Masterpieces

OF

Mystery

Masterpieces
OF
Mystery

The Old Masters

Selected by ELLERY QUEEN

CONTENTS

INTRODUCTION

DEAR READER:

The Old Masters are—why quarrel with a perfect phrase?—the Old Masters are the Old Masters. Consider the names of the contributors to this volume—some famous detective-mystery names from the past, some famous literary figures, some authors who could have been Nobel Prize winners. Do you realize that neither Leo Tolstoy nor Mark Twain was ever awarded the Nobel Prize for Literature?—and if we remember correctly, Tolstoy was nominated for the Nobel Prize no less than nine times!

As I write this Introduction, in my 73rd year, I can't help thinking of my colleagues who are now in their thirties and forties and fifties, and I can't help wondering if my young colleagues look upon me not as an old master but simply as an old man. If so, some of the authors in this collection are old, old masters, and some are ancient.

But—and it's an important but—the stories in this volume do not "read old." Most of them could have been written a mere few years ago—they are all timeless in their quality and grace, even the oldest one, by Voltaire, which was published 231 years ago!

And remember this old-forever-new truth in the art of reading: Any story you haven't read before is a new story.

So, happy reading! Fine stories, like fine vintage wines, improve with the connoisseur's care, and like the best wine, the stories by the old masters "goeth down sweetly" . . .

ELLERY QUEEN

THE DOG AND THE HORSE

BY VOLTAIRE

Voltaire was the pseudonym of Francois-Marie Arouet,
born in Paris, France, in 1694. He was educated by the
Jesuits and soon began to appear in free-thinking Paris
circles. His satiric writings caused him to be imprisoned
in the Bastille in 1717-18. He was exiled to England in
1726, and his exposure to the greater freedom there led
to his *Lettres philosophiques* (1734), which occasioned another scandal in France. *Candide* (1759) is his most
famous work. A dramatist, poet, philosopher, scientist,
novelist, and historian, Voltaire is considered the
epitome of the Age of Enlightenment. He died in Paris
in 1778.

ZADIG FOUND BY EXPERIENCE that the first month of marriage, as it is written in the book of Zend, is the moon of honey, and that the second is the moon of wormwood. He was some time after obliged to repudiate Azora, who became too difficult to be pleased; and he sought happiness in the study of nature.

"No man," said he, "can be happier than a philosopher, who reads in this great book which God hath placed before our eyes. The truths he discovers are his own; he nourishes and exalts his soul; he lives in peace; he fears nothing from men; and his tender spouse will not come to cut off his nose."

Possessed of these ideas, he retired to a country house on the banks of the Euphrates. There he did not employ himself in calculating how many inches of water flow in a second of time under the arches of a bridge, or whether there fell a cube-line of rain in the month of the mouse more than in the month of the sheep. He never dreamed of making silk of cobwebs, or porcelain of broken bottles; but he chiefly studied the properties of plants and animals; and soon acquired a sagacity that made him discover a thousand differences where other men see nothing but uniformity.

One day, as he was walking near a little wood, he saw one of the queen's eunuchs running toward him, followed by several officers, who appeared to be in great perplexity, and who ran to and fro like men distracted, eagerly searching for something of great value they had lost.

"Young man," said the first eunuch, "hast thou seen the queen's dog?"

"It is a bitch," replied Zadig, with modesty, "and not a dog."

"Thou art in the right," returned the first eunuch.

"It is a very small she-spaniel," added Zadig; "she has lately whelped; she limps on the left forefoot, and has very long ears."

"Thou hast seen her," said the first eunuch.

"No," replied Zadig, "I have not seen her, nor did I so much as know that the queen had a bitch."

Exactly at the same time, by one of the common freaks of fortune, the finest horse in the king's stable had escaped from the jockey in the plains of Babylon. The principal huntsman, and all the other officers, ran after him with as much eagerness and anxiety as the first eunuch had done after the bitch. The principal huntsman addressed himself to Zadig and asked him if he had not seen the king's horse passing by.

"He is the fleetest horse in the king's stable," replied Zadig; "he is five feet high, with very small hoofs and a tail three feet and an half in length; the studs on his bit are gold, of twenty-three carats, and his shoes are silver of eleven pennyweights."

"Where is he?" demanded the chief huntsman.

"I have not seen him," replied Zadig, "and never heard talk of him before."

The principal huntsman and the first eunuch never doubted but that Zadig had stolen the king's horse and the queen's dog. They therefore had him conducted before the assembly of the grand desterham, who condemned him to the knout, and to spend the rest of his days in Siberia. Hardly was the sentence passed, when the horse and the dog were both found. The judges were reduced to the disagreeable necessity of reversing their sentence; but they condemned Zadig to pay four hundred ounces of gold for having said that he had not seen what he had seen. This fine he was obliged to pay; after which, he was permitted to plead his cause before the council of the grand desterham, when he spoke to the following effect:

"Ye stars of justice, abyss of sciences, mirrors of truth, who have the weight of lead, the hardness of iron, the splendor of the diamond, and many of the properties of gold; since I am permitted to speak before this august assembly, I swear to you by Oromazes, that I have never seen the queen's respectable bitch, nor the sacred horse of the king of kings. The truth of the matter is as follows: I was walking toward the little wood, where I afterward met the venerable eunuch and the most illustrious chief huntsman. I observed on the sand the traces of an animal, and could easily perceive them to be those of a little dog. The light and long furrows impressed on little eminences of sand between the marks of the paws plainly discovered that it was a bitch, whose dugs were hanging down, and that therefore she must have whelped a few days before. Other traces of a different kind, that always appeared to have gently brushed the surface of the sand near the marks of the forefeet, showed me that she had very long ears; and as I remarked that there was always a slighter impression made on the sand by one foot than by the other three, I found that the bitch of our august queen was a little lame, if I may be allowed the expression. With regard to the horse of the king of kings, you will be pleased to know that walking in the lanes of this wood I observed the marks of a horse's shoes, all at equal distances. This must be a horse, said I to myself, that gallops excellently. The dust on the trees in a narrow road that was but seven feet wide was a little brushed off, at the distance of three feet and a half from the middle of the road. This horse, said I, has a tail three feet and a half long, which, being whisked to the right and left, has swept away the dust. I observed under the trees that formed an arbor five feet in height that the leaves of the branches were newly fallen, from whence I inferred that the horse had touched them, and that he must therefore be five feet high. As to his bit, it must be gold of twenty-three carats, for he had rubbed its bosses against a stone which I knew to be a touchstone, and which I have tried. In a word, from a mark made by his shoes on flints of another kind, I concluded that he was shod with silver eleven derniers fine."

All the judges admired Zadig for his acute and profound discernment. The news of this speech was carried even to the king and queen. Nothing was talked of but Zadig in the antechambers, the chambers, and the cabinet; and though many of the magi were of opinion that he ought to be burnt as a sorcerer, the king ordered his officers to restore him the four hundred ounces of gold which he had been obliged to pay. The register, the attorneys, and bailiffs went to his house with great formality to carry him back his four hundred ounces. They retained only three hundred ninety-eight of them to defray the expenses of justice.

Zadig saw how extremely dangerous it sometimes is to appear too knowing, and therefore resolved that on the next occasion he would not tell what he had seen.

Such an opportunity soon offered. A prisoner of state made his escape and passed under the windows of Zadig's house. Zadig was examined and made no answer. But it was proved that he had looked at the prisoner from this window. For this crime he was condemned to pay five hundred ounces of gold; and, according to the polite custom of Babylon, he thanked his judges for their indulgence.

"Great God!" said he to himself, "what a misfortune it is to walk in a wood through which the queen's dog or the king's horse have passed! How dangerous to look out of a window! And how difficult to be happy in this life!"

10

THE MAN OF THE CROWD

BY EDGAR ALLAN POE

Edgar Allan Poe was born in 1809 in Boston, Massachusetts. Orphaned at the age of two, he was raised by a wealthy couple, the Allans. He was educated in England and attended the University of Virginia for a time before entering the Army under a false name. In 1836 Poe married his thirteen-year-old cousin, Virginia Clemm. "The Murder in the Rue Morgue" (1841) is considered the first modern detective story. C. Auguste Dupin, Poe's fictional detective, also appeared in "The Mystery of Marie Roget" (1842) and "The Purloined Letter" (1844). Poe died in 1849 in Baltimore, Maryland.

Most of us are familiar with the recurring and seemingly inescapable tragedies in Edgar Allan Poe's life. For the second half of his nearly forty-one years he lived in shadow and darkness—the shadow of fear, the darkness of nightmare, alternating between anguish and despair, usually in unbelievable poverty and nearly always in profound misery. He was a tortured and tormented man, a haunted man who "still haunts our memory and our literature." He was possibly a dipsomaniac, possibly a maniac; he was either neglected or vilified, and certainly misunderstood; he was a failure in his own time—the highest salary he was ever paid as an editor was at the rate of $800 a year, and his stories earned so little that a single letter by Poe of even small literary interest is now likely to fetch at auction more than Poe earned in his entire literary career; indeed, some of Poe's books were published without royalties to him, his only payment having been "twenty copies for distribution to friends,"[1] and today first editions of his *Tamerlane and Other Poems* (1827), *Poems* (1831), and *The Raven and Other Poems* (1845) are rare and precious books. . . .

Is it any wonder that his morbidity and maladjustments, his persistent "evil fortune," caused him mental, physical, and emotional breakdowns? Yet his short life was one of intense creativity, full of imagination, originality, and otherworldliness. George Bernard Shaw called him "this finest of finest artists," and Poe's influence, both as a creator and critic, has been immeasurable.

The great problem in selecting a Poe story for this anthology was to choose one not already well-known to readers. The natural selection would have been a tale of C. Auguste Dupin—"The Murders in the Rue Morgue" (historically the most important, since it was the world's first detective story in a modern sense), or "The Purloined Letter" (Poe's finest balance of the two great 'tec tributaries—the "Intellectual" and the "Sensational"), or "The Mystery of Marie Rogêt" (which shows how Poe applied his new literary technique to the solution of a real-life case and which, in the opinion of so discerning a professional as Rex Stout, is not only Poe's outstanding achievement in the genre but also one of the ten best detective stories ever written). But all three Dupin stories have been anthologized numerous times.

---

[1] Quoted from Poe's letter of August 13, 1841, to his Philadelphia publishers, Lea & Blanchard.

A non-Dupin story? "The Gold-Bug" and even "Thou Art the Man" are also too familiar. One of Poe's tales of murder? Who does not know "The Cask of Amontillado," "The Tell-Tale Heart," "The Black Cat," even that lesser favorite, "Hop-Frog"?

No, for this anthology we needed something "different." So we dug into Poe's relatively "unknown" stories and we came up with a "discovery"—a story by Poe whose detective-crime significance has been unaccountably overlooked. The story is "The Man of the Crowd," and of it the perceptive and penetrating Philip Van Doren Stern has written: "It is one of Poe's least appreciated stories. It is almost never commented on in any critical review of his work, yet it is one of his most unusual stories, curiously modern in its psychology, and far more original than some of his better known tales."

And even Mr. Stern did not realize, or fully realize, the story's importance in the history of the detective story!

Further comments after you have read this "unhonored and unsung" tale—a tale of unusual "detection." . . .

Ce grand mal malheur, de ne pouvoir être seul.
LA BRUYÈRE

IT WAS WELL SAID OF A certain German book that *"es lässt sich nicht lesen"*—it does not permit itself to be read. There are some secrets which do not permit themselves to be told. Men die nightly in their beds, wringing the hands of ghostly confessors, and looking them piteously in the eyes—die with despair of heart and convulsion of throat, on account of the hideousness of mysteries which will not *suffer themselves* to be revealed. Now and then, alas, the conscience of the man takes up a burthen so heavy in horror that it can be thrown down only into the grave. And thus the essence of all crime is undivulged.

Not long ago, about the closing of an evening in the autumn, I sat at the large bow window of the D—— Coffee-House in London. For some months I had been ill in health, but was now convalescent, and, with returning strength, found myself in one of those happy moods which are so precisely the converse of *ennui*—moods of the keenest appetency, when the film from the mental vision departs—the $\alpha\chi\lambda\grave{\upsilon}\varsigma\ \eta\ \pi\rho\grave{\iota}\nu\ \epsilon\pi\eta\epsilon\nu$—and the intellect, electrified, surpasses as greatly its everyday condition as

13

does the vivid yet candid reason of Leibnitz, the mad and flimsy rhetoric of Gorgias.

Merely to breathe was enjoyment; and I derived positive pleasure even from many of the legitimate sources of pain. I felt a calm but inquisitive interest in everything. With a cigar in my mouth and a newspaper in my lap, I had been amusing myself for the greater part of the afternoon, now in poring over advertisements, now in observing the promiscuous company in the room, and now in peering through the smoky panes into the street.

This latter is one of the principal thoroughfares of the city, and had been very much crowded during the whole day. But, as the darkness came on, the throng momently increased; and by the time the lamps were well lighted, two dense and continuous tides of population were rushing past the door. At this particular period of the evening I had never before been in a similar situation, and the tumultuous seas of human heads filled me, therefore, with a delicious novelty of emotion. I gave up, at length, all care of things within the hotel, and became absorbed in contemplation of the scene without.

At first my observations took an abstract and generalizing turn. I looked at the passengers in masses, and thought of them in their aggregate relations. Soon, however, I descended to details, and regarded with minute interest the innumerable varieties of figure, dress, air, gait, visage, and expression of countenance.

By far the greater number of those who went by had a satisfied, business-like demeanor, and seemed to be thinking only of making their way through the press. Their brows were knit, and their eyes rolled quickly; when pushed against by fellow-wayfarers they evinced no symptom of impatience, but adjusted their clothes and hurried on. Others, still a numerous class, were restless in their movements, had flushed faces, and talked and gesticulated to themselves, as if feeling in solitude on account of the very denseness of the company around. When impeded in their progress, these people suddenly ceased muttering, but redoubled their gesticulations, and awaited, with an absent and overdone smile upon the lips, the course of the person impeding them. If jostled, they bowed profusely to the jostlers, and appeared overwhelmed with confusion.

There was nothing very distinctive about these two large classes beyond what I have noted. Their habiliments belonged to that order which is pointedly termed the decent. They were undoubtedly noblemen, merchants, attorneys, tradesmen, stock-jobbers—the Eupatrids and the commonplaces of society—men of leisure and men actively engaged in affairs of their own—conducting business upon their own responsibility. They did not greatly excite my attention.

The tribe of clerks was an obvious one; and here I discerned two remarkable divisions. There were the junior clerks of flash houses—young gentlemen with tight coats, bright boots, well-oiled hair, and supercilious lips. Setting aside a certain dapperness of carriage, which may be termed *deskism* for want of a better word, the manner of these persons seemed to me an exact facsimile of what had been the perfection of *bon ton* about twelve or eighteen months before. They wore the cast-off graces of the gentry;—and this, I believe, involves the best definition of the class.

The division of the upper clerks of staunch firms, or of the "steady old fellows," it was not possible to mistake. These were known by their coats and pantaloons of black or brown, made to sit comfortably, and white cravats and waistcoats, broad solid-looking shoes, and thick hose or gaiters.—They had all slightly bald heads, from which the right ears, long used to pen-holding, had an odd habit of standing off on end. I observed that they always removed or settled their hats with both hands, and wore watches, with short gold chains of a substantial and ancient pattern. Theirs was the affectation of respectability—if, indeed, there be an affectation so honorable.

There were many individuals of dashing appearance, whom I easily understood as belonging to the race of swell pickpockets, with which all great cities are infested. I watched these gentry with much inquisitiveness, and found it difficult to imagine how they should ever be mistaken for gentlemen by gentlemen themselves. Their voluminousness of wristband, with an air of excessive frankness, should betray them at once.

The gamblers, of whom I descried not a few, were still more easily recognizable. They wore every variety of dress, from that of the desperate thimble-rig bully, with velvet waistcoat, fancy neckerchief, gilt chains, and filigreed buttons, to that of the scrupulously inornate clergyman than which nothing could be less liable to suspicion. Still all were distinguished by a certain sodden swarthiness of complexion, a filmy dimness of eye, and pallor and compression of lip. There were two other traits,

15

moreover, by which I could always detect them—a guarded lowness of tone in conversation, and a more than ordinary extension of the thumb in a direction at right angles with the fingers.

Very often, in company with these sharpers, I observed an order of men somewhat different in habits, but still birds of a kindred feather. They may be defined as the gentlemen who live by their wits. They seem to prey upon the public in two battalions—that of the dandies and that of the military men. Of the first grade the leading features are long locks and smiles; of the second frogged coats and frowns.

Descending in the scale of what is termed gentility, I found darker and deeper themes for speculation. I saw peddlers, with hawk eyes flashing from countenances whose every other feature wore only an expression of abject humility; sturdy professional street beggars scowling upon mendicants of a better stamp, whom despair alone had driven forth into the night for charity; feeble and ghastly invalids, upon whom death had placed a sure hand, and who sidled and tottered through the mob, looking everyone beseechingly in the face, as if in search of some chance consolation, some lost hope; modest young girls returning from long and late labor to a cheerless home, and shrinking more tearfully than indignantly from the glances of ruffians, whose direct contact, even, could not be avoided; women of the town of all kinds and all ages—the unequivocal beauty in the prime of her womanhood, putting one in mind of the statue in Lucian, with the surface of Parian marble, and the interior filled with filth; the loathsome and utterly lost leper in rags— the wrinkled, bejeweled, and paint-begrimed beldame, making a last effort at youth—the mere child of immature form, yet, from long association, an adept in the dreadful coquetries of her trade, and burning with a rabid ambition to be ranked the equal of her elders in vice; drunkards innumerable and indescribable—some in shreds and patches, reeling, inarticulate, with bruised visage and lackluster eyes—some in whole although filthy garments, with a slightly unsteady swagger, thick, sensual lips, and hearty-looking rubicund faces—others clothed in materials which had once been good, and which even now were scrupulously well brushed—men who walked with a more than naturally firm and springy step, but whose countenances were fearfully pale, whose eyes were hideously wild and red, and who clutched with quivering fingers, as they strode

16

through the crowd, at every object which came within their reach; beside these, pie-men, porters, coal-heavers, sweeps; organ-grinders, monkey-exhibitors, and ballad-mongers, those who vended with those who sang; ragged artisans and exhausted laborers of every description, and all full of a noisy and inordinate vivacity which jarred discordantly upon the ear, and gave an aching sensation to the eye.

As the night deepened, so deepened to me the interest of the scene; for not only did the general character of the crowd materially alter (its gentler features retiring in the gradual withdrawal of the more orderly portion of the people, and its harsher ones coming out into bolder relief as the late hour brought forth every species of infamy from its den), but the rays of the gas-lamps, feeble at first in their struggle with the dying day, had now at length gained ascendancy, and threw over everything a fitful and garish luster. All was dark yet splendid—as that ebony to which has been likened the style of Tertullian.

The wild effect of the light enchained me to an examination of individual faces; and although the rapidity with which the world of light flitted before the window prevented me from casting more than a glance upon each visage, still it seemed that, in my then peculiar mental state, I could frequently read, even in their brief interval of a glance, the history of many long years.

With my brow to the glass, I was thus occupied in scrutinizing the mob, when suddenly there came into view a countenance (that of a decrepit man, some sixty-five or seventy years of age)—a countenance which at once arrested and absorbed my whole attention, on account of the absolute idiosyncrasy of its expression. Anything even remotely resembling that expression I had never seen before. I well remember that my first thought, upon beholding it, was that Retszch, had he viewed it, would have greatly preferred it to his own pictorial incarnation of the fiend.

As I endeavored, during the brief minute of my original survey, to form some analysis of the meaning conveyed, there arose confusedly and paradoxically within my mind the ideas of vast mental power, of caution, of penuriousness, of avarice, of coolness, of malice, of blood- thirstiness, of triumph, of merriment, of excessive terror, of intense—of extreme despair. I felt singularly aroused, startled, fascinated.

17

"How wild a history," I said to myself, "is written within that bosom!"

Then came a craving desire to keep the man in view—to know more of him. Hurriedly putting on an overcoat, and seizing my hat and cane, I made my way into the street, and pushed through the crowd in the direction which I had seen him take; for he had already disappeared. With some little difficulty I at length came within sight of him, approached, and followed him closely, yet cautiously, so as not to attract his attention.

I had now a good opportunity of examining his person. He was short in stature, very thin, and apparently very feeble. His clothes, generally, were filthy and ragged; but as he came, now and then, within the strong glare of a lamp, I perceived that his linen, although dirty, was of beautiful texture; and my vision deceived me, or, through a rent in a closely buttoned and evidently secondhand *roquelaure* which enveloped him, I caught a glimpse both of a diamond and a dagger. These observations heightened my curiosity, and I resolved to follow the stranger whithersoever he should go.

It was now fully nightfall, and a thick humid fog hung over the city, soon ending in a settled and heavy rain. This change of weather had an odd effect upon the crowd, the whole of which was at once put into new commotion, and overshadowed by a world of umbrellas. The waver, the jostle, and the hum increased in a tenfold degree. For my own part I did not much regard the rain—the lurking of an old fever in my system rendering the moisture somewhat too dangerously pleasant. Tying a handkerchief about my mouth, I kept on.

For half an hour the old man held his way with difficulty along the great thoroughfare; and I here walked close at his elbow through fear of losing sight of him. Never once turning his head to look back, he did not observe me. By and by he passed into a cross street which, although densely filled with people, was not quite so much thronged the main one he had quitted. Here a change in his demeanor became evident. He walked more slowly and with less object than before—more hesitatingly. He crossed and recrossed the way repeatedly without apparent aim; and the press was still so thick that, at every such movement, I was obliged to follow him closely.

The street was a narrow and long one, and his course lay within it for nearly an hour, during which the passengers had gradually diminished to about that number which is ordinarily

18

seen at noon in Broadway near the Park—so vast a difference is there between a London populace and that of the most frequented American city. A second turn brought us into a square, brilliantly lighted, and overflowing with life. The old manner of the stranger reappeared. His chin fell upon his breast, while his eyes rolled wildly from under his knit brows, in every direction, upon those who hemmed him in. He urged his way steadily and perseveringly. I was surprised, however, to find, upon his having made the circuit of the square, that he turned and retraced his steps. Still more was I astonished to see him repeat the same walk several times—once nearly detecting me as he came round with a sudden movement.

In this exercise the stranger spent another hour, at the end of which we met with far less interruption from passengers than at first. The rain fell fast; the air grew cool; and the people were retiring to their homes. With a gesture of impatience the wanderer passed into a by-street comparatively deserted. Down this, some quarter of a mile long, he rushed with an activity I could not have dreamed of seeing in one so aged, and which put me to some trouble in pursuit. A few minutes brought us to a large and busy bazaar, with the localities of which the stranger appeared well acquainted, and where his original demeanor again became apparent as he forced his way to and fro, without aim, among the host of buyers and sellers.

During the hour and a half, or thereabouts which we passed in this place, it required much caution on my part to keep him within reach without attracting his observation. Luckily I wore a pair of caoutchouc overshoes, and could move about in perfect silence. At no moment did he see that I watched him. He entered shop after shop, priced nothing, spoke no word, and looked at all objects with a wild and vacant stare. I was now utterly amazed at his behavior, and firmly resolved that we should not part until I satisfied myself in some measure respecting him.

A loud-toned clock struck eleven, and the company were fast deserting the bazaar. A shopkeeper, in putting up a shutter, jostled the old man, and at the instant I saw a strong shudder come over his frame. He hurried into the street, looked anxiously around him for an instant, and then ran with an incredible swiftness through many crooked and peopleless lanes, until we emerged once more upon the great thoroughfare whence we had started—the street of the D—— Hotel. It no longer

19

wore, however, the same aspect. It was still brilliant with gas; but the rain fell fiercely, and there were few persons to be seen.

The stranger grew pale. He walked moodily some paces up the once populous avenue, then, with a heavy sigh, turned in the direction of the river, and plunging through a great variety of devious ways, came out, at length, in view of one of the principal theaters. It was about being closed, and the audience were thronging from the doors. I saw the old man gasp as if for breath while he threw himself amid the crowd; but I thought that the intense agony of his countenance had, in some measure, abated. His head again fell upon his breast; he appeared as I had seen him at first. I observed that he now took the course in which had gone the greater number of the audience—but, upon the whole, I was at a loss to comprehend the waywardness of his actions.

As he proceeded, the company grew more scattered, and his old uneasiness and vacillation were resumed. For some time he followed closely a party of some ten or twelve roisterers; but from this number one by one dropped off, until three only remained together, in a narrow and gloomy lane little frequented.

The stranger paused, and, for a moment, seemed lost in thought; then, with every mark of agitation, pursued rapidly a route which brought us to the verge of the city, amid regions very different from those we had hitherto traversed. It was the most noisome quarter of London, where everything wore the worst impress of the most deplorable poverty, and of the most desperate crime. By the dim light of an accidental lamp, tall, antique, worm-eaten, wooden tenements were seen tottering to their fall, in directions so many and capricious that scarce the semblance of a passage was discernible between them. The paving-stones lay at random, displaced from their beds by the rankly growing grass. Horrible filth festered in the dammed-up gutters. The whole atmosphere teemed with desolation.

Yet, as we proceeded, the sounds of human life revived by sure degrees, and at length large bands of the most abandoned of a London populace were seen reeling to and fro. The spirits of the old man again flickered up, as a lamp which is near its death hour. Once more he strode onward with elastic tread. Suddenly a corner was turned, a blaze of light burst upon our sight, and we stood before one of the huge suburban temples of Intemperance—one of the palaces of the fiend, Gin.

20

It was now nearly daybreak; but a number of wretched inebriates still pressed in and out of the flaunting entrance. With a half shriek of joy the old man forced a passage within, resumed at once his original bearing, and stalked backward and forward, without apparent object, among the throng. He had not been thus long occupied, however, before a rush to the doors gave token that the host was closing them for the night.

It was something even more intense than despair that I then observed upon the countenance of the singular being whom I had watched so pertinaciously. Yet he did not hesitate in his career, but, with a mad energy, retraced his steps at once, to the heart of the mighty London. Long and swiftly he fled, while I followed him in the wildest amazement, resolute not to abandon a scrutiny in which I now felt an interest all-absorbing.

The sun rose while we proceeded, and, when we had once again reached that most thronged mart of the populous town, the street of the D—— Hotel, it presented an appearance of human bustle and activity scarcely inferior to what I had seen on the evening before. And here, long, amid the momently increasing confusion, did I persist in my pursuit of the stranger. But, as usual, he walked to and fro, and during the day did not pass from out the turmoil of that street. And, as the shades of the second evening came on, I grew wearied unto death, and, stopping fully in front of the wanderer, gazed at him steadfastly in the face. He noticed me not, but resumed his solemn walk, while I, ceasing to follow, remained absorbed in contemplation.

"This old man," I said at length, "is the type and the genius of deep crime. He refuses to be alone. *He is the man of the crowd.* It will be in vain to follow; for I shall learn no more of him, nor of his deeds. The worst heart of the world is a grosser book than the *Hortulus Animae*, and perhaps it is but one of the great mercies of God that *es lässt sich nicht lesen.*"

EDITORIAL COMMENT: "The Man of the Crowd" was first published in December 1840—simultaneously in Burton's *The Gentleman's Magazine* and in *The Casket*, the contents of which were identical because the two magazines were about to be combined into Graham's *Lady's and Gentleman's Magazine*. But mark the date—December 1840—*preceding* the first appearance in print of "The Murders in the Rue Morgue," in the April 1841 issue of *Graham's Magazine*.

In other words, "The Man of the Crowd" *antedated* the world's first detective story!

Was it a trial balloon? An experiment by Poe on the eve of his inventing the detective story? Does "The Man of the Crowd" foreshadow the first detective story?

Let us examine the internal evidence.

Surely the anonymous narrator begins as an armchair detective. He is interested in mystery and crime. He is an acute and accurate observer. He analyzes and deduces. Note the "ear" deduction identifying upper clerks: "They had all slightly bald heads, from which the right ears, long used to pen-holding, had an odd habit of standing off on end." Note the "Thumb" deduction identifying gamblers: I could always detect [significant word!] them . . . a more than ordinary extension of the thumb in a direction at right angles with the fingers"— the sign of a "sharper." Surely here is a detective (Poe almost uses the word) at work! Surely here are deductions of exactly the sort that Sherlock Holmes was to toss off so startlingly nearly half a century later!

But that is not all. The armchair detective changes to an *active* detective—when "the game is afoot." He follows his man; he tracks, trails (wearing "caoutchouc overshoes"—Poe's phrase for gumshoes), pursuing a tantalizing and baffling mystery; and as surely as the anonymous narrator is a detective, the man pursued is a criminal. And what of the detective's attitude, his point of view, during the chase? He describes himself as being in a "peculiar mental state" (how detective-like!) and he speaks of "darker and deeper themes for speculation" (how equally detective-like!).

Do you object, perhaps, that the mystery, except for psychological insight (how modern!), remains impenetrable, unsolved? But does this make the detective less of a detective? There is no principle in the genre, even in the fully developed technique of today, that *insists* the detective must always succeed. . . . Yes, in "The Man of the Crowd" the detective fails—but that was not only a new variation in 1840, it would be a comparatively new one by current standards. The mystery genre is still the most moral of all literary forms, since justice—legal as well as poetic—nearly always triumphs.

Here, then, in our opinion, is Poe's embryonic detective—the seed of C. Auguste Dupin, the world's first detective; here is the prototype—Poe's own prototype—of the private eye. . . .

There are, of course, other interpretations of "The Man of the Crowd." On a different level, one could theorize that the pursuer was pursuing *himself*. This would be a typically Poesque conception—an imaginative extension and variation of "William Wilson," and another of Poe's anticipations of the "Dr. Jekyll and Mr. Hyde" theme. The pursuer and the pursued are two halves of the same person, one half representing "good," the other half "evil."

If it were not for the disturbing fact (disturbing in a story by Poe) that the action is continuous and lasts longer than a full night—that is, occurs also in the daytime—the pursuer and the pursued could also be interpreted as the worldly mortal-self pursuing the unworldly dream-self (or vice-versa!), with one self never catching the other. Or—and this is too typically Poesque—the entire story could be interpreted as a dream, or nightmare, an unsuccessful attempt (as unsuccessful as Poe's own attempts) of a human being to free himself from the chains of earthly living, to reach that "wild weird clime that lieth, sublime, / Out of SPACE—out of TIME."

But these additional speculations are meant only to stimulate your imagination. Our main interest in "The Man of the Crowd" concerns its detective meanings, its historical and originative significance in the mystery genre. . . .

HUNTED DOWN

BY CHARLES DICKENS

Charles Dickens was born in Portsea, England, on February 7, 1812, and began working in a factory at the age of twelve. He later worked as a solicitor's clerk and as a stenographer for the *Morning Chronicle*. His first published work was a sketch in the *Monthly Magazine* in 1833, signed "Boz." *The Posthumous Papers of the Pickwick Club,* serialized in 1836-37, assured Dickens' fortune. He created some of the most famous and well-loved novels and characters in English literature. Most of his books contain crimes or mysteries, including *Oliver Twist, Great Expectations,* and *Bleak House.* In 1870 Dickens died while working on *The Mystery of Edwin Drood.*

THE PARTITION WHICH SEPARATED my own office from our general outer office in the City was of thick plate glass. I could see through it what passed in the outer office, without hearing a word. I had it put up in place of a wall that had been there for years—ever since the house was built. It is no matter whether I did or did not make the change in order that I might derive my first impression of strangers, who came to us on business, from their faces alone, without being influenced by anything they said. Enough to mention that I turned my glass partition to that account, and that a Life Assurance Office is at all times exposed to be practiced upon by the most crafty and cruel of the human race.

It was through my glass partition that I first saw the gentleman whose story I am going to tell.

He had come in without my observing it, and had put his hat and umbrella on the broad counter, and was bending over it to take some papers from one of the clerks. He was about forty or so, dark, exceedingly well dressed in black—being in mourning—and the hand he extended with a polite air, had a particularly well-fitting black kid glove upon it. His hair, which was elaborately brushed and oiled, was parted straight up the middle; and he presented this parting to the clerk, exactly (to my thinking) as if he had said, in so many words: "You must take me, if you please, my friend, just as I show myself. Come straight up here, follow the gravel path, keep off the grass, I allow no trespassing."

I conceived a very great aversion to that man the moment I thus saw him.

He had asked for some of our printed forms, and the clerk was giving them to him and explaining them. An obliged and agreeable smile was on his face, and his eyes met those of the clerk with a sprightly look. (I have known a vast quantity of nonsense talked about bad men not looking you in the face. Don't trust that conventional idea. Dishonesty will stare honesty out of the countenance, any day in the week, if there is anything to be got by it.)

I saw, in the corner of his eyelash, that he became aware of my looking at him. Immediately he turned the parting in his hair toward the glass partition, as if he said to me with a sweet smile, "Straight up here, if you please. Off the grass!"

In a few moments he had put on his hat and taken up his umbrella, and was gone.

I beckoned the clerk into my room, and asked, "Who was that?"

He had the gentleman's card in his hand. "Mr. Julius Slinkton, Middle Temple."

"A barrister, Mr. Adams?"

"I think not, sir."

"I should have thought him a clergyman, but for his having no Reverend here," said I.

"Probably, from his appearance," Mr. Adams replied, "he is reading for orders."

I should mention that he wore a dainty white cravat, and dainty linen altogether.

"What did he want, Mr. Adams?"

"Merely a form of proposal, sir, and form of reference."

"Recommended here? Did he say?"

"Yes, he said he was recommended here by a friend of yours. He noticed you, but said that as he had not the pleasure of your personal acquaintance, he would not trouble you."

"Did he know my name?"

"Oh, yes sir! He said, 'There *is* Mr. Sampson, I see!'"

"A well-spoken gentleman, apparently?"

"Remarkably so, sir."

"Insinuating manners, apparently?"

"Very much so, indeed, sir."

"Hah!" said I. "I want nothing at present, Mr. Adams."

Within a fortnight of that day I went to dine with a friend of mine, a merchant, a man of taste, who buys pictures and books, and the first man I saw among the company was Mr. Julius Slinkton. There he was, standing before the fire, with good large eyes and an open expression of face; but still (I thought) requiring everybody to come at him by the prepared way he offered, and by no other.

I noticed him ask my friend to introduce him to Mr. Sampson, and my friend did so. Mr. Slinkton was very happy to see me. Not too happy; there was no overdoing of the matter; happy in a thoroughly well-bred, perfectly unmeaning way.

"I thought you had met," our host observed.

"No," said Mr. Slinkton. "I did look in at Mr. Sampson's

office, on your recommendation; but I really did not feel justified in troubling Mr. Sampson himself, on a point in the everyday routine of a clerk."

I said I should have been glad to show him any attention on our friend's introduction.

"I am sure of that," said he, "and am much obliged. At another time, perhaps, I may be less delicate. Only, however, if I have real business; for I know, Mr. Sampson, how precious business time is, and what a vast number of impertinent people there are in the world."

I acknowledged his consideration with a slight bow. "You were thinking," said I, "of effecting a policy on your life."

"Oh dear no! I am afraid I am not so prudent as you pay me the compliment of supposing me to be, Mr. Sampson. I merely inquired for a friend. But you know what friends are in such matters. Nothing may ever come of it. I have the greatest reluctance to trouble men of business with inquiries for friends, knowing the probabilities to be a thousand to one that the friends will never follow them up. People are so fickle, so selfish, so inconsiderate. Don't you, in your business, find them so every day?"

I was going to give a qualified answer; but he turned his smooth, white parting on me with its "Straight up here, if you please!" and I answered "Yes."

"I hear, Mr. Sampson," he resumed presently, for our friend had a new cook, and dinner was not so punctual as usual, "that your profession has recently suffered a great loss."

"In money?" said I.

"No, in talent and vigor."

Not at once following out his allusion, I considered for a moment. "*Has* it sustained a loss of that kind?" said I. "I was not aware of it."

"Understand me, Mr. Sampson. I don't imagine that you have retired. It is not so bad as that. But Mr. Meltham—"

"Oh, to be sure!" said I. "Yes! Mr. Meltham, the young actuary of the 'Inestimable.' "

"Just so," he returned in a consoling way.

"He is a great loss. He was at once the most profound, the most original, and the most energetic man I have ever known connected with Life Assurance."

I spoke strongly; for I had a high esteem and admiration for Meltham; and my gentleman had indefinitely conveyed to me

27

some suspicion that he wanted to sneer at him. He recalled me to my guard by presenting that trim pathway up his head, with its infernal "Not on the grass, if you please—the gravel."

"You knew him, Mr. Slinkton?"

"Only by reputation. To have known him as an acquaintance or as a friend, is an honor I should have sought if he had remained in society, though I might never have had the good fortune to attain it, being a man of far inferior mark. He was scarcely above thirty, I suppose?"

"About thirty."

"Ah!" he sighed in his former consoling way. "What creatures we are! To break up, Mr. Sampson, and become incapable of business at that time of life!—Any reason assigned for the melancholy fact?"

("Humph!" thought I, as I looked at him. "But I WON'T go up the track, and I WILL go on the grass.")

"What reason have you heard assigned, Mr. Slinkton?" I asked, point-blank.

"Most likely a false one. You know what Rumor is, Mr. Sampson. I never repeat what I hear; it is the only way of paring the nails and shaving the head of the Rumor. But when *you* ask me what reason I have heard assigned for Mr. Meltham's passing away from among men, it is another thing. I am not gratifying idle gossip then. I was told, Mr. Sampson, that Mr. Meltham had relinquished all his avocations and all his prospects, because he was, in fact, broken-hearted. A disappointed attachment I heard—though it hardly seems probable, in the case of a man so distinguished and so attractive."

"Attractions and distinctions are no armor against death," said I.

"Oh, she died? Pray pardon me. I did not hear that. That, indeed, makes it very, very sad. Poor Mr. Meltham! Ah, dear me! Lamentable, lamentable!"

I still thought his pity was not quite genuine, and I still suspected an unaccountable sneer under all this, until he said, as we were parted, like the other knots of talkers, by the announcement of dinner:

"Mr. Sampson, you are surprised to see me so moved on behalf of a man whom I have never known. I am not so disinterested as you may suppose. I have suffered, and recently, too, from death myself. I have lost one of two charming nieces, who were my constant companions. She died young—barely three-

and-twenty; and even her remaining sister is far from strong. The world is a grave!"

He said this with deep feeling, and I felt reproached for the coldness of my manner. Coldness and distrust had been engendered in me, I knew, by my bad experiences; they were not so natural to me; and I often thought how much I had lost in life, losing trustfulness, and how little I had gained, gaining hard caution. This state of mind being habitual to me, I troubled myself more about this conversation than I might have troubled myself about a greater matter. I listened to his talk at dinner, and observed how readily other men responded to it, and with what a graceful instinct he adapted his subjects to the knowledge and habits of those he talked with. As, in talking with me, he had easily started the subject I might be supposed to understand best, and to be the most interested in, so, in talking with others, he guided himself by the same rule. The company was of a varied character; but he was not at fault, that I could discover, with any member of it. He knew just as much of each man's pursuit as made him agreeable to that man in reference to it, and just as little as made it natural in him to seek modestly for information when the theme was broached.

As he talked and talked—but really not too much, for the rest of us seemed to force it upon him—I became quite angry with myself. I took his face to pieces in my mind, like a watch, and examined it in detail. I could not say much against any of his features separately; I could say even less against them when they were put together. "Then is it not monstrous," I asked myself, "that because a man happens to part his hair straight up the middle of his head, I should permit myself to suspect, and even to detest him?"

(I may stop to remark that this was no proof of my sense. An observer of men who finds himself steadily repelled by some apparently trifling thing in a stranger is right to give it great weight. It may be the clue to the whole mystery. A hair or two will show where a lion is hidden. A very little key will open a very heavy door.)

I took my part in the conversation with him after a time, and we got on remarkably well. In the drawing room I asked the host how long he had known Mr. Slinkton. He answered, not many months; he had met him at the house of a celebrated painter then present, who had known him well when he was travelling with his nieces in Italy for their health. His plans in life being broken by the death of one of them, he was reading with the intention of going back to college as a matter of form, taking his degree, and going into orders. I could not but argue with myself that here was the true explanation of his interest in poor Meltham, and that I had been almost brutal in my distrust of that simple head.

On the very next day but one I was sitting behind my glass partition, as before, when he came into the outer office, as before. The moment I saw him again without hearing him, I hated him worse than ever.

It was only for a moment that I had this opportunity; for he waved his tight-fitting black glove the instant I looked at him, and came straight in.

"Mr. Sampson, good day! I presume, you see, upon your kind permission to intrude upon you. I don't keep my word in being justified by business, for my business here—if I may so abuse the word—is of the slightest nature."

I asked, was it anything I could assist him in?

"I thank you, no. I merely called to inquire outside whether my dilatory friend had been so false to himself as to be practical and sensible. But, of course, he has done nothing. I gave him your papers with my own hand, and he was hot upon the intention, but of course he has done nothing. Apart from the general human disinclination to do anything that ought to be done, I dare say there is a specialty about assuring one's life. You find it like will-making. People are so superstitious, and take it for granted that they will die soon afterwards."

"Up here, if you please; straight up here, Mr. Sampson. Neither to the right nor to the left." I almost fancied I could hear him breathe the words as he sat smiling at me, with that intolerable parting exactly opposite the bridge of my nose.

"There is such a feeling sometimes, no doubt," I replied: "but I don't think it obtains to any great extent."

"Well," said he, with a shrug and a smile, "I wish some good angel would influence my friend in the right direction. I rashly promised his mother and sister in Norfolk to see it done, and he promised them that he would do it. But I suppose he never will."

He spoke for a minute or two on indifferent topics, and went away.

I had scarcely unlocked the drawers of my writing-table next morning,when he reappeared. I noticed that he came straight to the door in the glass partition, and did not pause a single moment outside.

"Can you spare me two minutes, my dear Mr. Sampson?"

"By all means."

"Much obliged," laying his hat and umbrella on the table; "I came early, not to interrupt you. The fact is, I am taken by surprise in reference to the proposal my friend has made."

"Has he made one?" said I.

"Ye-es," he answered, deliberately looking at me; and then a bright idea seemed to strike him—"or he only tells me he has. Perhaps that may be a new way of evading the matter. By Jupiter, I never thought of that!"

Mr. Adams was opening the morning's letters in the outer office. "What is the name, Mr. Slinkton?" I asked.

"Beckwith."

I looked out at the door and requested Mr. Adams, if there were a proposal in that name, to bring it in. He had already laid it out of his hand on the counter. It was easily selected from the rest, and he gave it me. Alfred Beckwith. Proposal to effect a policy with us for two thousand pounds. Dated yesterday.

"From the Middle Temple, I see, Mr. Slinkton."

"Yes. He lives on the same staircase with me; his door is opposite. I never thought he would make me his reference though."

"It seems natural enough that he should."

"Quite so, Mr. Sampson; but I never thought of it. Let me see." He took the printed paper from his pocket. "How am I to answer all these questions?"

"According to the truth, of course," said I.

"Oh, of course!" he answered, looking up from the paper with a smile; "I meant there were so many. But you do right to be particular. It stands to reason that you must be particular. Will you allow me to use your pen and ink?"

"Certainly."

"And your desk?"

"Certainly."

He had been hovering about between his hat and his umbrella for a place to write on. He now sat down in my chair, at my blotting-paper and inkstand, with the long walk up his head in accurate perspective before me, as I stood with my back to the fire.

31

Before answering each question he ran over it aloud, and discussed it. How long had he known Mr. Alfred Beckwith? That he had to calculate by years upon his fingers. What were his habits? No difficulty about them; temperate in the last degree, and took a little too much exercise, if anything. All the answers were satisfactory. When he had written them all, he looked them over, and finally signed them in a very pretty hand. He supposed he had now done with the business. I told him he was not likely to be troubled any further. Should he leave the papers there? If he pleased. Much obliged. Good morning.

I had had one other visitor before him; not at the office, but at my own house. That visitor had come to my bedside when it was not yet daylight and had been seen by no one else but my faithful confidential servant.

A second reference paper (for we required always two) was sent down into Norfolk, and was duly received back by the post. This, likewise, was satisfactorily answered in every respect. Our forms were all complied with; we accepted the proposal, and the premium for one year was paid.

For six or seven months I saw no more of Mr. Slinkton. He called once at my house, but I was not at home; and he once asked me to dine with him in the Temple, but I was engaged. His friend's assurance was effected in March. Late in September or early in October I was down at Scarborough for a breath of sea air, where I met him on the beach. It was a hot evening; he came toward me with his hat in his hand; and there was the walk I had felt so strongly disinclined to take in perfect order again, exactly in front of the bridge of my nose.

He was not alone, but had a young lady on his arm.

She was dressed in mourning, and I looked at her with great interest. She had the appearance of being extremely delicate, and her face was remarkably pale and melancholy; but she was very pretty. He introduced her as his niece, Miss Niner.

"Are you strolling, Mr. Sampson? Is it possible you can be idle?"

It *was* possible, and I *was* strolling.

"Shall we stroll together?"

"With pleasure."

The young lady walked between us, and we walked on the cool sea sand, in the direction of Filey.

"There have been wheels here," said Mr. Slinkton. "And now I look again, the wheels of a handcarriage! Margaret, my love, your shadow without doubt!"

"Miss Niner's shadow?" I repeated, looking down at it on the sand.

"Not that one," Mr. Slinkton returned, laughing. "Margaret, my dear, tell Mr. Sampson."

"Indeed," said the young lady, turning to me, "there is nothing to tell—except that I constantly see the same invalid old gentleman at all times, wherever I go. I have mentioned it to my uncle, and he calls the gentleman my shadow."

"Does he live in Scarborough?" I asked.

"He is staying here."

"Do you live in Scarborough?"

"No, I am staying here. My uncle has placed me with a family here, for my health."

"And your shadow?" said I, smiling.

"My shadow," she answered, smiling too, "is—like myself—not very robust, I fear; for I lose my shadow sometimes, as my shadow loses me at other times. We both seem liable to confinement to the house. I have not seen my shadow for days and days; but it does oddly happen, occasionally, that wherever I go, for many days together, this gentleman goes. We have come together in the most unfrequented nooks on this shore."

"Is this he?" said I, pointing before us.

The wheels had swept down to the water's edge, and described a great loop on the sand in turning. Bringing the loop back towards us, and spinning it out as it came, was a hand-carriage drawn by a man.

"Yes," said Miss Niner, "this really is my shadow, uncle."

As the carriage approached us and we approached the carriage, I saw within it an old man, whose head was sunk on his breast, and who was enveloped in a variety of wrappers. He was drawn by a very quiet but very keen-looking man, with iron-gray hair, who was slightly lame. They had passed us, when the carriage stopped, and the old gentleman within, putting out his arm, called to me by name. I went back, and was absent from Mr. Slinkton and his niece for about five minutes.

When I rejoined them, Mr. Slinkton was the first to speak. Indeed, he said to me in a raised voice before I came up with him:

33

"It is well you have not been longer, or my niece might have died of curiosity to know who her shadow is, Mr. Sampson."

"An old East India Director," said I. "An intimate friend of our friend's, at whose house I first had the pleasure of meeting you. A certain Major Banks. You have heard of him?"

"Never."

"Very rich, Miss Niner; but very old and very crippled. An amiable man, sensible—much interested in you. He has just been expatiating on the affection that he has observed to exist between you and your uncle."

Mr. Slinkton was holding his hat again, and he passed his hand up the straight walk, as if he himself went up it serenely, after me.

"Mr. Sampson," he said, tenderly pressing his niece's arm in his, "our affection was always a strong one, for we have had but a few near ties. We have still fewer now. We have associations to bring us together, that are not of this world, Margaret."

"Dear uncle!" murmured the young lady, and turned her face aside to hide her tears.

"My niece and I have such remembrances and regrets in common, Mr. Sampson," he feelingly pursued, "that it would be strange indeed if the relations between us were cold or indifferent. If I remember a conversation we once had together, you will understand the reference I make. Cheer up, dear Margaret. Don't droop, don't droop. My Margaret! I cannot bear to see you droop!"

The poor young lady was very much affected, but controlled herself. His feelings, too, were very acute. In a word, he found himself under such great need of a restorative, that he presently went away, to take a bath of sea-water, leaving the young lady and me sitting by a point of rock, and probably presuming—but that you will say was a pardonable indulgence in a luxury—that she would praise him with all her heart.

She did, poor thing! With all her confiding heart, she praised him to me, for his care of her dead sister, and for his untiring devotion in her last illness. The sister had wasted away very slowly, and wild and terrible fantasies had come over her toward the end, but he had never been impatient with her, or at a loss; had always been gentle, watchful, and self-possessed. The sister had known him, as she had known him, to be the best of men, the kindest of men, and yet a man of such admirable strength of character, as to be a very tower for the support of

34

their weak natures while their poor lives endured.

"I shall leave him, Mr. Sampson, very soon," said the young lady; "I know my life is drawing to an end; and when I am gone, I hope he will marry and be happy. I am sure he has lived single so long, only for my sake, and for my poor, poor sister's."

The little hand-carriage had made another great loop on the damp sand, and was coming back again, gradually spinning out a slim figure of eight, half a mile long.

"Young lady," said I, looking around, laying my hand upon her arm, and speaking in a low voice, "time presses. You hear the gentle murmur of that sea?"

She looked at me with the utmost wonder and alarm saying, "Yes!"

"And you know what a voice is in it when the storm comes?"

"Yes!"

"You see how quiet and peaceful it lies before us, and you know what an awful sight of power without pity it might be, this very night!"

"Yes!"

"But if you had never heard or seen it, or heard of it in its cruelty, could you believe that it beats every inanimate thing in its way to pieces, without mercy, and destroys life without remorse?"

"You terrify me, sir, by these questions!"

"To save you, young lady, to save you! For God's sake, collect your strength and collect your firmness! If you were here alone, and hemmed in by the rising tide on the flow to fifty feet above your head, you could not be in greater danger than the danger you are now to be saved from."

The figure on the sand was spun out, and straggled off into a crooked little jerk that ended at the cliff very near us.

"As I am, before Heaven and the Judge of all mankind, your friend, and your dead sister's friend, I solemnly entreat you, Miss Niner, without one moment's loss of time, to come to this gentleman with me!"

If the little carriage had been less near to us, I doubt if I could have got her away; but it was so near that we were there before she had recovered the hurry of being urged from the rock. I did not remain there with her for two minutes. Certainly within five, I had the inexpressible satisfaction of seeing her— from the point we had sat on, and to which I had returned— half supported and half carried up some rude steps notched in the cliff, by the figure of an active man. With that figure beside her, I knew she was safe anywhere.

I sat alone on the rock, awaiting Mr. Slinkton's return. The twilight was deepening and the shadows were heavy, when he came round the point, with his hat hanging at his buttonhole, smoothing his wet hair with one of his hands, and picking out the old path with the other and a pocket-comb.

"My niece not here, Mr. Sampson?" he said, looking about.

"Miss Niner seemed to feel a chill in the air after the sun was down, and has gone home."

He looked surprised as though she were not accustomed to do anything without him.

"I persuaded Miss Niner," I explained.

"Ah!" said he. "She is easily persuaded—for her good. Thank you, Mr. Sampson; she is better within doors. The bathing-place was farther than I thought, to say the truth."

"Miss Niner is very delicate," I observed.

He shook his head and drew a deep sigh. "Very, very, very. You may recollect my saying so. The time that has since intervened has not strengthened her. The gloomy shadow that fell upon her sister so early in life seems, in my anxious eyes, to gather over her, ever darker, ever darker. Dear Margaret, dear Margaret! But we must hope."

The hand-carriage was spinning away before us at a most indecorous pace for an invalid vehicle, and was making most irregular curves upon the sand. Mr. Slinkton, noticing it, said:

"If I may judge from appearances, your friend will be upset, Mr. Sampson."

"It looks probable, certainly," said I.

"The servant must be drunk."

"The servants of old gentlemen will get drunk sometimes," said I.

"The major draws very light, Mr. Sampson."

"The major does draw light," said I.

By this time the carriage, much to my relief, was lost in the darkness. We walked on for a little, side by side over the sand, in silence. After a short while he said, in a voice still affected by the emotion that his niece's state of health had awakened in him,

"Do you stay here long, Mr. Sampson?"

"Why, no. I am going away tonight."

"So soon? But business always holds you in request. Men like

Mr. Sampson are too important to others, to be spared to their own need of relaxation and enjoyment."

"I don't know about that," said I. "However, I am going back. To London."

"I shall be there too, soon after you."

I knew that as well as he did. But I did not tell him so. Any more than I told him what defensive weapon my right hand rested on in my pocket, as I walked by his side. Any more than I told him why I did not walk on the sea side of him with the night closing in.

We left the beach, and our ways diverged. We exchanged good nights, and had parted indeed, when he said, returning,

"Mr. Sampson, *may* I ask? Poor Meltham, whom we spoke of—dead yet?"

"Not when I last heard of him; but too broken a man to live long, and hopelessly lost to his old calling."

"Dear, dear, dear!" said he, with great feeling. "Sad, sad, sad! The world is a grave!" And so went his way.

It was not his fault if the world were not a grave; but I did not call that observation after him, any more than I had mentioned those other things just now enumerated. He went his way, and I went mine with all expedition. This happened, as I have said, either at the end of September or beginning of October. The next time I saw him, and the last, was late in November.

I had a very particular engagement to breakfast in the Temple. It was a bitter northeasterly morning, and the sleet and slush lay inches deep in the streets. I could get no conveyance, and was soon wet to the knees; but I should have been true to that appointment, though I had to wade to it up to my neck in the same impediments.

The appointment took me to some chambers in the Temple. They were at the top of a lonely corner house overlooking the river. The name, MR. ALFRED BECKWITH, was painted on the outer door. On the door opposite, on the same landing, the name MR. JULIUS SLINKTON. The doors of both sets of chambers stood open, so that anything said aloud in one set could be heard in the other.

I had never been in those chambers before. They were dismal, close, unwholesome, and oppressive; the furniture, originally good, and not yet old, was faded and dirty—the rooms were in great disorder; there was a strong prevailing smell of opium, brandy and tobacco; the grate and fire-irons were splashed all over with unsightly blotches of rust: and on a sofa by the fire, in the room where breakfast had been prepared, lay the host, Mr. Beckwith, a man with all the appearance of the worst kind of drunkard, very far advanced upon his shameful way to death.

"Slinkton is not come yet," said this creature, staggering up when I went in; "I'll call him—Halloa! Julius Ceasar! Come and drink!" As he hoarsely roared this out, he beat the poker and tongs together in a mad way, as if that were his usual manner of summoning his associate.

The voice of Mr. Slinkton was heard through the clatter from the opposite side of the staircase, and he came in. He had not expected the pleasure of meeting me. I have seen several artful men brought to a stand, but I never saw a man so aghast as he was when his eyes rested on mine.

"Julius Caesar," cried Beckwith, staggering between us, "Mist' Sampson! Mist' Sampson, Julius Caesar! Julius, Mist' Sampson, is the friend of my soul. Julius keeps me plied with liquor, morning, noon, and night. Julius is a real benefactor. Julius threw the tea and coffee out of window when I used to have any. Julius empties all the water-jugs of their contents, and fills 'em with spirits. Julius winds me up and keeps me going—Boil the brandy, Julius!"

There was a rusty and furred saucepan in the ashes—the ashes looked like the accumulation of weeks—and Beckwith, rolling and staggering between us as if he were going to plunge headlong into the fire, got the saucepan out, and tried to force it into Slinkton's hand.

"Boil the brandy, Julius Caesar! Come! Do your usual office. Boil the brandy!"

He became so fierce in his gesticulations with the saucepan, that I expected to see him lay open Slinkton's head with it. I therefore put out my hand to check him. He reeled back to the sofa, and sat there panting, shaking, and red-eyed, in his rags of dressing-gown, looking at us both. I noticed then that there was nothing to drink on the table but brandy, and nothing to eat but some salted herrings, and a dish of hot, sickly, highly peppered stew.

"At all events, Mr. Sampson," said Slinkton, offering me the smooth gravel path for the last time, "I thank you for interfering between me and this unfortunate man's violence. However you came here, Mr. Sampson, or with whatever motive you came here, at least I thank you for that."

Without gratifying his desire to know how I came there, I said, quietly, "How is your niece, Mr. Slinkton?"

He looked hard at me and I looked hard at him.

"I am sorry to say, Mr. Sampson, that my niece has proved treacherous and ungrateful to her best friend. She left me without a word of notice or explanation. She was misled, no doubt, by some designing rascal. Perhaps you may have heard of it."

"I did hear that she was misled by a designing rascal. In fact, I have proof of it."

"Are you sure of that?" said he.

"Quite."

"Boil the brandy," muttered Beckwith. "Company to breakfast, Julius Caesar. Do your usual office—provide the usual breakfast, dinner, tea, and supper. Boil the brandy!"

The eyes of Slinkton looked from him to me, and he said, after a moment's consideration,

"Mr. Sampson, you are a man of the world, and so am I. I will be plain with you."

"And I tell you you will not," said I. "I know all about you. *You* plain with any other? Nonsense, nonsense!"

"I plainly tell you, Mr. Sampson," he went on, with a manner almost composed, "that I understand your object. You want to save your funds, and escape from your liabilities; these are old tricks of the trade with you Office-gentlemen. But you will not do it sir; you will not succeed. You have not an easy adversary to play against, when you play against me. We shall have to inquire in due time, when and how Mr. Beckwith fell into his present habits. With that remark, sir, I put this poor creature, and his incoherent wanderings of speech, aside, and wish you a good morning and a better case next time."

While he was saying this, Beckwith had filled a half-pint glass with brandy. At this moment, he threw the brandy at his face, and threw the glass after it. Slinkton put his hands up, half blinded with the spirit, and cut with the glass across the forehead. At the sound of the breakage, a fourth person came into the room, closed the door, and stood at it; he was a very quiet but very keen-looking man, with iron-gray hair, and slightly lame.

Slinkton pulled out his handkerchief, assuaged the pain in

his smarting eyes, and dabbled the blood on his forehead. He was a long time about it, and I saw that in the doing of it, a tremendous change came over him, occassioned by the change in Beckwith—who ceased to pant and tremble, sat upright, and never took his eyes off him. I never in my life saw a face in which abhorrence and determination were so forcibly painted as in Beckwith's then.

"Look at me, you villain," said Beckwith, "and see me as I really am. I took these rooms, to make them a trap for you. I came into them as a drunkard, to bait the trap for you. You fell into the trap, and you will never leave it alive. On the morning when you last went to Mr. Sampson's office, I had seen him first. Your plot has been known to both of us, all along, and you have been counterplotted all along. What? Having been cajoled into putting that prize of two thousand pounds in your power, I was to be done to death with brandy, and, brandy not proving quick enough, with something quicker? Have I never seen you, when you thought my senses gone, pouring from your little bottle into my glass? Why, you murderer and forger, alone here with you in the dead of night, as I have so often been, I have had my hand upon the trigger of a pistol, twenty times, to blow your brains out!"

This sudden starting up of the thing that he had supposed to be his imbecile victim into a determined man, with a settled resolution to hunt him down and be the death of him, mercilessly expressed from head to foot, was, in the first shock, too much for him. Without any figure of speech, he staggered under it. But there is no greater mistake than to suppose that a man who is a calculating criminal, is, in any phase of his guilt, otherwise than true to himself, and perfectly consistent with his whole character. Such a man commits murder, and murder is the natural culmination of his course; such a man has to outface murder, and will do it with hardihood and effrontery. It is a sort of fashion to express surprise that any notorious criminal having such crime upon his conscience, can so brave it out. Do you think that if he had it on his conscience at all, or had a conscience to have it upon, he would ever have committed the crime?

Perfectly consistent with himself, as I believe all such monsters to be, this Slinkton recovered himself, and showed a defiance that was sufficiently cold and quiet. He was white, he was haggard, he was changed; but only as a sharper who had played for a great stake and had at the end been outwitted.

"Listen to me, you villain," said Beckwith, "and let every word you hear me say be a stab in your wicked heart. When I took these rooms, to throw myself in your way and lead you on to the scheme that I knew my appearance and supposed character and habits would suggest to such a devil, how did I know that? Because you were no stranger to me. I knew you well. And I knew you to be the cruel wretch who, for so much money, had killed one innocent girl while she trusted him implicitly, and who was by inches killing another."

Slinkton took out a snuff-box, took a pinch of snuff, and laughed.

"But see here," said Beckwith, never looking away, never raising his voice, never relaxing his face, never unclenching his hand. "See what a dull wolf you have been, after all! The infatuated drunkard who never drank a fiftieth part of the liquor you plied him with, but poured it away, here, there, everywhere—almost before your eyes; who brought over the fellow you set to watch him and to ply him, by outbidding you in his bribe, before he had been at work three days—with whom you have observed no caution, yet who was so bent on ridding the earth of you as a wild beast, that he should have defeated you if you had been ever so prudent—that drunkard whom you have, many a time, left on the floor of this room, and who has even let you go out of it, alive and undeceived, when you have turned him over with your foot—has, almost as often, on the same night, within an hour, within a few minutes, watched you awake, had his hand at your pillow when you were asleep, turned over your papers, taken samples from your bottles and packets of powder, changed their contents, rifled every secret of your life!"

He had another pinch of snuff in his hand, but had gradually let it drop from between his fingers to the floor; where he now smoothed it out with his foot, looking down at it the while.

"That drunkard," said Beckwith, "who had free access to your rooms at all times, that he might drink the strong drinks that you left in his way and be the sooner ended, holding no more terms with you than he would hold with a tiger, has had his master-key for all your locks, his test for all your poisons, his clue to your cipher-writing. He can tell you, as well as you can tell him, how long it took to complete that deed, what doses there were, what intervals, what signs of gradual decay upon mind and body; what distempered fancies were produced, what observable changes, what physical pain. He can tell you, as well as you can tell him, that all this was recorded day by day, as a lesson of experience for future service. He can tell you, better than you can tell him, where that journal is now."

Slinkton stopped the action of his foot, and looked at Beckwith.

"No," said the latter, as if answering a question from him. "Not in the drawer of the writing-desk that opens with a spring; it is not there, and it never will be there again."

"Then you are a thief!" said Slinkton.

Without any change whatever in the inflexible purpose, which it was quite terrific even to me to contemplate, and from the power of which I had always felt convinced it was impossible for this wretch to escape, Beckwith returned,

"I am your niece's shadow, too."

With an imprecation Slinkton put his hand to his head, tore out some hair, and flung it to the ground. It was the end of the smooth walk; he destroyed it in the action, and it will soon be seen that his use for it was past.

Beckwith went on: "Whenever you left here, I left here. Although I understood that you found it necessary to pause in the completion of that purpose, to avert suspicion, still I watched you close, with the poor confiding girl. When I had the diary, and could read it word by word—it was only about the night before your last visit to Scarborough—you remember the night? you slept with a small flat vial tied to your wrist—I sent to Mr. Sampson, who was kept out of view. This is Mr. Sampson's trusty servant standing by the door. We three saved your niece among us."

Slinkton looked at us all, took an uncertain step or two from the place where he had stood, returned to it, and glanced about him in a very curious way—as one of the meaner reptiles might, looking for a hole to hide in. I noticed at the same time, that a singular change took place in the figure of the man—as if it collapsed within his clothes, and they consequently became ill-shapen and ill-fitting.

"You shall know," said Beckwith, "for I hope the knowledge will be bitter and terrible to you, why you have been pursued by one man, and why, when the whole interest that Mr. Sampson represents would have expended any money in hunting you down, you have been tracked to death at a single individual's charge. I hear you have had the name of Meltham on your lips sometimes?"

I saw, in addition to those other changes, a sudden stoppage come upon his breathing.

"When you sent the sweet girl you murdered (you know with what artfully made-out surroundings and probabilities you sent her) to Meltham's office, before taking her abroad to originate the transaction that doomed her to the grave, it fell to Meltham's lot to see her and to speak with her. It did not fall to his lot to save her, though I know he would freely give his own life to have done it. He admired her—I would say he loved her deeply, if I thought it possible that you could understand the word. When she was sacrificed, he was thoroughly assured of your guilt. Having lost her, he had but one object left in life, and that was to avenge her and destroy you.

"That man Meltham," Beckwith steadily pursued, "was as absolutely certain that you could never elude him in this world, if he devoted himself to your destruction with his utmost fidelity and earnestness, and if he divided the sacred duty with no other duty in life, as he was certain that in achieving it he would be a poor instrument in the hands of Providence, and would do well before Heaven in striking you out from among living men. I am that man, and I thank God I have done my work!"

If Slinkton had been running for his life from swift-footed savages, a dozen miles, he could not have shown more emphatic signs of being oppressed at heart and laboring for breath, than he showed now, when he looked at the pursuer who had so relentlessly hunted him down.

"You never saw me under my right name before; you see me under my right name now. You shall see me once again in the body, when you are tried for your life. You shall see me once again in the spirit, when the cord is around your neck, and the crowd are crying against you!"

When Meltham had spoken these last words, the miscreant suddenly turned away his face, and seemed to strike his mouth with his open hand. At the same instant, the room was filled with a new and powerful odor, and, almost at the same instant, he broke into a crooked run, leap, start—I have no name for the spasm—and fell, with a dull weight that shook the heavy old doors and windows.

That was the fitting end of him.

When we saw that he was dead, we drew away from the room, and Meltham, giving me his hand, said, wearily, "I have no more work on earth, my friend. But I shall see her again else-where."

It was in vain that I tried to rally him. He might have saved her, he said; he had not saved her, and he reproached himself; he had lost her, and he was broken-hearted.

"The purpose that sustained me is over, Sampson, and there is nothing now to hold me to life. I am not fit for life; I am weak and spiritless; I have no hope and no object."

In truth, I could hardly have believed that the broken man who then spoke to me was the man who had so strongly and so differently impressed me when his purpose was before him. I used such entreaties with him, as I could; but he still said and always said, in a patient, undemonstrative way—nothing could avail him—he was broken-hearted.

He died early in the next spring. He was buried by the side of the poor young lady for whom he had cherished those tender and unhappy regrets; and he left all he had to her sister. She lived to be a happy wife and mother; she married my sister's son, who succeeded poor Meltham; she is living now, and her children ride about the garden on my walking-stick when I go to see her.

THE BITER BIT

BY WILKIE COLLINS

William Wilkie Collins was born in London on January 8, 1824. While apprenticed to a tea merchant at the age of seventeen, he wrote his first novel, *Antonina*, which was published in 1850. He later studied law. He often collaborated on articles and stories with his close friend, Charles Dickens. Collins' tales of mystery and suspense include *The Woman in White* (1860) and *The Moonstone* (1868), which introduced his rose-growing detective, Sergeant Cuff. Other novels include *No Name* (1862), *Hide and Seek* (1854), and *The Law and the Lady* (1875), based on the famous poisoning trial of Madeleine Smith. Collins died on September 23, 1889.

THE BITER BIT

LONDON, *4th July*, 18—

SERGEANT BULMER,—This is to inform you that you are wanted to assist in looking up a case of importance, which will require all the attention of an experienced member of the force. The matter of the robbery on which you are now engaged, you will please to shift over to the young man who brings you this letter. You will tell him all the circumstances of the case, just as they stand; you will put him up to the progress you have made (if any) towards detecting the person or persons by whom the money has been stolen; and you will leave him to make the best he can of the matter now in your hands. He is to have the whole responsibility of the case, and the whole credit of his success, if he is successful.

So much for the orders that I am desired to communicate to you.

A word in your ear, next, about this new man who is to take your place. His name is Matthew Sharpin; and he is to have the chance given him of dashing into our office at a jump—supposing he turns out strong enough to take it. You will naturally ask me how he comes by this privilege. I can only tell you that he has some uncommonly strong interest to back him in certain high quarters which you and I had better not mention except under our breaths. He has been a lawyer's clerk; and he is wonderfully conceited in his opinion of himself, as well as mean and underhanded to look at. According to his own account, he leaves his old trade and joins ours of his own free will and preference. You will no more believe that than I do. My notion is that he has managed to ferret out some private information in connection with the affairs of one of his master's clients, which makes him rather an awkward customer to keep in the office for the future, and which, at the same time, gives him hold enough over his employer to make it dangerous to drive him into a corner by turning him away. I think that giving him this unheard-of chance among us is, in plain words, pretty

46

much like giving him hush-money to keep him quiet. However that may be, Mr. Matthew Sharpin is to have the case now in your hands; and if he succeeds with it, he pokes his ugly nose into our office, as sure as fate. I put you up to this, Sergeant, so that you may not stand in your own light by giving the new man any cause to complain of you at headquarters, and remain yours,

FRANCIS THEAKSTONE

FROM MR. MATTHEW SHARPIN
TO CHIEF INSPECTOR THEAKSTONE

LONDON, 5th July, 18—

DEAR SIR,—Having now been favored with the necessary instructions from Sergeant Bulmer, I beg to remind you of certain directions which I have received, relating to the report of my future proceedings which I am to prepare for examination at headquarters.

The object of my writing, and of your examining what I have written, before you send it in to the higher authorities, is, I am informed, to give me, as an untried hand, the benefit of your advice, in case I want it (which I venture to think I shall not) at any stage of my proceedings. As the extraordinary circumstances of the case on which I am now engaged make it impossible for me to absent myself from the place where the robbery was committed, until I have made some progress towards discovering the thief, I am necessarily precluded from consulting you personally. Hence the necessity of my writing down the various details, which might, perhaps, be better communicated by word of mouth. This, if I am not mistaken, is the position in which we are now placed. I state my own impressions on the subject, in writing, in order that we may clearly understand each other at the outset; and have the honor to remain, your obedient servant,

MATTHEW SHARPIN

FROM CHIEF INSPECTOR THEAKSTONE
TO MR. MATTHEW SHARPIN

LONDON, 5th July, 18—

SIR,—You have begun by wasting time, ink, and paper. We both of us perfectly well knew the position we stood in towards each other when I sent you with my letter to Sergeant Bulmer. There was not the least need to repeat it in writing. Be so good as to employ your pen, in future, on the business actually in hand.

You have now three separate matters on which to write to me. First, you have to draw up a statement of your instructions received from Sergeant Bulmer, in order to show us that nothing has escaped your memory, and that you are thoroughly acquainted with all the circumstances of the case which has been entrusted to you. Secondly, you are to inform me what it is you propose to do. Thirdly, you are to report every inch of your progress (if you make any) from day to day, and, if need be, from hour to hour as well. This is *your* duty. As to what *my* duty may be, when I want you to remind me of it, I will write and tell you so. In the meantime, I remain, yours,

FRANCIS THEAKSTONE

FROM MR. MATTHEW SHARPIN TO
CHIEF INSPECTOR THEAKSTONE

LONDON, 6th *July*, 18—

SIR,—You are rather an elderly person and, as such, naturally inclined to be a little jealous of men like me, who are in the prime of their lives and their faculties. Under these circumstances, it is my duty to be considerate towards you, and not to bear too hardly on your small failings. I decline, therefore, altogether, to take offense at the tone of your letter; I give you the full benefit of the natural generosity of my nature; I sponge the very existence of your surly communication out of my memory—in short, Chief Inspector Theakstone, I forgive you, and proceed to business.

My first duty is to draw up a full statement of the instructions I have received from Sergeant Bulmer. Here they are at your service, according to my version of them:

At number 13 Rutherford Street, Soho, there is a stationer's shop. It is kept by one Mr. Yatman. He is a married man, but has no family. Besides Mr. and Mrs. Yatman, the other inmates in the house are a young single man named Jay, who lodges in the front room on the second floor—a shopman, who sleeps in one of the attics—and a servant-of-all-work, whose bed is in the back-kitchen. Once a week a charwoman comes for a few hours in the morning only, to help this servant. These are all the persons who, on ordinary occasions, have means of access to the interior of the house.

Mr. Yatman has been in business for many years, carrying on his affairs prosperously enough to realize a handsome independence for a person in his position. Unfortunately for himself he endeavored to increase the amount of his property by speculating. He ventured boldly in his investments, luck went against him, and rather less than two years ago he found himself a poor man again. All that was saved out of the wreck of his property was the sum of two hundred pounds.

Although Mr. Yatman did his best to meet his altered circumstances, by giving up many of the luxuries and comforts to which he and his wife had been accustomed, he found it impossible to retrench so far as to allow him to put by any money from the income produced by the shop. The business has been declining of late years—the cheap advertising stationers having done it injury with the public. Consequently, up to the last week the only surplus property possessed by Mr. Yatman consisted of the two hundred pounds which had been recovered from the wreck of his fortune. This sum was placed as a deposit in a joint-stock bank of the highest possible character.

Eight days ago Mr. Yatman and his lodger, Mr. Jay, held a conversation on the subject of the commercial difficulties which are hampering trade in all directions at the present time. Mr. Jay (who lives by supplying the newspapers with short paragraphs relating to incidents, offenses, and brief records of remarkable occurrences in general—who is, in short, what they call a penny-a-liner) told his landlord that he had been in the city that day, and had heard unfavorable rumors on the subject of the joint-stock banks. The rumors to which he alluded had already reached the ears of Mr. Yatman from other quarters; and the confirmation of them by his lodger had such an effect on his mind—predisposed as it was to alarm by the experience of his former losses—that he resolved to go at once to the bank and withdraw his deposit.

It was then getting on towards the end of the afternoon; and he arrived just in time to receive his money before the bank closed.

He received the deposit in banknotes of the following amounts: one fifty-pound note, three twenty-pound notes, six ten-pound notes, and six five-pound notes.

He brought the money back in an envelope placed in his

breast-pocket; and asked his shopman, on getting home, to look for a small flat tin cashbox, which had not been used for years, and which, as Mr. Yatman remembered it, was exactly the right size to hold the banknotes. For some time the cashbox was searched for in vain. Mr. Yatman called to his wife to know if she had any idea where it was. The question was overheard by the servant-of-all-work, who was taking up the tea-tray at the time, and by Mr. Jay, who was coming downstairs on his way out to the theater. Ultimately the cashbox was found by the shopman. Mr. Yatman placed the banknotes in it, secured them by a padlock, and put the box in his coatpocket. It stuck out of the coatpocket very little, but enough to be seen. Mr. Yatman remained at home, upstairs, all the evening. No visitors called. At eleven o'clock he went to bed, and put the cashbox, along with his clothes, on a chair by the bedside.

When he and wife woke the next morning, the box was gone. Payment of the notes was immediately stopped at the Bank of England; but no news of the money has been heard of since that time.

So far, the circumstances of the case are perfectly clear. They point unmistakably to the conclusion that the robbery must have been committed by some person living in the house. Suspicion falls, therefore, upon the servant-of-all-work, upon the shopman, and upon Mr. Jay. The first two knew that the cashbox was being inquired for by their master, but did not know what it was he wanted to put into it. They would assume, of course, that it was money. They both had opportunities (the servant, when she took away the tea—and the shopman, when he came, after shutting up, to give the keys of the till to his master) of seeing the cashbox in Mr. Yatman's pocket, and of inferring naturally, from its position there, that he intended to take it into his bedroom with him at night.

Mr. Jay, on the other hand, had been told, during the afternoon's conversation on the subject of joint-stock banks, that his landlord had a deposit of two hundred pounds in one of them. He also knew that Mr. Yatman left him with the intention of drawing that money out; and he heard the inquiry for the cashbox, afterwards, when he was coming downstairs. He must, therefore, have inferred that the money was in the house, and that the cashbox was the receptacle intended to contain it. That he could have had any idea, however, of the place in which Mr. Yatman intended to keep it for the night is impossible, seeing that he went out before the box was found, and did not return till his landlord was in bed. Consequently, if he committed the robbery, he must have gone into the bedroom purely on speculation.

Speaking of the bedroom reminds me of the necessity of noticing the situation of it in the house, and the means that exist of gaining easy access to it at any hour of the night.

The room in question is the backroom on the first floor. In consequence of Mrs. Yatman's constitutional nervousness on the subject of fire (which makes her apprehend being burned alive in her room, in case of accident, by the hampering of the lock if the key is turned in it) her husband has never been accustomed to lock the bedroom door. Both he and his wife are, by their own admission, heavy sleepers. Consequently, the risk to be run by any evil-disposed persons wishing to plunder the bedroom was of the most trifling kind. They could enter the room by merely turning the handle of the door; and if they moved with ordinary caution, there was no fear of their waking the sleepers inside. This fact is of importance. It strengthens our conviction that the money must have been taken by one of the inmates of the house.

Such are the circumstances, as they were related to Sergeant Bulmer, when he was first called in to discover the guilty parties and, if possible, to recover the lost banknotes. The strictest inquiry which he could institute failed to produce the smallest fragment of evidence against any of the persons on whom suspicion naturally fell. Their language and behavior, on being informed of the robbery, were perfectly consistent with the language and behavior of innocent people. Sergeant Bulmer felt from the first that this was a case for private inquiry and secret observation. He began by recommending Mr. and Mrs. Yatman to affect a feeling of perfect confidence in the innocence of the persons living under their roof; and he then opened the campaign by employing himself in following the goings and comings, and in discovering the friends, the habits, and the secrets of the maid-of-all-work.

Three days and nights of exertions on his own part, and on that of others who were competent to assist his investigations, were enough to satisfy him that there was no sound cause for suspicion against the girl.

He next practiced the same precaution in relation to the shopman. There was more difficulty and uncertainty in privately clearing up this person's character without his knowledge, but the obstacles were at last smoothed away with tolerable success; and though there is not the same amount of certainty in this case which there was in that of the girl, there is still fair reason for supposing that the shopman has had nothing to do with the robbery of the cashbox.

As a necessary consequence of these proceedings, the range of suspicion now becomes limited to the lodger, Mr. Jay.

When I presented your letter of introduction to Sergeant Bulmer, he had already made some inquiries on the subject of this young man. The result, so far, has not been at all favorable. Mr. Jay's habits are irregular; he frequents public houses, and seems to be familiarly acquainted with a great many dissolute characters; he is in debt to most of the tradespeople whom he employs; he has not paid his rent to Mr. Yatman for the last month; yesterday evening he came home excited by liquor, and last week he was seen talking to a prizefighter. In short, though Mr. Jay does call himself a journalist, by virtue of his penny-a-line contributions to the newspapers, he is a young man of low tastes, vulgar manners, and bad habits.

I have now reported, down to the very last details, all the particulars communicated to me by Sergeant Bulmer. I believe you will not find an omission anywhere; and I think you will admit, though you are prejudiced against me, that a clearer statement of facts was never laid before you than the statement I have now made. My next duty is to tell you what I propose to do now.

In the first place, it is clearly my business to take up the case at the point where Sergeant Bulmer has left it. On his authority, I am justified in assuming that I have no need to trouble myself about the maid-of-all-work and the shopman. Their characters are now to be considered as cleared up. What remains to be privately investigated is the question of the guilt or innocence of Mr. Jay.

This is the plan that I have adopted, with the full approval of Mr. and Mrs. Yatman.

I propose, today, to present myself at the house in the character of a young man who is looking for lodgings. The back room on the second floor will be shown to me as the room to let; and I shall establish myself there tonight, as a person from the country who has come to London to look for a situation in a respectable shop or office.

52

By this means I shall be living next to the room occupied by Mr. Jay. The partition between us is mere lath and plaster. I shall make a small hole in it, near the cornice, through which I can see what Mr. Jay does in his room, and hear every word that is said when any friend happens to call on him. Whenever he is at home, I shall be at my post of observation. Whenever he goes out, I shall be after him. By employing these means of watching him I believe I may look forward to the discovery of his secret—if he knows anything about the lost banknotes—as to a dead certainty.

What you may think of my plan of observation I cannot undertake to say. It appears to me to unite the invaluable merits of boldness and simplicity. Fortified by this conviction, I close the present communication with feelings of the most sanguine description in regard to the future, and remain your obedient servant,

MATTHEW SHARPIN.

FROM THE SAME TO THE SAME

7th July.

SIR,—As you have not honored me with any answer to my last communication, I assume that, in spite of your prejudices against me, it has produced the favorable impression on your mind which I ventured to anticipate. Gratified beyond measure by the token of approval which your eloquent silence conveys to me, I proceed to report the progress that has been made in the course of the last twenty-four hours.

I am now comfortably established next door to Mr. Jay; and I am delighted to say that I have two holes in the partition, instead of one. My natural sense of humor has led me into the pardonable extravagance of giving them appropriate names. One I call my Peep-hole, and the other my Pipe-hole. The name of the first explains itself; the name of the second refers to a small tin pipe, or tube, inserted in the hole, and twisted so that the mouth of it comes close to my ear, while I am standing at my post of observation. Thus, while I am looking at Mr. Jay through my Peep-hole, I can hear every word that may be spoken in his room through my Pipe-hole.

Perfect candor—a virtue which I have possessed from my childhood—compels me to acknowledge, before I go any further, that the ingenious notion of adding a Pipe-hole to my

53

proposed Peep-hole originated with Mrs. Yatman. This lady—a most intelligent and accomplished person, simple, and yet distinguished, in her manners—has entered into all my little plans with an enthusiasm and intelligence which I cannot too highly praise. Mr. Yatman is so cast down by his loss that he is quite incapable of affording me any assistance. Mrs. Yatman, who is evidently most tenderly attached to him, feels her husband's sad condition of mind even more acutely than she feels the loss of the money; and is mainly stimulated to exertion by her desire to assist in raising him from the miserable state of prostration into which he has now fallen.

"The money, Mr. Sharpin," she said to me yesterday evening, with tears in her eyes, "the money may be regained by rigid economy and strict attention to business. It is my husband's wretched state of mind that makes me so anxious for the discovery of the thief. I may be wrong, but I felt hopeful of success as soon as you entered the house; and I believe, if the wretch who has robbed us is to be found, you are the man to discover him." I accepted this gratifying compliment in the spirit in which it was offered—firmly believing that I shall be found, sooner or later, to have thoroughly deserved it.

Let me now return to business.

I have enjoyed some hours of calm observation of Mr. Jay. Though rarely at home, as I understand from Mrs. Yatman, on ordinary occasions, he has been indoors the whole of this day. That is suspicious, to begin with. I have to report, further, that he rose at a late hour this morning (always a bad sign in a young man), and that he lost a great deal of time, after he was up, in yawning and complaining to himself of headache. Like other debauched characters, he ate little or nothing for breakfast. His next proceeding was to smoke a pipe—a dirty clay pipe, which a gentleman would have been ashamed to put between his lips. When he had done smoking, he took out pen, ink, and paper, and sat down to write with a groan—whether of remorse for having taken the banknotes, or of disgust at the task before him, I am unable to say. After writing a few lines (too far away from my Peep-hole to give me a chance of reading over his shoulder), he leaned back in his chair, and amused himself by humming the tunes of certain popular songs. Whether these do, or do not, represent secret signals by which he communicates with his accomplices remains to be seen. After he had amused himself for some time by humming, he got up and began to walk about the room, occasionally stopping to add a sentence to the paper on his desk. Before long, he went to a locked cupboard and opened it. I strained my eyes eagerly, in expectation of making a discovery. I saw him take something carefully out of the cupboard—he turned round—and it was only a pint bottle of brandy! Having drunk some of the liquor, this extremely indolent reprobate lay down on his bed again, and in five minutes was fast asleep.

After hearing him snoring for at least two hours, I was recalled to my Peep-hole by a knock at his door. He jumped up and opened it with suspicious activity.

A very small boy, with a very dirty face, walked in, said, "Please, sir, they're waiting for you," sat down on a chair, with his legs a long way from the ground, and instantly fell asleep! Mr. Jay swore an oath, tied a wet towel round his head, and going back to his paper, began to cover it with writing as fast as his fingers could move the pen. Occasionally getting up to dip the towel in water and tie it on again, he continued at this employment for nearly three hours; then folded up the leaves of writing, woke the boy, and gave them to him, with this remarkable expression: "Now, then, young sleepyhead, quick—march! If you see the governor, tell him to have the money ready when I call for it." The boy grinned, and disappeared. I was sorely tempted to follow "sleepyhead," but, on reflection, considered it safest still to keep my eye on the proceedings of Mr. Jay.

In half an hour's time he put on his hat and walked out. Of course, I put on my hat and walked out also. As I went downstairs, I passed Mrs. Yatman going up. The lady has been kind enough to undertake, by previous arrangement between us, to search Mr. Jay's room, while he is out of the way, and while I am necessarily engaged in the pleasing duty of following him wherever he goes. On the occasion to which I now refer, he walked straight to the nearest tavern, and ordered a couple of mutton chops for his dinner. I placed myself in the next box to him, and ordered a couple of mutton chops for my dinner. Before I had been in the room a minute, a young man of highly suspicious manners and appearance, sitting at a table opposite, took his glass of port and joined Mr. Jay.

"Jack has been here inquiring after you," says the young man.

"Did he leave any message?" asks Mr. Jay.

"Yes," says the other. "He told me, if I met you, to say that he wished very particularly to see you tonight, and that he would give you a look in, at Rutherford Street, at seven o'clock."

"All right," says Mr. Jay. "I'll get back in time to see him."

Upon this, the suspicious-looking young man finished his port, and saying that he was rather in a hurry, took leave of his friend (perhaps I should not be wrong if I said his accomplice) and left the room.

At twenty-five minutes and a half past six—in these serious cases it is important to be particular about time—Mr. Jay finished his chops and paid his bill. At twenty-six minutes and three-quarters I finished my chops and paid mine. In ten minutes more I was inside the house in Rutherford Street, and was received by Mrs. Yatman in the passage. That charming woman's face exhibited an expression of melancholy and disappointment which it quite grieved me to see.

"I am afraid, Ma'am," says I, "that you have not hit on any little incriminating discovery in the lodger's room?"

She shook her head and sighed. It was a soft, languid, fluttering sigh—and, upon my life, it quite upset me.

"Don't despair, Ma'am," I said, with an insinuating mildness which seemed to touch her. "I have heard a mysterious conversation—I know of a guilty appointment—and I expect great things from my Peep-hole and my Pipe-hole tonight. I think we are on the brink of a discovery."

Here my enthusiastic devotion to business got the better of my tender feelings. I looked—winked—nodded—left her.

When I got back to my observatory, I found Mr. Jay digesting his mutton chops in an armchair, with his pipe in his mouth. On his table were two tumblers, a jug of water, and the pint bottle of brandy. It was then close upon seven o'clock. As the hour struck, the person described as "Jack" walked in.

He looked agitated—I am happy to say he looked violently agitated. The cheerful glow of anticipated success diffused itself (to use a strong expression) all over me, from head to foot. With breathless interest I looked through my Peep-hole, and saw the visitor—the "Jack" of this delightful case—sit down, facing me, at the opposite side of the table to Mr. Jay. Making allowance for the difference in expression which their countenances just now happened to exhibit, these two abandoned villains were so much alike in other respects as to lead at once to the conclusion that they were brothers. Jack was the cleaner

56

man and the better dressed of the two. I admit that, at the outset. It is, perhaps, one of my failings to push justice and impartiality to their utmost limits. I am no Pharisee; and where Vice has its redeeming point, I say, let Vice have its due—yes, yes, by all manner of means, let Vice have its due.

"What's the matter now, Jack?" says Mr. Jay.

"Can't you see it in my face?" says Jack. "My dear fellow, delays are dangerous. Let us have done with suspense, and risk it the day after tomorrow."

"So soon as that?" cried Mr. Jay, looking very much astonished. "Well, I'm ready, if you are. But, I say, Jack, is Somebody Else ready too? Are you quite sure of that?"

He smiled as he spoke—a frightful smile—and laid a very strong emphasis on those two words, "Somebody Else." There is evidently a third ruffian, a nameless desperado, concerned in the business.

"Meet us tomorrow," says Jack, "and judge for yourself. Be in the Regent's Park at eleven in the morning."

"I'll be there," says Mr. Jay. "Have a drop of brandy and water? What are you getting up for? You're not going already?"

"Yes, I am," says Jack. "The fact is, I'm so excited and agitated that I can't sit still anywhere for five minutes together. Ridiculous as it may appear to you, I'm in a perpetual state of nervous flutter. I can't, for the life of me, help fearing that we shall be found out. I fancy that every man who looks twice at me in the street is a spy—"

At those words I thought my legs would have given way under me. Nothing but strength of mind kept me at my Peephole—nothing else, I give you my word of honor.

"Stuff and nonsense!" cried Mr. Jay, with all the effrontery of a veteran in crime. "We have kept the secret up to this time, and we will manage cleverly to the end. Have a drop of brandy and water, and you will feel as certain about it as I do."

Jack steadily refused the brandy and water, and steadily persisted in taking his leave.

"I must try if I can't walk it off," he said. "Remember tomorrow morning—eleven o'clock, Avenue Road side of the Regent's Park."

With those words he went out. His hardened relative laughed desperately, and resumed the dirty clay pipe.

I sat down on the side of my bed, actually quivering with excitement.

It is clear to me that no attempt has yet been made to change the stolen banknotes; and I may add that Sergeant Bulmer was of that opinion also, when he left the case in my hands. What is the natural conclusion to draw from the conversation which I have just set down? Evidently, that the confederates meet to-morrow to take their respective shares in the stolen money, and to decide on the safest means of getting the notes changed the day after. Mr. Jay is, beyond a doubt, the leading criminal in this business, and he will probably run the chief risk—that of changing the fifty-pound note. I shall, therefore, still make it my business to follow him—attending at the Regent's Park to-morrow, and doing my best to hear what is said there. If another appointment is made the day after, I shall, of course, go to it. In the meantime, I shall want the immediate assistance of two competent persons (supposing the rascals separate after their meeting) to follow the two minor criminals. It is only fair to add that if the rogues all retire together, I shall probably keep my subordinates in reserve. Being naturally ambitious, I desire, if possible, to have the whole credit of discovering this robbery to myself.

8th July.

I have to acknowledge, with thanks, the speedy arrival of my two subordinates—men of very average abilities, I am afraid; but, fortunately, I shall always be there to direct them in their duties.

My first business this morning was, necessarily, to prevent mistakes by accounting to Mr. and Mrs. Yatman for the presence of two strangers on the scene. Mr. Yatman (between ourselves, a poor feeble man) only shook his head and groaned. Mrs. Yatman (that superior woman) favored me with a charming look of intelligence.

"Oh, Mr. Sharpin!" she said, "I am so sorry to see those two men! Your sending for their assistance looks as if you were beginning to be doubtful of success."

I privately winked at her (she is very good in allowing me to do so without taking offense), and told her, in my facetious way, that she labored under a slight mistake.

"It is because I am sure of success, Ma'am, that I send for them. I am determined to recover the money, not for my own sake only, but for Mr. Yatman's sake—and for yours."

I laid a considerable amount of stress on those last three words. She said, "Oh, Mr. Sharpin!" again—and blushed a heavenly red—and looked down at her work. I could go to the world's end with that woman, if Mr. Yatman would only die.

I sent off the two subordinates to wait, until I wanted them, at the Avenue Road gate of the Regent's Park. Half an hour afterwards I was following in the same direction myself, at the heels of Mr. Jay.

The two confederates were punctual to the appointed time, but the third rogue—the nameless desperado of my report, or if you prefer it, the mysterious "Somebody Else" of the conversation between the two brothers—is a Woman! And, what is worse, a young woman! And what is more lamentable still, a nice-looking woman! I have long resisted a growing conviction that, wherever there is mischief in this world, an individual of the fair sex is inevitably certain to be mixed up in it. After the experience of this morning I can struggle against that sad conclusion no longer. I give up the sex—excepting Mrs. Yatman, I give up the sex.

The man named "Jack" offered the woman his arm. Mr. Jay placed himself on the other side of her. The three then walked away slowly among the trees. I followed them at a respectful distance. My two subordinates, at a respectful distance also, followed me.

It was, I deeply regret to say, impossible to get near enough to them to overhear their conversation, without running too great a risk of being discovered. I could only infer from their gestures and actions that they were all three talking with extraordinary earnestness on some subject which deeply interested them. After having been engaged in this way a full quarter of an hour, they suddenly turned round to retrace their steps. My presence of mind did not forsake me in this emergency. I signed to the two subordinates to walk on carelessly and pass them, while I myself slipped dexterously behind a tree. As they came by me, I heard "Jack" address these words to Mr. Jay:

"Let us say half-past ten tomorrow morning. And mind you come in a cab. We had better not risk taking one in this neighborhood."

Mr. Jay made some brief reply, which I could not overhear. They walked back to the place at which they had met, shaking hands there with an audacious cordiality which it quite sickened me to see. They then separated. I followed Mr. Jay. My subordinates paid the same delicate attention to the other two.

Instead of taking me back to Rutherford Street, Mr. Jay led me to the Strand. He stopped at a dingy, disreputable-looking house which, according to the inscription over the door, was a newspaper office, but which, in my judgment, had all the external appearance of a place devoted to the reception of stolen goods.

After remaining inside for a few minutes, he came out, whistling, with his finger and thumb in his waistcoat pocket. A less discreet man than myself would have arrested him on the spot. I remembered the necessity of catching the two confederates, and the importance of not interfering with the appointment that had been made for the next morning. Such coolness as this, under trying circumstances, is rarely to be found, I should imagine, in a young beginner, whose reputation as a detective policeman is still to be made.

From the house of suspicious appearance Mr. Jay betook himself to a cigar-divan, and read the magazines over a cheroot. I sat at a table near him, and read the magazines likewise over a cheroot. From the divan he strolled to the tavern and had his chops. I strolled to the tavern and had my chops. When he had done, he went back to his lodging. When I had done, I went back to mine. He was overcome with drowsiness early in the evening, and went to bed. As soon as I heard him snoring, I was overcome with drowsiness, and went to bed also.

Early in the morning my two subordinates came to make their report.

They had seen the man named "Jack" leave the woman near the gate of an apparently respectable villa-residence, not far from the Regent's Park. Left to himself, he took a turning to the right, which led to a sort of suburban street, principally inhabited by shopkeepers. He stopped at the private door of one of the houses, and let himself in with his own key—looking about him as he opened the door, and staring suspiciously at my men as they lounged along on the opposite side of the way. These were all the particulars which the subordinates had to communicate. I mounted to my Peep-hole to have a look at Mr. Jay.

He was occupied in dressing himself, and was taking extraordinary pains to destroy all traces of the natural slovenliness of his appearance. This was precisely what I expected. A vagabond like Mr. Jay knows the importance of giving himself a respectable look when he is going to run the risk of changing a stolen banknote. At five minutes past ten o'clock he had given the last brush to his shabby hat and the last scouting with bread-crumb to his dirty gloves. At ten minutes past ten he was in the street on his way to the nearest cab-stand, and I and my subordinates were close on his heels.

He took a cab, and we took a cab. I had not overheard them appoint a place of meeting, when following them in the Park on the previous day; but I soon found that we were proceeding in the old direction of the Avenue Road gate.

The cab in which Mr. Jay was riding turned into the Park slowly. We stopped outside, to avoid exciting suspicion. I got out to follow the cab on foot. Just as I did so, I saw it stop, and detected the two confederates approaching it from among the trees. They got in, and the cab was turned about directly. I ran back to my own cab, and told the driver to let them pass him, and then to follow as before.

The man obeyed my directions, but so clumsily as to excite their suspicions. We had been driving after them about three minutes (returning along the road by which we had advanced) when I looked out of the window to see how far they might be ahead of us. As I did this, I saw two hats popped out of the windows of their cab, and two faces looking back at me. I sank into my place in a cold sweat; the expression is coarse, but no other form of words can describe my condition at that trying moment.

"We are found out!" I said faintly to my two subordinates. They stared at me in astonishment. My feelings changed instantly from the depth of despair to the height of indignation.

"It is the cabman's fault. Get out, one of you," I said, with dignity, "get out and punch his head."

Instead of following my directions (I should wish this act of disobedience to be reported at headquarters) they both looked out of the window. Before I could pull them back, they both sat down again. Before I could express my just indignation, they both grinned and said to me, "Please look out, sir!"

I did look out. The thieves' cab had stopped. Where?

At a church door!!!

What effect this discovery might have had upon the ordinary run of men, I don't know. Being of a strong religious turn myself, it filled me with horror. I have often read of the unprincipled cunning of criminal persons; but I never before heard of three thieves attempting to double on their pursuers by entering a church! The sacrilegious audacity of that proceeding is, I should think, unparalleled in the annals of crime.

I checked my grinning subordinates by a frown. It was easy to see what was passing in their superficial minds. If I had not been able to look below the surface, I might, on observing two nicely dressed men and one nicely dressed woman enter a church before eleven in the morning on a weekday, have come to the same hasty conclusion at which my inferiors had evidently arrived. As it was, appearances had no power to impose on *me*. I got out, and, followed by one of my men, entered the church. The other man I sent round to watch the vestry door. You may catch a weasel asleep—but not your humble servant, Matthew Sharpin!

We stole up the gallery stairs, diverged to the organ loft, and peered through the curtains in front. There they were, all three, sitting in a pew below.

Before I could determine what to do, a clergyman made his appearance in full canonicals, from the vestry door, followed by a clerk. My brain whirled and my eyesight grew dim. Dark remembrances of robberies committed in vestries floated through my mind. I trembled for the excellent man in full canonicals—I even trembled for the clerk.

The clergyman placed himself inside the altar rails. The three desperadoes approached him. He opened his book, and began to read. What?—you will ask.

I answer, without the slightest hesitation, the first lines of the Marriage Service.

My subordinate had the audacity to look at me, and then to stuff his pocket handkerchief into his mouth. I scorned to pay any attention to him. After I had discovered that the man "Jack" was the bridegroom, and that the man Jay acted the part of father, and gave away the bride, I left the church, followed by my man, and joined the other subordinate outside the vestry door. Some people in my position would now have felt rather crestfallen, and would have begun to think that they had made a very foolish mistake. Not the faintest misgiving of any kind troubled me. And even now, after a lapse of three hours, my mind remains, I am happy to say, in the same calm and hopeful condition.

As soon as I and my subordinates were assembled together

outside the church, I intimated my intention of still following the other cab, in spite of what had occurred. My reason for deciding on this course will appear presently. The two subordinates were astonished at my resolution. One of them had the impertinence to say to me:

"If you please, sir, who is it that we are after? A man who has stolen money, or a man who has stolen a wife?"

The other low person encouraged him by laughing. Both have deserved an official reprimand; and both, I sincerely trust, will be sure to get it.

When the marriage ceremony was over, the three got into their cab; and once more our vehicle (neatly hidden round the corner of the church, so that they could not suspect it to be near them) started to follow theirs.

We traced them to the terminus of the South-Western Railway. The newly married couple took tickets for Richmond—paying their fare with a half-sovereign, and so depriving me of the pleasure of arresting them, which I should certainly have done, if they had offered a banknote. They parted from Mr. Jay, saying, "Remember the address—Fourteen Babylon Terrace. You dine with us tomorrow a week." Mr. Jay accepted the invitation, and added, jocosely, that he was going home at once to get off his clean clothes, and to be comfortable and dirty again for the rest of the day. I have to report that I saw him home safely, and that he is comfortable and dirty again (to use his own disgraceful language) at the present moment.

Here the affair rests, having by this time reached what I may call its first stage.

I know very well what persons of hasty judgment will be inclined to say of my proceedings thus far. They will assert that I have been deceiving myself all through, in the most absurd way; they will declare that the suspicious conversations which I have reported, referred solely to the difficulties and dangers of successfully carrying out a runaway match; and they will appeal to the scene in the church as offering undeniable proof of the correctness of their assertions. So let it be. I dispute nothing up to this point. But I ask a question, out of the depths of my own sagacity as a man of the world, which the bitterest of my enemies will not, I think, find it particularly easy to answer.

Granted the fact of the marriage, what proof does it afford me of the innocence of the three persons concerned in that clandestine transaction? It gives me none. On the contrary, it strengthens my suspicions against Mr. Jay and his confederates, because it suggests a distinct motive for their stealing the money. A gentleman who is going to spend his honeymoon at Richmond wants money; and a gentleman who is in debt to all his tradespeople wants money. Is this an unjustifiable imputation of bad motives? In the name of outraged morality, I deny it. These men have combined together, and have stolen a woman. Why should they not combine together, and steal a cashbox? I take my stand on the logic of rigid virtue; and I defy all the sophistry of vice to move me an inch out of my position.

Speaking of virtue, I may add that I have put this view of the case to Mr. and Mrs. Yatman. That accomplished and charming woman found it difficult, at first, to follow the close chain of my reasoning. I am free to confess that she shook her head, and shed tears, and joined her husband in premature lamentation over the loss of the two hundred pounds. But a little careful explanation on my part, and a little attentive listening on hers, ultimately changed her opinion. She now agrees with me, that there is nothing in this unexpected circumstance of the clandestine marriage which absolutely tends to divert suspicion from Mr. Jay, or Mr. "Jack," or the runaway lady. "Audacious hussy" was the term my fair friend used in speaking of her, but let that pass. It is more to the purpose to record that Mrs. Yatman has not lost confidence in me and that Mr. Yatman promises to follow her example, and do his best to look hopefully for future results.

I have now, in the new turn that circumstances have taken, to await advice from your office. I pause for fresh orders with all the composure of a man who has got two strings to his bow. When I traced the three confederates from the church door to the railway terminus, I had two motives for doing so. First, I followed them as a matter of official business, believing them still to have been guilty of the robbery. Secondly, I followed them as a matter of private speculation, with a view of discovering the place of refuge to which the runaway couple intended to retreat, and of making my information a marketable commodity to offer to the young lady's family and friends. Thus, whatever happens, I may congratulate myself beforehand on not having wasted my time. If the office approves of my conduct, I have my plan ready for further proceedings. If the office blames me, I shall take myself off, with my marketable information, to the genteel villa-residence in the neighborhood of the Regent's Park. Anyway, the affair puts money into my pocket, and does credit to me.

I have only one word more to add, and it is this: If any individual ventures to assert that Mr. Jay and his confederates are innocent of all share in the stealing of the cashbox, I, in return, defy that individual—though he may even be Chief Inspector Theakstone himself—to tell me who has committed the robbery at Rutherford Street, Soho.

Your very obedient servant,

MATTHEW SHARPIN

FROM CHIEF INSPECTOR THEAKSTONE
TO SERGEANT BULMER

BIRMINGHAM, 9th July

SERGEANT BULMER,—That empty-headed puppy, Mr. Matthew Sharpin, has made a mess of the case at Rutherford Street, exactly as I expected he would. Business keeps me in this town; so I write to you to set the matter straight. I enclose, with this, the pages of feeble scribble-scrabble which the creature, Sharpin, calls a report. Look them over; and when you have made your way through all the gabble, I think you will agree with me that the conceited booby has looked for the thief in every direction but the right one. You can lay your hand on the guilty person in five minutes, now. Settle the case at once; forward your report to me at this place; and tell Mr. Sharpin that he is suspended till further notice.

Yours,

FRANCIS THEAKSTONE

FROM SERGEANT BULMER TO
CHIEF INSPECTOR THEAKSTONE

LONDON, 10th July

INSPECTOR THEAKSTONE,—Your letter and enclosure came safe to hand. Wise men, they say, may always learn something, even from a fool. By the time I had got through Sharpin's maundering report of his own folly, I saw my way clear enough to the end of the Rutherford Street case, just as you thought I should. In half an hour's time I was at the house. The first

65

person I saw there was the incomparable Mr. Sharpin himself.

"Have you come to help me?" says he.

"Not exactly," says I. "I've come to tell you that you are suspended till further notice."

"Very good," says he, not taken down by so much as a single peg in his own estimation. "I thought you would be jealous of me. It's very natural; and I don't blame you. Walk in, pray, and make yourself at home. I'm off to do a little detective business on my own account, in the neighborhood of the Regent's Park. Ta-ta, sergeant, ta-ta!"

With those words he took himself out of the way—which was exactly what I wanted him to do.

As soon as the maidservant had shut the door, I told her to inform her master that I wanted to say a word to him in private. She showed me into the parlor behind the shop; and there was Mr. Yatman, all alone.

"About this matter of the robbery, sir," says I.

He cut me short, peevishly enough—being naturally a poor, weak, womanish sort of man. "Yes, yes, I know," says he. "You have come to tell me that your wonderfully clever man, who has bored holes in my second-floor partition, has made a mistake, and is off the scent of the scoundrel who it is that has stolen my money."

"Yes, sir," says I. "That *is* one of the things I came to tell you. But I have got something else to say, besides that."

"Can you tell me who the thief is?" says he, more pettish than ever.

"Yes, sir," says I, "I think I can."

He put down the newspaper and began to look rather anxious and frightened.

"Not my shopman?" says he. "I hope, for the man's own sake, it's not my shopman."

"Guess again, sir," says I.

"That idle slut, the maid?" says he.

"She is idle, sir," says I, "and she is also a slut; my first inquiries about her proved as much as that. But she's not the thief."

"Then in the name of heaven, who is?" says he.

"Will you please prepare yourself for a very disagreeable surprise, sir?" says I. "And in case you lose your temper, will you excuse my remarking that I am the stronger man of the two, and that, if you allow yourself to lay hands on me, I may

66

unintentionally do you an injury, in pure self-defense?"

He turned as pale as ashes, and pushed his chair two or three feet away from me.

"You have asked me to tell you, sir, who has taken your money," I went on. "If you insist on my giving you an answer—"

"I do insist," he said, faintly. "Who has taken it?"

"Your wife has taken it," I said very quietly, and very positively at the same time.

He jumped out of the chair as if I had put a knife into him, and struck his fist on the table, so heavily that the wood cracked again.

"Steady, sir," says I. "Flying into a passion won't help you to the truth."

"It's a lie!" says he, with another smack of his fist on the table, "a base, vile, infamous lie! How dare you—"

He stopped, and fell back into the chair again, looked about him in a bewildered way, and ended by bursting out crying.

"When your better sense comes back to you, sir," says I, "I am sure you will be gentleman enough to make an apology for the language you have just used. In the meantime, please listen, if you can, to a word of explanation. Mr. Sharpin has sent in a report of the most irregular and ridiculous kind; setting down, not only all his own foolish doings and sayings, but the doings and sayings of Mrs. Yatman as well. In most cases such a document would have been fit for the wastepaper basket; but, in this particular case, it so happens that Mr. Sharpin's budget of nonsense leads to a certain conclusion, which the simpleton of a writer has been quite innocent of suspecting from the beginning to the end. Of that conclusion I am so sure that I will forfeit my place, if it does not turn out that Mrs. Yatman has been practicing upon the folly and conceit of this young man, and that she has tried to shield herself from discovery by purposely encouraging him to suspect the wrong persons. I tell you that confidently; and I will even go further. I will undertake to give a decided opinion as to why Mrs. Yatman took the money, and what she has done with it, or with a part of it. Nobody can look at that lady, sir, without being struck by the great taste and beauty of her dress—"

As I said those last words, the poor man seemed to find his powers of speech again. He cut me short directly, as haughtily as if he had been a duke instead of a stationer.

"Try some other means of justifying your vile calumny against my wife," says he. "Her milliner's bill for the past year is on my file of receipted accounts at this moment."

"Excuse me, sir," says I, "but that proves nothing. Milliners, I must tell you, have a certain rascally custom which comes within the daily experience of our office. A married lady who wishes it can keep two accounts at her dressmaker's; one is the account which her husband sees and pays; the other is the private account which contains all the extravagant items and which the wife pays secretly, by installments, whenever she can. According to our usual experience, these installments are mostly squeezed out of the housekeeping money. In your case, I suspect no installments have been paid; proceedings have been threatened; Mrs. Yatman, knowing your altered circumstances, has felt herself driven into a corner; and she has paid her account out of your cashbox."

"I won't believe it," says he. "Every word you speak is an abominable insult to me and to my wife."

"Are you man enough, sir," says I, taking him up short, in order to save time and words, "to get that receipted bill you spoke of just now off the file, and come with me at once to the milliner's shop where Mrs. Yatman deals?"

He turned red in the face at that, got the bill directly, and put on his hat. I took out of my pocketbook the list containing the numbers of the lost notes, and we left the house together immediately.

Arrived at the milliner's (one of the expensive West End houses, as I expected), I asked for a private interview, on important business, with the mistress of the concern. It was not the first time that she and I had met over the same delicate investigation. The moment she set eyes on me, she sent for her husband. I mentioned who Mr. Yatman was, and what we wanted.

"This is strictly private?" inquires the milliner's husband. I nodded my head.

"And confidential?" says his wife. I nodded again.

"Do you see any objection, dear, to obliging the sergeant with a sight of the books?" says the husband.

"None in the world, love, if you approve of it," says the wife.

All this while poor Mr. Yatman sat looking the picture of astonishment and distress, quite out of place at our polite conference. The books were brought—and one minute's look at the pages in which Mrs. Yatman's name figured was enough, and more than enough, to prove the truth of every word I had spoken.

There, in one book, was the husband's account, which Mr. Yatman had settled. And there, in the other, was the private account, crossed off also; the date of settlement being the very day after the loss of the cashbox. This said private account amounted to the sum of a hundred and seventy-five pounds, odd shillings; and it extended over a period of three years. Not a single installment had been paid on it. Under the last line was an entry to this effect: "Written to for the third time, June 23rd." I pointed to it, and asked the milliner if that meant "last June." Yes, it did mean last June; and she now deeply regretted to say that it had been accompanied by a threat of legal proceedings.

"I thought you gave good customers more than three years' credit?" says I.

The milliner looks at Mr. Yatman, and whispers to me—"Not when a lady's husband gets into difficulties."

She pointed to the account as she spoke. The entries after the time when Mr. Yatman's circumstances became involved were just as extravagant, for a person in his wife's situation, as the entries for the year before that period. If the lady had economized in other things, she had certainly not economized in dress.

There was nothing left now but to examine the cashbook, for form's sake. The money had been paid in notes, the amounts and numbers of which exactly tallied with the figures set down in my list.

After that, I thought it best to get Mr. Yatman out of the house immediately. He was in such a pitiable condition that I called a cab and accompanied him home in it. At first he cried and raved like a child: but I soon quieted him—and I must add to his credit, that he made me a most handsome apology for his language, as the cab drew up at his house door. In return, I tried to give him some advice about how to set matters right, for the future, with his wife. He paid very little attention to me, and went upstairs muttering to himself about a separation. Whether Mrs. Yatman will come cleverly out of the scrape or not seems doubtful. I should say, myself, that she will go into screeching hysterics, and so frighten the poor man into forgiving her. But this is no business of ours. So far as we are concerned, the case is now at an end; and the present report may come to a conclusion along with it.

I remain, accordingly, yours to command,

THOMAS BULMER

P.S.—I have to add, that, on leaving Rutherford Street, I met Mr. Matthew Sharpin coming to pack up his things.

"Only think!" says he, rubbing his hands in great spirits, "I've been to the genteel villa-residence; and the moment I mentioned my business, they kicked me out directly. There were two witnesses of the assault; and it's worth a hundred pounds to me, if it's worth a farthing."

"I wish you joy of your luck," says I.

"Thank you," says he. "When may I pay you the same compliment on finding the thief?"

"Whenever you like," says I, "for the thief is found."

"Just what I expected," says he. "I've done all the work; and now you cut in and claim all the credit—Mr. Jay, of course?"

"No," says I.

"Who is it then?" says he.

"Ask Mrs. Yatman," says I. "She's waiting to tell you."

"All right! I'd much rather hear it from that charming woman than from you," says he, and goes into the house.

What do you think of that, Inspector Theakstone? Would you like to stand in Mr. Sharpin's shoes? I shouldn't, I can promise you!

FROM CHIEF INSPECTOR THEAKSTONE
TO MR. MATTHEW SHARPIN

12th July

SIR,—Sergeant Bulmer has already told you to consider yourself suspended until further notice. I have now authority to add that your services as a member of the Detective Police are positively declined. You will please to take this letter as notifying officially your dismissal from the force.

I may inform you, privately, that your rejection is not intended to cast any reflection on your character. It merely implies that you are not quite sharp enough for our purpose. If we *are* to have a new recruit among us, we should infinitely prefer Mrs. Yatman.

Your obedient servant,

FRANCIS THEAKSTONE

THE BLUE WASH MYSTERY

BY ANNA KATHARINE GREEN

Anna Katharine Green was born on November 11, 1846, in Brooklyn, New York, where her father was a well-known criminal lawyer. Educated at Ripley Female College in Poultney, Vermont, she published a volume of verse, *The Defense of the Bride and Other Poems* (1882), and a verse drama, *Risifi's Daughter* (1887). Her first detective novel, *The Leavenworth Case* (1878), was an immediate success and introduced her police detective, Ebenezer Gryce. She also wrote books involving female detectives Violet Strange and Amelia Butterworth. She produced over thirty works of fiction, most of them in the mystery field. She died on April 11, 1935.

ONE SUMMER DAY, several years ago now, a gentleman was walking down Broadway, when he encountered Mr. Hardy of. the firm of Hanson, Gregg & Hardy, House Painters and Decorators. Being friends, they both stopped.

"Well met," cried the former. "I am just on my way to spend a couple of weeks with my family at Lake George, and your face reminds me of a pleasant surprise I can give my wife upon our return. Our front parlor needs to be freshly frescoed and painted, or so she has been saying for the past six months. Now if it could be done while I am gone, her wishes would be gratified and I would escape a confounded nuisance. What do you think about it? Can you manage to do it at such short notice?"

"Yes," was the sturdy reply, "if you can let us into the house today. I have two men on hand waiting for orders this morning. If I could make use of them I think there would be no difficulty about the matter."

"But I haven't the key—I gave it to Henry, who is going to sleep in the house while I am gone, and he went to Newark this morning, and won't be home till midnight. Won't tomorrow do? Or stay, I have an idea. Our house is a corner one as you know, and my room looks out on G—— Street. If your men will put a ladder up on that side of the house, they can get in through the farther window on the second floor. I left it up this morning with injunctions to Henry to close it when he came home tonight. Won't that do? The furniture you can put in the back room, the carpet you can cover up—anything so my wife gets her surprise."

"Well, we'll try." And the gentlemen parted.

Now to you lady readers, the mystery will be that any man in his sane mind would dare to order his parlor furniture removed and the ceiling torn over a first-class axminster carpet, without warning his wife of the destruction that loomed over her favorite property. But that is not the mystery of this tale. The mystery of this story is one that a man can comprehend, even a boy, I think. So listen and be patient while I relate a few further facts.

Well, then, Mr. Hardy, who was of a prompt and energetic disposition, went immediately to his store and notified his two men of what he wanted done. Being fully engaged that morning, he could not go with them himself, but he told them expressly where the house was and by what means they were to enter, adding that he would be with them by noon when he hoped they would have the walls scraped and the blue wash on, ready for whatever final coloring he should decide upon employing.

"Remember," said he, "the large double-house on the northeast corner of G—— Street and Seventh Avenue. You cannot mistake it as there is but one house of that sort on the block." And conscious of having displayed the efficiency of his character, he left the store to attend to the business more immediately demanding his attention.

The men started. Pushing before them their hand-cart with its long ladder, they proceeded slowly uptown, and arriving at G—— Street, turned down toward Seventh Avenue. Soon they came to a corner on which was a large double-house. Looking up, they saw it was closed, all but the one window on the second floor which they had expected to find open. Stopping, they put up their ladder, entered the house, made their way unmolested to the parlor, carried out the furniture into the back room, tore up the carpet and laid it in a heap in the center. Then they scraped the walls and having put on the blue wash as had been ordered, went upstairs to look out of the window by which they had entered, in order to see if Mr. Hardy was coming. He was. He was just passing the corner. Without a glance in their direction, he was going quickly by, when one of the men whistled. That made him stop. Astonished, almost aghast, he looked up.

"What are you doing here?" cried he, coming hastily to the foot of the ladder.

"Scraping the walls as you ordered," exclaimed the man, alarmed at the expression on the face that met his gaze from below.

"But this is not the house!" cried Mr. Hardy. "I told you the large double-house on the corner of Seventh Avenue. This is Sixth!"

It was true. The men, misled by the appearance of things, had failed to notice what avenue they were on and had stopped one block short of their real destination.

Shaking the ladder in his wrath, Mr. Hardy cried, "Have you scraped the walls?"

The man nodded.

"Good heavens! And put on the blue wash?"

"Yes, sir."

"Thunder and lightning!—and I don't even know the name of the man who lives here. Is the house empty?"

"Yes, sir, empty and ready to be swept," said the workman.

"Sweep it then, you idiots, and put things back in their place, while I go and see what can be done."

He went to one of the neighbors, a man he knew, and told him of the mistake his men had made, and asked who lived in the house thus invaded. He was told:

"A Mr. Crippens, sir. The bitterest old curmudgeon and the worst man to irritate you ever saw. Once let him know that anyone has dared to invade his premises and do what you have done, and no amount of apology—no, nor damages either— would ever appease him. He would hound you and hinder you and get in your way all the rest of your life. Nothing is too mean for him to do, nothing too much trouble. You might as well arouse the Evil One himself."

"But what is to be done, then?" exclaimed Mr. Hardy in dismay.

"Nothing. Take off your men, shut up the house, and keep quiet. The neighbors are all away but myself and you may be sure he will learn nothing from me. Let him stamp his feet and howl over the matter if he will. 'Twill ease his mind and do him just as much good as if he spent time and money in ruining the business of a respectable man."

And Mr. Hardy partially followed this advice. He had the carpet put back and the furniture restored to its place, left a suitable sum of money on the mantel, but beyond that did nothing by way of explanation or remedy for the havoc he had caused.

And now what is the mystery? The mystery is this. What did that same old curmudgeon and his family think when they returned to their home and found the walls of their parlor denuded of every particle of paint? What explanation were they ever able to make to themselves of this startling occurrence? And if any of them are living yet, what do they think today when they remember the surprise of that moment and how the long years have passed without offering them any solution to the enigma?

MARKHEIM

BY ROBERT LOUIS STEVENSON

Robert Louis Stevenson was born in Edinburgh, Scotland, on November 13, 1850, and studied at the University of Edinburgh. An invalid for most of his life, he eventually settled with his wife in Samoa in 1888. He wrote much popular children's literature, including *Treasure Island, Kidnapped,* and *A Child's Garden of Verses.* His first mystery writing was a collection of short stories, *New Arabian Nights* (1882), which included such classic tales as "The Suicide Club" and "The Pavilion on the Links." He also wrote *The Strange Case of Dr. Jekyll and Mr. Hyde* and *The Wrong Box.* Stevenson died on December 3, 1894.

"YES," SAID THE DEALER, "OUR windfalls are of various kinds. Some customers are ignorant, and then I touch a dividend of my superior knowledge. Some are dishonest," and here he held up the candle, so that the light fell strongly on his visitor, "and in that case," he continued, "I profit by my virtue."

Markheim had but just entered from the daylight streets, and his eyes had not yet grown familiar with the mingled shine and darkness in the shop. At these pointed words, and before the near presence of the flame, he blinked painfully and looked aside.

The dealer chuckled. "You come to me on Christmas Day," he resumed, "when you know that I am alone in my house, put up my shutters, and make a point of refusing business. Well, you will have to pay for that; you will have to pay for my loss of time, when I should be balancing my books; you will have to pay, besides, for a kind of manner that I remark in you today very strongly. I am the essence of discretion, and ask no awkward questions; but when a customer cannot look me in the eye, he has to pay for it." The dealer once more chuckled; and then changed to his usual business voice, though still with a note of irony. "You can give, as usual, a clear account of how you came into the possession of the object?" he continued. "Still your uncle's cabinet? A remarkable collector, sir!"

And the little, pale, round-shouldered dealer stood almost on tiptoe, looking over the top of his gold spectacles, and nodding his head with every mark of disbelief. Markheim returned his gaze with one of infinite pity, and a touch of horror.

"This time," said he, "you are in error. I have not come to sell, but to buy. I have no curios to dispose of; my uncle's cabinet is bare to the wainscot; even were it still intact, I have done well on the Stock Exchange, and should more likely add to it than otherwise, and my errand today is simplicity itself. I seek a Christmas present for a lady," he continued, waxing more fluent as he struck into the speech he had prepared; "and certainly I owe you every excuse for thus disturbing you upon so small a matter. But the thing was neglected yesterday; I must produce my little compliment at dinner; and, as you very well know, a rich marriage is not a thing to be neglected."

There followed a pause, during which the dealer seemed to weigh this statement increduously. The ticking of many clocks among the curious lumber of the shop, and the faint rushing of the cabs in a near thoroughfare, were all that filled up the interval of silence.

"Well, sir," said the dealer, "be it so. You are an old customer after all; and if, as you say, you have the chance of a good marriage, far be it from me to be an obstacle. Here is a nice thing for a lady now," he went on, "this hand glass—fifteenth century, warranted; comes from a good collection, too; but I reserve the name, in the interests of my customer, who was just like yourself, my dear sir, the nephew and sole heir of a remarkable collector."

The dealer, while he thus ran on in his dry and biting voice, had stopped to take the object from its place; and, as he had done so, a shock had passed through Markheim, a start both of hand and foot, a sudden leap of many tumultuous passions to the face. It passed as swiftly as it came, and left no trace beyond a certain trembling of the hand that now received the glass.

"A glass," he said hoarsely, and then paused, and repeated it more clearly. "A glass? For Christmas? Surely not?"

"And why not?" cried the dealer. "Why not a glass?"

Markheim was looking upon him with an indefinable expression. "You ask me why not?" he said. "Why look here—look in it—look at yourself! Do you like to see it? No! nor I—nor any man."

The little man had jumped back when Markheim had so suddenly confronted him with the mirror; but now, perceiving there was nothing worse on hand, he chuckled. "Your future lady, sir, must be pretty hard favored," said he.

"I ask you," said Markheim, "for a Christmas present, and you give me this—this damned reminder of years and sins and follies—this hand-conscience! Did you mean it? Had you a thought in your mind? Tell me. It will be better for you if you do. Come, tell me about yourself. I hazard a guess now, that you are in secret a very charitable man?"

The dealer looked closely at his companion. It was very odd, Markheim did not appear to be laughing; there was something in his face like an eager sparkle of hope, but not mirth.

"What are you driving at?" the dealer asked.

"Not charitable?" returned the other, gloomily. "Not charitable; not pious; not scrupulous; unloving, unbeloved; a hand to get money, a safe to keep it. Is that all? Dear God, man, is that all?"

"I will tell you what it is," began the dealer, with some sharpness, and then broke off again into a chuckle. "But I see this is a love match of yours, and you have been drinking the lady's health."

"Ah!" cried Markheim, with a strange curiosity. "Ah, have you been in love? Tell me about that."

"I," cried the dealer, "I in love! I never had the time, nor have I the time today for all this nonsense. Will you take the glass?"

"Where is the hurry?" returned Markheim. "It is very pleasant to stand here talking; and life is so short and insecure that I would not hurry away from any pleasure—no, not even from so mild a one as this. We should rather cling, cling to what little we can get, like a man at a cliff's edge. Every second is a cliff, if you think upon it—a cliff a mile high—high enough, if we fall, to dash us out of every feature of humanity. Hence it is best to talk pleasantly. Let us talk to each other; why should we wear this mask? Let us be confidential. Who knows, we might become friends?"

"I have just one word to say to you," said the dealer. "Either make your purchase, or walk out of my shop."

"True, true," said Markheim. "Enough fooling. To business. Show me something else."

The dealer stooped once more, this time to replace the glass upon the shelf, his thin blond hair falling over his eyes as he did so. Markheim moved a little nearer, with one hand in the pocket of his greatcoat; he drew himself up and filled his lungs; at the same time many different emotions were depicted together in his face—terror, horror and resolve, fascination and a physical repulsion; and through a haggard lift of his upper lip, his teeth looked out.

"This, perhaps, may suit," observed the dealer; and then as he began to re-arise, Markheim bounded from behind upon his victim. The long skewerlike dagger flashed and fell. The dealer struggled like a hen, striking his temple on the shelf, and then tumbled on the floor in a heap.

Time had some score of small voices in that shop, some stately and slow as was becoming to their great age; others garrulous and hurried. All these told out the seconds in an intricate chorus of tickings. Then the passage of a lad's feet, heavily running on the pavement, broke in upon these smaller voices and startled Markheim into the consciousness of his surroundings. He looked about him awfully. The candle stood on the counter, its flame solemnly wagging in a draught; and by that inconsiderable movement, the whole room was filled with noiseless bustle and kept heaving like a sea: the tall shadows nodding, the gross blots of darkness swelling and dwindling as with respiration, the faces of the portraits and the china gods changing and wavering like images in water. The inner door stood ajar, and peered into that leaguer of shadows with a long slit of daylight like a pointing finger.

From these fear-stricken rovings, Markheim's eyes returned to the body of the victim, where it lay both humped and sprawling, incredibly small and strangely meaner than in life. In these poor, miserly clothes, in that ungainly attitude, the dealer lay like so much sawdust. Markheim had feared to see it, and, lo! it was nothing. And yet, as he gazed, this bundle of old clothes and pool of blood began to find eloquent voices. There it must lie; there was none to work the cunning hinges or direct the miracle of locomotion—there it must lie till it was found. Found! ay, and then? Then would this dead flesh lift up a cry that would ring over England, and fill the world with the echoes of pursuit. Ay, dead or not, this was still the enemy. "Time was that when the brains were out," he thought; and the first word struck into his mind. Time, now that the deed was accomplished—time which had closed for the victim, had become momentous for him.

The thought was yet in his mind, when, first one and then another, with every variety of pace and voice—one deep as the bell from a cathedral turret, another ringing on its treble notes the prelude of a waltz—the clocks began to strike the hour of three in the afternoon.

The sudden outbreak of so many tongues in that dumb chamber staggered him. He began to bestir himself, going to and fro with the candle, beleaguered by moving shadows, and startled to the soul by chance reflections. In many rich mirrors, some of home designs, some from Venice or Amsterdam, he saw his face repeated and repeated, as it were an army of spies; his own eyes met and detected him; and the sound of his own steps, lightly as they fell, vexed the surrounding quiet. And still as he continued to fill his pockets, his mind accused him with a sickening iteration, of the thousand faults of his design. He should have chosen a more quiet hour; he should have prepared an alibi; he should not have used a knife; he should have been more cautious, and only bound and gagged the dealer, and not killed him; he should have been more bold, and killed the servant also; he should have done all things otherwise; poignant regrets, weary, incessant toiling of the mind to change what was unchangeable, to plan what was now useless, to be the architect of the irrevocable past. Meanwhile, and behind all this activity, brute terrors, like the scurrying of rats in a deserted attic, filled the more remote chambers of his brain with riot; the hand of the constable would fall heavy on his shoulder, and his nerves would jerk like a hooked fish; or he beheld, in galloping defile, the dock, the prison, the gallows and the black coffin.

Terror of the people in the street sat down before his mind like a besieging army. It was impossible, he thought, but that some rumor of the struggle must have reached their ears and set an edge on their curiosity; and now, in all the neighboring houses, he divined them sitting motionless and with uplifted ear—solitary people, condemned to spend Christmas dwelling alone on memories of the past, and now startlingly recalled from that tender excercise; happy family parties, struck into silence around the table, the mother still with raised finger: every degree and age and humor, but all, by their own hearts, prying and hearkening and weaving the rope that was to hang him. Sometimes it seemed to him he could not move too softly; the clink of the tall Bohemian goblets rang out loudly like a bell; and alarmed by the bigness of the ticking, he was tempted to stop the clocks. And then, again, with a swift transition of his terrors, the very silence of the place appeared a source of peril, and a thing to strike and freeze the passerby; and he would step more boldly, and bustle aloud among the contents of the shop, and imitate, with elaborate bravado, the movements of a busy man at ease in his own house.

But he was now so pulled about by different alarms that, while one portion of his mind was still alert and cunning, another trembled on the brink of lunacy. One hallucination in particular took a strong hold on his credulity. The neighbor hearkening with white face beside his window, the passerby arrested by a horrible surmise on the pavement—these could at worst suspect, they could not know; through the brick walls and shuttered windows only sounds could penetrate. But here, within the house, was he alone? He knew he was; he had watched the servant set forth sweethearting, in her poor best, "out for the day" written in every ribbon and smile. Yes, he was alone, of course, and yet, in the bulk of empty house above him, he could surely hear a stir of delicate footing—he was surely conscious, inexplicably conscious of some presence. Ay, surely; to every room and corner of the house his imagination followed it; and now it was a faceless thing, and yet had eyes to see with; and again it was a shadow of himself; and yet again behold the image of the dead dealer, reinspired with cunning and hatred.

At times, with a strong effort, he would glance at the open door which still seemed to repel his eyes. The house was tall, the skylight small and dirty, the day blind with fog; and the light that filtered down to the ground story was exceedingly faint, and showed dimly on the threshold of the shop. And yet, in that strip of doubtful brightness, did there not hang, wavering, a shadow?

Suddenly, from the street outside, a very jovial gentleman began to beat with a staff on the shop door, accompanying his blows with shouts and railleries in which the dealer was continually called upon by name. Markheim, smitten into ice, glanced at the dead man. But no! he lay quite still; he was fled away far beyond earshot of these blows and shoutings; he was sunk beneath seas of silence; and his name, which would have once caught his notice above the howling of a storm, had become an empty sound. And presently the jovial gentleman desisted from his knocking and departed.

Here was a broad hint to hurry what remained to be done, to get forth from this accusing neighborhood, to plunge into a bath of London multitudes, and to reach, on the other side of day, that haven of safety and apparent innocence—his bed. One visitor had come; at any moment another might follow and be more obstinate. To have done the deed, and yet not to reap the profit, would be too abhorrent a failure. The money, that was now Markheim's concern; and as a means to that, the keys.

He glanced over his shoulder at the open door, where the shadow was still lingering and shivering; and with no conscious repugnance of the mind, yet with a terror of the belly, he drew near the body of his victim. The human character had quite departed. Like a suit half stuffed with bran, the limbs lay scattered, the trunk doubled, on the floor; and yet the thing repelled him. Although so dingy and inconsiderable to the eye, he feared it might have more significance to the touch. He took the body by the shoulders, and turned it on its back. It was strangely light and supple, and the limbs, as if they had been broken, fell into the oddest postures. The face was robbed of all expression; but it was as pale as wax, and shockingly smeared with blood about one temple. That was, for Markheim, the one displeasing circumstance. It carried him back, upon the instant, to a certain fair day in a fishers' village; a gray day, a piping wind, a large crowd upon the street, the blare of brasses, the booming of drums, the nasal voice of a ballad singer; and a boy going to and fro, buried over head in the crowd and divided between interest and fear, until, coming out upon the chief place of concourse, he beheld a booth and a great screen with pictures, dismally designed, garishly colored: Brownrigg with her apprentice; the Mannings with their murdered guest; Weare in the death-grip of Thurtell; and a score besides of famous crimes. The thing was as clear as an illusion; he was once again that little boy; he was looking once again, and with the same sense of physical revolt, at these vile pictures; he was still stunned by the thumping of the drums. A bar of that day's music returned upon his memory; and at that, for the first time, a qualm came over him, a breath of nausea, a sudden weakness of the joints, which he must instantly resist and conquer.

He judged it more prudent to confront than to flee from these considerations looking the more hardily in the dead face, bending his mind to realize the nature and greatness of his crime. So little a while ago, that face had moved with every change of sentiment, that pale mouth had spoken, that body had been all on fire with governable energies; and now, and by his act, that piece of life had been arrested, as the horologist, with interjected finger, arrests the beating of the clock. So he reasoned in vain; he could rise to no more remorseful consciousness; the same heart which had shuddered before the painted effigies of crime, looked on its reality unmoved. At best, he felt a gleam of pity for one who had been endowed in vain with all those faculties that can make the world a garden of enchantment, one who has never lived and was now dead. But of penitence, no, not a tremor.

With that, shaking himself clear of these considerations, he found the keys and advanced towards the open door of the shop. Outside, it had begun to rain smartly; and the sound of the shower upon the roof had banished silence. Like some dripping cavern, the chambers of the house were haunted by an incessant echoing, which filled the ear and mingled with the ticking of the clocks. And, as Markheim approached the door, he seemed to hear, in answer to his own cautious tread, the steps of another foot withdrawing up the stair. The shadow still palpitated loosely on the threshold. He threw a ton's weight of resolve upon his muscles, and drew back the door.

The faint, foggy daylight glimmered dimly on the bare floor and stairs; on the bright suit of armor posted, halberd in hand, upon the landing; and on the dark woodcarvings, and framed pictures that hung against the yellow panels of the wainscot. So loud was the beating of the rain through all the house that, in Markheim's ears, it began to be distinguished into many different sounds. Footsteps and sighs, the tread of regiments marching in the distance, the clink of money in the counting, and the creaking of doors held stealthily ajar, appeared to mingle with the patter of the drops upon the cupola and the gushing of water in the pipes. The sense that he was not alone grew upon him to the verge of madness. On every side he was haunted and begirt by presences. He heard them moving in the upper chambers; from the shop, he heard the dead man getting to his legs; and as he began with a great effort to mount the stairs, feet fled quietly before him and followed stealthily behind. If he were but deaf, he thought, how tranquilly he would possess his soul! And then again, and harkening with ever-fresh attention, he blessed himself for that unresting sense which held the outposts and stood a trusty sentinel upon his life. His head turned continually on his neck; his eyes, which seemed starting from their orbits, scouted on every side, and on every side were half rewarded as with the tail of something nameless vanishing. The four-and-twenty steps to the first floor were four-and-twenty agonies.

On that first story the doors stood ajar, three of them like three ambushes, shaking his nerves like the throats of cannon. He could never again, he felt, be sufficiently immured and fortified from men's observing eyes; he longed to be home, girt in by walls, buried among bedclothes, and invisible to all but God. And at that thought he wondered a little, recollecting tales of other murderers and the fear they were said to entertain of heavenly avengers. It was not so, at least, with him. He feared the laws of nature, lest, in their callous and immutable procedure, they should preserve some damning evidence of his crime. He feared tenfold more, with a slavish, superstitious terror, some scission in the continuity of man's experience, some willful illegality of nature. He played a game of skill, depending on the rules, calculating consequence from cause; and what if nature, as the defeated tyrant overthrew the chessboard, should break the mold of their succession? The like had befallen Napoleon (so writers said) when the winter changed the time of its appearance. The like might befall Markheim; the solid walls might become transparent and reveal his doings like those of bees in a glass hive; the stout planks might yield under his foot like quicksands and detain him in their clutch; ay, and there were soberer accidents that might destroy him: if, for instance, the house should fall and imprison him beside the body of his victim; or the house next door should fly on fire, and the fireman invade him from all sides. These things he feared; and, in a sense, these things might be called the hands of God reached forth against sin. But about God himself he was at ease, his act was doubtless exceptional, but so were his excuses, which God knew; it was there, and not among men, that he felt sure of justice.

When he had got safe into the drawingroom, and shut the door behind him, he was aware of a respite from alarms. The room was quite dismantled, uncarpeted besides, and strewn with packaging-cases and incongruous furniture; several great pier-glasses, in which he beheld himself at various angles, like an actor on a stage; many pictures, framed and unframed, standing, with their faces to the wall; a fine Sheraton sideboard, a cabinet of marquetry, and a great old bed, with tapestry hangings. The windows opened to the floor; but by great good-fortune the lower part of the shutters had been closed, and this concealed him from the neighbors. Here, then, Markheim drew in a packing-case before the cabinet, and began to search among the keys. It was a long business for there were many; and it was irksome besides; for, after all, there might be nothing in the cabinet, and time was on the wing. But the closeness of the occupation sobered him. With the tail of his eye he saw the door—even glanced at it from time to time directly, like a besieged commander pleased to verify the good estate of his defenses. But in truth he was at peace. The rain falling in the street sounded natural and pleasant. Presently, on the other side, the notes of a piano were awakened to the music of a hymn, and the voices of many children took up the air and words. How stately, how comfortable was the melody! How fresh the youthful voices! Markheim gave ear to it, smilingly, as he sorted out the keys; and his mind was thronged with answerable ideas and images; churchgoing children and the pealing of the high organ; children afield, bathers by the brookside, ramblers on the brambly common, kite-fliers in the windy and cloud-navigated sky; and then, at another cadence of the hymn, back again to church, and the somnolence of summer Sundays, and the high genteel voice of the parson (which he smiled a little to recall) and the painted Jacobean tombs, and the dim lettering of the Ten Commandments in the chancel.

And as he sat thus, at once busy and absent, he was startled to his feet. A flash of ice, a flash of fire, a bursting gush of blood, went over him, and then he stood transfixed and thrilling. A step mounted the stair slowly and steadily, and presently a hand was laid upon the knob, and the lock clicked and the door opened.

Fear held Markheim in a vise. What to expect he knew not, whether the dead man walking, or the official ministers of human justice, or some chance witness blindly stumbling in to consign him to the gallows. But when a face was thrust into the aperture, glanced around the room, looked at him, nodded and smiled as if in friendly recognition, and then withdrew again, and the door closed behind it, his fear broke lose from his control in a hoarse cry. At the sound of this the visitant returned.

"Did you call me?" he asked, pleasantly, and with that he entered the room and closed the door behind him.

Markheim stood and gazed at him with all his eyes. Perhaps there was a film upon his sight, but the outlines of the new-comer seemed to change and waver like those of the idols in the wavering candlelight of the shop; and at times he thought he knew him; and at times he thought he bore a likeness to himself; and always, like a lump of living terror, there lay in his bosom the conviction that this thing was not of the earth and not of God.

And yet the creature had a strange air of the commonplace, as he stood looking at Markheim with a smile; and when he added: "You are looking for the money, I believe?" it was in the tones of everyday politeness.

Markheim made no answer.

"I should warn you," resumed the other, " that the maid has

85

left her sweetheart earlier than usual and will soon be here. If Mr. Markheim be found in this house, I need not describe to him the consequences."

"You know me?" cried the murderer.

The visitor smiled. "You have long been a favorite of mine," he said; "and I have long observed and often sought to help you."

"What are you?" cried Markheim: "the devil?"

"What I may be," returned the other, "cannot affect the service I propose to render you."

"It can," cried Markheim; "it does! Be helped by you? No, never, not by you! You do not know me yet; thank God, you do not know me!"

"I know you," replied the visitant, with a sort of kind severity or rather firmness. "I know you to the soul."

"Know me!" cried Markheim. "Who can do so? My life is but a travesty and slander on myself. I have lived to belie my nature. All men do; all men are better than this disguise that grows about and stifles them. You see each dragged away by life, like one whom bravos have seized and muffled in a cloak. If they had their own control—if you could see their faces, they would be altogether different, they would shine out for heroes and saints! I am worse than most; my self is more overlaid; my excuse is known to me and God. But had I the time, I could disclose myself."

"To me?" inquired the visitant.

"To you before all," returned the murderer. "I supposed you were intelligent. I thought—since you exist—you would prove a reader of the heart. And yet you would propose to judge me by my acts! Think of it; my acts! I was born and have lived in a land of giants; giants have dragged me by the wrists since I was born out of my mother—the giants of circumstance. And you would judge me by my acts! But can you not look within? Can you not understand that evil is hateful to me? Can you not see within me the clear writing of conscience, never blurred by any willful sophistry, although too often disregarded? Can you not read me for a thing that surely must be common as humanity—the unwilling sinner?"

"All this is very feelingly expressed," was the reply, "but it regards me not. These points of consistency are beyond my province, and I care not in the least by what compulsion you may have been dragged away, so as you are but carried in the right direction. But time flies; the servant delays, looking in the faces of the crowd and at the pictures on the boardings, but still she keeps moving nearer; and remember, it is as if the gallows itself were striding towards you through the Christmas streets! Shall I help you; I, who know all? Shall I tell you where to find the money?"

"For what price?" asked Markheim.

"I offer you the service for a Christmas gift," returned the other.

Markheim could not refrain from smiling with a kind of bitter triumph. "No," said he, "I will take nothing at your hands; if I were dying of thirst, and it was your hand that put the pitcher to my lips, I should find the courage to refuse. It may be credulous, but I will do nothing to commit myself to evil."

"I have no objection to a death-bed repentance," observed the visitant.

"That is because you disbelieve their efficacy!" Markheim cried.

"I do not say so," returned the other; "but I look on these things from a different side, and when the life is done my interest falls. The man has lived to serve me, to spread black looks under color of religion, or to sow tares in the wheatfield, as you do, in a course of weak compliance with desire. Now that he draws so near to his deliverance, he can add but one act of service—to repent, to die, smiling, and thus to build up in confidence and hope the more timorous of my surviving followers. I am not so hard a master. Try me. Accept my help. Please yourself in life as you have done hitherto; please yourself more amply, spread your elbows at the board; and when the night begins to fall and the curtains to be drawn, I tell you, for your greater comfort, that you will find it even easy to compound your quarrel with your conscience, and to make a truckling peace with God. I came but now from such a death-bed, and the room was full of sincere mourners, listening to the man's last words: and when I looked into that face, which had been set as a flint against mercy, I found it smiling with hope."

"And do you, then, suppose me such a creature?" asked Markheim. "Do you think I have no more generous aspirations than to sin, and sin, and at last, sneak into heaven? My heart rises at the thought. Is this, then, your experience of mankind? or is it because you find me with red hands that you presume such baseness? And is this crime of murder indeed so impious as to dry up the very springs of good?"

"Murder to me is no special category," replied the other. "All sins are murder, even as all life is war. I behold your race, like starving mariners on a raft, plucking crusts out of the hands of famine and feeding on each other's lives. I follow sins beyond the moment of their acting; I find in all that the last consequence is death; and to my eyes, the pretty maid who thwarts her mother with such taking graces on a question of a ball, drips no less visibly with human gore than such a murderer as yourself. Do I say that I follow sins? I follow virtues also; they differ not by the thickness of a nail, they are both scythes for the reaping angel of Death. Evil, for which I live, consists not in action but in character. The bad man is dear to me; not the bad act, whose fruits, if we could follow them far enough down the hurtling cataract of the ages, might yet be found more blessed than those of the rarest virtues. And it is not because you have killed a dealer, but because you are Markheim that I offered to forward your escape."

"I will lay my heart open to you," answered Markheim. "This crime on which you find me is my last. On my way to it I have learned many lessons; itself is a lesson, a momentous lesson. Hitherto I have been driven with revolt to what I would not; I was a bondslave to poverty, driven and scourged. There are robust virtues that can stand in these temptations; mine was not so; I had a thirst for pleasure. But today, and out of this deed, I pluck both warning and riches—both the power and a fresh resolve to be myself. I become in all things a free actor in the world; I begin to see myself all changed, these hands the agents of good, this heart at peace. Something comes over me out of the past; something of what I have dreamed on Sabbath evenings to the sound of the church organ, of what I forecast when I shed tears over noble books, or talked, an innocent child, with my mother. There lies my life; I have wandered a few years, but now I see once more my city of destination."

"You are to use this money on the Stock Exchange, I think?" remarked the visitor; "and there, if I mistake not, you have already lost some thousands?"

"Ah," said Markheim, "but this time—this time I have a sure thing."

"This time, again, you will lose," replied the visitor quietly.

"Ah, but I keep back the half!" cried Markheim.

"That also you will lose," said the other.

The sweat started upon Markheim's brow. "Well, then, what matter?" he exclaimed. "Say it be lost, say I am plunged again in poverty, shall one part of me, and that the worst, continue until the end to override the better? Evil and good run strong in me, hauling me both ways. I do not love the one thing, I love all. I can conceive great deeds, renunciations, martyrdoms; and though I be fallen to such a crime as murder, pity is no stranger to my thoughts. I pity the poor; who knows their trials better than myself? I pity and help them; I prize love, I love honest laughter; there is no good thing nor true thing on earth but I love it from my heart. And are my vices only to direct my life, and my virtues to lie without effect, like some passive lumber of the mind? Not so; good, also, is a spring of acts."

But the visitant raised his finger. "For six-and-thirty years that you have been in this world," said he, "through many changes of fortune and varieties of humor, I have watched you steadily fall. Fifteen years ago you would have started at a theft. Three years back you would have blanched at the name of murder. Is there any crime, is there any cruelty or meanness, from which you still recoil—five years from now I shall detect you in the fact! Downward, downward, lies your way; nor can anything but death avail to stop you."

"It is true," Markheim said huskily, "I have in some degree complied with evil. But it is so with all: the very saints, in the mere excercise of living, grow less dainty, and take on the tone of their surroundings."

"I will propound to you one simple question," said the other; "and as you answer, I shall read to you your moral horoscope. You have grown in many things more lax; possibly you do right to do so; and at any account, it is the same with all men. But granting that, are you in any one particular, however trifling, more difficult to please with your own conduct, or do you go in all things with a looser rein?"

"In any one?" repeated Markheim, with an anguish of consideration. "No," he added, with despair, "in none! I have gone down in all."

"Then," said the visitor, "content yourself with what you are, for you will never change; and the words of your part are irrevocably written."

Markheim stood for a long while silent, and indeed it was the visitor who first broke the silence. "That being so," he said, "shall I show you the money?"

"And grace?" cried Markheim.

"Have you not tried it?" returned the other. "Two or three years ago, did I not see you on the platform of revival meetings, and was not your voice the loudest in the hymn?"

"It is true," said Markheim; "and I see clearly what remains for me by way of duty. I thank you for these lessons from my soul; my eyes are opened, and I behold myself at last for what I am."

At this moment, the sharp note of the doorbell rang through the house; and the visitant, as though this were some concerted signal for which he had been waiting, changed at once in his demeanor.

"The maid!" he cried. "She has returned, as I forewarned you, and there is now before you one more difficult passage. Her master, you must say, is ill; you must let her in, with an assured but rather serious countenance—no smiles, no over-acting, and I promise you success! Once the girl within, and the door closed, the same dexterity that has already rid you of the dealer will relieve you of this last danger in your path. Thenceforward you have the whole evening—the whole night, if needful—to ransack the treasures of the house and to make good your safety. This is help that comes to you with the mask of danger. Up!" he cried: "up, friend; your life hangs trembling in the scales: up, and act!"

Markheim steadily regarded his counselor. "If I be condemned to evil acts," he said, "there is still one door of freedom open—I can cease from action. If my life be an ill thing, I can lay it down. Though I be, as you say truly, at the beck of every small temptation, I can yet, by one decisive gesture, place myself beyond the reach of all. My love of good is damned to barrenness; it may, and let it be! But I have still my hatred of evil; and from that, to your galling disappointment, you shall see that I can draw both energy and courage."

The features of the visitor began to undergo a wonderful and lovely change: they brightened and softened with a tender triumph; and, even as they brightened, faded and dislimned. But Markheim did not pause to watch or understand the transformation. He opened the door and went downstairs very slowly, thinking to himself. His past went soberly before him; he beheld it as it was, ugly and strenuous like a dream, random as a chance medley—a scene of defeat. Life, as he thus reviewed it, tempted him no longer; but on the further side he perceived a quiet haven for his bark. He paused in the passage, and looked into the shop, where the candle still burned by the dead body. It was strangely silent. Thoughts of the dealer swarmed into his mind, as he stood gazing. And then the bell once more broke out into impatient clamor.

He confronted the maid upon the threshold with something like a smile.

"You had better go for the police," said he: "I have killed your master."

THE REIGATE PUZZLE

BY A. CONAN DOYLE

Arthur Conan Doyle was born on May 22, 1859, in Edinburgh, Scotland, and received his medical degree from the University of Edinburgh in 1885. Conan Doyle wrote four novels and five volumes of short stories about Sherlock Holmes, the most popular detective in literature, and also wrote historical novels, adventure tales, and other mysteries. He was knighted in 1902 for his work on behalf of the British propaganda effort during the Boer War. He died on July 7, 1930. The Baker Street Irregulars, an organization of Sherlock Holmes enthusiasts, hold their annual dinner on the first Friday of every year to celebrate Holmes' birth (January 6, 1854).

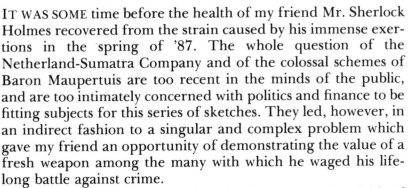

IT WAS SOME time before the health of my friend Mr. Sherlock Holmes recovered from the strain caused by his immense exertions in the spring of '87. The whole question of the Netherland-Sumatra Company and of the colossal schemes of Baron Maupertuis are too recent in the minds of the public, and are too intimately concerned with politics and finance to be fitting subjects for this series of sketches. They led, however, in an indirect fashion to a singular and complex problem which gave my friend an opportunity of demonstrating the value of a fresh weapon among the many with which he waged his life-long battle against crime.

On referring to my notes I see that it was upon the 14th of April that I received a telegram from Lyons which informed me that Holmes was lying ill in the Hotel Dulong. Within twenty-four hours I was in his sickroom, and was relieved to find that there was nothing formidable in his symptoms. Even his iron constitution, however, had broken down under the strain of the investigation which had extended over two months, during which period he had never worked less than fifteen hours a day, and had more than once, as he assured me, kept to his task for five days at a stretch. Even the triumphant issue of his labors could not save him from the reaction after so terrible an exertion, and at a time when Europe was ringing with his name and when his room was literally ankle-deep with congratulatory telegrams, I found him a prey to the blackest depression. Even the knowledge that he had succeeded where the police of the three countries had failed, and that he had outmaneuvered at every point the most accomplished swindler in Europe, was insufficient to rouse him from his nervous prostration.

Three days later we were back in Baker Street together; but it was evident that my friend would be much the better for a change, and the thought of a week of springtime in the country was full of attractions to me also. My old friend, Colonel Hayter, who had come under my professional care in Afghanistan, had now taken a house near Reigate in Surrey, and had frequently asked me to come down to him upon a visit. On the last occasion he had remarked that if my friend would only come with me he would be glad to extend his hospitality to him also. A little diplomacy was needed, but when Holmes understood that the establishment was a bachelor one, and that he would be allowed the fullest freedom, he fell in with my plans and a week after our return from Lyons we were under the Colonel's roof. Hayter was a fine old soldier who had seen much of the world, and he soon found, as I had expected, that Holmes and he had much in common.

On the evening of our arrival we were sitting in the Colonel's gun-room after dinner, Holmes stretched upon the sofa, while Hayter and I looked over his little armory of Eastern weapons.

"By the way," said he suddenly, "I think I'll take one of these pistols upstairs with me in case we have an alarm."

"An alarm!" said I.

"Yes, we've had a scare in this part lately. Old Acton, who is one of our county magnates, had his house broken into last Monday. No great damage done, but the fellows are still at large."

"No clue?" asked Holmes, cocking his eye at the Colonel.

"None as yet. But the affair is a pretty one, one of our little country crimes, which must seem too small for your attention, Mr. Holmes, after this great international affair."

Holmes waved away the compliment, though his smile showed that it had pleased him.

"Was there any feature of interest?"

"I fancy not. The thieves ransacked the library and got very little for their pains. The whole place was turned upside down, drawers burst open, and presses ransacked, with the result that an odd volume of Pope's 'Homer,' two plated candlesticks, an ivory letter-weight, a small oak barometer, and a ball of twine are all that have vanished."

"What an extraordinary assortment!" I exclaimed.

"Oh, the fellows evidently grabbed hold of everything they could get."

Holmes grunted from the sofa.

"The county police ought to make something of that," said he; "why it is surely obvious that—"

But I held up a warning finger.

"You are here for a rest, my dear fellow. For Heaven's sake don't get started on a new problem when your nerves are all in shreds."

Holmes shrugged his shoulders with a glance of comic resignation towards the Colonel, and the talk drifted away into less dangerous channels.

It was destined, however, that all my professional caution should be wasted, for next morning the problem obtruded itself upon us in such a way that it was impossible to ignore it, and our country visit took a turn which neither of us would have anticipated. We were at breakfast when the Colonel's butler rushed in with all his propriety shaken out of him.

"Have you heard the news, sir?" he gasped. "At the Cunninghams', sir!"

"Burglary!" cried the Colonel, with his coffe-cup in midair.

"Murder!"

The Colonel whistled. "By Jove!" said he. "Who's killed, then? The J.P. or his son?"

"Neither, sir. It was William the coachman. Shot through the heart, sir, and never spoke again."

"Who shot him, then?"

"The burglar, sir. He was off like a shot and got clean away. He'd just broke in at the pantry window when William came in on him and met his end in saving his master's property."

"What time?"

"It was last night, sir, somewhere about twelve."

"Ah, then we'll step over afterwards," said the Colonel, coolly settling down to his breakfast again. "It's a baddish businesss," he added when the butler had gone; "he's our leading man about here, is old Cunningham, and a very decent fellow too. He'll be cut up over this, for the man has been in his service for years and was a good servant. It's evidently the same villains who broke into Acton's."

"And stole that very singular collection," said Holmes, thoughtfully.

"Precisely."

"Hum! It may prove the simplest matter in the world, but all the same at first glance this is just a little curious, is it not? A gang of burglars acting in the country might be expected to vary the scene of their operations, and not to crack two cribs in the same district within a few days. When you spoke last night of taking precautions I remember that it passed through my mind that this was probably the last parish in England to which the thief or thieves would be likely to turn their attention—which shows that I have still much to learn."

"I fancy it's some local practitioner," said the Colonel. "In

95

that case, of course, Acton's and Cunningham's are just the places he would go for, since they are far the largest about here."

"And richest?"

"Well, they ought to be, but they've had a lawsuit for some years which has sucked the blood out of both of them, I fancy. Old Acton has some claim on half Cunningham's estate, and the lawyers have been at it with both hands."

"If it's a local villain there should not be much difficulty in running him down," said Holmes with a yawn. "All right, Watson, I don't intend to meddle."

"Inspector Forrester, sir," said the butler, throwing open the door.

The official, a smart, keen-faced young fellow, stepped into the room. "Good-morning, Colonel," said he; "I hope I don't intrude, but we hear that Mr. Holmes of Baker Street is here."

The Colonel waved his hand towards my friend, and the Inspector bowed.

"We thought that perhaps you would care to step across, Mr. Holmes."

"The fates are against you, Watson," said he, laughing. "We were chatting about the matter when you came in, Inspector. Perhaps you can let us have a few details." As he leaned back in the chair in the familiar attitude I knew the case was hopeless.

"We had no clue in the Acton affair. But here we have plenty to go on, and there's no doubt it is the same party in each case. The man was seen."

"Ah!"

"Yes, sir. But he was off like a deer after the shot that killed poor William Kirwan was fired. Mr. Cunningham saw him from the bedroom window, and Mr. Alec Cunningham saw him from the back passage. It was quarter to twelve when the alarm broke out. Mr. Cunningham had just gone to bed, and Mr. Alec was smoking a pipe in his dressing-gown. They both heard William the coachman calling for help, and Mr. Alec ran down to see what was the matter. The back door was open, and as he came to the foot of the stairs he saw two men wrestling together outside. One of them fired a shot, the other dropped, and the murderer rushed across the garden and over the hedge. Mr. Cunningham, looking out of his bedroom, saw the fellow as he gained the road, but lost sight of him at once. Mr. Alec stopped to see if he could help the dying man, and so the villain got clean away. Beyond the fact that he was a middle-sized man and dressed in some dark stuff, we have no personal clue; but we are making energetic inquiries, and if he is a stranger we shall soon find him out."

"What was this William doing there? Did he say anything before he died?"

"Not a word. He lives at the lodge with his mother, and as he was a very faithful fellow we imagine that he walked up to the house with the intention of seeing that all was right there. Of course this Acton business has put everyone on their guard. The robber must have just burst open the door—the lock has been forced—when William came upon him."

"Did William say anything to his mother before going out?"

"She is very old and deaf, and we can get no information from her. The shock has made her half-witted, but I understand that she was never very bright. There is one very important circumstance, however. Look at this!"

He took a small piece of torn paper from a notebook and spread it out upon his knee.

"This was found between the finger and thumb of the dead man. It appears to be a fragment torn from a larger sheet. You will observe that the hour mentioned upon it is the very time at which the poor fellow met his fate. You see that the murderer might have torn the rest of the sheet from him or he might have taken this fragment from the murderer. It reads almost as if it were an appointment."

Holmes took up the scrap of paper, a facsimile of which is here reproduced.

"Presuming that it is an appointment," continued the Inspector, "it is of course a conceivable theory that this William Kirwan—though he had the reputation of being an honest man, may have been in league with the thief. He may have met him there, may even have helped him break into the door, and

97

then they may have fallen out between themselves."

"This writing is of extraordinary interest," said Holmes, who had been examining it with intense concentration. "These are much deeper waters than I had thought." He sank his head upon his hands, while the Inspector smiled at the effect which his case had had upon the famous London specialist.

"Your last remark," said Holmes, presently, "as to the possibility of there being an understanding between the burglar and the servant, and this being a note of appointment from one to the other, is an ingenious and not an entirely impossible supposition. But this writing opens up—" He sank his head into his hands again and remained for some minutes in the deepest thought. When he raised his face again, I was surprised to see that his face was tinged with color, and his eyes as bright as before his illness. He sprang to his feet with very much his old energy.

"I'll tell you what," said he, "I should like to have a quiet little glance into the details of this case. There is something in it which fascinates me extremely. If you will permit me, Colonel, I will leave my friend Watson and you, and I will step'round with the Inspector to test the truth of one or two little fancies of mine. I will be with you again in half an hour."

An hour and a half had elapsed before the Inspector returned alone.

"Mr. Holmes is walking up and down in the field outside," said he. "He wants us all four to go up to the house together."

"To Mr. Cunningham's?"

"Yes, sir."

"What for?"

The Inspector shrugged his shoulders. "I don't quite know, sir. Between ourselves, I think Mr. Holmes has not quite got over his illness yet. He's been behaving very queerly, and he is very much excited."

"I don't think you need alarm yourself," said I. "I have usually found that there was method in his madness."

"Some folk might say there was madness in his method," muttered the Inspector. "But he's all on fire to start, Colonel, so we had best go out if you are ready."

We found Holmes pacing up and down in the field, his chin sunk upon his breast, and his hands thrust into his trouser pockets.

"The matter grows in interest," said he. "Watson, your country trip has been a distinct success. I have had a charming morning."

"You have been up to the scene of the crime, I understand," said the Colonel.

"Yes, the Inspector and I have made quite a little reconnaissance together."

"Any success?"

"Well, we have seen some very interesting things. I'll tell you what we did as we walk. First of all, we saw the body of this unfortunate man. He certainly died from a revolver wound as reported."

"Had you doubted it, then?"

"Oh, it is as well to test everything. Our inspection was not wasted. We then had an interview with Mr. Cunningham and his son, who were able to point out the exact spot where the murderer had broken through the garden hedge in his flight. That was of great interest."

"Naturally."

"Then we had a look at this poor fellow's mother. We could get no information from her, however, as she is very old and feeble."

"And what is the result of your investigation?"

"The conviction that the crime is a very peculiar one. Perhaps our visit now may do something to make it less obscure. I think that we are both agreed, Inspector, that the fragment of paper in the dead man's hand, bearing, as it does, the very hour of his death written upon it, is of extreme importance."

"It should give a clue, Mr. Holmes."

"It *does* give a clue. Whoever wrote that note was the man who brought William Kirwan out of his bed at that hour. But where is the rest of that sheet of paper?"

"I examined the ground carefully in the hope of finding it," said the Inspector.

"It was torn out of the dead man's hand. Why was some one so anxious to get possession of it? Because it incriminated him. And what would he do with it? Thrust it into his pocket, most likely, never noticing that a corner of it had been left in the grip of the corpse. If we could get the rest of that sheet it is obvious that we should have gone a long way towards solving the mystery."

"Yes, but how can we get at the criminal's pocket before we catch the criminal?"

"Well, well, it was worth thinking over. Then there is another obvious point. The note was sent to William. The man who wrote it could not have taken it; otherwise, of course, he might have delivered his own message by word of mouth. Who brought the note, then? Or did it come through the post?"

"I have made inquiries," said the Inspector. "William received a letter by the afternoon post yesterday. The envelope was destroyed by him."

"Excellent!" cried Holmes, clapping the Inspector on the back. "You've seen the postman. It is a pleasure to work with you. Well, here is the lodge, and if you will come up, Colonel, I will show you the scene of the crime."

We passed the pretty cottage where the murdered man had lived, and walked up an oak-lined avenue to the fine old Queen Anne house, which bears the date of Malplaquet upon the lintel of the door. Holmes and the Inspector led us round it until we came to the side gate, which is separated by a stretch of garden from the hedge which lines the road. A constable was standing at the kitchen door.

"Throw the door open, officer," said Holmes. "Now, it was on those stairs that young Mr. Cunningham stood and saw the two men struggling just where we are. Old Mr. Cunningham was at that window—the second on the left—and he saw the fellow get away just to the left of that bush. So did the son. They are both sure of it on account of the bush. Then Mr. Alec ran out and knelt beside the wounded man. The ground is very hard, you see, and there are no marks to guide us." As he spoke two men came down the garden path, from round the angle of the house. The one was an elderly man, with a strong, deep-lined, heavy-eyed face; the other a dashing young fellow, whose bright, smiling expression and showy dress were in strange contrast with the business which had brought us there.

"Still at it, then?" said he to Holmes. "I thought you Londoners were never at fault. You don't seem to be so quick, after all."

"Ah, you must give us a little time," said Holmes good-humoredly.

"You'll want it," said young Alec Cunningham. "Why, I don't see that we have any clue at all."

"There's only one," answered the Inspector. "We thought that if we could only find—Good heavens, Mr. Holmes! What is the matter?"

My poor friend's face had suddenly assumed the most dreadful expression. His eyes rolled upwards, his features writhed in agony, and with a suppressed groan he dropped on his face upon the ground. Horrified at the suddenness and severity of the attack, we carried him into the kitchen, where he lay back in a large chair, and breathed heavily for some minutes. Finally, with a shamefaced apology for his weakness, he rose once more.

"Watson would tell you that I have only just recovered from a severe illness," he explained. "I am liable to these sudden nervous attacks."

"Shall I send you home in my trap?" asked old Cunningham.

"Well, since I am here, there is one point on which I should like to feel sure. We can very easily verify it."

"What was it?"

"Well, it seems to me that it is just possible that the arrival of this poor fellow William was not before, but after, the entrance of the burglar into the house. You appear to take it for granted that, although the door was forced, the robber never got in."

"I fancy that is quite obvious," said Mr. Cunningham, gravely. "Why, my son Alec had not yet gone to bed, and he would certainly have heard anyone moving about."

"Where was he sitting?"

"I was smoking in my dressing-room."

"Which window is that?"

"The last on the left, next to my father's."

"Both of your lamps were lit, of course?"

"Undoubtedly."

"There are some very singular points here," said Holmes, smiling. "Is it not extraordinary that a burglar—and a burglar who had had some previous experience—should deliberately break into a house at a time when he could see from the lights that two of the family were still afoot?"

"He must have been a cool hand."

"Well, of course, if the case were not an odd one we should not have been driven to ask you for an explanation," said young Mr. Alec. "But as to your ideas that the man had robbed the house before William tackled him, I think it a most absurd notion. Wouldn't we have found the place disarranged, and missed the things which he had taken?"

"It depends on what the things were," said Holmes. "You must remember that we are dealing with a burglar who is a very peculiar fellow, and who appears to work on lines of his own.

Look, for example, at the queer lot of things he took from Acton's—what was it?—a ball of string, a letter-weight, and I don't know what other odds and ends."

"Well, we are quite in your hands, Mr. Holmes," said old Cunningham. "Anything which you or the Inspector may suggest will most certainly be done."

"In the first place," said Holmes, "I should like you to offer a reward—coming from yourself, for the officials may take a little time before they would agree upon the sum, and these things cannot be done too promptly. I have jotted down the form here if you would not mind signing it. Fifty pounds was quite enough, I thought."

"I would willingly give five hundred," said the J.P., taking the slip of paper and the pencil which Holmes handed to him. "This is not quite correct, however," he added, glancing over the document.

"I wrote it rather hurriedly."

"You see you begin, 'Whereas, at about a quarter to one on Tuesday morning an attempt was made,' and so on. It was a quarter to twelve, as a matter of fact."

I was pained at the mistake, for I knew how keenly Holmes would feel any slip of the kind. It was his specialty to be accurate as to fact, but his recent illness had shaken him, and this one little incident was enough to show me that he was still far from being himself. He was obviously embarrassed for an instant, while the Inspector raised his eyebrows, and Alec Cunningham burst into a laugh. The old gentleman corrected the mistake, however, and handed the paper back to Holmes.

"Get it printed as soon as possible," he said; "I think your idea is an excellent one."

Holmes put the slip of paper carefully away into his pocket-book.

"And now," said he, "it really would be a good thing that we should all go over the house together and make certain that this rather erratic burglar did not, after all, carry anything away with him."

Before entering, Holmes made an examination of the door which had been forced. It was evident that a chisel or strong knife had been thrust in, and the lock forced back with it. We could see the marks in the wood where it had been pushed in.

"You don't use bars, then?" he asked.

"We have never found it necessary."

"You don't keep a dog?"

"Yes, but it is chained on the other side of the house."

"When do the servants go to bed?"

"About ten."

"I understand that William was usually in bed also at that hour."

"Yes."

"It is singular that on this particular night he should have been up. Now, I should be very glad if you should have the kindness to show us over the house, Mr. Cunningham."

A stone-flagged passage, with the kitchens branching away from it, led by a wooden staircase directly to the first floor of the house. It came out upon the landing opposite to a second, more ornamental stair which came up from the front hall. Out of this landing opened the drawing-room and several bedrooms, including those of Mr. Cunningham and his son. Holmes walked slowly, taking keen note of the architecture of the house. I could tell from his expression that he was on a hot scent, and yet I could not in the least imagine in what direction his inferences were leading him.

"My good sir," said Mr. Cunningham with some impatience, "this is surely very unnecessary. That is my room at the end of the stairs, and my son's is the one beyond it. I leave it to your judgment whether it was possible for the thief to have come up here without disturbing us."

"You must try round and get on a fresh scent, I fancy," said the son with a rather malicious smile.

"Still, I must ask you to humor me a little further. I should like, for example, to see how far the windows of the bedrooms command the front. This, I understand, is your son's room"—he pushed open the door—"and that, I presume, is the dressing-room in which he sat smoking when the alarm was given. Where does the window of that look out to?" He stepped across the bedroom, pushed open the door, and glanced round the other chamber.

"I hope that you are satisfied now?" said Mr. Cunningham, tartly.

"Thank you, I think I have seen all that I wished."

"Then if it is really necessary we can go into my room."

"If it is not too much trouble."

The J.P. shrugged his shoulders, and led the way into his own chamber, which was a plainly furnished and commonplace room. As we moved across it in the direction of the window, Holmes fell back until he and I were the last of the group. Near the foot of the bed stood a dish of oranges and a carafe of water. As we passed it Holmes, to my unutterable astonishment, leaned over in front of me and deliberately knocked the whole thing over. The glass smashed into a thousand pieces and the fruit rolled about into every corner of the room.

"You've done it now, Watson," said he coolly. "A pretty mess you've made of the carpet."

I stooped in some confusion and began to pick up the fruit, understanding for some reason my companion desired me to take the blame upon myself. The others did the same, and set the table on its legs again.

"Hullo!" cried the Inspector, "where's he got to?"

Holmes had disappeared.

"Wait here an instant," said young Alec Cunningham. "The fellow is off his head, in my opinion. Come with me, father, and see where he has got to!"

They rushed out of the room, leaving the Inspector, the Colonel, and me staring at each other.

" 'Pon my word, I am inclined to agree with Master Alec," said the official. "It may be the effect of this illness, but it seems to me that—"

His words were cut short by a sudden scream of "Help! Help! Murder!" With a thrill I recognized the voice as that of my friend. I rushed madly from the room on to the landing. The cries, which had sunk down into a hoarse, inarticulate shouting, came from the room which we had first visited. I dashed in, and on into the dressing-room beyond. The two Cunninghams were bending over the prostrate figure of Sherlock Holmes, the younger clutching his throat with both hands, while the elder seemed to be twisting one of his wrists. In an instant the three of us had torn them away from him, and Holmes staggered to his feet, very pale and evidently exhausted.

"Arrest these men, Inspector," he gasped.

"On what charge?"

"That of murdering their coachman, William Kirwan."

The Inspector stared about him in bewilderment. "Oh, come now, Mr. Holmes," said he at last, "I'm sure you don't really mean to—"

"Tut, man, look at their faces!" cried Holmes, curtly.

Never certainly have I seen a plainer confession of guilt upon human countenances. The older man seemed numb and dazed, with a heavy, sullen expression upon his strongly marked face. The son, on the other hand, had dropped all that jaunty, dashing style which had characterized him, and the ferocity of a dangerous wild beast gleamed in his dark eyes and distorted his handsome features. The Inspector said nothing, but, stepping to the door, he blew the whistle. Two of his constables came at the call.

"I have no alternative, Mr. Cunningham," said he. "I trust that this may all prove to be an absurd mistake, but you can see that—Ah, would you? Drop it!" He struck out with his hand, and a revolver which the younger man was in the act of cocking clattered down upon the floor.

"Keep that," said Holmes, quietly putting his foot upon it; "you will find it useful at the trial. But this is what we really wanted." He held up a little crumpled piece of paper.

"The remainder of the sheet!" cried the Inspector.

"Precisely."

"And where was it?"

"Where I was sure it must be. I'll make the whole matter clear to you presently. I think, Colonel, that you and Watson might return now, and I will be with you again in an hour at the furthest. The Inspector and I must have a word with the prisoners, but you will certainly see me back at luncheon time."

Sherlock Holmes was as good as his word, for about one o'clock he rejoined us in the Colonel's smoking room. He was accompanied by a little elderly gentleman, who was introduced to me as the Mr. Acton whose house had been the scene of the original burglary.

"I wished Mr. Acton to be present while I demonstrated this small matter to you," said Holmes, "for it is natural that he should take an interest in the details. I am afraid, my dear Colonel, that you must regret the hour that you took in such a stormy petrel as I am."

"On the contrary," answered the Colonel, warmly, "I consider it the greatest privilege to have been permitted to study your methods of working. I confess that they quite surpass my expectations, and that I am utterly unable to account for your result. I have not yet seen the vestige of a clue."

"I am afraid that my explanation may disillusion you but it has always been my habit to hide none of my methods, either from my friend Watson or from anyone who might take an inteligent interest in them. But, first, as I am rather shaken by the knocking about which I had in the dressing-room, I think that I shall help myself to a dash of your brandy, Colonel. My strength has been rather tried of late."

"I trust that you had no more of those nervous attacks."

Sherlock Holmes laughed heartily. "We will come to that in its turn," said he. "I will lay an account of the case before you in its due order, showing you the various points which guided me in my decision. Pray interrupt me if there is any inference which is not perfectly clear to you.

"It is of the highest importance in the art of detection to be able to recognize, out of a number of facts, which are incidental and which are vital. Otherwise your energy and attention must be dissipated instead of being concentrated. Now, in this case there was not the slightest doubt in my mind from the first that the key of the whole matter must be looked for in the scrap of paper in the dead man's hand.

"Before going into this, I would draw your attention to the fact that, if Alec Cunningham's narrative was correct, and if the assailant, after shooting William Kirwan, had *instantly* fled, then it obviously could not be he who tore the paper from the dead man's hand. But if it was not he, it must have been Alec Cunningham himself, for by the time that the old man had descended several servants were on the scene. The point is a simple one, but the Inspector had overlooked it because he had started with the supposition that these county magnates had had nothing to do with the matter. Now, I make a point of never having any prejudices, and of following docilely wherever fact may lead me, and so, in the very first stage of the investigation, I found myself looking a little askance at the part which had been played by Mr. Alec Cunningham.

"And now I made a very careful examination of the corner of paper which the Inspector had submitted to us. It was at once clear to me that it formed part of a very remarkable document. Here it is. Do you not now observe something very suggestive about it?"

"It has a very irregular look," said the Colonel.

"My dear sir," cried Holmes, "there cannot be the least doubt in the world that it has been written by two persons doing alternate words. When I draw your attention to the strong *t*'s of 'at' and 'to,' and ask you to compare them with the weak ones of 'quarter' and 'twelve,' you will instantly recognize the fact. A very brief analysis of these four words would enable you to say with the utmost confidence that the 'learn' and the 'maybe' are written in the stronger hand, and the 'what' in the weaker."

"By Jove, it's as clear as day!" cried the Colonel. "Why on earth should two men write a letter in such a fashion?"

"Obviously the business was a bad one, and one of the men who distrusted the other was determined that, whatever was done, each should have an equal hand in it. Now, of the two men, it is clear that the one who wrote the 'at' and 'to' was the ringleader."

"How do you get at that?"

"We might deduce it from the mere character of the one hand as compared with the other. But we have more assured reasons than for supposing it. If you examine this scrap with attention you will come to the conclusion that the man with the stronger hand wrote all his words first, leaving blanks for the other to fill up. These blanks were not always sufficient, and you can see that the second man had a squeeze to fit his 'quarter' in between the 'at' and 'to,' showing that the latter were already written. The man who wrote all his words first is undoubtedly the man who planned the affair."

"Excellent!" cried Mr. Acton.

"But very superficial," said Holmes. "We come now, however, to a point which is of importance. You may not be aware that the deduction of a man's age from his writing is one which has been brought to considerable accuracy by experts. In normal cases one can place a man in his true decade with tolerable confidence. I say normal cases, because ill-health and physical weakness produce the signs of old age, even when the invalid is a youth. In this case, looking at the bold strong hand of the one, and the rather broken-backed appearance of the other, which still retains its legibility through the t's have begun to lose their crossing, we can say that the one was a young man and the other was advanced in years without being positively decrepit."

"Excellent!" cried Mr. Acton again.

"There is a further point, however, which is subtler and of greater interest. There is something in common between these hands. They belong to men who are blood relatives. It may be most obvious to you in the Greek e's, but to me there are so many small points which indicate the same thing. I have no doubt at all that a family mannerism can be traced in these two specimens of writing. I am only, of course, giving you the leading results now of my examination of the paper. There were twenty-three other deductions which would be of more interest to experts than to you. They all tend to deepen the impression upon my mind that the Cunninghams, father and son, had written this letter.

"Having got so far, my next step was, of course, to examine into the details of the crime, and to see how far they would help us. I went up to the house with the Inspector, and saw all that was to be seen. The wound upon the dead man, as I was able to determine with absolute confidence, fired from a revolver at the distance of something over four yards. There was no powder-blackening on the clothes. Evidently, therefore, Alec Cunningham had lied when he said that the two men were struggling when the shot was fired. Again, both father and son agreed as to the place where the man escaped into the road. At that point, however, as it happens, there is a broadish ditch, moist at the bottom. As there were no indications of boot marks about this ditch, I was absolutely sure not only that the Cunninghams had again lied, but that there had never been any unknown man upon the scene at all.

"And now I have to consider the motive of this singular crime. To get at this, I endeavored first of all to solve the reason of the original burglary at Mr. Acton's. I understood, from something which the Colonel told us, that a lawsuit had been going on between you, Mr. Acton, and the Cunninghams. Of course, it instantly occurred to me that they had broken into your library with the intention of getting at some document which might be of importance in the case."

"Precisely so," said Mr. Acton. "There can be no possible doubt as to their intentions. I have the clearest claim upon half of their present estate, and if they could have found a single paper—which, fortunately, was in the strong-box of my solicitors—they would undoubtedly have crippled our case."

"There you are," said Holmes, smiling. "It was a dangerous, reckless attempt, in which I seem to trace the influence of young Alec. Having found nothing, they tried to divert suspicion by making it appear to be an ordinary burglary, to which end they carried off whatever they could lay their hands upon. That is all clear enough, but there was much that was still obscure. What I wanted above all was to get the missing part of that note. I was certain that Alec had torn it out of the dead man's hand, and almost certain that he must have thrust it into the pocket of his dressing-gown. Where else could he have put it? The only question was whether it was still there. It was worth an effort to find out, and for that object we all went up to the house.

"The Cunninghams joined us, as you doubtless remember, outside the kitchen door. It was, of course, of the very first importance that they should not be reminded of the existence of this paper, otherwise they would naturally destroy it without delay. The Inspector was about to tell them the importance which we attached to it when, by the luckiest chance in the world, I tumbled down in a sort of fit and so changed the conversation."

"Good heavens!" cried the Colonel, laughing, "do you mean to say all our sympathy was wasted and your fit an imposture?"

"Speaking professionally, it was admirably done," cried I, looking in amazement at this man who was forever confounding me with some new phase of his astuteness.

"It is an art which is often useful," said he. "When I recovered I managed, by a device which had perhaps some little merit of ingenuity, to get old Cunningham to write the word twelve, so that I might compare it with the 'twelve' upon the paper."

"Oh, what an ass I have been!" I exclaimed.

"I could see that you were commiserating me over my weakness," said Holmes, laughing. "I was sorry to cause you the sympathetic pain which I knew that you felt. We then went upstairs together, and having entered the room and seen the dressing-gown hanging up behind the door, I contrived, by upsetting a table, to engage their attention for the moment, and slipped back to examine the pockets. I had hardly got the paper, however—which was, as I had expected, in one of them—when the two Cunninghams were on me, and would, I verily believe, have murdered me then and there but for your prompt and friendly aid. As it is, I feel that young man's grip on my throat now, and the father has twisted my wrist round in the effort to get the paper out of my hand. They saw that I must know all about it, you see, and the sudden change from absolute security to complete despair made them perfectly desperate.

"I had a little talk with old Cunningham afterwards as to the motive of the crime. He was tractable enough, though his son was a perfect demon, ready to blow out his own or anybody else's brains if he could have got to his revolver. When Cunningham saw that the case against him was so strong he lost all heart and made a clean breast of everything. It seems that William had secretly followed his two masters on the night when they made their raid upon Mr. Acton's, and having thus got them into his power, proceeded, under threats of exposure, to levy blackmail upon them. Mr. Alec, however, was a dangerous man to play games of that sort with. It was a stroke of positive genius on his part to see in the burglary scare which was convulsing the countryside an opportunity of plausibly getting rid of the man whom he feared. Wiilliam was decoyed up and shot, and had they only gotten the whole of the note and paid a little more attention to detail in their accessories, it is very possible that suspicion may never have been aroused."

"And the note?" I asked.

Sherlock Holmes placed the subjoined paper before us.

If you will only come round' to the east gate you will will very much surprise you and be of the greatest service to you and also to Annie Morrison. But say nothing to anyone upon the matter.

"It is very much the sort of thing that I expected," said he. "Of course, we do not yet know what the relations may have been between Alec Cunningham, William Kirwan, and Annie Morrison. The result shows that the trap was skilfully baited. I am sure that you cannot fail to be delighted with the traces of heredity shown in the *p*'s and in the tails of the *g*'s. The absence of the *i*-dots in the old man's writing is also most characteristic. Watson, I think our quiet rest in the country has been a distinct success, and I shall certainly return much invigorated to Baker Street tomorrow."

THE FLITTERBAT LANCERS

BY ARTHUR MORRISON

Arthur Morrison was born in England in 1863 and
worked as a journalist for several years. His first book,
Tales of Mean Streets, contained fictionalized accounts of
life in the London slums. He wrote four volumes of
stories about private detective Martin Hewitt, whose in-
vestigative methods resembled those of Sherlock
Holmes. These include *The Chronicles of Martin Hewitt*
and *The Red Triangle. Cunning Murrell* and *The Hole in the
Wall* did not feature Hewitt. An art collector and an
expert on Oriental masters, Morrison wrote *The Painters
of Japan* (1911), which remains a standard reference in
the field. He died in 1945.

IT WAS LATE ON A SUMMER EVENING, two or three years back, that I drowsed in my armchair over a particularly solid and ponderous volume of essays on social economy. I was doing a good deal of reviewing at the time, and I remember well that this particular volume had a property of such exceeding toughness that I had already made three successive attacks on it, on as many successive evenings, each attack having been defeated in the end by sleep. The weather was hot, my chair was very comfortable, and the book had somewhere about its strings of polysyllables an essence as of laudanum. Still something had been done on each evening, and now on the fourth I strenuously endeavored to finish the book. I was just beginning to feel that the words before me were sliding about and losing their meanings, when a sudden crash and a jingle of broken glass behind me woke me with a start, and I threw the book down. A pane of glass in my window was smashed, and I hurried across and threw up the sash to see, if I could, whence the damage had come.

The building in which my chambers (and Martin Hewitt's office) were situated was accessible—or rather visible, for there was no entrance—from the rear. There was, in fact, a small courtyard, reached by a passage from the street behind, and into this courtyard, my sitting-room window looked.

"Hullo, there!" I shouted. But there came no reply. Nor could I distinguish anybody in the courtyard. Some men had been at work during the day on a drainpipe, and I reflected that probably their litter had provided the stone with which my window had been smashed. As I looked, however, two men came hurrying from the passage into the court, and going straight into the deep shadow of one corner, presently appeared again in a less obscure part, hauling forth a third man, who must have already been there in hiding. The third man struggled fiercely, but without avail, and was dragged across toward the passage leading to the street beyond. But the most remarkable feature of the whole thing was the silence of all three men. No cry, no exclamation, escaped any of them. In perfect silence the two hauled the third across the courtyard, and in perfect silence he swung and struggled to resist and escape. The matter astonished me not a little, and the men were entering the passage before I found voice to shout at them. But they took no notice, and disappeared. Soon after I heard cab wheels in the street beyond, and had no doubt that the two men had carried off their prisoner.

I turned back into my room a little perplexed. It seemed probable that the man who had been borne off had broken my window. But why? I looked about on the floor, and presently found the missile. It was, as I had expected, a piece of broken concrete, but it was wrapped up in a worn piece of paper, which had partly opened out as it lay on my carpet, thus indicating that it had just been crumpled round the stone.

I disengaged the paper and spread it out. Then I saw it to be a rather hastily written piece of manuscript music, whereof I append a reduced facsimile:

This gave me no help. I turned the paper this way and that, but could make nothing of it. There was not a mark on it that I could discover, except the music and the scrawled title, *Flitterbat Lancers*, at the top. The paper was old, dirty, and cracked. What did it all mean? One might conceive of a person in certain circumstances sending a message—possibly an appeal for help—through a friend's window, wrapped round a stone, but this seemed to be nothing of that sort.

Once more I picked up the paper, and with an idea to hear what the *Flitterbat Lancers* sounded like, I turned to my little pianette and strummed over the notes, making my own time and changing it as seemed likely. But I could by no means extract from the notes anything resembling an air. I half thought of trying Martin Hewitt's office door, in case he might still be there and offer a guess at the meaning of my smashed window and the scrap of paper, when Hewitt himself came in. He had stayed late to examine a bundle of papers in connection with a case just placed in his hands, and now, having finished, came to find if I were disposed for an evening stroll before turning in. I handed him the paper and the piece of concrete, observing, "There's a little job for you, Hewitt, instead of the stroll." And I told him the complete history of my smashed window.

Hewitt listened attentively, and examined both the paper and the fragment of paving. "You say these people made absolutely no sound whatever?" he asked.

"None but that of scuffling, and even that they seemed to do quietly."

"Could you see whether or not the two men gagged the other, or placed their hands over his mouth?"

"No, they certainly didn't do that. It was dark, of course, but not so dark as to prevent my seeing generally what they were doing."

Hewitt stood for half a minute in thought, and then said, "There's something in this, Brett—what, I can't guess at the moment, but something deep, I fancy. Are you sure you won't come out now?"

I told Hewitt that I was sure, and that I should stick to my work.

"Very well," he said; "then perhaps you will lend me these articles?" holding up the paper and the stone.

"Delighted," I said. "If you get no more melody out of the clinker than I did out of the paper, you won't have a musical evening. Goodnight!"

Hewitt went away with the puzzle in his hand, and I turned once more to my social economy, and, thanks to the gentleman who smashed my window, conquered.

At this time my only regular daily work was on an evening paper so that I left home at a quarter to eight on the morning following the adventure of my broken window, in order, as usual, to be at the office at eight; consequently it was not until lunchtime that I had an opportunity of seeing Hewitt. I went to my own rooms first, however, and on the landing by my door I found the housekeeper in conversation with a shortish, sun-browned man, whose accent at once convinced me that he hailed from across the Atlantic. He had called, it appeared, three or four times during the morning to see me, getting more impatient each time. As he did not seem even to know my name, the housekeeper had not considered it expedient to give

114

him any information about me, and he was growing irascible under the treatment. When I at last appeared, however, he left her and approached me eagerly.

"See here, sir," he said, "I've been stumpin' these here durn stairs o' yours half through the mornin'. I'm anxious to apologize, and fix up some damage."

He had followed me into my sitting-room, and was now standing with his back to the fireplace, a dripping umbrella in one hand, and the forefinger of the other held up shoulder-high and pointing, in the manner of a pistol, to my window, which, by the way, had been mended during the morning, in accordance with my instructions to the housekeeper.

"Sir," he continued, "last night I took the extreme liberty of smashin' your winder."

"Oh," I said, "that was you, was it?"

"It was, sir—me. For that I hev come humbly to apologize. I trust the draft has not discommoded you, sir. I regret the accident, and I wish to pay for the fixin' up and the general inconvenience." He placed a sovereign on the table. "I 'low you'll call that square now, sir, and fix things friendly and comfortable as between gentlemen, an' no ill will. Shake."

And he formally extended his hand.

I took it at once. "Certainly," I said. "As a matter of fact, you haven't inconvenienced me at all; indeed, there were some circumstances about the affair that rather interested me." And I pushed the sovereign toward him.

"Say now," he said, looking a trifle disappointed at my unwillingness to accept his money, "didn't I startle your nerves?"

"Not a bit," I answered, laughing. "In fact, you did me a service by preventing me going to sleep just when I shouldn't; so we'll say no more of that."

"Well—there was one other little thing," he pursued, looking at me rather sharply as he pocketed the sovereign. "There was a bit o' paper round that pebble that came in here. Didn't happen to notice that, did you?"

"Yes, I did. It was an old piece of manuscript music."

"That was it—exactly. Might you happen to have it handy now?"

"Well," I said, "as a matter of fact a friend of mine has it now. I tried playing it over once or twice, as a matter of curiosity, but I couldn't make anything of it, and so I handed it to him."

"Ah!" said my visitor, watching me narrowly, "that's a puzzler, that *Flitterbat Lancers*—a real puzzler. It whips 'em all. Ha, ha!" He laughed suddenly—a laugh that seemed a little artificial. "There's music fellers as 'lows to set right down and play off anything right away that can't make anything of the *Flitterbat Lancers*. That was two of 'em that was monkeyin' with me last night. They never could make anythin' of it at all, and I was tantalizing them with it all along till they got real mad, and reckoned to get it out o' my pocket and learn it at home. Ha, ha! So I got away for a bit, and just rolled it round a stone and heaved it through your winder before they could come up, your winder being the nearest one with a light in it. Ha, ha! I'll be considerable obliged if you'll get it from your friend right now. Is he stayin' hereabout?"

The story was so ridiculously lame that I determined to confront my visitor with Hewitt, and observe the result. If he had succeeded in making any sense of the *Flitterbat Lancers*, the scene might be amusing. So I answered at once, "Yes; his office is on the floor below; he will probably be in at about this time. Come down with me."

We went down, and found Hewitt in his outer office. "This gentleman," I told him with a solemn intonation, "has come to ask for his piece of manuscript music, the *Flitterbat Lancers*. He is particularly proud of it, because nobody who tries to play it can make any sort of tune out of it, and it was entirely because two dear friends of his were anxious to drag it out of his pocket and practice it over on the quiet that he flung it through my windowpane last night, wrapped round a piece of concrete."

The stranger glanced sharply at me, and I could see that my manner and tone rather disconcerted him. But Hewitt came forward at once. "Oh, yes," he said. "Just so—quite a natural sort of thing. As a matter of fact, I quite expected you. Your umbrella's wet—do you mind putting it in the stand? Thank you. Come into my private office."

We entered the inner room, and Hewitt, turning to the stranger, went on: "Yes, that is a very extraordinary piece of music, that *Flitterbat Lancers*. I have been having a little bit of practice with it myself, though I'm really nothing of a musician. I don't wonder you are anxious to keep it to yourself. Sit down."

The stranger, with a distrustful look at Hewitt, complied. At this moment, Hewitt's clerk, Kerrett, entered from the outer office with a slip of paper. Hewitt glanced at it, and crumpled it in his hand. "I am engaged just now," was his remark, and Kerret vanished.

"And now," Hewitt said, as he sat down and suddenly turned to the stranger with an intent gaze, "and now, Mr. Hooker, we'll talk of this music."

The stranger started and frowned. "You've the advantage of me, sir," he said; "you seem to know my name, but I don't know yours."

Hewitt smiled pleasantly. "My name," he said, "is Hewitt—Martin Hewitt, and it is my business to know a great many things. For instance, I know that you are Mr. Reuben B. Hooker, of Robertsville, Ohio."

The visitor pushed his chair back, and stared. "Well—that gits me," he said. "You're a pretty smart chap, Mr. Hewitt. I've heard your name before, of course. And—and so you've been a-studyin' the *Flitterbat Lancers*, have you?" This with a keen glance at Hewitt's face. "Well, s'pose you have. What's your idea?"

"Why," answered Hewitt, still keeping his steadfast gaze on Hooker's eyes, "I think it's pretty late in the century to be fishing about for the Wedlake jewels."

These words astonished me almost as much as they did Mr. Hooker. The great Wedlake jewel robbery is, as many will remember, a traditional story of the 'sixties. I remembered no more of it at the time than probably most men do who have at some time or another read the *causes célèbres* of the century. Sir Francis Wedlake's country house had been robbed, and the whole of Lady Wedlake's magnificent collection of jewels stolen. A man named Shiels, a strolling musician, had beeen arrested and had been sentenced to a long term of penal servitude. Another man named Legg—one of the comparatively wealthy scoundrels who finance promising thefts or swindles and pocket the greater part of the proceeds—had also been punished, but only a very few of the trinkets, and those quite unimportant items, had been recovered. The great bulk of the booty was never brought to light. So much I remembered, and Hewitt's sudden mention of the Wedlake jewels in connection with my broken window, Mr. Reuben B. Hooker, and the *Flitterbat Lancers*, astonished me not a little.

As for Hooker, he did his best to hide his perturbation, but with little success. "Wedlake jewels, eh?" he said; "and—and what's that to do with it, anyway?"

"To do with it?" responded Hewitt, with an air of carelessness. "Well, well, I had my idea, nothing more. If the Wedlake jewels have nothing to do with it, we'll say no more about it, that's all. Here's your paper, Mr. Hooker—only a little crumpled." He rose and placed the article in Mr. Hooker's hand, with the manner of terminating the interview.

Hooker rose, with a bewildered look on his face, and turned toward the door. Then he stopped, looked at the floor, scratched his cheek, and finally sat down and put his hat on the ground. "Come," he said, "we'll play a square game. That paper *has* something to do with the Wedlake jewels, and, win or lose, I'll tell you all I know about it. You're a smart man and whatever I tell you, I guess it won't do me no harm; it ain't done me no good yet, anyway."

"Say what you please, of course," Hewitt answered, "but think first. You might tell me something you'd be sorry for afterward."

"Say, will you listen to what I say, and tell me if you think I've been swindled or not? My two hundred and fifty dollars is gone now, and I guess I won't go skirmishing after it anymore if you think it's no good. Will you do that much?"

"As I said before," Hewitt replied, "tell me what you please, and if I can help you I will. But remember, I don't ask for your secrets."

"That's all right, I guess, Mr. Hewitt. Well, now, it was all like this." And Mr. Reuben B. Hooker plunged into a detailed account of his adventures since his arrival in London.

Relieved of repetitions, and put as directly as possible, it was as follows: Mr. Hooker was a wagon-builder, had made a good business from very humble beginnings, and intended to go on and make it still a better. Meantime, he had come over to Europe for a short holiday—a thing he had promised himself for years. He was wandering about the London streets on the second night after his arrival in the city, when he managed to get into conversation with two men at a bar. They were not very prepossessing men, though flashily dressed. Very soon they suggested a game of cards. But Reuben B. Hooker was not to be had in that way, and after a while, they parted. The two were amusing enough fellows in their way, and when Hooker saw them again the next night in the same bar, he made no difficulty in talking with them freely. After a succession of drinks, they told him that they had a speculation on hand—a speculation that meant thousands if it succeeded—and to carry out which they were only waiting for a paltry sum of £50. There was a house, they said, in which was hidden a great number of jewels of immense value, which had been deposited there by a man who was now dead. Exactly in what part of the house the jewels were to be found they did not know. There was a paper, they said, which was supposed to contain some information, but as yet they hadn't been quite able to make it out. But that would really matter very little if once they could get possession of the house. Then they would simply set to work and search from the topmost chimney to the lowermost brick, if necessary. The only present difficulty was that the house was occupied, and that the landlord wanted a large deposit of rent down before he would consent to turn out his present tenants and give them possession at a higher rental. This deposit would come to £50, and they hadn't the money. However, if any friend of theirs who meant business would put the necessary sum at their disposal, and keep his mouth shut, they would make him an equal partner in the proceeds with themselves; and as the value of the whole haul would probably be something not very far off £20,000, the speculation would bring a tremendous return to the man who was smart enough to put down his £50.

Hooker, very distrustful, skeptically demanded more detailed particulars of the scheme. But these two men (Luker and Birks were their names, he found, in course of talking) inflexibly refused to communicate.

"Is it likely," said Luker, "that we should give the 'ole thing away to anybody who might easily go with his fifty pounds and clear out the bloomin' show? Not much. We've told you what the game is, and if you'd like to take a flutter with your fifty, all right; you'll do as well as anybody, and we'll treat you square. If you don't—well, don't, that's all. We'll get the oof from somewhere—there's blokes as 'ud jump at the chance. Anyway, we ain't going to give the show away before you've done somethin' to prove you're on the job, straight. Put your money in, and you shall know as much as we do."

Then there were more drinks, and more discussion. Hooker was still reluctant, though tempted by the prospect, and growing more venturesome with each drink.

"Don't you see," said Birks, "that if we was a-tryin' to 'ave you we should out with a tale as long as yer arm, all complete, with the address of the 'ouse and all. Then I s'pose you'd lug out the pieces on the nail, without askin' a bloomin' question. As it is, the thing's so perfectly genuine that we'd rather lose the chance and wait for some other bloke to find the money than run a chance of givin' the thing away. It's a matter o' business, simple and plain, that's all. It's a question of either us trustin' you with a chance of collarin' twenty thousand pounds or you trustin' us with a paltry fifty. We don't lay out no 'igh moral sentiments, we only say the weight o' money is all on one side. Take it or leave it, that's all. 'Ave another Scotch?"

The talk went on and the drinks went on, and it all ended, at "chucking-out time," in Reuben B. Hooker handing over five £10 notes, with smiling, though slightly incoherent, assurances of his eternal friendship for Luker and Birks.

In the morning he awoke to the realization of a bad head, a bad tongue, and a bad opinion of his proceedings of the previous night. In his sober senses it seemed plain that he had been swindled. All day he cursed his fuddled foolishness, and at night he made for the bar that had been the scene of the transaction, with little hope of seeing either Luker or Birks, who had agreed to be there to meet him. There they were, however, and, rather to his surprise, they made no demand for more money. They asked him if he understood music, and showed him the worn old piece of paper containing the *Flitterbat Lancers*. The exact spot, they said, where the jewels were hidden was supposed to be indicated somehow on that piece of paper. Hooker did not understand music, and could find nothing on the paper that looked in the least like a direction to a hiding-place for jewels or anything else.

Luker and Birks then went into full particulars of their project. First, as to its history. The jewels were the famous Wedlake jewels, which had been taken from Sir Francis Wedlake's house in 1866 and never heard of again. A certain Jerry Shiels had been arrested in connection with the robbery, had been given a long sentence of penal servitude, and had died in jail. This Jerry Shiels was an extraordinarily clever criminal, and traveled about the country as a street musician. Although an expert burglar, he very rarely perpetrated robberies himself, but acted as a sort of traveling fence, receiving stolen property and transmitting it to London or out of the country. He also acted as the agent of a man named Legg, who had money, and who financed any likely looking project of a criminal nature that Shiels might arrange.

Jerry Shiels traveled with a "pardner"—a man who played the harp and acted as his assistant and messenger in affairs wherein Jerry was reluctant to appear personally. When Shiels was arrested, he had in his possession a quantity of printed and manuscript music, and after his first remand his "pardner," Jimmy Snape, applied for the music to be given up to him, in order, as he explained, that he might earn his living. No objection was raised to this, and Shiels was quite willing that Snape should have it, and so it was handed over. Now among the music was a small slip, headed *Flitterbat Lancers*, which Shiels had shown to Snape before the arrest. In case of Shiels being taken, Snape was to take this slip to Legg as fast as he could.

But as chance would have it, on that very day Legg himself was arrested, and soon after was sentenced also to a term of years. Snape hung about in London for a little while, and then emigrated. Before leaving, however, he gave the slip of music to Luker's father, a rag-shop keeper, to whom he owed money. He explained its history, and Luker senior made all sorts of fruitless efforts to get at the information concealed in the paper. He had held it to the fire to bring out concealed writing, had washed it, had held it to the light till his eyes ached, had gone over it with a magnifying glass—all in vain. He had got musicians to strum out the notes on all sorts of instruments— backwards, forwards, alternately, and in every other way he could think of. If at any time he fancied a resemblance in the resulting sound to some familiar song-tune, he got that song and studied all its words with loving care, upside-down, right-side up—every way. He took the words *Flitterbat Lancers* and transposed the letters in all directions, and did everything else he could think of. In the end he gave it up, and died. Now, lately, Luker junior had been impelled with a desire to see into the matter. He had repeated all the parental experiments, and more, with the same lack of success. He had taken his "pal" Birks into his confidence, and together they had tried other experiments till at last they began to believe that the message had probably been written in some sort of invisible ink which the subsequent washings had erased altogether. But he had done one other thing: he had found the house which Shiels had rented at the time of his arrest, and in which a good quantity of stolen property—not connected with the Wedlake case—was discovered. Here, he argued, if anywhere, Jerry Shiels had hidden the jewels. There was no other place where he could be

121

found to have lived, or over which he had sufficient control to warrant his hiding valuables therein. Perhaps, once the house could be properly examined, something about it might give a clue as to what the message of the *Flitterbat Lancers* meant.

Hooker, of course, was anxious to know where the house in question stood, but this Luker and Birks would on no account inform him. "You've done your part," they said, "and now you leave us to do ours. There's a bit of a job about gettin' the tenants out. They won't go, and it'll take a bit of time before the landlord can make them. So you just hold your jaw and wait. When we're safe in the 'ouse, and there's no chance of anybody else pokin' in, then you can come and help find the stuff."

Hooker went home that night sober, but in much perplexity. The thing might be genuine, after all; indeed, there were many little things that made him think it was. But then, if it were, what guarantee had he that he would get his share, supposing the search turned out successful? None at all. But then it struck him for the first time that these jewels, though they may have lain untouched so long, were stolen property after all. The moral aspect of the affair began to trouble him a little, but the legal aspect troubled him more. That consideration, however, he decided to leave over for the present. He had no more than the word of Luker and Birks that the jewels (if they existed) *were* those of Lady Wedlake, and Luker and Birks themselves only professed to know from hearsay. At any rate, he made up his mind to have some guarantee for his money. In accordance with this resolve, he suggested, when he met the two men the next day, that he should take charge of the slip of music and make an independent study of it. This proposal, however, met with an instant veto.

Hooker resolved to make up a piece of paper, folded as like the slip of music as possible, and substitute one for the other at their next meeting. Then he would put the *Flitterbat Lancers* in some safe place, and face his fellow conspirators with a hand of cards equal to their own. He carried out his plan the next evening with perfect success, thanks to the contemptuous indifference with which Luker and Birks had begun to regard him. He got the slip in his pocket, and left the bar. He had not gone far, however, before Luker discovered the loss, and soon he became conscious of being followed. He looked for a cab, but he was in a dark street, and no cab was near. Luker and Birks turned the corner and began to run. He saw they must catch him. Everything now depended on his putting the *Flitterbat Lancers* out of their reach, but where he could himself recover it. He ran till he saw a narrow passageway on his right, and into this he darted. It led into a yard where stones were lying about, and in a large building before him he saw the window of a lighted room a couple of floors up. It was a desperate expedient, but there was no time for consideration. He wrapped a stone in the paper and flung it with all his force through the lighted window. Even as he did it he heard the feet of Luker and Birks as they hurried down the street. The rest of the adventure in the court I myself saw.

Luker and Birks kept Hooker in their lodgings all that night. They searched him unsuccessfully for the paper; they bullied, they swore, they cajoled, they entreated, they begged him to play the game square with his pals. Hooker merely replied that he had put the *Flitterbat Lancers* where they couldn't easily find it, and that he intended playing the game square as long as they did the same. In the end they released him, apparently with more respect than they had before entertained, advising him to get the paper into his possession as soon as he could.

"And now," said Mr. Hooker, in conclusion of his narrative, "perhaps you'll give me a bit of advice. Am I playin' a fool-game running after these toughs, or ain't I?"

Hewitt shrugged his shoulders. "It all depends," he said, "on your friends Luker and Birks. They may want to swindle you, or they may not. I'm afraid they'd like to, at any rate. But perhaps you've got some little security in this piece of paper. One thing is plain: they certainly believe in the deposit of the jewels themselves, else they wouldn't have taken so much trouble to get the paper back."

"Then I guess I'll go on with the thing, if that's it."

"That depends, of course, on whether you care to take trouble to get possession of what, after all, is somebody else's lawful property."

Hooker looked a little uneasy. "Well," he said, "there's that, of course. I didn't know nothin' of that at first, and when I did I'd parted with my money and felt entitled to get something back for it. Anyway, the stuff ain't found yet. When it is, why then, you know, I might make a deal with the owner. But, say, how did you find out my name, and about this here affair being jined up with the Wedlake jewels?"

Hewitt smiled. "As to the name and address, you just think it over a little when you've gone away, and if you don't see how I did it, you're not so cute as I think you are. In regard to the jewels—well, I just read the message of the *Flitterbat Lancers*, that's all."

"You read it? Whew! And what does it say? How did you do it?" Hooker turned the paper over eagerly in his hands as he spoke.

"See, now," said Hewitt, "I won't tell you all that, but I'll tell you something, and it may help you to test the real knowledge of Luker and Birks. Part of the message is in these words, which you had better write down: *Over the coals the fifth dancer slides, says Jerry Shiels the horney.*"

"What?" Hooker exclaimed, "fifth dancer slides over the coals? That's mighty odd. What's it all about?"

"About the Wedlake jewels, as I said. Now you can go and make a bargain with Luker and Birks. The only other part of the message is an address, and that they already know, if they have been telling the truth about the house they intend taking. You can offer to tell them what I have told you of the message, after they have told you where the house is, and proved to you that they are taking the steps they talked of. If they won't agree to that, I think you had best treat them as common rogues and charge them with obtaining your money under false pretenses."

Nothing more would Hewitt say than that, despite Hooker's many questions; and when at last Hooker had gone, almost as troubled and perplexed as ever, my friend turned to me and said, "Now, Brett, if you haven't lunched and would like to see the end of this business, hurry!"

"The end of it?" I said. "Is it to end so soon? How?"

"Simply by a police raid on Jerry Shiels's old house with a search warrant. I communicated with the police this morning before I came here."

"Poor Hooker!" I said.

"Oh, I had told the police before I saw Hooker, or heard of him, of course. I just conveyed the message on the music slip—that was enough. But I'll tell you all about it when there's more time; I must be off now. With the information I have given him, Hooker and his friends may make an extra push and get into the house soon, but I couldn't resist the temptation to give the unfortunate Hooker some sort of sporting chance—though it's a poor one, I fear. Get your lunch as quickly as you can, and go at once to Colt Row, Bankside—Southwark way, you know.

Probably we shall be there before you. If not, wait."

Colt Row was not difficult to find. It was one of those places that decay with an excess of respectability, like Drury Lane and Clare Market. Once, when Jacob's Island was still an island, a little farther down the river, Colt Row had evidently been an unsafe place for a person with valuables about him, and then it probably prospered, in its own way. Now it was quite respectable, but very dilapidated and dirty. Perhaps it was sixty yards long—perhaps a little more. It was certainly a very few yards wide, and the houses at each side had a patient and forlorn look of waiting for a metropolitan improvement to come along and carry them away to their rest.

I could see no sign of Hewitt, nor of the police, so I walked up and down the narrow pavement for a little while. As I did so, I became conscious of a face at the window of the least ruinous house in the row, a face that I fancied expressed particular interest in my movements. The house was an old gabled structure, faced with plaster. What had apparently once been a shopwindow on the ground floor was now shuttered up, and the face that watched me—an old woman's—looked out from the window above. I had noted these particulars with some curiosity, when, arriving again at the street corner, I observed Hewitt approaching, in company with a police inspector, and followed by two unmistakable plainclothesmen.

"Well," Hewitt said, "you're first here after all. Have you seen any more of our friend Hooker?"

"No, nothing."

"Very well—probably he'll be here before long, though."

The party turned into Colt Row, and the inspector, walking up to the door of the house with the shuttered bottom window, knocked sharply. There was no response, so he knocked again, equally in vain.

"All out," said the inspector.

"No," I said; "I saw a woman watching me from the window above not three minutes ago."

"Ho, ho!" the inspector replied. "That's so, eh? One of you—you, Johnson—step round to the back, will you?"

One of the plainclothesmen started off, and after waiting another minute or two the inspector began a thundering cannonade of knocks that brought every available head out of the window of every inhabited room in the Row. At this the

125

woman opened the window, and began abusing the inspector with a shrillness and fluency that added a street-corner audience to that already congregated at the windows.

"Go away, you blaggards!" the lady said, "you ought to be 'orse-w'ipped, every one of ye! A-comin' 'ere a-tryin' to turn decent people out o' 'ouse and 'ome! Wait till my 'usband comes 'ome—'e'll show yer, ye mutton-cadgin' scoundrels! Payin' our rent reg'lar, and good tenants as is always been—and I'm a respectable married woman, that's what I am, ye dirty great cow-ards!"—this last word with a low, tragic emphasis.

Hewitt remembered what Hooker had said about the present tenants refusing to quit the house on the landlord's notice. "She thinks we've come from the landlord to turn her out," he said to the inspector.

"We're not here from the landlord, you old fool!" the inspector said. "We don't want to turn you out. We're the police, with a search warrant, and you'd better let us in or you'll get into trouble."

"'Ark at 'im!" the woman screamed, pointing at the inspector. "'Ark at 'im! Thinks I was born yesterday, that feller! Go 'ome, ye dirty pie-stealer, go 'ome!"

The audience showed signs of becoming a small crowd, and the inspector's patience gave out. "Here, Bradley," he said, addressing the remaining plainclothesman, "give a hand with these shutters," and the two—both powerful men—seized the iron bar which held the shutters and began to pull. But the garrison was undaunted, and, seizing a broom, the woman began to belabor the invaders about the shoulders and head from above. But just at this moment, the woman, emitting a terrific shriek, was suddenly lifted from behind and vanished. Then the head of the plainclothesman who had gone round to the back appeared, with the calm announcement, "There's a winder open behind, sir. But I'll open the front door if you like."

In a minute the bolts were shot, and the front door swung back. The placid Johnson stood in the passage, and as we passed in he said, "I've locked 'er in the back room upstairs."

"It's the bottom staircase, of course," the inspector said; and we tramped down into the basement. A little way from the stairfoot Hewitt opened a cupboard door, which enclosed a receptacle for coals. "They still keep the coals here, you see," he said, striking a match and passing it to and fro near the sloping

126

roof of the cupboard. It was of plaster, and covered the underside of the stairs.

"And now for the fifth dancer," he said, throwing the match away and making for the staircase again. "One, two, three, four, five," and he tapped the fifth stair from the bottom.

The stairs were uncarpeted, and Hewitt and the inspector began a careful examination of the one he had indicated. They tapped it in different places, and Hewitt passed his hands over the surfaces of both tread and riser. Presently, with his hand at the outer edge of the riser, Hewitt spoke. "Here it is, I think," he said; "it is the riser that slides."

He took out his pocketknife and scraped away the grease and paint from the edge of the old stair. Then a joint was plainly visible. For a long time the plank, grimed and set with age, refused to shift; but at last, by dint of patience and firm fingers, it moved, and was drawn clean out from the end.

Within, nothing was visible but grime, fluff, and small rubbish. The inspector passed his hand along the bottom angle. "Here's something," he said. It was the gold hook of an old-fashioned earring, broken off short.

Hewitt slapped his thigh. "Somebody's been here before us," he said, "and a good time back too, judging from the dust. That hook's a plain indication that jewelry was here once. There's plainly nothing more, except—except this piece of paper." Hewitt's eyes had detected—black with loose grime as it was—a small piece of paper lying at the bottom of the recess. He drew it out and shook off the dust. "Why, what's this?" he exclaimed. "More music!"

We went to the window, and there saw in Hewitt's hand a piece of written musical notation, thus:

Hewitt pulled out from his pocket a few pieces of paper. "Here is a copy I made this morning of the *Flitterbat Lancers*, and a note or two of my own as well," he said. He took a pencil, and, constantly referring to his own papers, marked a letter under each note on the last-found slip of music. When he had done this, the letters read:

You are a clever cove whoever you are but there was a cleverer says Jim Snape the horney's mate.

"You see?" Hewitt said, handing the inspector the paper. "Snape, the unconsidered messenger, finding Legg in prison, set to work and got the jewels for himself. The thing was a cryptogram, of course, of a very simple sort, though uncommon in design. Snape was a humorous soul, too, to leave this message here in the same cipher, on the chance of somebody else reading the *Flitterbat Lancers*."

"But," I asked, "why did he give that slip of music to Luker's father?"

"Well, he owed him money, and got out of it that way. Also, he avoided the appearance of 'flushness' that paying the debt might have given him, and got quietly out of the country with his spoils."

The shrieks upstairs had grown hoarser, but the broom continued vigorously. "Let that woman out," said the inspector, "and we'll go and report. Not much good looking for Snape now, I fancy. But there's some satisfaction in clearing up that old quarter-century mystery."

We left the place pursued by the execrations of the broom wielder, who bolted the door behind us, and from the window defied us to come back, and vowed she would have us all searched before a magistrate for what we had probably stolen. In the very next street we hove in sight of Reuben B. Hooker in the company of two swell-mob-looking fellows, who sheered off down a side turning in sight of our group. Hooker, too, looked rather shy at the sight of the inspector.

"The meaning of the thing was so very plain," Hewitt said to me afterwards, "that the duffers who had the *Flitterbat Lancers* in hand for so long never saw it at all. If Shiels had made an ordinary clumsy cryptogram, all letters and figures, they would have seen what it was at once, and at least would have tried to read it; but because it was put in the form of music, they tried everything else but the right way. It was a clever dodge of

Shiels's, without a doubt. Very few people, police officers or not, turning over a heap of old music, would notice or feel suspicious of that little slip among the rest. But once one sees it is a cryptogram (and the absence of bar lines and of notes beyond the stave would suggest that) the reading is as easy as possible. For my part I tried it as a cryptogram at once. You know the plan—it has been described a hundred times. See here—look at this copy of the *Flitterbat Lancers*. Its only difficulty—and that is a small one—is that the words are not divided. Since there are positions for less than a dozen notes on the stave, and there are twenty-six letters to be indicated, it follows that crotchets, quavers, and semiquavers on the same line or space must mean different letters. The first step is obvious. We count the notes to ascertain which sign occurs most frequently, and we find that the crotchet in the top space is the sign required—it occurs no less than eleven times. Now the letter most frequently occurring in an ordinary sentence of English is *e*. Let us then suppose that this represents *e*. At once a coincidence strikes us. In ordinary musical notation in the treble clef the note occupying the top space would be E. Let us remember that presently. Now the most common word in the English language is *the*. We know the sign for *e*, the last letter of this word, so let us see if in more than one place that sign is preceded by two others identical in each case. If so, the probability is that the other two signs will represent *t* and *h*, and the whole word will be *the*. Now it happens in no less than four places the sign *e* is preceded by the same two other signs—once in the first line, twice in the second, and once in the fourth. No word of three letters ending in *e* would be in the least likely to occur four times in a short sentence except *the*. Then we will call it *the*, and note the signs preceding the *e*. They are a quaver under the bottom line for the *t*, and a crotchet on the first space for the *h*. We travel along the stave, and wherever these signs occur we mark them with *t* or *h*, as the case may be. But now we remember that *e*, the crotchet in the top space, is in its right place as a musical note, while the crotchet in the bottom space means *h*, which is no musical note at all. Considering this for a minute, we remember that among the notes which are expressed in ordinary music on the treble stave, without the use of ledger lines, *d e* and *f* are repeated at the lower and at the upper part of the stave. Therefore, anybody making a cryptogram of musical notes would probably use one set of these duplicate positions to indicate other letters, and as *h* is in the lower part of the stave, that is where the variation comes in. Let us experiment by assuming that all the crotchets above *f* in ordinary musical notation have their usual values, and let us set the letters over their respective notes. Now things begin to shape. Look toward the end of the second line: there is the word *the* and the letters *f f t h*, with another note between the two *f*s. Now that word can only possibly be fifth, so that now we have the sign for *i*. It is the crotchet on the bottom line. Let us go through and mark the *i*'s. And now observe. The first sign of the lot is *i*, and there is one other sign before the word *the*. The only words possible here beginning with *i*, and of two letters, are *it*, *if*, *is* and *in*. Now we have the signs for *t* and *f*, so we know that it isn't *it* or *if*. *Is* would be unlikely here, because there is a tendency, as you see, to regularity in these signs, and *t*, the next letter alphabetically to *s*, is at the bottom of the stave. Let us try *n*. At once we get the word *dance* at the beginning of line three. And now we have got enough to see the system of the thing. Make a stave and put G A B C and the higher D E F in their proper musical places. Then fill in the blank places with the next letters of the alphabet downward, *h i j*, and we find that *h* and *i* fall in the places we have already discovered for them as crotchets. Now take quavers, and go on with *k l m n o*, and so on as before, beginning on the A space. When you have filled the quavers, do the same with semiquavers—there are only six alphabetical letters left for this—*u v w x y z*. Now you will find that this exactly agrees with all we have ascertained already, and if you will use the other letters to fill up over the signs still unmarked you will get the whole message:

"In the Colt Row ken over the coals the fifth dancer slides says Jerry Shiels the horney.

" 'Dancer,' as perhaps you didn't know, is thieves' slang for a stair, and 'horney' is the strolling musician's name for cornet player. Of course the thing took a little time to work out, chiefly because the sentence was short, and gave one few opportunities. But anybody with the key, using the cipher as a means of communication, would read it easily.

"As soon as I had read it, of course I guessed the purport of the *Flitterbat Lancers*. Jerry Shiels's name is well-known to anybody with half my knowledge of the criminal records of the century, and his connection with the missing Wedlake jewels, and his death in prison, came to my mind at once. Certainly

130

here was something hidden, and as the Wedlake jewels seemed most likely, I made the shot in talking to Hooker."

"But you terribly astonished him by telling him his name and address. How was that?" I asked curiously.

Hewitt laughed aloud. "That," he said; "why, that was the thinnest trick of all. Why, the man had it engraved on the silver band of his umbrella handle. When he left his umbrella outside, Kerrett (I had indicated the umbrella to him by a sign) just copied the lettering on one of the ordinary visitors' forms, and brought it in. You will remember I treated it as an ordinary visitor's announcement." And Hewitt laughed again.

THE CRIMINOLOGISTS' CLUB

BY E. W. HORNUNG

Ernest William Hornûng was born in Yorkshire, England in 1866, and served in France during World War I. He was married to Constance Doyle, sister of Arthur Conan Doyle. His most famous fictional creation is A. J. Raffles, who made his first appearance in a story, "The Amateur Cracksman," in 1899. Hornung wrote three short-story collections and one novel, *Mr. Justice Raffles* (1909), about Raffles and his companion, Bunny Manders. Hornung also wrote romantic novels of crime and adventure in Australia. His book, *The Crime Doctor* (1914), is a collection of stories about psychologist-detective Dr. John Dollar. Hornung died in 1921.

"BUT WHO ARE THEY, Raffles, and where's their house? There's no such club on the list in Whitaker."

"The Criminologists, my dear Bunny, are too few for a local habitation, and too select to tell their name in Gath. They are merely so many solemn students of contemporary crime, who meet and dine periodically at each other's clubs or houses."

"But why in the world should they ask us to dine with them?"

And I brandished the invitation which had brought me hot-foot to the Albany: it was from the Right Hon. the Earl of Thornaby, K.G.; and it requested the honor of my company at dinner, at Thornaby House, Park Lane, to meet the members of the Criminologists' Club. That in itself was a disturbing compliment: judge then of my dismay on learning that Raffles had been invited too!

"They have got it into their heads," said he, "that the gladiatorial element is the curse of most modern sport. They tremble especially for the professional gladiator. And they want to know whether my experience tallies with their theory."

"So they say!"

"They quote the case of a league player, *sus per coll.*, and any number of suicides. It really is rather in my public line."

"In yours, if you like, but not in mine," said I. "No, Raffles, they've got their eye on us both, and mean to put us under the microscope, or they never would have pitched on *me*."

Raffles smiled on my perturbation.

"I almost wish you were right, Bunny! It would be even better fun than I mean to make it as it is. But it may console you to hear that it was I who gave them your name. I told them you were a far keener criminologist than myself. I am delighted to hear they have taken my hint, and that we are to meet at their gruesome board."

"If I accept," said I, with the austerity he deserved.

"If you don't," rejoined Raffles, "you will miss some sport after both our hearts. Think of it, Bunny! These fellows meet to wallow in all the latest crimes; we wallow with them as though we knew no more about it than themselves. Perhaps we don't, for few criminologists have a soul above murder; and I quite expect to have the privilege of lifting the discussion into our own higher walk. They shall give their morbid minds to the fine art of burgling, for a change; and while we're about it, Bunny, we may as well extract their opinion of our noble selves. As authors, as collaborators, we will sit with the flower of our critics, and find our own level in the expert eye. It will be a piquant experience, if not an invaluable one; if we are sailing too near the wind, we are sure to hear about it, and can trim our yards accordingly. Moreover, we shall get a very good dinner into the bargain, or our noble host will belie a European reputation."

"Do you know him?" I asked.

"We have a pavilion acquaintance, when it suits my lord," replied Raffles, chuckling. "But I know all about him. He was president one year of the M.C.C., and we never had a better. He knows the game, though I believe he never played cricket in his life. But then he knows most things and has never done any of them. He has never even married, and never opened his lips in the House of Lords. Yet they say there is no better brain in the august assembly, and he certainly made us a wonderful speech last time the Australians were over. He has read everything and (to his credit in these days) never written a line. All round he is a whale for theory and a sprat for practice—but he looks quite capable of both at crime!"

I now longed to behold this remarkable peer in the flesh, and with the greater curiosity since another of the things which he evidently never did was to have his photograph published for the benefit of the vulgar. I told Raffles that I would dine with him at Lord Thornaby's, and he nodded as though I had not hesitated for a moment. I see now how deftly he had disposed of my reluctance. No doubt he had thought it all out before: his little speeches look sufficiently premeditated as I set them down at the dictates of an excellent memory. Let it, however, be borne in mind that Raffles did not talk exactly like a Raffles book: he said the things, but he did not say them in so many consecutive breaths. They were punctuated by puffs from his eternal cigarette, and the punctuation was often in the nature of a line of asterisks, while he took a silent turn up and down his room. Nor was he ever more deliberate than when he seemed most nonchalant and spontaneous. I came to see it in the end. But these were early days, in which he was more plausible to me than I can hope to render him to another human being.

And I saw a good deal of Raffles just then; it was, in fact, the one period at which I can remember his coming round to see me more frequently than I went round to him. Of course he would come at his own odd hours, often just as one was dressing to go out and dine, and I can even remember finding him there when I returned, for I had long since given him a key of the flat. It was the inhospitable month of February, and I can recall more than one cosy evening when we discussed anything and everything but our own malpractices; indeed, there were none to discuss just then. Raffles, on the contrary, was showing himself with some industry in the most respectable society, and by his advice I used the club more than ever.

"There is nothing like it at this time of year," said he. "In the summer I have my cricket to provide me with decent employment in the sight of men. Keep yourself before the public from morning to night, and they'll never think of you in the still small hours."

Our behavior, in fine, had so long been irreproachable that I rose without misgiving on the morning of Lord Thornaby's dinner to the other Criminologists and guests. My chief anxiety was to arrive under the ægis of my brilliant friend, and I had begged him to pick me up on his way; but at five minutes to the appointed hour there was no sign of Raffles or his cab. We were bidden at a quarter to eight for eight o'clock, so after all I had to hurry off alone.

Fortunately, Thornaby House is almost at the end of my street that was; and it seemed to me another fortunate circumstance that the house stood back, as it did and does, in its own august courtyard; for, as I was about to knock, a hansom came twinkling in behind me, and I drew back, hoping it was Raffles at the last moment. It was not, and I knew it in time to melt from the porch, and wait yet another minute in the shadows, since others were as late as I. And out jumped these others, chattering in stage whispers as they paid their cab.

"Thornaby has a bet about it with Freddy Vereker, who can't come, I hear. Of course, it won't be lost or won to-night. But the dear man thinks he's been invited as a cricketer!"

"I don't believe he's the other thing," said a voice as brusque as the first was bland. "I believe it's all bunkum. I wish I didn't, but I do!"

"I think you'll find it's more than that," rejoined the other, as the doors opened and swallowed the pair.

I flung out limp hands and smote the air. Raffles bidden to

what he had well called this "gruesome board," not as a cricketer but as a suspected criminal! Raffles wrong all the time, and I right for once in my original apprehension! And still no Raffles in sight—no Raffles to warn—no Raffles, and the clocks striking eight!

Well may I shirk the psychology of such a moment, for my belief is that the striking clocks struck out all power of thought and feeling, and that I played my poor part the better for that blessed surcease of intellectual sensation. On the other hand, I was never more alive to the purely objective impressions of any hour of my existence, and of them the memory is startling to this day. I hear my mad knock at the double doors; they fly open in the middle, and it is like some sumptuous and solemn rite. A long slice of silken-legged lackey is seen on either hand; a very prelate of a butler bows a benediction from the sanctuary steps. I breathe more freely when I reach a book-lined library where a mere handful of men do not overflow the Persian rug before the fire. One of them is Raffles, who is talking to a large man with the brow of a demigod and the eyes and jowl of a degenerate bulldog. And this is our noble host.

Lord Thornaby stared at me with inscrutable stolidity as we shook hands, and at once handed me over to a tall, ungainly man whom he addressed as Ernest, but whose surname I never learned. Ernest in turn introduced me, with a shy and clumsy courtesy, to the two remaining guests. They were the pair who had driven up in the hansom; one turned out to be Kingsmill, Q.C.; the other I knew at a glance from his photographs as Parrington, the backwoods novelist. They were admirable foils to each other, the barrister being plump and dapper, with a Napoleonic cast of countenance, and the author one of the shaggiest dogs I have ever seen in evening clothes. Neither took much stock of me, but both had an eye on Raffles as I exchanged a few words with each in turn. Dinner, however, was immediately announced, and the six of us had soon taken our places round a brilliant little table stranded in a great dark room.

I had not been prepared for so small a party, and at first I felt relieved. If the worst came to the worst, I was fool enough to say in my heart, they were but two to one. But I was soon sighing for that safety which the adage associates with numbers. We were far too few for the confidential duologue with one's neighbor in which I, at least, would have taken refuge from the perils of a general conversation. And the general conversation soon resolved itself into an attack, so subtly concerted and so artistically delivered that I could not conceive how Raffles should ever know it for an attack, and that against himself, or how to warn him of his peril. But to this day I am not convinced that I also was honored by the suspicions of the club; it may have been so, and they may have ignored me for the bigger game.

It was Lord Thornaby himself who fired the first shot, over the very sherry. He had Raffles on his right hand, and the backwoodsman of letters on his left. Raffles was hemmed in by the law on his right, while I sat between Parrington and Ernest, who took the foot of the table, and seemed a sort of feudatory cadet of the noble house. But it was the motley lot of us that my lord addressed, as he sat back blinking his baggy eyes.

"Mr. Raffles," he said, "has been telling me about that poor fellow who suffered the extreme penalty last March. A great end, gentlemen, a great end! It is true that he had been unfortunate enough to strike a jugular vein, but his own end should take its place among the most glorious traditions of the gallows. You tell them, Mr. Raffles: it will be as new to my friends as it is to me."

"I tell the tale as I heard it last time I played at Trent Bridge; it was never in the papers, I believe," said Raffles gravely. "You may remember the tremendous excitement over the Test Matches out in Australia at the time: It seems that the result of the crucial game was expected onthe condemned man's last day on earth, and he couldn't rest until he knew it. We pulled it off, if you will recollect, and he said it would make him swing happy."

"Tell 'em what else he said!" cried Lord Thornaby, rubbing his podgy hands.

"The chaplain remonstrated with him on his excitement over a game at such a time, and the convict is said to have replied: 'Why, it's the first thing they'll ask me at the other end of the drop!' "

The story was new even to me, but I had no time to appreciate its points. My concern was to watch its effect upon the other members of the party. Ernest, on my left, doubled up with laughter, and tittered and shook for several minutes. My other neighbor, more impressionable by temperament, winced first, and then worked himself into a state of enthusiasm which

137

culminated in an assault upon his shirt cuff with a joiner's pencil. Kingsmill, Q.C., beaming tranquilly on Raffles, seemed the one least impressed, until he spoke.

"I am glad to hear that," he remarked in a high bland voice. "I thought that man would die game."

"Did you know anything about him, then?" inquired Lord Thornaby.

"I led for the Crown," replied the barrister, with a twinkle. "You might almost say that I measured the poor man's neck."

The point must have been quite unpremeditated; it was not the less effective for that. Lord Thornaby looked askance at the callous silk. It was some moments before Ernest tittered and Parrington felt for his pencil; and in the interim I had made short work of my hock, though it was Johannisberger. As for Raffles, one had but to see his horror to feel how completely he was off his guard.

"In itself, I have heard, it was not a sympathetic case," was the remark with which he broke the general silence.

"Not a bit."

"That must have been a comfort to you," said Raffles dryly.

"It would have been to me," vowed our author, while the barrister merely smiled. "I should have been very sorry to have had a hand in hanging Peckham and Solomons the other day."

"Why Peckham and Solomons?" inquired my lord.

"They never meant to kill that old lady."

"But they strangled her in her bed with her own pillowcase!"

"I don't care," said the uncouth scribe. "They didn't break in for that. They never thought of scragging her. The foolish old person would make a noise, and one of them tied too tight. I call it jolly bad luck on them."

"On quiet, harmless, well-behaved thieves," added Lord Thornaby, "in the unobtrusive exercise of their humble vocation."

And, as he turned to Raffles with his puffy smile, I knew that we had reached that part of the program which had undergone rehearsal: it had been perfectly timed to arrive with the champagne, and I was not afraid to signify my appreciation of that small mercy. But Raffles laughed so quickly at his lordship's humor, and yet with such a natural restraint, as to leave no doubt that he had taken kindly to my own old part, and was playing the innocent inimitably in his turn, by reason of his very innocence. It was a poetic judgment on old Raffles, and in my momentary enjoyment of the novel situation I was able to enjoy some of the good things of this rich man's table. The saddle of mutton more than justified its place in the menu; but it had not spoiled me for my wing of pheasant, and I was even looking forward to a sweet, when a further remark from the literary light recalled me from the table to its talk.

"But, I suppose," said he to Kingsmill, "it's 'many a burglar *you've* restored to his friends and his relations.'"

"Let us say many a poor fellow who has been charged with burglary," replied the cheery Q.C. "It's not quite the same thing, you know, nor is 'many' the most accurate word. I never touch criminal work in town."

"It's the only kind I should care about," said the novelist, eating jelly with a spoon.

"I quite agree with you," our host chimed in. "And of all the criminals one might be called upon to defend, give me the enterprising burglar."

"It must be the breeziest branch of the business," remarked Raffles, while I held my breath.

But his touch was as light as gossamer, and his artless manner a triumph of even his incomparable art. Raffles was alive to the danger at last. I saw him refuse more champagne, even as I drained my glass again. But it was not the same danger to us both. Raffles had no reason to feel surprise or alarm at such a turn in a conversation frankly devoted to criminology; it must have seemed as inevitable to him as it was sinister to me, with my fortuitous knowledge of the suspicions that were entertained. And there was little to put him on his guard in the touch of his adversaries, which was only less light than his own.

"I am not very fond of Mr. Sikes," announced the barrister, like a man who had got his cue.

"But he was prehistoric," rejoined my lord. "A lot of blood has flowed under the razor since the days of Sweet William."

"True; we have had Peace," said Parrington, and launched out into such glowing details of that criminal's last moments that I began to hope the diversion might prove permanent. But Lord Thornaby was not to be denied.

"William and Charles are both dead monarchs," said he. "The reigning king in their department is the fellow who gutted poor Danby's place in Bond Street."

There was a guilty silence on the part of the three conspirators—for I had long since persuaded myself that

139

Ernest was not in their secret—and then my blood froze.

"I know him well," said Raffles, looking up.

Lord Thornaby stared at him in consternation. The smile on the Napoleonic countenance of the barrister looked forced and frozen for the first time during the evening. Our author, who was nibbling cheese from a knife, left a bead of blood upon his beard. The futile Ernest alone met the occasion with a hearty titter.

"What!" cried my lord. *"You know the thief?"*

"I wish I did," rejoined Raffles chuckling. "No, Lord Thornaby, I only meant the jeweler, Danby. I go to him when I want a wedding present."

I heard three deep breaths drawn as one before I drew my own.

"Rather a coincidence," observed our host dryly, "for I believe you also know the Milchester people, where Lady Melrose had her necklace stolen a few months afterward."

"I was staying there at the time," said Raffles eagerly. No snob was ever quicker to boast of basking in the smile of the great.

"We believe it to be the same man," said Lord Thornaby, speaking apparently for the Criminologists' Club, and with much less severity of voice.

"I only wish I could come across him," continued Raffles heartily. "He's a criminal much more to my mind than your murderers who swear on the drop or talk cricket in the condemned cell!"

"He might be in the house now," said Lord Thornaby, looking Raffles in the face. But his manner was that of an actor in an unconvincing part and a mood to play it gamely to the bitter end; and he seemed embittered, as even a rich man may be in the moment of losing a bet.

"What a joke if he were!" cried the Wild West writer.

"Absit omen!" murmured Raffles, in better taste.

"Still, I think you'll find it's a favorite time," argued Kingsmill, Q.C. "And it would be quite in keeping with the character of this man, so far as it is known, to pay a little visit to the president of the Criminologists' Club, and to choose the evening on which he happens to be entertaining the other members."

There was more conviction in this sally than in that of our noble host; but this I attributed to the trained and skilled dissimulation of the bar. Lord Thornaby, however, was not to be amused by the elaboration of his own idea, and it was with some asperity that he called upon the butler, now solemnly superintending the removal of the cloth.

"Leggett! Just send upstairs to see if all the doors are open and the rooms in proper order. That's an awful idea of yours, Kingsmill, or of mine!" added my lord, recovering the courtesy of his order by an effort that I could follow. "We should look fools. I don't know which of us it was, by the way, who seduced the rest from the main stream of blood into this burglarious backwater. Are you familiar with De Quincey's masterpiece on 'Murder as a Fine Art,' Mr. Raffles?"

"I believe I once read it," replied Raffles doubtfully.

"You must read it again," pursued the earl. "It is the last word on a great subject; all we can hope to add is some baleful illustration or blood-stained footnote, not unworthy of De Quincey's text. Well, Leggett?"

The venerable butler stood wheezing at his elbow. I had not hitherto observed that the man was an asthmatic.

"I beg your lordship's pardon, but I think your lordship must have forgotten."

The voice came in rude gasps, but words of reproach could scarcely have achieved a finer delicacy.

"Forgotten, Leggett! Forgotten what, may I ask?"

"Locking your lordship's dressing room door behind your lordship, my lord," stuttered the unfortunate Leggett, in the short spurts of a winded man, a few stertorous syllables at a time. "Been up myself, my lord. Outer door—inner door—both locked inside!"

But by this time the noble master was in worse case than the man. His fine forehead was a tangle of livid cords; his baggy jowl filled out like a balloon. In another second he had abandoned his place as our host and fled the room; and in yet another we had forgotten ours as his guests and rushed headlong at his heels.

Raffles was as excited as any of us now: he outstripped us all. The cherubic little lawyer and I had a fine race for the last place but one, which I secured, while the panting butler and his satellites brought up a respectful rear. It was our unconventional author, however, who was the first to volunteer his assistance and advice.

"No use pushing, Thornaby!" cried he. "If it's been done with a wedge and gimlet, you may smash the door, but you'll never force it. Is there a ladder in the place?"

"There's a rope ladder somewhere, in case of fire, I believe," said my lord vaguely, as he rolled a critical eye over our faces. "Where is it kept, Leggett?"

"William will fetch it, my lord."

And a pair of noble calves went flashing to the upper regions.

"No need for him to bring it down," cried Parrington, who had thrown back to the wilds in his excitement. "Let him hang it out of the window above your own and let me climb down and do the rest! I'll undertake to have one or other of these doors open in two two's!"

The fastened doors were at right angles on the landing which we filled between us. Lord Thornaby smiled grimly on the rest of us, when he had nodded and dismissed the author like a hound from the leash.

"It's a good thing we know something about our friend Parrington," said my lord. "He takes more kindly to all this than I do, I can tell you."

"It's grist to his mill," said Raffles charitably.

"Exactly! We shall have the whole thing in his next book."

"I hope to have it at the Old Bailey first," remarked Kingsmill, Q.C.

"Refreshing to find a man of letters such a man of action too!"

It was Raffles who said this, and the remark seemed rather trite for him, but in the tone there was something that just caught my private ear. And for once I understood: The officious attitude of Parrington, without being seriously suspicious in itself, was admirably calculated to put a previously suspected person in a grateful shade. This literary adventurer had elbowed Raffles out of the limelight, and gratitude for the service was what I had detected in Raffle's voice. No need to say how grateful I felt myself. But my gratitude was shot with flashes of unwonted insight. Parrington was one of those who suspected Raffles, or, at all events, one who was in the secret of those suspicions. What if he had traded on the suspect's presence in the house? What if he were a deep villain himself, and *the* villain of this particular piece? I had made up my mind about him, and that in a tithe of the time I take to make it up as a rule, when we heard my man in the dressing room. He greeted us with an impudent shout; in a few moments the door was open, and there stood Parrington, flushed and dishevelled, with a gimlet in one hand and a wedge in the other.

Within was a scene of eloquent disorder. Drawers had been pulled out, and now stood on end, their contents heaped upon the carpet. Wardrobe doors stood open; empty stud cases strewed the floor; a clock, tied up in a towel, had been tossed into a chair at the last moment. But a long tin lid protruded from an open cupboard in one corner. And one had only to see Lord Thornaby's wry face behind the lid to guess that it was bent over a somewhat empty tin trunk.

"What a rum lot to steal!" said he, with a twitch of humor at the corners of his canine mouth. "My peer's robes, with coronet complete!"

We rallied round him in a seemly silence. I thought our scribe would put in his word. But even he either feigned or felt a proper awe. "You may say it was a rum place to keep 'em," continued Lord Thornaby. "But where would you gentlemen stable your white elephants? And these were elephants as white as snow; by Jove, I'll job them for the future!"

And he made merrier over his loss than any of us could have imagined the minute before; but the reason dawned on me a little later, when we all trooped downstairs, leaving the police in possession of the theater of crime. Lord Thornaby linked arms with Raffles as he led the way. His step was lighter, his gaiety no longer sardonic; his very looks had improved. And I divined the load that had been lifted from the hospitable heart of our host.

"I only wish," said he, "that this brought us any nearer to the identity of the gentleman we were discussing at dinner, for, of course, we owe it to all our instincts to assume that it was he."

"I wonder!" said old Raffles, with a foolhardy glance in my direction.

"But I'm sure of it, my dear sir," cried my lord. "The audacity is his and his alone. I look no further than the fact of his honoring me on the one night of the year when I endeavor to entertain my brother Criminologists. That's no coincidence, sir, but a deliberate irony, which would have occurred to no other criminal mind in England."

"You may be right," Raffles had the sense to say this time, though I think it was my face that made him.

"What is still more certain," resumed our host, "is that no other criminal in the world would have crowned so delicious a conception with so perfect an achievement. I feel sure the inspector will agree with us."

The policeman in command had knocked and been admitted to the library as Lord Thornaby spoke.

"I didn't hear what you said, my lord."

"Merely that the perpetrator of this amusing outrage can be no other than the swell mobsman who relieved Lady Melrose of her necklace and poor Danby of half his stock a year or two ago."

"I believe your lordship has hit the nail on the head," the inspector said.

"The man who took the Thimblely diamonds and returned them to Lord Thimblely, you know."

"Perhaps he'll treat your lordship the same."

"Not he! I don't mean to cry over *my* spilt milk. I only wish the fellow joy of all he had time to take. Anything fresh upstairs by the way?"

"Yes, my lord: the robbery took place between a quarter past eight and the half-hour."

"How on earth do you know?"

"The clock that was tied up in the towel had stopped at twenty past."

"Have you interviewed my man?"

"I have, my lord. He was in your lordship's room until close on the quarter, and reports that all was as it should be when he left it."

"Then do you suppose the burglar was hiding in the house?"

"It's impossible to say, my lord. He's not in the house now, for he could only be in your lordship's bedroom or dressing room, and we have searched every inch of both."

Lord Thornaby turned to us when the inspector had retreated, caressing his peaked cap.

"I told him to clear up these points first," he explained, jerking his head toward the door. "I had reason to think my man had been neglecting his duties up there. I am glad to find myself mistaken."

I ought to have been no less glad that I was mistaken. My suspicions of our officious author were thus proved to have been as wild as himself. I owed the man no grudge, and yet in my human heart I felt vaguely disappointed. My theory had gained color from his behavior ever since he had admitted us to the dressing room; it had changed all at once from the familiar to the morose; and only now was I just enough to remember that Lord Thornaby, having tolerated those familiarities as long

144

as they were connected with useful service, had administered a relentless snub the moment that service had been well and truly performed.

But if Parrington was exonerated in my mind, so also was Raffles reinstated in the regard of those who had entertained a far graver and more dangerous hypothesis. It was a miracle of good luck, a coincidence among coincidences, which had whitewashed him in their sight at the very moment when they were straining the expert eye to sift him through and through. But the miracle had been performed, and its effect was visible in every face and audible in every voice. I except Ernest, who had never been in the secret; moreover, that gay Criminologist had been palpably shaken by his first little experience of crime. But the other three vied among themselves to do honor where they had done injustice. I heard Kingsmill, Q.C., telling Raffles the best time to catch him at chambers, and promising a seat in court for any trial he might ever like to hear. Parrington spoke of a presentation set of his books, and in doing homage to Raffles made his peace with our host. As for Lord Thornaby, I did overhear the name of the Athenæum Club, a reference to his friends on the committee, and a whisper (as I thought) of Rule II. But he and Raffles had their heads too close together for one to swear honestly to the rule.

The police were still in possession when we went our several ways, and it was all that I could do to drag Raffles up to my rooms, though, as I have said, they were just round the corner. He consented at last as a lesser evil than talking of the burglary in the street; and in my rooms I told him of his late danger and my own dilemma, of the few words I had overheard in the beginning, of the thin ice on which he had cut figures without a crack. It was all very well for him. He had never realized his peril. But let him think of me—listening, watching, yet unable to lift a finger—unable to say one warning word.

Raffles heard me out, but a weary sigh followed the last symmetrical whiff of a Sullivan which he flung into my fire before he spoke.

"No, I won't have another, thank you. I'm going to talk to you, Bunny. Do you really suppose I didn't see through these wiseacres from the first?"

I flatly refused to believe he had done so before that evening. Why had he never mentioned his idea to me? It had been quite the other way, as I indignantly reminded Raffles. Did he mean

145

me to believe he was the man to thrust his head into the lion's mouth for fun? And what point would there be in dragging me there to see the fun?

"I might have wanted you, Bunny. I very nearly did."

"For my face?"

"It has been my fortune before to-night, Bunny. It has also given me more confidence than you are likely to believe at this time of day. You stimulate me more than you think."

"Your gallery and your prompter's box in one?"

"Capital, Bunny! But it was no joking matter with me either, my dear fellow; it was touch-and-go at the time. I might have called on you at any moment, and it was something to know I should not have called in vain."

"But what to do, Raffles?"

"Fight our way out and bolt!" he answered, with a mouth that meant it, and a fine gay glitter of the eyes.

I shot out of my chair.

"You don't mean to tell me you had a hand in the job!"

"I had the only hand in it, my dear Bunny."

"Nonsense! You were sitting at table at the time. No, but you may have taken some other fellow into the show. I always thought you would!"

"One's quite enough, Bunny," said Raffles dryly; he leaned back in his chair and took out another cigarette. And I accepted of yet another from his case; for it was no use losing one's temper with Raffles; and his incredible statement was not, after all, to be ignored.

"Of course," I went on, " if you really had brought off this thing on your own, I should be the last to criticize your means of reaching such an end. You have not only scored off a far superior force, which had laid itself out to score off you, but you have put them in the wrong about you, and they'll eat out of your hand for the rest of their days. But don't ask me to believe that you've done all this alone! By George," I cried, in a sudden wave of enthusiasm, "I don't care how you've done it or who has helped you. It's the biggest thing you ever did in your life!"

And certainly I had never seen Raffles look more radiant, or better pleased with the world and himself, or nearer that elation which he usually left to me.

"Then you shall hear all about it, Bunny, if you'll do what I ask you."

146

"Ask away, old chap, and the thing's done."

"Switch off the electric lights."

"All of them?"

"I think so."

"There, then."

"Now go to the back window and up with the blind."

"Well?"

"I'm coming to you. Splendid! I never had a look so late as this. It's the only window left alight in the house!"

His cheek against the pane, he was pointing slightly downward and very much aslant through a long lane of mews to a little square light like a yellow tile at the end. But I had opened the window and leaned out before I saw it for myself.

"You don't mean to say that's Thornaby House?"

I was not familiar with the view from my back windows.

"Of course I do, you rabbit! Have a look through your own race glass. It has been the most useful thing of all."

But before I had the glass in focus more scales had fallen from my eyes; and now I knew why I had seen so much of Raffles these last few weeks, and why he had always come between seven and eight o'clock in the evening, and waited at this very window, with these very glasses at his eyes. I saw through them sharply now. The one lighted window pointed out by Raffles came tumbling into the dark circle of my vision. I could not see into the actual room, but the shadows of those within were quite distinct on the lowered blind. I even thought a black thread still dangled against the square of light. It was, it must be, the window to which the intrepid Parrington had descended from the one above.

"Exactly!" said Raffles in answer to my exclamation. "And that's the window I have been watching these last few weeks. By daylight you can see the whole lot above the ground floor on this side of the house; and by good luck one of them is the room in which the master of the house arrays himself in all his nightly glory. It was easily spotted by watching at the right time. I saw him shaved one morning before you were up! In the evening his valet stays behind to put things straight; and that has been the very mischief. In the end I had to find out something about the man, and wire to him from his girl to meet her outside at eight o'clock. Of course he pretends he was at his post at the time: that I foresaw, and did the poor fellow's work before my own. I folded and put away every garment before I permitted

147

myself to rag the room."

"I wonder you had time!"

"It took me one more minute, and it put the clock on exactly fifteen. By the way, I did that literally, of course, in the case of the clock they found. It's an old dodge, to stop a clock and alter the time; but you must admit that it looked as though one had wrapped it up all ready to cart away. There was thus any amount of *prima-facie* evidence of the robbery having taken place when we were all at table. As a matter of fact, Lord Thornaby left his dressing room one minute, his valet followed him the minute after, and I entered the minute after that."

"Through the window?"

"To be sure. I was waiting below in the garden. You have to pay for your garden in town, in more ways than one. You know the wall, of course, and that jolly old postern? The lock was beneath contempt."

"But what about the window? It's on the first floor, isn't it?"

Raffles took up the cane which he had laid down with his overcoat. It was a stout bamboo with a polished ferrule. He unscrewed the ferrule, and shook out of the cane a diminishing series of smaller canes, exactly like a child's fishing rod, which I afterward found to have been their former state. A double hook of steel was now produced and quickly attached to the tip of the top joint; then Raffles undid three buttons of his waistcoat; and lapped round and round his waist I beheld the finest of Manila ropes, with the neatest of foot loops at regular intervals.

"Is it necessary to go any further?" asked Raffles when he had unwound the rope. "This end is made fast to that end of the hook, the other half of the hook fits over anything that comes its way, and you leave your rod dangling while you swarm up your line. Of course, you must know what you've got to hook on to; but a man who has had a porcelain bath fixed in his dressing room is the man for me. The pipes were all outside, and fixed to the wall in just the right place. You see I had made a reconnaissance by day in addition to many by night; it would hardly have been worth while constructing my ladder on chance."

"So you made it on purpose!"

"My dear Bunny," said Raffles, as he wound the hemp girdle round his waist once more, "I never did care for ladderwork, but I always said that if I ever used a ladder it should be the best of its kind yet invented. This one may come in useful again."

"But how long did the whole thing take you?"

"From mother earth to mother earth? About five minutes, tonight, and one of those was spent doing another man's work."

"What!" I cried. " You mean to tell me you climbed up and down, in and out and broke into that cupboard and that big tin box, and wedged up the doors and cleared out with a peer's robes and all the rest of it in five minutes?"

"Of course I don't, and of course I didn't."

"Then what do you mean, and what did you do?"

"Made two bites at the cherry, Bunny! I had a dress rehearsal in the dead of last night, and it was then I took the swag. Our noble friend was snoring next door all the time, but the effort may still stand high among my small exploits, for I not only took all I wanted, but left the whole place exactly as I found it, and shut things after me like a good little boy. All that took a good deal longer; tonight I had simply to rag the room a bit, sweep up some studs and links, and leave ample evidence of having boned those rotten robes *tonight.* That, if you come to think of it, was what a *Chronicle* critic would call the quintessential Q.E.D. I have not only shown these dear Criminologists that I couldn't possibly have done this trick, but that there's some other fellow who could and did, and whom they've been perfect asses to confuse with me."

You may figure me as gazing on Raffles all this time in mute and rapt amazement. But I had long been past that pitch. If he had told me now that he had broken into the Bank of England, or the Tower, I should not have disbelieved him for a moment. I was prepared to go home with him to the Albany and find the regalia in his hatbox. And I took down my overcoat as he put on his. But Raffles would not hear of my accompanying him that night.

"No, my dear Bunny, I am short of sleep and fed up with excitement. You mayn't believe it—you may look upon me as a plaster devil—but those five minutes you wot of were rather too crowded even for my taste. The dinner was nominally at a quarter to eight, and I don't mind telling you now that I counted on twice as long as I had. But no one came until twelve minutes to, and so our host took his time. I didn't want to be the last to arrive, and I was in the drawing room five minutes before the hour. But it was a quicker thing than I care about, when all is said."

And his last word on the matter, as he nodded and went his

149

way, may well be mine; for one need be no criminologist, much less a member of the Criminologists' Club, to remember what Raffles did with the robes and coronet of the Right Hon. the Earl of Thornaby, K.G. He did with them exactly what he might have been expected to do by the gentlemen with whom we had foregathered; and he did it in a manner so characteristic of himself as surely to remove from their minds the last aura of the idea that he and himself were the same person. Carter Paterson was out of the question, and any labelling or addressing to be avoided on obvious grounds. But Raffles stabled the white elephants in the cloakroom at Charing Cross—and sent Lord Thornaby the ticket.

THE STOLEN RUBENS

BY JACQUES FUTRELLE

Jacques Futrelle was born in Pike County, Georgia, on April 9, 1875. He was a theatrical manager for a time and later worked for the *Boston American,* which published many of his fictional works. The author of several light romantic novels and short stories, Futrelle is best remembered for his stories about Professor Augustus S. F. X. Van Deusen, "The Thinking Machine." In addition to these, he wrote several crime and mystery novels, including *The Diamond Master* (1909) and *My Lady's Garter* (1912). Futrelle died on the *Titanic* on April 15, 1912.

MATTHEW KALE MADE fifty million dollars out of axle grease, after which he began to patronize the high arts. It was simple enough: He had the money, and Europe had the old masters. His method of buying was simplicity itself. There were five thousand square yards, more or less, in the huge gallery of his marble mansion which were to be covered, so he bought five thousand yards, more or less, of art. Some of it was good, some of it fair, and much of it bad. The chief picture of the collection was a Rubens, which he had picked up in Rome for fifty thousand dollars.

Soon after acquiring his collection, Kale decided to make certain alterations in the vast room where the pictures hung. They were all taken down and stored in the ballroom, equally vast, with their faces toward the wall. Meanwhile Kale and his family took refuge in a nearby hotel.

It was at this hotel that Kale met Jules de Lesseps. De Lesseps was distinctly the sort of Frenchman whose conversation resembles calisthenics. He was nervous, quick, and agile, and he told Kale in confidence that he was not only a painter himself, but a connoisseur in the high arts. Pompous in the pride of possession, Kale went to a good deal of trouble to exhibit his private collection for de Lesseps' delectation. It happened in the ballroom, and the true artist's delight shone in the Frenchman's eyes as he handled the pieces which were good. Some of the others made him smile, but it was an inoffensive sort of smile.

With his own hands Kale lifted the precious Rubens and held it before the Frenchman's eyes. It was a "Madonna and Child," one of those wonderful creations which have endured through the years with all the sparkle and color beauty of their pristine days. Kale seemed disappointed because de Lesseps was not particularly enthusiastic about this picture.

"Why, it's a Rubens!" he exclaimed.

"Yes, I see," replied de Lesseps.

"It cost me fifty thousand dollars."

"It is perhaps worth more than that," and the Frenchman shrugged his shoulders as he turned away.

Kale looked at him in chagrin. Could it be that de Lesseps did not understand that it was a Rubens, and that Rubens was a painter? Or was it that he had failed to hear him say that it cost him fifty thousand dollars? Kale was accustomed to seeing people bob their heads and open their eyes when he said fifty thousand dollars; therefore, "Don't you like it?" he asked.

"Very much indeed," replied de Lesseps; "but I have seen it before. I saw it in Rome just a week or so before you purchased it."

They rummaged on through the pictures, and at last a Whistler was turned up for their inspection. It was one of the famous Thames series, a water color. De Lesseps' face radiated excitement, and several times he glanced from the water color to the Rubens as if mentally comparing the exquisitely penciled and colored newer work with the bold, masterly technic of the older painting.

Kale misunderstood his silence. "I don't think much of this one myself," he explained apologetically. "It's a Whistler, and all that, and it cost me five thousand dollars, and I sort of had to have it, but still it isn't just the kind of thing that I like. What do you think of it?"

"I think it is perfectly wonderful!" replied the Frenchman enthusiastically. "It is the essence, the superlative, of Whistler's work. I wonder if it would be possible," and he turned to face Kale, "for me to make a copy of that? I have some slight skill in painting myself, and dare say I could make a fairly creditable copy of it."

Kale was flattered. He was more and more impressed each moment with the picture. "Why certainly," he replied. "I will have it sent up to the hotel, and you can—"

"No, no, no!" interrupted de Lesseps quickly. "I wouldn't care to accept the responsibility of having the picture in my charge. There is always danger of fire. But if you would give me permission to come here—this room is large and airy and light—and besides it is quiet—"

"Just as you like," said Kale magnanimously. "I merely thought the other way would be most convenient for you."

De Lesseps laid one hand on the millionaire's arm. "My dear friend," he said earnestly, "if these pictures were my pictures, I shouldn't try to accommodate anybody where they were concerned. I dare say the collection as it stands cost you—"

"Six hundred and eighty-seven thousand dollars," volunteered Kale proudly.

"And surely they must be well protected here in your house during your absence?"

"There are about twenty servants in the house, while the workmen are making the alterations," said Kale, "and three of them don't do anything but watch this room. No one can go in or out except by the door we entered—the others are locked and barred—and then only with my permission, or a written order from me. No, sir, nobody can get away with anything in this room."

"Excellent—excellent!" said de Lesseps admiringly. He smiled a little. "I am afraid I did not give you credit for being the farsighted businessman that you are." He turned and glanced over the collection of pictures abstractedly. "A clever thief, though," he ventured, "might cut a valuable painting, for instance the Rubens, out of the frame, roll it up, conceal it under his coat, and escape."

Kale laughed and shook his head.

It was a couple of days later at the hotel that de Lesseps brought up the subject of copying the Whistler. He was profuse in his thanks when Kale volunteered to accompany him into the mansion and witness the preliminary stages of the work. They paused at the ballroom door.

"Jennings," said Kale to the liveried servant there, "this is Mr. De Lesseps. He is to come and go as he likes. He is going to do some work in the ballroom here. See that he isn't disturbed."

De Lesseps noticed the Rubens leaning carelessly against some other pictures, with the holy face of the Madonna turned toward them. "Really, Mr. Kale," he protested, "that picture is too valuable to be left about like that. If you will let your servants bring me some canvas, I shall wrap it and place it up on this table off the floor. Suppose there were mice here!"

Kale thanked him. The necessary orders were given, and finally the picture was carefully wrapped and placed beyond harm's reach, whereupon de Lesseps adjusted himself, paper, easel, stool, and all, and began his work. There Kale left him.

Three days later Kale found the artist still at his labor.

"I just dropped by," he explained, "to see how the work in the gallery was getting along. It will be finished in another week. I hope I am not disturbing you?"

"Not at all," said de Lesseps; "I have nearly finished. See how I am getting along?" He turned the easel toward Kale.

The millionaire gazed from that toward the original which

stood on a chair nearby, and frank admiration for the artist's efforts was in his eyes. "Why, it's fine!" he exclaimed. "It's just as good as the other one, and I bet you don't want any five thousand dollars for it—eh?"

That was all that was said about it at the time. Kale wandered about the house for an hour or so, then dropped into the ballroom where de Lesseps was getting his paraphernalia together, and they walked back to the hotel. The artist carried under one arm his copy of the Whistler, loosely rolled up.

Another week passed, and the workmen who had been engaged in refinishing and decorating the gallery had gone. De Lesseps volunteered to assist in the work of rehanging the pictures, and Kale gladly turned the matter over to him. It was in the afternoon of the day this work began that de Lesseps, chatting pleasantly with Kale, ripped loose the canvas which enshrouded the precious Rubens. Then he paused with an exclamation of dismay. The picture was gone; the frame which had held it was empty. A thin strip of canvas around the inside edge showed that a sharp penknife had been used to cut out the painting.

All of these facts came to the attention of Professor Augustus S.F.X. Van Dusen—The Thinking Machine. This was a day or so after Kale had rushed into Detective Mallory's office at police headquarters with the statement that his Rubens had been stolen. He banged his fist down on the detective's desk, and roared at him.

"It cost me fifty thousand dollars! Why don't you do something? What are you sitting there staring at me for?"

"Don't excite yourself, Mr. Kale," the detective advised. "I will put my men at work right now to recover the—the—What is a Rubens, anyway?"

"It's a picture!" bellowed Kale. "A piece of canvas with some paint on it, and it cost me fifty thousand dollars—don't you forget that!"

So the police machinery was set in motion to recover the picture. And in time the matter fell under the watchful eye of Hutchinson Hatch, reporter. He learned the facts preceding the disappearance of the picture and then called on de Lesseps. He found the artist in a state of excitement bordering on hysteria; an intimation from the reporter of the object of his visit caused de Lesseps to burst into words.

"*Mon Dieu!* It is outrageous! What can I do? I was the only one in the room for several days. I was the one who took such pains to protect the picture. And now it is gone! The loss is irreparable. What can I do?"

Hatch didn't have any very definite idea as to just what he could do, so he let him go on. "As I understand it, Mr. de Lesseps," he interrupted at last, "no one else was in the room, except you and Mr. Kale, all the time you were there?"

"No one else."

"And I think Mr. Kale said that you were making a copy of some famous water color; weren't you?"

"Yes, a Thames scene by Whistler," was the reply. "That is it, hanging over the fireplace."

Hatch glanced at the picture admiringly. It was an exquisite copy, and showed the deft touch of a man who was himself an artist of great ability.

De Lesseps read the admiration in his face. "It is not bad," he said modestly. "I studied with Carolus Duran."

With all else that was known, and this little additional information, which seemed of no particular value to the reporter, the entire matter was laid before The Thinking Machine. That distinguished man listened from beginning to end without comment.

"Who had access to the room?" he asked finally.

"That is what the police are working on now," said Hutchinson Hatch. "There are a couple of dozen servants in the house, and I suppose, in spite of Kale's rigid orders, there was a certain laxity in their enforcement."

"Of course that makes it more difficult," said The Thinking Machine in the perpetually irritated voice which was so characteristic a part of himself. "Perhaps it would be best for us to go to Mr. Kale's home and personally investigate."

Kale received them with the reserve which rich men usually show in the presence of representatives of the press. He stared frankly and somewhat curiously at the diminutive figure of the scientist, who explained the object of their visit.

"I guess you fellows can't do anything with this," the millionaire assured them. "I've got some regular detectives on it."

"Is Mr. Mallory here now?" asked The Thinking Machine curtly.

"Yes, he is upstairs in the servants' quarters."

"May we see the room from which the picture was taken?"

inquired the scientist, with a suave intonation which Hatch knew well.

Kale granted the permission with a wave of the hand, and ushered them into the ballroom, where the pictures had been stored. From the center of this room The Thinking Machine surveyed it all. The windows were high. Half a dozen doors leading out into the hallways, the conservatory, quiet nooks of the mansion offered innumerable possibilities of access. After this one long comprehensive squint, The Thinking Machine went over and picked up the frame from which the Rubens had been cut. For a long time he examined it. Kale's impatience was evident. Finally the scientist turned to him.

"How well do you know M. de Lesseps?"

"I've known him for only a month or so. Why?"

"Did he bring you letters of introduction, or did you meet him merely casually?"

Kale regarded him with displeasure. "My own personal affairs have nothing whatever to do with this matter! Mr. de Lesseps is a gentleman of integrity, and certainly he is the last whom I would suspect of any connection with the disappearance of the picture."

"That is usually the case," remarked The Thinking Machine tartly. He turned to Hatch. "Just how good a copy was that he made of the Whistler picture?"

"I have never seen the original," Hatch replied; "but the workmanship was superb. Perhaps Mr. Kale wouldn't object to us seeing—"

"Oh, of course not," said Kale resignedly. "Come in; it's in the gallery."

Hatch submitted the picture to a careful scrutiny. "I should say the copy is well-nigh perfect," was his verdict. "Of course, in its absence, I can't say exactly; but it is certainly a superb work."

The curtains of a wide door almost in front of them were thrown aside suddenly, and Detective Mallory entered. He carried something in his hand, but at sight of them concealed it behind him. Unrepressed triumph was in his face.

"Ah, professor, we meet often; don't we?" he said.

"This reporter here and his friend seem to be trying to drag de Lesseps into this affair somehow," Kale complained to the detective. "I don't want anything like that to happen. He is liable to go out and print anything. They always do."

The Thinking Machine glared at him unwaveringly for an

instant, then extended his hand toward Mallory. "Where did you find it?" he asked.

"Sorry to disappoint you, professor," said the detective sarcastically, "but this is the time when you were a little late," and he produced the object which he held behind him. "Here is your picture, Mr. Kale."

Kale gasped in relief and astonishment, and held up the canvas with both hands to examine it. "Fine!" he told the detective. "I'll see that you don't lose anything by this. Why, that thing cost me fifty thousand dollars!"

The Thinking Machine leaned forward to squint at the upper righthand corner of the canvas. "Where did you find it?" he asked again.

"Rolled up tight, and concealed in the bottom of a trunk in the room of one of the servants," explained Mallory. "The servant's name is Jennings. He is now under arrest."

"Jennings!" exclaimed Kale. "Why, he has been with me for years."

"Did he confess?" asked the scientist imperturbably.

"Of course not," said Mallory. "He says some of the other servants must have hidden it there."

The Thinking Machine nodded at Hatch. "I think perhaps that is all," he remarked. "I congratulate you, Mr. Mallory, upon bringing the matter to such a quick and satisfactory conclusion."

Ten minutes later they left the house and took a taxi for the scientist's home. Hatch was a little chagrined at the unexpected termination of the affair.

"Mallory does show an occasional gleam of human intelligence, doesn't he?"

"Not that I ever noticed," remarked The Thinking Machine crustily.

"But he found the picture," Hatch insisted.

"Of course he found it. It was put there for him to find."

"Put there for him to find!" repeated the reporter. "Didn't Jennings steal it?"

"If he did, he's a fool."

"Well, if he didn't steal it, who put it there?"

"De Lesseps."

"De Lesseps!" echoed Hatch. "Why the deuce did he steal a fifty-thousand dollar picture and put it in a servant's trunk to be found?"

158

The Thinking Machine twisted around in his seat and squinted at him coldly for a moment. "At times, Mr. Hatch, I am absolutely amazed at your stupidity. I can understand it in a man like Mallory, but I have always given you credit for being an astute, quick-witted man."

Hatch smiled at the reproach. It was not the first time he had heard it. But nothing bearing on the problem in hand was said until they reached The Thinking Machine's house.

"The only real question in my mind, Mr. Hatch," said the scientist then, "is whether or not I should take the trouble to restore Mr. Kale's picture at all. He is perfectly satisfied, and will probably never know the difference. So—"

Suddenly Hatch saw something. "Great Scott!" he exclaimed. "Do you mean that the picture Mallory found was—"

"A copy of the original," snapped the scientist. "Personally I know nothing whatever about art; therefore, I could not say from observation that it is a copy, but I know it from the logic of the thing. When the original was cut from the frame, the knife swerved a little at the upper right-hand corner. The canvas remaining in the frame told me that. The picture that Mr. Mallory found did not correspond in this detail with the canvas in the frame. The conclusion is obvious."

"And de Lesseps has the original?"

"De Lesseps has the original. How did he get it? In any one of a dozen ways. He might have rolled it up and stuck it under his coat. He might have had a confederate. But I don't think that any ordinary method of theft would have appealed to him. I am giving him credit for being clever, as I must when we review the whole case.

"For instance, he asked for permission to copy the Whistler, which you saw was the same size as the Rubens. It was granted. He copied it practically under guard, always with the chance that Mr. Kale himself would drop in. It took him three days to copy it, so he says. He was alone in the room all that time. He knew that Mr. Kale had not the faintest idea of art. Taking advantage of that, what would have been simpler than to have copied the Rubens in oil? He could have removed it from the frame immediately after he canvased it over, and kept it in a position near him where it could be quickly concealed if he was interrupted. Remember, the picture is worth fifty thousand dollars; therefore, was worth the trouble.

"De Lesseps is an artist—we know that—and dealing with a

159

man who knew nothing whatever of art, he had no fears. We may suppose his idea all along was to use the copy of the Rubens as a sort of decoy after he got away with the original. You saw that Mallory didn't know the difference, and it was safe for him to suppose that Mr. Kale wouldn't. His only danger until he could get away gracefully was of some critic or connoisseur, perhaps, seeing the copy. His boldness we see readily in the fact that he permitted himself to discover the theft; that he discovered it after he had volunteered to assist Mr. Kale in the general work of rehanging the pictures in the gallery. Just how he put the picture in Jennings' trunk I don't happen to know. We can imagine many ways." He lay back in his chair for a minute without speaking, eyes steadily turned upward, fingers placed precisely tip to tip.

"But how did he take the picture from the Kale home?" asked Hatch.

"He took it with him probably under his arm the day he left the house with Mr. Kale," was the astonishing reply.

Hatch was staring at him in amazement. After a moment the scientist rose and passed into the adjoining room, and the telephone bell there jingled. When he joined Hatch again he picked up his hat and they went out together.

De Lesseps was in when their cards were sent up, and received them. They conversed about the case generally for ten minutes, while the scientist's eyes were turned inquiringly here and there about the room. At last there came a knock on the door.

"It is Detective Mallory, Mr. Hatch," remarked The Thinking Machine. "Open the door for him."

De Lesseps seemed startled for just one instant, then quickly recovered. Mallory's eyes were full of questions when he entered.

"I should like, Mr. Mallory," began The Thinking Machine quietly, "to call your attention to this copy of Mr. Kale's picture by Whistler—over the mantel here. Isn't it excellent? You have seen the original?"

Mallory grunted. De Lesseps' face, instead of expressing appreciation of the compliment, blanched, and his hands closed tightly. Again he recovered himself and smiled.

"The beauty of this picture lies not only in its faithfulness to the original," the scientist went on, "but also in the fact that it was painted under extraordinary circumstances. For instance, I

160

don't know if you know, Mr. Mallory, that it is possible so to combine glue and putty and a few other commonplace things into a paste which will effectually blot out an oil painting, and offer at the same time an excellent surface for water color work!"

There was a moment's pause, during which the three men stared at him silently—with conflicting emotions.

"This water color—this copy of Whistler," continued the scientist evenly—"is painted on such a paste as I have described. That paste in turn covers the original Rubens picture. It can be removed with water without damage to the picture, which is in oil, so that instead of a copy of the Whistler painting, we have an original by Rubens, worth fifty thousand dollars. That is true; isn't it, M. De Lesseps?"

There was no reply to the question—none was needed.

It was an hour later, after de Lesseps was safely in his cell, that Hatch called up The Thinking Machine and asked one question.

"How did you know that the water color was painted over the Rubens?"

"Because it was the only absolutely safe way in which the Rubens could be hopelessly lost to those who were looking for it, and at the same time perfectly preserved," was the answer. "I told you de Lesseps was a clever man, and a little logic did the rest. Two and two always make four, Mr. Hatch, not sometimes, but all the time."

THE RED SILK SCARF

BY MAURICE LEBLANC

Maurice Leblanc was born in Rouen, France, in 1864, and educated in Germany and England. He worked as a journalist and published his first novel, *A Woman,* in 1887. His writing career was undistinguished until 1906, when he was asked by the editor of *Je Sais Tout,* a new publication, to write a crime story as a filler. The result was the gentleman burglar Arsene Lupin, the "Prince of Thieves," who appeared in many novels and short stories and brought Leblanc fame and financial success. Leblanc lived near Paris until the Nazi occupation. He died in Perpignan on November 6, 1941.

ON LEAVING HIS HOUSE one morning at his usual early hour for going to the Law Courts, Chief Inspector Ganimard noticed the curious behavior of an individual who was walking along the Rue Pergolèse in front of him. Shabbily dressed and wearing a straw hat, though the day was the first of December, the man stooped at every thirty or forty yards to fasten his bootlace, or pick up his stick, or for some other reason. And, each time, he took a little piece of orange peel from his pocket and laid it stealthily on the curb of the pavement. It was probably a mere display of eccentricity, a childish amusement to which no one else would have paid attention; but Ganimard was one of those shrewd observers who are indifferent to nothing that strikes their eyes and who are never satisfied until they know the secret causes of things. He therefore began to follow the man.

Now, at the moment when the fellow was turning to the right, into the Avenue de la Grande-Armée, the inspector caught him exchanging signals with a boy of twelve or thirteen, who was walking along the houses on the lefthand side. Twenty yards farther, the man stooped and turned up the bottom of his trousers legs. A bit of orange peel marked the place. At the same moment, the boy stopped and, with a piece of chalk, drew a white cross, surrounded by a circle, on the wall of the house next to him.

The two continued on their way. A minute later, a fresh halt. The strange individual picked up a pin and dropped a piece of orange peel; and the boy at once made a second cross on the wall and again drew a white circle round it.

"By Jove!" thought the chief inspector, with a grunt of satisfaction. "This is rather promising. . . . What on earth can those two merchants be plotting?"

The two "merchants" went down the Avenue Friedland and the Rue du Faubourg-Saint-Honoré, but nothing occurred that was worthy of special mention. The double performance was repeated at almost regular intervals and, so to speak, mechanically. Nevertheless, it was obvious, on the one hand, that the man with the orange peel did not do his part of the business until after he had picked out with a glance the house that was to be marked and, on the other hand, that the boy did not mark that particular house until after he had observed his companion's signal. It was certain, therefore, that there was an agreement between the two; and the proceedings presented no small interest in the chief inspector's eyes.

At the Place Beauveau the man hesitated. Then, apparently making up his mind, he twice turned up and twice turned down the bottom of his trousers legs. Hereupon, the boy sat down on the curb, opposite the sentry who was mounting guard outside the Ministry of the Interior, and marked the flagstone with two little crosses contained within two circles. The same ceremony was gone through a little farther on, when they reached the Elysée. Only, on the pavement where the President's sentry was marching up and down, there were three signs instead of two.

"Hang it all!" muttered Ganimard, pale with excitement and thinking, in spite of himself, of his inveterate enemy, Lupin, whose name came to his mind whenever a mysterious circumstance presented itself. "Hang it all, what does it mean?"

He was nearly collaring and questioning the two "merchants." But he was too clever to commit so gross a blunder. The man with the orange peel had now lit a cigarette; and the boy, also placing a cigarette end between his lips, had gone up to him, apparently with the object of asking for a light.

They exchanged a few words. Quick as thought, the boy handed his companion an object which looked—at least, so the inspector believed—like a revolver. They both bent over this object; and the man, standing with his face to the wall, put his hand six times in his pocket and made a movement as though he were loading a weapon.

As soon as this was done, they walked briskly to the Rue de Surène; and the inspector, who followed them as closely as he was able to, saw them enter the gateway of an old house of which all the shutters were closed, with the exception of those on the third or top floor.

He hurried in after them. At the end of the carriage entrance he saw a large courtyard, with a house painter's sign at the back and a staircase on the left.

He went up the stairs and, as soon as he reached the first floor, ran still faster, because he heard, right up at the top, a din as of a free fight.

When he came to the last landing he found the door open. He entered, listened for a second, caught the sound of a struggle, rushed to the room from which the sound appeared to

164

proceed and remained standing on the threshold, very much out of breath and greatly surprised to see the man of the orange peel and the boy banging the floor with chairs.

At that moment a third person walked out of an adjoining room. It was a young man of twenty-eight or thirty, wearing a pair of short whiskers in addition to his moustache, spectacles, and a smoking jacket with an astrakhan collar and looking like a foreigner, a Russian.

"Good morning, Ganimard," he said. And turning to the two companions, "Thank you, my friends, and all my congratulations on the successful result."

He gave them a hundred-franc note, pushed them outside and shut both doors.

"I am sorry, old chap," he said to Ganimard. "I wanted to talk to you . . . wanted to talk to you badly."

He offered him his hand and, seeing that the inspector remained flabbergasted and that his face was still distorted with anger, he exclaimed:

"Why, you don't seem to understand! . . . And yet it's clear enough . . . I wanted to see you particularly. . . . So what could I do?" And, pretending to reply to an objection, "No, no, old chap," he continued. "You're quite wrong. If I had written or telephoned, you would not have come . . . or else you would have come with a regiment. Now I wanted to see you all alone; and I thought the best thing was to send those two decent fellows to meet you, with orders to scatter bits of orange peel and draw crosses and circles, in short, to mark out your road to this place. . . . Why, you look quite bewildered! What is it? Perhaps you don't recognize me? Lupin. . . . Arsène Lupin. . . . Ransack your memory. . . . Doesn't the name remind you of anything?"

"You dirty scoundrel!" Ganimard snarled between his teeth.

Lupin seemed greatly distressed and said affectionately:

"Are you vexed? Yes, I can see it in your eyes. . . . The Dugrival business, I suppose. I ought to have waited for you to come and take me in charge? . . . There now, the thought never occurred to me! I promise you, next time . . ."

"You scum of the earth!" growled Ganimard.

"And I thinking I was giving you a treat! Upon my word, I did. I said to myself, 'That dear old Ganimard! We haven't met for an age. He'll simply rush at me when he sees me after so long!'"

Ganimard, who had not yet stirred a limb, seemed to be waking from his stupor. He looked all around him, looked at Lupin, visibly asked himself whether he would not do well to rush at him in reality and then, controlling himself, took hold of a chair and settled himself in it, as though he had suddenly made up his mind to listen to his enemy:

"Speak," he said. "And don't waste my time with any nonsense. I'm in a hurry."

"That's it," said Lupin, "let's talk. You can't imagine a quieter place than this. It's an old manor house, which once stood in the open country, and it belongs to the Duc de Rochelaure. The duke, who has never lived in it, lets this floor to me and the outhouses to a painter and decorator. I always keep up a few establishments of this kind: it's a sound, practical plan. Here, in spite of my looking like a Russian nobleman, I am M. Daubreuil, an ex-cabinet minister. . . . You understand, I had to select a rather overstocked profession, so as not to attract attention."

"Do you think I care a hang about all this?" said Ganimard, interrupting him.

"Quite right, I'm wasting words and you're in a hurry. Forgive me. I shan't be long now. . . . Five minutes, that's all. . . . I'll start at once. . . . Have a cigar? No? Very well, no more will I."

He sat down also, drummed his fingers on the table, while thinking, and began in this fashion:

"On the seventeenth of October, 1599, on a warm and sunny autumn day . . . Do you follow me? . . . But, now that I come to think of it, is it really necessary to go back to the reign of Henry IV, and tell you all about the building of the Pont-Neuf? No, I don't suppose you are very well up in French history; and I should only end by muddling you. Suffice it, then, for you to know that, last night, at one o'clock in the morning, a boatman passing under the last arch of the Pont-Neuf aforesaid, along the left bank of the river, heard something drop into the front part of his barge. The thing had been flung from the bridge and its evident destination was the bottom of the Seine. The bargee's dog rushed forward, barking, and, when the man reached the end of his craft, he saw the animal worrying a piece of newspaper that had served to wrap up a number of objects. He took from the dog such of the contents as had not fallen into the water, went to his cabin and examined them carefully. The result struck him as interesting; and, as the man is connected

166

with one of my friends, he very thoughtfully sent to let me know. This morning I was waked up and placed in possession of the facts and of the objects which the man had collected. Here they are."

He pointed to them, spread out on a table. There were, first of all, the torn pieces of a newspaper. Next came a large cut-glass inkstand, with a long piece of string fastened to the lid. There was a bit of broken glass and a sort of flexible cardboard, reduced to shreds. Lastly, there was a piece of bright scarlet silk, ending in a tassel of the same material and color.

"You see our exhibits, friend of my youth," said Lupin. "No doubt, the problem would be more easily solved if we had the other objects which went overboard owing to the stupidity of the dog. But it seems to me, all the same, that we ought to be able to manage, with a little reflection and intelligence. And those are just your great qualities. How does the business strike you?"

Ganimard did not move a muscle. He was willing to stand Lupin's chaff, but his dignity commanded him not to speak a single word in answer nor even to give a nod or shake of the head that might have been taken to express approval or criticism.

"I see that we are entirely of one mind," continued Lupin, without appearing to remark the chief inspector's silence. "And I can sum up the matter briefly, as told us by these exhibits. Yesterday evening, between nine and twelve o'clock, a showily dressed young woman was wounded with a knife and then caught round the throat and choked to death by a well-dressed gentleman, wearing a single eyeglass and interested in racing, with whom the aforesaid showily dressed young lady had been eating three meringues and a coffee éclair."

Lupin lit a cigarette and, taking Ganimard by the sleeve, said animatedly:

"Aha, that's up against you, Chief Inspector! You thought that, in the domain of police deductions, such feats as those were prohibited to outsiders! Wrong, sir! Lupin juggles with inferences and deductions for all the world like a detective in a novel. My proofs are dazzling and absolutely simple."

And, pointing to the objects one by one, as he demonstrated his statement, he resumed:

"I said, after nine o'clock yesterday evening. This scrap of newspaper bears yesterday's date, with the words, 'Evening edition.' Also, you will see here, pasted to the paper, a bit of one of those yellow wrappers in which the subscribers' copies are sent out. These copies are always delivered by the nine-o'clock post. Therefore, it was after nine o'clock. I said a well-dressed man. Please observe that this tiny piece of glass has the round hole of a single eyeglass at one of the edges and that the single eyeglass is an essentially aristocratic article of wear. This well-dressed man walked into a pastry cook's shop. Here is the very thin cardboard, shaped like a box, and still showing a little of the cream of the meringues and éclairs which were packed in it in the usual way. Having got his parcel, the gentleman with the eyeglass joined a young person whose eccentricity in the matter of dress is pretty clearly indicated by this bright red silk scarf. Having joined her, for some reason as yet unknown, he first stabbed her with a knife and then strangled her with the help of this same scarf. Take your magnifying glass, Chief Inspector, and you will see, on the silk, stains of a darker red which are, here, the marks of a knife wiped on the scarf and, there, the marks of a hand, covered with blood, clutching the material. Having committed the murder, his next business is to leave no trace behind him. So he takes from his pocket, first, the news-paper to which he subscribes—a racing-paper, as you will see by glancing at the contents of this scrap; and you will have no difficulty in discovering the title—and, secondly, a cord, which, on inspection, turns out to be a length of whipcord. These two details prove—do they not?—that our man is interested in racing and that he himself rides. Next, he picks up the frag-ments of his eyeglass, the cord of which has been broken in the struggle. He takes a pair of scissors—observe the hacking of the scissors—and cuts off the stained part of the scarf, leaving the other end, no doubt, in his victim's clenched hands. He makes a ball of the confectioner's cardboard box. He also puts in certain things that would have betrayed him, such as the knife, which must have slipped into the Seine. He wraps everything in news-paper, ties it with the cord and fastens this cut-glass inkstand to it, as a makeweight. Then he makes himself scarce. A little later, the parcel falls into the waterman's barge. And there you are. Oof, it's hot work! . . . What do you say to the story?"

He looked at Ganimard to see what impression his speech had produced on the inspector. Ganimard did not depart from his attitude of silence.

Lupin began to laugh:

"As a matter of fact, you're annoyed and surprised. But you're suspicious as well: 'Why should that confounded Lupin hand the business over to me,' say you, 'instead of keeping it for himself, hunting down the murderer and rifling his pockets, if there was a robbery?' The question is quite logical, of course. But—there is a 'but'—I have no time, you see. I am full up with work at the present moment: a burglary in London, another at Lausanne, an exchange of children at Marseilles, to say nothing of having to save a young girl who is at this moment shadowed by death. That's always the way: it never rains but it pours. So I said to myself, 'Suppose I handed the business over to my dear old Ganimard? Now that it is half solved for him, he is quite capable of succeeding. And what a service I shall be doing for him! How magnificently he will be able to distinguish himself!' No sooner said than done. At eight o'clock in the morning, I sent the joker with the orange peel to meet you. You swallowed the bait; and you were here by nine, all on edge and eager for the fray."

Lupin rose from his chair. He went over to the inspector and, with his eyes on Ganimard's, said:

"That's all. You now know the whole story. Presently, you will know the victim: some ballet dancer, probably, some singer at a music hall. On the other hand, the chances are that the criminal lives near the Pont-Neuf, most likely on the left bank. Lastly, here are all the exhibits. I make you a present of them. Set to work. I shall only keep this end of the scarf. If ever you want to piece the scarf together, bring me the other end, the one which the police will find round the victim's neck. Bring it to me in four weeks from now to the day, that is to say, on the twenty-ninth of December, at ten o'clock in the morning. You can be sure of finding me here. And don't be afraid: this is all perfectly serious, friend of my youth; I swear it is. No humbug, honor bright. You can go straight ahead. Oh, by the way, when you arrest the fellow with the eyeglass, be a bit careful: he is left-handed! Good-by, old dear, and good luck to you!"

Lupin spun round on his heel, went to the door, opened it and disappeared beford Ganimard had even thought of taking a decision. The inspector rushed after him, but at once found that the handle of the door, by some trick of mechanism which he did not know, refused to turn. It took him ten minutes to unscrew the lock and ten minutes more to unscrew the lock of the hall door. By the time that he had scrambled down the three flights of stairs, Ganimard had given up all hope of catching Arsène Lupin.

Besides, he was not thinking of it. Lupin inspired him with a queer, complex feeling, made up of fear, hatred, involuntary admiration and also the vague instinct that he, Ganimard, in spite of all his efforts, in spite of the persistency of his endeavors, would never get the better of this particular adversary. He pursued him from a sense of duty and pride, but with the continual dread of being taken in by that formidable hoaxer and flouted and fooled in the face of a public that was always only too willing to laugh at the chief inspector's mishaps.

This business of the red scarf, in particular, struck him as most suspicious. It was interesting, certainly, in more ways than one, but so very improbable! And Lupin's explanation, apparently so logical, would never stand the test of a severe examination!

"No," said Ganimard, "this is all swank: a parcel of suppositions and guesswork based upon nothing at all. I'm not to be caught with chaff."

When he reached the headquarters of police, at 36 Quai des Orfèvres, he had quite made up his mind to treat the incident as though it had never happened.

He went up to the Criminal Investigation Department. Here, one of his fellow inspectors said:

"Seen the chief?"

"No."

"He was asking for you just now."

"Oh, was he?"

"Yes, you had better go after him."

"Where?"

"To the Rue de Berne ... there was a murder there last night."

"Oh! Who's the victim?"

"I don't know exactly ... a music-hall singer, I believe."

Ganimard simply muttered:—

"By Jove!"

Twenty minutes later he stepped out of the underground railway station and made for the Rue de Berne.

The victim, who was known in the theatrical world by her stage name of Jenny Saphir, occupied a small flat on the second floor of one of the houses. A policeman took the chief inspector upstairs and showed him the way, through two sitting rooms, to a bedroom, where he found the magistrates in charge of the inquiry, together with the divisional surgeon and M. Dudouis, the head of the detective service.

Ganimard started at the first glance which he gave into the room. He saw, lying on a sofa, the corpse of a young woman whose hands clutched a strip of red silk! One of the shoulders, which appeared above the low-cut bodice, bore the marks of two wounds surrounded with clotted blood. The distorted and almost blackened features still bore an expression of frenzied terror.

The divisional surgeon, who had just finished his examination, said:

"My first conclusions are very clear. The victim was twice stabbed with a dagger and afterward strangled. The immediate cause of death was asphyxia."

"By Jove!" thought Ganimard again, remembering Lupin's words and the picture which he had drawn of the crime.

The examining magistrate objected:

"But the neck shows no discoloration."

"She may have been strangled with a napkin or a handkerchief," said the doctor.

"Most probably," said the chief detective, "with this silk scarf, which the victim was wearing and a piece of which remains, as though she had clung to it with her two hands to protect herself."

"But why does only that piece remain?" asked the magistrate. "What has become of the other?"

"The other may have been stained with blood and carried off by the murderer. You can plainly distinguish the hurried slashing of the scissors."

"By Jove!" said Ganimard, between his teeth, for the third time. "That brute of a Lupin saw everything without seeing a thing!"

"And what about the motive of the murder?" asked the magistrate. "The locks have been forced, the cupboards turned upside down. Have you anything to tell me, M. Dudouis?"

The chief of the detective service replied:

"I can at least suggest a supposition, derived from the statements made by the servant. The victim, who enjoyed a greater reputation on account of her looks than through her talent as a singer, went to Russia, two years ago, and brought back with

171

her a magnificent sapphire, which she appears to have received from some person of importance at the court. Since then, she went by the name of Jenny Saphir and seems generally to have been very proud of that present, although, for prudence's sake, she never wore it. I daresay that we shall not be far out if we presume the theft of the sapphire to have been the cause of the crime."

"But did the maid know where the stone was?"

"No, nobody did. And the disorder of the room would tend to prove that the murderer did not know either."

"We will question the maid," said the examining magistrate.

M. Dudouis took the chief inspector aside and said:

"You're looking very old-fashioned, Ganimard. What's the matter? Do you suspect anything?"

"Nothing at all, chief."

"That's a pity. We could do with a bit of showy work in the department. This is one of a number of crimes, all of the same class, of which we have failed to discover the perpetrator. This time we want the criminal . . . and quickly!"

"A difficult job, chief."

"It's got to be done. Listen to me, Ganimard. According to what the maid says, Jenny Saphir led a very regular life. For a month past she was in the habit of frequently receiving visits, on her return from the music hall, that is to say, at about half past ten, from a man who would stay until midnight or so. 'He's a society man,' Jenny Saphir used to say, 'and he wants to marry me.' This society man took every precaution to avoid being seen, such as turning up his coat collar and lowering the brim of his hat when he passed the porter's box. And Jenny Saphir always made a point of sending away her maid, even before he came. This is the man whom we have to find."

"Has he left no traces?"

"None at all. It is obvious that we have to deal with a very clever scoundrel, who prepared his crime beforehand and committed it with every possible chance of escaping unpunished. His arrest would be a great feather in our cap. I rely on you, Ganimard."

"Ah, you rely on me, chief?" replied the inspector. "Well, we shall see . . . we shall see. . . . I don't say no. . . . Only it's that . . ."

He seemed in a very nervous condition, and his agitation struck M. Dudouis.

172

"Only," continued Ganimard, "only I swear . . . do you hear, chief? I swear . . ."

"What do you swear?"

"Nothing. . . . We shall see, chief . . . we shall see. . . ."

Ganimard did not finish his sentence until he was outside, alone. And he finished it aloud, stamping his foot, in a tone of the most violent anger:

"Only, I swear to Heaven that the arrest shall be effected by my own means, without my employing a single one of the clues with which that villain has supplied me. Ah, no! Ah, no! . . ."

Railing against Lupin, furious at being mixed up in this business and resolved, nevertheless, to get to the bottom of it, he wandered aimlessly about the streets. His brain was seething with irritation; and he tried to adjust his ideas a little and to discover, among the chaotic facts, some trifling details, unperceived by all, unsuspected by Lupin himself, that might lead him to success.

He lunched hurriedly at a bar, resumed his stroll and suddenly stopped, petrified, astounded and confused. He was walking under the gateway of the very house in the Rue de Surène to which Lupin had enticed him a few hours earlier! A force stronger than his own will was drawing him there once more. The solution of the problem lay there. There and there alone were all the elements of the truth. Do and say what he would, Lupin's assertions were so precise, his calculations so accurate, that, worried to the innermost recesses of his being by so prodigious a display of perspicacity, he could not do other than take up the work at the point where his enemy had left it.

Abandoning all further resistance, he climbed the three flights of stairs. The door of the flat was open. No one had touched the exhibits. He put them in his pocket and walked away.

From that moment, he reasoned and acted, so to speak, mechanically, under the influence of the master whom he could not choose but obey.

Admitting that the unknown person whom he was seeking lived in the neighborhood of the Pont-Neuf, it became necessary to discover, somewhere between that bridge and the Rue de Berne, the first-class confectioner's shop, open in the evenings, at which the cakes were bought. This did not take long to find. A pastry cook near the Gare Saint-Lazare showed him some little cardboard boxes, identical in material and shape with the one in Ganimard's possession. Moreover, one of the shopgirls remembered having served, on the previous evening, a gentleman whose face was almost concealed in the collar of his fur coat, but whose eyeglass she had happened to notice.

"That's one clue checked," thought the inspector. "Our man wears an eyeglass."

He next collected the pieces of the racing paper and showed them to a news vendor, who easily recognized the *Turf Illustré*. Ganimard at once went to the offices of the *Turf* and asked to see the list of subscribers. Going through the list, he jotted down the names and addresses of all those who lived anywhere near the Pont-Neuf and principally—because Lupin had said so—those on the left bank of the river.

He then went back to the Criminal Investigation Department, took half a dozen men and packed them off with the necessary instructions.

At seven o'clock in the evening, the last of these men returned and brought good news with him. A certain M. Prévailles, a subscriber to the *Turf*, occupied an entresol flat on the Quai des Augustins. On the previous evening, he left his place, wearing a fur coat, took his letters and his paper, the *Turf Illustré*, from the porter's wife, walked away and returned home at midnight. This M. Prévailles wore a single eyeglass. He was a regular race-goer and himself owned several hacks which he either rode himself or jobbed out.

The inquiry had taken so short a time and the results obtained were so exactly in accordance with Lupin's predictions that Ganimard felt quite overcome on hearing the detective's report. Once more he was measuring the prodigious extent of the resources at Lupin's disposal. Never in the course of his life—and Ganimard was already well advanced in years—had he come across such perspicacity, such a quick and far-seeing mind.

He went in search of M. Dudouis.

"Everything's ready, chief. Have you a warrant?"

"Eh?"

"I said, everything is ready for the arrest, chief."

"You know the name of Jenny Saphir's murderer?"

"Yes."

"But how? Explain yourself."

Ganimard had a sort of scruple of conscience, blushed a little and nevertheless replied:

"An accident, chief. The murderer threw everything that was

174

likely to compromise him into the Seine. Part of the parcel was picked up and handed to me."

"By whom?"

"A boatman who refused to give his name, for fear of getting into trouble. But I had all the clues I wanted. It was not so difficult as I expected."

And the inspector described how he had gone to work.

"And you call that an accident!" cried M. Dudouis. "And you say that it was not difficult! Why, it's one of your finest performances! Finish it yourself, Ganimard, and be prudent."

Ganimard was eager to get the business done. He went to the Quai des Augustins with his men and distributed them around the house. He questioned the portress, who said that her tenant took his meals out of doors, but made a point of looking in after dinner.

A little before nine o'clock, in fact, leaning out of her window, she warned Ganimard, who at once gave a low whistle. A gentleman in a tall hat and a fur coat was coming along the pavement beside the Seine. He crossed the road and walked up to the house.

Ganimard stepped forward:

"M. Prévailles, I believe?"

"Yes, but who are you?"

"I have a commission to . . ."

He had not time to finish his sentence. At the sight of the men appearing out of the shadow, Prévailles quickly retreated to the wall and faced his adversaries, with his back to the door of a shop on the ground floor, the shutters of which were closed.

"Stand back!" he cried.

His right hand brandished a heavy stick, while his left was slipped behind him and seemed to be trying to open the door.

Ganimard had an impression that the man might escape through this way and through some secret outlet:

"None of this nonsense," he said, moving closer to him. "You're caught. . . . You had better come quietly."

But, just as he was laying hold of Prévailles's stick, Ganimard remembered the warning which Lupin gave him: Prévailles was left-handed; and it was his revolver for which he was feeling behind his back.

The inspector ducked his head. He had noticed the man's sudden movement. Two reports rang out.

175

A second later, Prévailles received a blow under the chin from the butt end of a revolver, which brought him down where he stood. He was entered at the Dépôt soon after nine o'clock.

Ganimard enjoyed a great reputation even at that time. But this capture, so quickly effected, by such very simple means, and at once made public by the police, won him a sudden celebrity. Prévailles was forthwith saddled with all the murders that had remained unpunished; and the newspapers vied with one another in extolling Ganimard's prowess.

The case was conducted briskly at the start. It was first of all ascertained that Prévailles, whose real name was Thomas Derocq, had already been in trouble. Moreover, the search instituted in his rooms, while not supplying any fresh proofs, at least led to the discovery of a ball of whipcord similar to the cord used for doing up the parcel and also to the discovery of daggers which would have produced a wound similar to the wounds on the victim.

But, on the eighth day, everything was changed. Until then Prévailles had refused to reply to the questions put to him; but now, assisted by his counsel, he pleaded a circumstantial alibi and maintained that he was at the Folies-Bergère on the night of the murder.

As a matter of fact, the pockets of his dinner jacket contained the counterfoil of a stall ticket and a program of the performance, both bearing the date of that evening.

"An alibi prepared in advance," objected the examining magistrate.

"Prove it," said Prévailles.

The prisoner was confronted with the witnesses for the prosecution. The young lady from the confectioner's "thought she knew" the gentleman with the eyeglass. The hall porter in the Rue de Berne "thought he knew" the gentleman who used to come to see Jenny Saphir. But nobody dared to make a more definite statement.

The examination, therefore, led to nothing of a precise character, provided no solid basis whereon to found a serious accusation.

The judge sent for Ganimard and told him of his difficulty.

"I can't possibly persist, at this rate. There is no evidence to support the charge."

"But surely you are convinced in your own mind, monsieur *le juge d'instruction*! Prévailles would never have resisted his arrest unless he was guilty."

"He says that he thought he was being assaulted. He also says that he never set eyes on Jenny Saphir; and, as a matter of fact, we can find no one to contradict his assertion. Then again, admitting that the sapphire has been stolen, we have not been able to find it at his flat."

"Nor anywhere else," suggested Ganimard.

"Quite true, but that is no evidence against him. I'll tell you what we shall want, M. Ganimard, and that very soon: the other end of this red scarf."

"The other end?"

"Yes, for it is obvious that, if the murderer took it away with him, the reason was that the stuff is stained with the marks of the blood on his fingers."

Ganimard made no reply. For several days he had felt that the whole business was tending to this conclusion. There was no other proof possible. Given the silk scarf—and no other circumstances—Prévailles's guilt was certain. Now Ganimard's position required that Prévailles's guilt should be established. He was responsible for the arrest, it had cast a glamor around him, he had been praised to the skies as the most formidable adversary of criminals; and he would look absolutely ridiculous if Prévailles were released.

Unfortunately, the one and only indispensable proof was in Lupin's pocket. How was he to get hold of it?

Ganimard cast about, exhausted himself with fresh investigations, went over the inquiry from start to finish, spent sleepless nights in turning over the mystery of the Rue de Berne, studied the records of Prévailles's life, sent ten men hunting after the sapphire. Everything was useless.

On the 28th of December, the examining magistrate stopped him in one of the passages of the Law Courts:

"Well, M. Ganimard, any news?"

"No, monsieur *le juge d'instruction*."

"Then I shall dismiss the case."

"Wait one day longer."

"What's the use? We want the other end of the scarf; have you got it?"

"I shall have it tomorrow."

"Tomorrow!"

"Yes, but please lend me the piece in your possession."

"What if I do?"

"If you do, I promise to let you have the whole scarf complete."

"Very well, that's understood."

Ganimard followed the examining magistrate to his room and came out with the piece of silk:

"Hang it all!" he growled. "Yes, I will go and fetch the proof and I shall have it too . . . always presuming that Master Lupin has the courage to keep the appointment."

In point of fact, he did not doubt for a moment that Master Lupin would have this courage, and that was just what exasperated him. Why had Lupin insisted on this meeting? What was his object, in the circumstances?

Anxious, furious and full of hatred, he resolved to take every precaution necessary not only to prevent his falling into a trap himself, but to make his enemy fall into one, now that the opportunity offered. And, on the next day, which was the 29th of December, the date fixed by Lupin, after spending the night in studying the old manor house in the Rue de Surène and convincing himself that there was no other outlet than the front door, he warned his men that he was going on a dangerous expedition and arrived with them on the field of battle.

He posted them in a café and gave them formal instructions: if he showed himself at one of the third-floor windows, or if he failed to return within an hour, the detectives were to enter the house and arrest anyone who tried to leave it.

The chief inspector made sure that his revolver was in working order and that he could take it from his pocket easily. Then he went upstairs.

He was surprised to find things as he had left them, the doors open and the locks broken. After ascertaining that the windows of the principal room looked out on the street, he visited the three other rooms that made up the flat. There was no one there.

"Master Lupin was afraid," he muttered, not without a certain satisfaction.

"Don't be silly," said a voice behind him.

Turning round, he saw an old workman, wearing a housepainter's long smock, standing in the doorway.

"You needn't bother your head," said the man. "It's I, Lupin. I have been working in the painter's shop since early morning.

178

This is when we knock off for breakfast. So I came upstairs."

He looked at Ganimard with a quizzing smile and cried:

" 'Pon my word, this is a gorgeous moment I owe you, old chap! I wouldn't sell it for ten years of your life; and yet you know how I love you! What do you think of it, artist? Wasn't it well thought out and well foreseen? Foreseen from alpha to omega? Did I understand the business? Did I penetrate the mystery of the scarf? I'm not saying that there were no holes in my argument, no links missing in the chain. . . . But what a masterpiece of intelligence! Ganimard, what a reconstruction of events! What an intuition of everything that had taken place and of everything that was going to take place, from the discovery of the crime to your arrival here in search of a proof! What really marvelous divination! Have you the scarf?"

"Yes, half of it. Have you the other?"

"Here it is. Let's compare."

They spread the two pieces of silk on the table. The cuts made by the scissors corresponded exactly. Moreover, the colors were identical.

"But I presume," said Lupin, "that this was not the only thing you came for. What you are interested in seeing is the marks of the blood. Come with me, Ganimard: it's rather dark in here."

They moved into the next room, which, though it overlooked the courtyard, was lighter; and Lupin held his piece of silk against the windowpane:

"Look," he said, making room for Ganimard.

The inspector gave a start of delight. The marks of the five fingers and the print of the palm were distinctly visible. The evidence was undeniable. The murderer had seized the stuff in his bloodstained hand, in the same hand that had stabbed Jenny Saphir, and tied the scarf round her neck.

"And it is the print of a left hand," observed Lupin. "Hence my warning, which had nothing miraculous about it, you see. For, though I admit, friend of my youth, that you may look upon me as a superior intelligence, I won't have you treat me as a wizard."

Ganimard had quickly pocketed the piece of silk. Lupin nodded his head in approval:

"Quite right, old boy, it's for you. I'm so glad you're glad! And, you see, there was no trap about all this . . . only the wish to oblige . . . a service between friends, between pals. . . . And also, I confess, a little curiosity. . . . Yes, I wanted to examine

179

this other piece of silk, the one the police had . . . Don't be afraid: I'll give it back to you. . . . Just a second. . . ."

Lupin, with a careless movement, played with the tassel at the end of his half of the scarf, while Ganimard listened to him in spite of himself:

"How ingenious these little bits of women's work are! Did you notice one detail in the maid's evidence? Jenny Saphir was very handy with her needle and used to make all her own hats and frocks. It is obvious that she made this scarf herself. . . . I noticed that from the first. Besides, I am naturally curious, as I have already told you, and I made a thorough examination of the piece of silk which you have just put in your pocket. Inside the tassel, I found a little sacred medal, which the poor girl had stitched into it to bring her luck. Touching, isn't it, Ganimard? A little medal of Our Lady of Good Succor."

The inspector felt greatly puzzled and did not take his eyes off the other. And Lupin continued:

"Then I said to myself, 'How interesting it would be to explore the other half of the scarf, the one which the police will find round the victim's neck!' For this other half, which I hold in my hands at last, is finished off in the same way . . . so I shall be able to see if it has a hiding place too and what's inside it. . . . But look, my friend, isn't it cleverly made? And so simple! All you have to do is to take a skein of red cord and braid it round a wooden cup, leaving a little recess, a little empty space in the middle, very small, of course, but large enough to hold a medal of a saint . . . or anything . . . A precious stone, for instance. . . . Such as a sapphire. . . ."

At that moment he finished pushing back the silk cord and, from the hollow of a cup he took between his thumb and forefinger a wonderful blue stone, perfect in respect of size and purity.

"Ha! What did I tell you, friend of my youth?"

He raised his head. The inspector had turned livid and was staring wild-eyed, as though fascinated by the stone that sparkled before him. He at last realized the whole plot:

"You dirty scoundrel!" he muttered, repeating the insults which he had used at the first interview. "You scum of the earth!"

The two men were standing one against the other.

"Give me back that," said the inspector.

Lupin held out the piece of silk.

"And the sapphire," said Ganimard, in a peremptory tone.

"Don't be silly."

"Give it back, or . . ."

"Or what, you idiot!" cried Lupin. "Look here, do you think I put you on to this soft thing for nothing?"

"Give it back!"

"You haven't noticed what I've been about, that's plain! What! For four weeks I've kept you on the move like a deer; and you want to! . . . Come, Ganimard, old chap, pull yourself together! . . . Don't you see that you've been playing the good dog for four weeks on end? . . . Fetch it, Rover! . . . There's a nice blue pebble over there, which master can't get at. Hunt it, Ganimard, fetch it . . . bring it to master. . . . Ah, he's his master's own good little dog! . . . Sit up! Beg! . . . Does'ms want a bit of sugar, then? . . ."

Ganimard, containing the anger that seethed within him, thought only of one thing, summoning his detectives. And, as the room in which he now was looked out on the courtyard, he tried gradually to work his way round to the communicating door. He would then run to the window and break one of the panes.

"All the same," continued Lupin, "what a pack of dunderheads you and the rest must be! You've had the silk all this time and not one of you ever thought of feeling it, not one of you ever asked himself the reason why the poor girl hung on to her scarf. Not one of you! You just acted at haphazard, without reflecting, without foreseeing anything. . . ."

The inspector had attained his object. Taking advantage of a second when Lupin had turned away from him, he suddenly wheeled round and grasped the door handle. But an oath escaped him: the handle did not budge.

Lupin burst into a fit of laughing:

"Not even that! You did not even foresee that! You lay a trap for me and you won't admit that I may perhaps smell the thing out beforehand. . . . And you allow yourself to be brought into this room without asking whether I am not bringing you here for a particular reason and without remembering that the locks are fitted with a special mechanism. Come now, speaking frankly, what do you think of it yourself?"

"What do I think of it?" roared Ganimard, beside himself with rage.

He had drawn his revolver and was pointing it straight at

Lupin's face.

"Hands up!" he cried. "That's what I think of it!"

Lupin placed himself in front of him and shrugged his shoulders:

"Sold again!" he said.

"Hands up, I say, once more!"

"And sold again, say I. Your deadly weapon won't go off."

"What?"

"Old Catherine, your housekeeper, is in my service. She damped the charges this morning while you were having your breakfast coffee."

Ganimard made a furious gesture, pocketed the revolver and rushed at Lupin.

"Well?" said Lupin, stopping him short with a well aimed kick on the shin.

Their clothes were almost touching. They exchanged defiant glances, the glances of two adversaries who mean to come to blows. Nevertheless, there was no fight. The recollection of the earlier struggles made any present struggle useless. And Ganimard, who remembered all his past failures, his vain attacks, Lupin's crushing reprisals, did not lift a limb. There was nothing to be done. He felt it. Lupin had forces at his command against which any individual force simply broke to pieces. So what was the good?

"I agree," said Lupin, in a friendly voice, as though answering Ganimard's unspoken thought, "you would do better to let things be as they are. Besides, friend of my youth, think of all that this incident has brought you: fame, the certainty of quick promotion and, thanks to that, the prospect of a happy and comfortable old age! Surely, you don't want the discovery of the sapphire and the head of poor Arsène Lupin in addition! It wouldn't be fair. To say nothing of the fact that poor Arsène Lupin saved your life. . . . Yes, sir! Who warned you, at this very spot, that Prévailles was left-handed? . . . And is this the way you thank me? It's not pretty of you, Ganimard. Upon my word, you make me blush for you!"

While chattering, Lupin had gone through the same performance as Ganimard and was now near the door. Ganimard saw that his foe was about to escape him. Forgetting all prudence, he tried to block his way and received a tremendous butt in the stomach, which sent him rolling.

Lupin dexterously touched a spring, turned the handle,

opened the door and slipped away, roaring with laughter as he went.

Twenty minutes later, when Ganimard at last succeeded in joining his men, one of them said to him:—

"A house painter left the house, as his mates were coming back from breakfast, and put a letter in my hand. 'Give that to your governor,' he said. 'Which governor?' I asked; but he was gone. I suppose it's meant for you."

"Let's have it."

Ganimard opened the letter. It was hurriedly scribbled in pencil and contained these words:—

This is to warn you, friend of my youth, against excessive credulity. When a fellow tells you that the cartridges in your revolver are damp, however great your confidence in that fellow may be, even though his name be Arsène Lupin, never allow yourself to be taken in. Fire first; and, if the fellow hops the twig, you will have acquired the proof (1) that the cartridges are not damp: and (2) that old Catherine is the most honest and respectable of housekeepers.

One of these days, I hope to have the pleasure of making her acquaintance.

Meanwhile, friend of my youth, believe me always affectionately and sincerely yours,

ARSÈNE LUPIN

THE MISSING MORTGAGEE

BY R. AUSTIN FREEMAN

Richard Austin Freeman was born in London's Soho district on May 11, 1862, and trained as a surgeon at Middlesex Hospital Medical College. He served on the African Gold Coast as an assistant colonial surgeon for several years, was invalided out for ill health in 1891, and never returned to the practice of medicine on a full-time basis. He published a travel book in 1898 and collaborated on his first fictional work, *The Adventures of Romney Pringle,* published in 1902. Best known for his scientific detective, Dr. Thorndyke, Freeman also invented the "inverted" detective story with "The Singing Bone" (1912). He died in 1943.

I. The Story of the Crime

EARLY IN THE AFTERNOON of a warm, humid November day Thomas Elton sauntered dejectedly along the Margate esplanade, casting an eye now on the slate-colored sea with its pall of slate-colored sky, and now on the harbor, where the ebb tide was just beginning to expose the mud. It was a dreary prospect, and Elton varied it by observing the few fishermen and fewer promenaders who walked foot to foot with their distorted reflections in the wet pavement; and thus it was that his eye fell on a smartly dressed man who had just stepped into a shelter to light a cigar.

Now, something in the aspect of the broad back that was presented to his view, in that of the curly, black hair and the exuberant raiment, suggested to Elton a suspicion of disagreeable familiarity. The man backed out of the shelter, diffusing azure clouds, and, drawing an envelope from his pocket, read something that was written on it. Then he turned quickly—and so did Elton, but not quickly enough. For he was a solitary figure on that bald and empty expanse, and the other had seen him at the first glance. Elton walked away slowly, but he had not gone a dozen paces when he felt the anticipated slap on the shoulder and heard the too well-remembered voice:

"Blow me, if I don't believe you were trying to cut me, Tom."

Elton looked round with ill-assumed surprise.

"Hallo, Gordon! Who the deuce would have thought of seeing you here?"

Gordon laughed thickly. "Not you, apparently; and you don't look as pleased as you might now that you have seen me. Whereas I'm delighted to see you, and especially to see that things are going so well with you."

"What do you mean?" asked Elton sullenly.

"Taking your winter holiday by the sea, like a blooming duke."

"I'm not taking a holiday," said Elton. "I was so worn out that I had to have some sort of change; but I've brought my work down with me, and I put in a full eight hours every day."

"That's right," said Gordon. " 'Consider the ant.' Nothing

185

like steady industry. I've brought my work down with me too; a little slip of paper with a stamp on it. You know the article, Tom."

"I know. But it isn't due till tomorrow, is it?"

"Isn't it, by gum! It's due this very day, the twentieth of the month. That's why I'm here. Knowing your little weakness in the matter of dates, and having a small item to collect in Canterbury, I thought I'd just come on and save you the useless expense that results from forgetfulness."

Elton understood the hint, and his face grew rigid.

"I can't do it, Gordon; I can't really. Haven't got it, and shan't have it until I'm paid for the drawings I'm working on now."

"Oh, what a pity!" exclaimed Gordon. "Here you are, blueing your capital on seaside jaunts and reducing your income at a stroke by a clear four pounds a year."

"How do you make that out?" demanded Elton.

"Tut, tut," protested Gordon, "what an unbusinesslike chap you are! Here's a little matter of twenty pounds—a quarter's interest. If it's paid now, it's twenty. If it isn't, it goes on to the principal, and there's another four pounds a year to be paid. Why don't you try to be more economical, dear boy?"

Elton looked askance at the vampire by his side; at the plump, blue-shaven cheeks, the thick black eyebrows, and the full red lips that embraced the cigar, and though he was a mild-tempered man, he felt that he could have battered that sensual, complacent face out of all human likeness with something uncommonly like enjoyment. But of these thoughts nothing appeared in his reply, for a man cannot afford to say all he would wish to a creditor who could ruin him with a word.

"You mustn't be too hard on me, Gordon," said he. "Give me a little time. I'm doing all I can, you know. I earn every penny that I am able, and I have kept my insurance paid up regularly. I shall be paid for this work in a week or two and then we can settle up."

Gordon made no immediate reply, and the two men walked slowly eastward, a curiously ill-assorted pair: the one prosperous, jaunty, overdressed; the other pale and dejected, and, with his well-brushed but napless clothes, his patched boots and shiny-brimmed hat, the very type of decent, struggling poverty.

They had just passed the pier and were coming to the base of the jetty when Gordon next spoke.

"Can't we get off this beastly wet pavement?" he asked, look-

186

ing down at his dainty and highly-polished boots. "What's it like down on the sands?"

"Oh, it's very good walking," said Elton, "between here and Foreness, and probably drier than the pavement."

"Then," said Gordon, "I vote we go down"; and accordingly they descended the sloping way beyond the jetty. The stretch of sand left by the retiring tide was as smooth and firm as a sheet of asphalt, and far more pleasant to walk upon.

"We seem to have the place all to ourselves," remarked Gordon, "with the exception of some half-dozen dukes like yourself."

As he spoke, Gordon changed over from one arm to the other the heavy fur-lined overcoat that he was carrying. "Needn't have brought this beastly thing," he remarked, "if I'd known it was going to be so warm."

"Shall I carry it for you a little way?" asked the naturally polite Elton.

"If you would, dear boy," replied Gordon. "It's difficult to manage an overcoat, an umbrella and a cigar all at once."

He handed over the coat with a sigh of relief. Presently their footsteps led them to the margin of the weed-covered rocks, and here, from under a high heap of bladder-wrack, a large green shore crab rushed out and menaced them with uplifted claws. Gordon stopped and stared at the creature with Cockney surprise, prodding it with his umbrella, and speculating aloud as to whether it was good to eat. The crab, as if alarmed at the suggestion, suddenly darted away and began to scuttle over the green-clad rocks, finally plunging into a large, deep pool. Gordon pursued it, hobbling awkwardly over the slippery rocks, until he came to the edge of the pool, over which he stooped, raking inquisitively among the weedy fringe with his umbrella. He was so much interested in his quarry that he failed to allow for the slippery surface on which he stood. The result was disastrous. Of a sudden, one foot began to slide forward, and when he tried to recover his balance, was instantly followed by the other. For a moment he struggled frantically to regain his footing, executing a sort of splashing, stamping dance on the margin. Then, the circling sea birds were startled by a yell of terror, an ivory-handled umbrella flew across the rocks, and Mr. Gordon took a complete header into the deepest part of the pool. What the crab thought of it history does not relate. What Mr. Gordon thought of it is not suitable for publi-

187

cation; he rose looking like an extremely up-to-date merman.

"It's a good job you brought your overcoat, after all," Elton remarked. Gordon made no reply but staggered towards the hospitable overcoat, holding out his dripping arms. Having inducted him into the garment and buttoned him up, Elton hurried off to recover the umbrella and, having secured it, angled with it for the smart billycock which was floating across the pool.

It was surprising what a change the last minute or two had wrought. The positions of the two men were now reversed. Despite his shabby clothing, Elton seemed to walk quite jauntily as compared with his shuddering companion, who trotted by his side with short, miserable steps, shrinking into the uttermost depths of his enveloping coat, like an alarmed winkle into its shell, puffing out his cheeks and anathematizing the Universe in general.

They hurried along towards the slope by the jetty when, suddenly, Elton asked: "What are you going to do, Gordon? You can't travel like that."

"Can't you lend me a change?" asked Gordon.

Elton reflected. He had another suit, his best suit, which he had been careful to preserve in good condition for use on those occasions when a decent appearance was indispensable. He looked askance at the man by his side and something told him that the treasured suit would probably receive less careful treatment than it was accustomed to. Still the man couldn't be allowed to go about in wet clothes.

"I've got a spare suit," he said. "It isn't quite up to your style, and may not be much of a fit, but I daresay you'll be able to put up with it for an hour or two."

"It'll be dry anyhow," mumbled Gordon, "so we won't trouble about the style. How far is it to your rooms?"

The plural number was superfluous. Elton's room was in a little ancient flint house at the bottom of a narrow close in the old quarter of the town. You reached it without any formal preliminaries of bell or knocker by simply letting yourself in by a street door, crossing a tiny room, opening the door of what looked like a narrow cupboard, and squeezing up a diminutive flight of stairs, which was unexpectedly exposed to view. By following this procedure the two men reached a small bed-sitting-room; that is to say, it was a bedroom, but by sitting down on the bed, you converted it into a sitting-room.

188

Gordon puffed out his cheeks and looked round distastefully.

"You might ring for some hot water, old chappie," he said.

Elton laughed aloud. "Ring!" he exclaimed. "Ring what? Your clothes are the only thing that are likely to get wrung."

"Well, then, sing out for the servant," said Gordon.

Elton laughed again. "My dear fellow," said he, "we don't go in for servants. I look after my room myself. You'll be all right if you have a good rubdown."

Gordon groaned, and emerged reluctantly from the depths of his overcoat, while Elton brought forth from the chest of drawers the promised suit and the necessary undergarments. One of these latter Gordon held up with a sour smile, as he regarded it with extreme disfavor.

"I shouldn't think," said he, "you need have been at the trouble of marking them so plainly. No one's likely to want to run away with them."

The undergarments certainly contrasted very unfavorably with the delicate garments which he was peeling off, excepting in one respect; they were dry; and that had to console him for the ignominious change.

The clothes fitted quite fairly, notwithstanding the difference between the figures of the two men; for while Gordon was a slender man grown fat, Elton was a broad man grown thin; which, in a way, averaged their superficial area.

Elton watched the process of investment and noted the caution with which Gordon smuggled the various articles from his own pockets into those of the borrowed garments without exposing them to view; heard the jingle of money; saw the sumptuous gold watch and massive chain transplanted, and noted with interest the large leather wallet that came forth from the breast pocket of the wet coat. He got a better view of this from the fact that Gordon himself examined it narrowly, and even opened it to inspect its contents.

"Lucky that wasn't an ordinary pocket-book," he remarked. "If it had been, your receipt would have got wet, and so would one or two other little articles that wouldn't have been improved by salt water. And, talking of the receipt, Tom, shall I hand it over now?"

"You can if you like," said Elton; "but as I told you, I haven't got the money." On which Gordon muttered: "Pity, pity," and thrust the wallet into his, or rather, Elton's breast pocket.

189

A few minutes later the two men came out together into the gathering darkness, and as they walked slowly up the close, Elton asked: "Are you going up to town tonight, Gordon?"

"How can I?" was the reply. "I can't go without my clothes. No, I shall run over to Broadstairs. A client of mine keeps a boarding-house there. He'll have to put me up for the night, and if you can get my clothes cleaned and dried I can come over for them tomorrow."

These arrangements having been settled, the two men adjourned, at Gordon's suggestion, for tea at one of the restaurants on the Front; and after that, again at Gordon's suggestion, they set forth together along the cliff path that leads to Broadstairs by way of Kingsgate.

"You may as well walk with me into Broadstairs," said Gordon; "I'll stand you the fare back." And to this Elton agreed, not because he was desirous of the other man's company, but because he still had some lingering hopes of being able to adjust the little difficulty respecting the installment.

"Look here, Gordon," he said at length, "can't you manage to give me a bit more time to pay up this installment? It doesn't seem quite fair to keep sending up the principal like this."

"Well, dear boy," replied Gordon, "it's your own fault, you know. If you would only bear the dates in mind it wouldn't happen."

"But," pleaded Elton, "just consider what I'm paying you. I originally borrowed fifty pounds from you, and I'm now paying you eighty pounds a year in addition to the insurance premium. That's close on a hundred a year; just about half what I manage to earn. If you stick it up any farther you won't leave me enough to keep body and soul together; which really means that I shan't be able to pay you at all."

There was a brief pause; then Gordon said dryly:

"You talk about not paying, dear boy, as if you had forgotten about that promissory note."

Elton set his teeth. His temper was rising rapidly. But he restrained himself.

"I should have a pretty poor memory if I had," he replied, "considering the number of reminders you've been at pains to give me."

"You've needed them, Tom," said the other. "I've never met a slacker man in keeping to his engagements."

At this Elton lost his temper completely.

"That's a lie!" he exclaimed, "and you know it, you infernal, dirty, blood-sucking parasite!"

Gordon stopped dead.

"Look here, my friend," said he; "none of that. If I've any of your sauce, I'll give you a sound good hammering."

"The deuce you will!" said Elton, whose fingers were itching, not for the first time, to take some recompense for all that he had suffered from the insatiable usurer. "Nothing's preventing you now, you know, but I fancy twenty percent is more in your line than fighting."

"Give me any more and you'll see," said Gordon.

"Very well," was the quiet rejoinder. "I have great pleasure in informing you that you are a human maw-worm. How does that suit you?"

For reply, Gordon threw down his overcoat and umbrella on the grass at the side of the path, and deliberately slapped Elton on the cheek.

The reply followed instantly in the form of a smart left-hander, which took effect on the bridge of Gordon's nose. Thus the battle was fairly started, and it proceeded with all the fury of accumulated hatred on the one side and sharp physical pain on the other. What little science there was appertained to Elton, in spite of which, however, he had to give way to his heavier, better nourished, and more excitable opponent. Regardless of the punishment he received, the infuriated Gordon rushed at him, and, by sheer weight of onslaught, drove him backward across the little green.

Suddenly, Elton, who knew the place by daylight, called out in alarm.

"Look out, Gordon! Get back, you fool!"

But Gordon, blind with fury, and taking this as a maneuver to escape, only pressed him harder. Elton's pugnacity died out instantly in mortal terror. He shouted out another warning and, as Gordon still pressed him, battering furiously, he did the only thing that was possible: he dropped to the ground. And then, in the twinkling of an eye, came the catastrophe. Borne forward by his own momentum, Gordon stumbled over Elton's prostrate body, staggered forward a few paces, and fell. Elton heard a muffled groan that faded quickly and mingled with the sound of falling earth and stones. He sprang to his feet and looked round and saw that he was alone.

For some moments he was dazed by the suddenness of the

191

awful thing that had happened. He crept timorously towards the unseen edge of the cliff, and listened. But there was no sound save the distant surge of the breakers, and the scream of an invisible sea-bird. It was useless to try to look over. Near as he was, he could not, even now, distinguish the edge of the cliff from the dark beach below. Suddenly he thought of a narrow cutting that led down from the cliff to the shore. Quickly crossing the green, and mechanically stooping to pick up Gordon's overcoat and umbrella, he made his way to the head of the cutting and ran down the rough chalk roadway. At the bottom he turned to the right.

Soon there loomed up against the murky sky the shadowy form of the little headland on which he and Gordon had stood; and almost at the same moment there grew out of the darkness of the beach a darker spot amid a constellation of smaller spots of white. As he drew nearer the dark spot took shape: a horrid shape with sprawling limbs and a head strangely awry. He stepped forward, trembling, and spoke the name the thing had borne. He grasped the flabby hand, and laid his fingers on the wrist; but it only told him the same tale as did that strangely misplaced head. The body lay face downwards, and he had not the courage to turn it over; but that his enemy was dead he had not the faintest doubt. He stood up amidst the litter of fallen chalk and earth and looked down at the horrible, motionless thing, wondering numbly and vaguely what he should do. Should he go and seek assistance? The answer to that came in a another question. How came the body to be lying on the beach? And what answer should he give to the inevitable questions?

A minute later, a panic-stricken man stole with stealthy swiftness up the narrow cutting and set forth towards Margate.

Little sleep was there that night for Elton in his room in the old flint house. The dead man's clothes, which greeted him on his arrival, hanging limply on the towel-horse where he had left them, haunted him through the night. In the darkness the sour smell of damp cloth assailed him with an endless reminder of their presence, and after each brief doze, he would start up in alarm and hastily light his candle; only to throw its flickering light on those dank, drowned-looking vestments. His thoughts, half-controlled, as night thoughts are, flitted erratically from the unhappy past to the unstable present, and thence to the incalculable future. Once he lighted the candle specially to look at his watch to see if the tide had yet crept up to that solitary

192

figure on the beach; nor could he rest again until the time of high water was well past. And all through these wanderings of his thoughts there came, recurring like a horrible refrain, the question, what would happen when the body was found? Could he be connected with it and, if so, would he be charged with murder? At last he fell asleep and slumbered on until the land-lady thumped at the staircase door to announce that she had brought his breakfast.

As soon as he was dressed he went out. He went straight on down to the beach; with what purpose he could hardly have said, but an irresistible impulse drove him thither to see if it was there. He went down by the jetty and struck out eastward over the smooth sand, looking about him with dreadful expectation for some small crowd or hurrying messenger.

It was less than half an hour later that the fatal headland opened out beyond Whiteness. Not a soul had he met along that solitary beach, and though, once or twice, he had started at the sight of some mass of driftwood or heap of seaweed, the dreadful thing he was seeking had not yet appeared. He passed the opening of the cutting and approached the headland, breathing fast and looking about him fearfully.

Then, rounding the headland, he came in sight of a black hole at the cliff foot, the entrance to a deep cave. He ap-proached yet more slowly, sweeping his eye round the little bay, and looking apprehensively at the cavity before him. Suppose the thing should have washed in there. It was quite possible. Many things did wash into that cave, for he had once visited it and had been astonished at the quantity of seaweed and jetsam that had accumulated within it. But it was an uncomfortable thought. It would be doubly horrible to meet the awful thing in the dim twilight of the cavern. And yet, the black archway seemed to draw him on, step by step, until he stood at the portal and looked in. It was an eerie place, chilly and damp, the clammy walls and roof stained green and purple, and black with encrusting lichens.

At first he could see nothing but the smooth sand near the opening; then, as his eyes grew more accustomed to the gloom, he could make out the great heap of seaweed on the floor of the cave. Insensibly, he crept in, with his eyes riveted on the weedy mass and, as he left the daylight behind him, so did the twilight of the cave grow clearer. His feet left the firm sand and trod the springy mass of weed.

And then, in an instant, he saw it. From a heap of weed, a few paces ahead, projected a boot: his own boot. He recognized the patch on the sole, and at the sight his heart seemed to stand still. Though he had somehow expected to find it here, its presence seemed to strike him with a greater shock of horror from that very circumstance.

How long would the body lie here undiscovered? And what would happen when it was found? What was there to connect him with it? Of course, there was his name on the clothing, but there was nothing incriminating in that, if he had only had the courage to give information at once. But it was too late to think of that now. Besides, it suddenly flashed upon him, there was the receipt in the wallet. That receipt mentioned him by name and referred to a loan. Obviously, its suggestion was most sinister, coupled with his silence. It was a deadly item of evidence against him. But no sooner had he realized the appalling significance of this document that he also realized that it was still within his reach. Why should he leave it there to be brought in evidence—in false evidence, too—against him?

Slowly he began to lift the slimy, tangled weed. As he drew aside the first bunch, he gave a gasp of horror and quickly replaced it. The body was lying on its back and as he lifted the weed, he had uncovered—not the face, for the thing had no face. It had struck either the cliff or a stone upon the beach and—but there is no need to go into particulars: it had no face. When he had recovered a little, Elton groped shudderingly among the weed until he found the breast-pocket from which he quickly drew out the wallet, now clammy and sodden.

Elton stood up and took a deep breath. He resolved instantly to take out and destroy the receipt and put back the wallet. But this was easier thought of than done. The receipt was soaked with sea-water, and refused utterly to light when he applied a match to it. In the end he tore it up into little fragments and deliberately swallowed them, one by one.

But to restore the wallet was more than he was equal to just now. The receipt was gone now, and with it the immediate suggestion of motive. There remained only the clothes with their too legible markings. They certainly connected him with the body, but they offered no proof of his presence at the catastrophe. And then, suddenly, another idea occurred to him. Who could identify the body—the body that had no face? There was the wallet, it was true, but he could take that away with him; and there was a ring on the finger, and some articles in the pockets which might be identified. But these things were removable, too. And if he removed them, what then? Why, then, the body was that of Thomas Elton, a friendless, poverty-stricken artist.

He pondered on this new situation profoundly. It offered him a choice of alternatives. Either he might choose the imminent risk of being hanged for a murder that he had not committed, or he might surrender his identity forever and move away to a new environment.

He smiled faintly. His identity! What might that be worth to barter against his life? Only yesterday he would gladly have surrendered it as the bare price of emancipation from the vampire who had fastened on to him.

He thrust the wallet into his pocket and buttoned his coat.

"Thomas Elton" was dead.

II: Dr. Thorndyke's Investigation

FROM various causes the insurance business that passed through Dr. Thorndyke's hands had, of late, considerably increased. The number of companies which regularly employed him had grown larger, and, since the remarkable case of Percival Bland,* the "Griffin" had made it a routine practice to send all inquest cases to us for report.

It was a reference to one of these that Mr. Stalker, a senior member of the staff of that office, called on us one afternoon in December.

"I've brought you another inquest case," said he; "a rather queer one, quite interesting from your point of view. As far as we can see, it has no particular interest for us excepting that it does rather look as if our examining medical officer had been a little casual.

"On the twenty-fourth of last month some men who were collecting seaweed, to use as manure, discovered in a cave at Kingsgate in the Isle of Thanet the body of a man, lying under a mass of accumulated weed. As the tide was rising, they put the body into their cart and conveyed it to Margate, where, of course, an inquest was held, and the following facts were elicited. The body was that of a man named Thomas Elton. It was

*See "Percival Bland's Proxy" in MASTERPIECES OF MYSTERY: *Detective Directory—II.*

195

identified by the name-marks on the clothing, by the visiting-cards and a couple of letters which were found in the pockets. From the address on the letters, it was seen that Elton had been staying in Margate, and on inquiry at the address, it was learned from the old woman who let the lodgings that he had been missing about four days. The landlady was taken to the mortuary, and at once identified the body as that of her lodger. It remained only to decide how the body came into the cave; and this did not seem to present much difficulty; for the neck had been broken by a tremendous blow, which had practically destroyed the face, and there were distinct evidences of a breaking away of a portion of the top of the cliff, only a few yards from the position of the cave. There was apparently no doubt that Elton had fallen sheer from the top of the overhanging cliff onto the beach. Now, one would suppose with the evidence of this fall of about a hundred and fifty feet, the smashed face, and broken neck, there was not much room for doubt as to the cause of death. I think you will agree with me, Dr. Jervis?"

"Certainly," I replied; "it must be admitted that a broken neck is a condition that tends to shorten life."

"Quite so," agreed Stalker; "but our friend, the local coroner, is a gentleman who takes nothing for granted—a very Thomas Didymus, who apparently agrees with Dr. Thorndyke that if there is no post-mortem, there is no inquest. So he ordered a postmortem, which would have appeared to me an absurdly unnecessary proceeding, as I think even you will agree with me, Dr. Thorndyke."

But Thorndyke shook his head.

"Not at all," said he. "It might, for instance, be much easier to push a drugged or poisoned man over a cliff than to put over the same man in his normal state. The appearance of violent accident is an excellent mask for the less obvious forms of murder."

"That's perfectly true," said Stalker; "and I suppose that is what the coroner thought. At any rate, he had the postmortem made, and the result was most curious; for it was found, on opening the body, that the deceased had suffered from a smallish thoracic aneurysm, which had burst. Now, as the aneurysm must obviously have burst during life, it leaves the cause of death—so I understand—uncertain; at any rate, the medical witness was unable to say whether the deceased fell over the cliff in consequence of the bursting of the aneurysm or burst the

196

aneurysm in consequence of falling over the cliff. Of course, it doesn't matter to us which way the thing happened; the only question which interests us is, whether a comparatively recently insured man ought to have had an aneurysm at all."

"Have you paid the claim?" asked Thorndyke.

"No, certainly not. We never pay a claim until we have had your report. But, as a matter of fact, there is another circumstance that is causing delay. It seems that Elton had mortgaged his policy to a moneylender, named Gordon, and it is by him that the claim has been made—or rather, by a clerk of his, named Hyams. Now, we have had a good many dealings with this man, Gordon, and hitherto he has always acted in person; and as he is a somewhat slippery gentleman, we have thought it desirable to have the claim actually signed by him. And that is the difficulty. For it seems that Mr. Gordon is abroad, and his whereabouts unknown to Hyams; so, as we certainly couldn't take Hyams's receipt for payment, the matter is in abeyance until Hyams can communicate with his principal. And now, I must be running away. I have brought you, as you will see, all the papers, including the policy and the mortgage deed."

As soon as he was gone, Thorndyke gathered up the bundle of papers and sorted them out in what he apparently considered the order of their importance.

"The medical evidence," he remarked, "is very full and complete. Both the coroner and the doctor seem to know their business."

"Seeing that the man apparently fell over a cliff," said I, "the medical evidence would not seem to be of first importance. It would seem to be more to the point to ascertain how he came to fall over."

"That's quite true," replied Thorndyke; "and yet, this report contains some rather curious matter. The deceased had an aneurysm of the arch; that was probably rather recent. But he also had some slight, old-standing aortic disease, with full compensory hypertrophy. He also had a nearly complete set of false teeth. Now, doesn't it strike you, Jervis, as rather odd that a man who was passed only five years ago as a first-class life, should, in that short interval, have become actually uninsurable?"

"It certainly does look," said I, "as if the fellow had had rather bad luck. What does the proposal form say?"

I took the document up and ran my eyes over it. On

Thorndyke's advice, medical examiners for the "Griffin" were instructed to make a somewhat fuller report than is usual in some companies. In this case, the ordinary answers set forth that the heart was perfectly healthy and the teeth exceptionally good, and then, in the summary at the end, the examiner remarked: "The proposer seems to be a completely sound and healthy man; he presents no physical defects whatever, with the exception of a bony ankylosis of the first joint of the third finger of the left hand, which he states to have been due to an injury."

Thorndyke looked up quickly. "Which finger, did you say?" he asked.

"The third finger of the left hand," I replied.

Thorndyke looked thoughtfully at the paper that he was reading. "It's very singular," said he, "for I see that the Margate doctor states that the deceased wore a signet ring on the third finger of the left hand. Now, of course, you couldn't get a ring onto a finger with bony ankylosis of the joint."

I admitted that it was very singular indeed, and we then resumed our study of the respective papers. But presently I noticed that Thorndyke had laid the report upon his knee.

"If we take the small and unimpressive items and add them together," he said, after a few moments, "you will see that a quite considerable sum of discrepancy results. Thus:

"In 1903 Thomas Elton, aged thirty-one, had a set of sound teeth. In 1908, at the age of thirty-six, he was more than half toothless.

"Again, at the age of thirty-one, his heart was perfectly healthy. At the age of thirty-six he had old aortic disease, with fully established compensation, and an aneurysm that was possibly due to it.

"When he was examined he had a noticeable incurable malformation; no such malformation is mentioned in connection with the body.

"He appears to have fallen over a cliff; and he had also burst an aneurysm. Now, the bursting of the aneurysm must obviously have occurred during life; but it would occasion practically instantaneous death. Therefore, if the fall was accidental, the rupture must have occurred either as he stood at the edge of the cliff, as he was in the act of falling, or on striking the beach.

"At the place where he apparently fell, the footpath is some thirty yards distant from the edge of the cliff.

"It is not known how he came to that spot, or whether he was alone at the time.

"Someone is claiming five-hundred pounds as the immediate result of his death.

"There, you see, Jervis, are seven propositions, none of them extremely striking, but rather suggestive when taken together."

"You seem," said I, "to suggest a doubt as to the identity of the body."

"I do," he replied. "The identity was not at all clearly established."

"And the old woman—" I suggested, but he interrupted me.

"My dear Jervis," he exclaimed; "I'm surprised at you. How many times has it happened within our knowledge that women have identified the bodies of total strangers as those of their husbands, fathers, or brothers. The thing happens almost every year. As to this old woman, she saw a body with an unrecognizable face, dressed in the clothes of her missing lodger. Of course, it was the clothes that she identified."

"I suppose it was," I agreed; and then I said: "You seem to suggest the possibility of foul play."

"Well," he replied, "if you consider those seven points, you will agree with me that they present a cumulative discrepancy which it is impossible to ignore.

"Then," he continued, after a pause, "there is this mortgage deed. It looks quite regular and is correctly stamped, but it seems to me that the surface of the paper is slightly altered in one or two places, and if one holds the document up to the light, the paper looks a little more transparent in those places." He examined the document for a few seconds with his pocket lens, and then passing lens and document to me, said: "Have a look at it, Jervis, and tell me what you think."

I scrutinized the paper closely, taking it over to the window to get a better light; and to me, also, the paper appeared to be changed in certain places.

"Are we agreed as to the position of the altered places?" Thorndyke asked.

"I only see three patches," I answered. "Two correspond to the name, Thomas Elton, and the third to one of the figures in the policy number."

"Exactly," said Thorndyke, "and the significance is obvious. If the paper has really been altered, it means that some other name has been erased and Elton's substituted; by which arrangement, of course, the correctly dated stamp would be secured. And this—the alteration of an old document—is the only form of forgery that is possible with a dated, impressed stamp."

"Wouldn't it be rather a stroke of luck?" I asked, "for a forger

199

to happen to have in his possession a document needing only these two alterations?"

"I see nothing remarkable in it," Thorndyke replied. "A moneylender would have a number of documents of this kind in hand, and you observe that he as not bound down to any particular date. Any date within a year or so of the issue of the policy would answer his purpose. This document is, in fact, dated, as you see, about six months after the issue of the policy."

"I suppose," said I, "that you will draw Stalker's attention to this matter."

"He will have to be informed, of course," Thorndyke replied: "but I think it would be interesting in the first place to call on Mr. Hyams. You will have noticed that there are some rather mysterious features in this case, and Mr. Hyams's conduct suggests that he may have some special information." He glanced at his watch and after a few moments' reflection added: "I don't see why we shouldn't make our little ceremonial call at once."

Mr. Hyams was "discovered," as the playwrights have it, in a small office at the top of a high building in Queen Victoria Street. He was a small gentleman, of sallow and greasy aspect, with heavy eyebrows.

"Are you Mr. Gordon?" Thorndyke suavely inquired as we entered.

Mr. Hyams seemed to experience a momentary doubt on the subject, but finally decided that he was not. "But perhaps," he added brightly, "I can help you."

"I daresay you can," Thorndyke agreed significantly; on which we were conducted into an inner den.

"Now," said Mr. Hyams, shutting the door ostentatiously, "what can I do for you?"

"I want you," Thorndyke replied, "to answer one or two questions with reference to the claim made by you on the 'Griffin' Office in respect of Thomas Elton."

My Hyams's manner underwent a sudden change. He began rapidly to turn over papers, and opened and shut the drawers of his desk, with an air of restless preoccupation.

"Did the 'Griffin' people send you here?" he demanded brusquely.

Thorndyke produced a card and laid it on the table. Mr.

Hyams had apparently seen the name before, for he suddenly grew rather pale and very serious.

"What is the nature of the questions that you wished to ask?" he inquired.

"They refer to this claim," replied Thorndyke. "The first question is, where is Mr. Gordon?"

"I don't know," said Hyams.

"Where do you think he is?" asked Thorndyke.

"I don't think at all," replied Hyams, turning a shade paler and looking everywhere but at Thorndyke.

"Very well," said the latter, "then the next question is, are you satisfied that this claim is really payable?"

"I shouldn't have made it if I hadn't been," replied Hyams.

"Quite so," said Thorndyke; "and the third question is, are you satisfied that the mortgage deed was executed as it purports to have been?"

"I can't say anything about that," replied Hyams, who was growing every moment paler and more fidgety. "It was done before my time."

"Thank you," said Thorndyke. "You will, of course, understand why I am making these inquiries."

"I don't," said Hyams.

"Then," said Thorndyke, "perhaps I had better explain. We are dealing, Mr. Hyams, with the case of a man who has met with a violent death under somewhat mysterious circumstances. We are dealing, also, with another man who has disappeared, leaving his affairs to take care of themselves; and with a claim, put forward by a *third* party, on behalf of the one man in respect of the other. When I say that the dead man has been imperfectly identified, and that the document supporting the claim presents certain peculiarities, you will see that the matter certainly calls for further inquiry."

There was an appreciable interval of silence. Mr. Hyams had turned a tallowy white, and looked furtively about the room, as if anxious to avoid the stony gaze of my colleague.

"Can you give us no assistance?" Thorndyke inquired, at length. Mr. Hyams chewed a pen-holder ravenously, as he considered the question. At length, he burst out in an agitated voice: "Look here, sir, if I tell you what I know, will you treat the information as confidential?"

"I can't agree to that, Mr. Hyams," replied Thorndyke. "It might amount to compounding a felony. But you will be wiser to tell me what you know. The document is a side issue, which my clients may never raise, and my own concern is with the death."

Hyams looked distinctly relieved. "If that's so," said he, "I'll tell you all I know, which is precious little, and which just amounts to this: Two days after Elton was killed, someone came to this office in my absence and opened the safe. I discovered the fact the next morning. Someone had rummaged over all the papers. It wasn't Gordon, because he knew where to find everything; and it wasn't an ordinary thief because no cash or valuables had been taken. In fact, the only thing that I missed was a promissory note, drawn by Elton."

"You didn't miss a mortgage deed?" suggested Thorndyke, and Hyams, having snatched a little further refreshment from the pen-holder, said he did not.

"And the policy," suggested Thorndyke, "was apparently not taken?"

"No," replied Hyams; "but it was looked for. Three bundles of policies had been untied, but this one happened to be in a drawer of my desk and I had the only key."

"And what do you infer from this visit?" Thorndyke asked.

"Well," replied Hyams, "the safe was opened with keys, and they were Gordon's keys—or, at any rate, they weren't mine— and the person who opened it wasn't Gordon; and the thing that was taken concerned only Elton. Naturally I smelled a rat; and when I read of the finding of the body, I smelled a fox."

An exhumation, consequent on Thorndyke's challenge of the identity of the deceased, showed that the body was that of Gordon. A hundred pounds reward was offered for information as to Elton's whereabouts. But no one ever earned it. A letter, bearing the postmark of Marseilles, and addressed by the missing man to Thorndyke, gave a plausible account of Gordon's death; which was represented as having occurred accidentally at the moment when Gordon chanced to be wearing a suit of Elton's clothes.

Of course, this account may have been correct, or again, it may have been false; but whether it was true or false, Elton, from that moment, vanished from our ken and has never since been heard of.

THE QUEER FEET

BY G. K. CHESTERTON

Born in London on May 24, 1874, Gilbert Keith Chesterton was educated at St. Paul's School and the Slade Art College of University College, London. He wrote thousands of poems, reviews, stories, and essays on literature, politics, religion, and philosophy. His first mystery fiction was a collection of short stories, *The Club of Queer Trades*. His famous fictional detective, Father Brown's exploits often border on the occult and the fantastic. Chesterton's other detectives include Horne Fisher, whose adventures are collected in *The Man Who Knew Too Much* (1922). Chesterton lived at Beaconsfield in the Chiltern Hills, where he died on June 14, 1936.

IF YOU MEET A MEMBER of that select club, The Twelve True Fishermen, entering the Vernon Hotel for the annual club dinner, you will observe, as he takes off his overcoat, that his evening coat is green and not black. If (supposing that you have the star-defying audacity to address such a being) you ask him why, he will probably answer that he does it to avoid being mistaken for a waiter. You will then retire crushed. But you will leave behind you a mystery as yet unsolved and a tale worth telling.

If (to pursue the same vein of improbable conjecture) you were to meet a mild, hardworking little priest, named Father Brown, and were to ask him what he thought was the most singular luck of his life, he would probably reply that upon the whole his best stroke was at the Vernon Hotel, where he had averted a crime and, perhaps, saved a soul, merely by listening to a few footsteps in a passage. He is perhaps a little proud of this wild and wonderful guess of his, and it is possible that he might refer to it. But since it is immeasurably unlikely that you will ever rise high enough in the social world to find The Twelve True Fishermen, or that you will ever sink low enough among slums and criminals to find Father Brown, I fear you will never hear the story at all unless you hear it from me.

The Vernon Hotel at which The Twelve True Fishermen held their annual dinners was an institution such as can only exist in an oligarchical society which has almost gone mad on good manners. It was that topsy-turvy product—an "exclusive" commercial enterprise. That is, it was a thing which paid not by attracting people, but actually by turning people away. In the heart of a plutocracy tradesmen become cunning enough to be more fastidious than their customers. They positively create difficulties so that their wealthy and weary clients may spend money and diplomacy in overcoming them. If there were a fashionable hotel in London which no man could enter who was under six feet, society would meekly make up parties of six-foot men to dine in it. If there were an expensive restaurant which by a mere caprice of its proprietor was only open on Thursday afternoon, it would be crowded on Thursday afternoon. The Vernon Hotel stood, as if by accident, in the corner of a square in Belgravia. It was a small hotel; and a very inconvenient one. But its very inconveniences were considered as walls protecting a particular class. One inconvenience, in particular, was held to be of vital importance: the fact that practically only twenty-four people could dine in the place at once. The only big dinner table was the celebrated terrace table, which stood open to the air on a sort of veranda overlooking one of the most exquisite old gardens in London. Thus it happened that even the twenty-four seats at this table could only be enjoyed in warm weather; and this making the enjoyment yet more difficult made it yet more desired. The existing owner of the hotel was a Jew named Lever; and he made nearly a million out of it, by making it difficult to get into. Of course he combined with this limitation in the scope of his enterprise the most careful polish in its performance. The wines and cooking were really as good as any in Europe, and the demeanor of the attendants exactly mirrored the fixed mood of the English upper class. The proprietor knew all his waiters like the fingers on his hand; there were only fifteen of them all told. It was much easier to become a Member of Parliament than to become a waiter in that hotel. Each waiter was trained in terrible silence and smoothness, as if he were a gentleman's servant. And, indeed, there was generally at least one waiter to every gentleman who dined.

The club of The Twelve True Fishermen would not have consented to dine anywhere but in such a place, for it insisted on a luxurious privacy; and would have been quite upset by the mere thought that any other club was even dining in the same building. On the occasion of their annual dinner the Fishermen were in the habit of exposing all their treasures, as if they were in a private house, especially the celebrated set of fish knives and forks which were, as it were, the insignia of the society, each being exquisitely wrought in silver in the form of a fish, and each loaded at the hilt with one large pearl. These were always laid out for the fish course, and the fish course was always the most magnificent in that magnificent repast. The society had a vast number of ceremonies and observances, but it had no history and no object; that was where it was so very aristocratic. You did not have to be anything in order to be one of the Twelve Fishers; unless you were already a certain sort of person, you never even heard of them. It had been in existence twelve years. Its president was Mr. Audley. Its vice-president was the Duke of Chester.

If I have in any degree conveyed the atmosphere of this appalling hotel, the reader may feel a natural wonder as to how I came to know anything about it, and may even speculate as to how so ordinary a person as my friend Father Brown came to find himself in that golden galley. As far as that is concerned, my story is simple, or even vulgar. There is in the world a very aged rioter and demagogue who breaks into the most refined retreats with the dreadful information that all men are brothers, and wherever this leveller went on his pale horse it was Father Brown's trade to follow. One of the waiters, an Italian, had been struck down with a paralytic stroke that afternoon; and his Jewish employer, marveling mildly at such superstitions, had consented to send for the nearest Popish priest. With what the waiter confessed to Father Brown we are not concerned, for the excellent reason that the cleric kept it to himself; but apparently it involved him in writing out a note or statement for the conveying of some message or the righting of some wrong. Father Brown, therefore, with a meek impudence which he would have shown equally in Buckingham Palace, asked to be provided with a room and writing materials. Mr. Lever was torn in two. He was a kind man, and had also that bad imitation of kindness, the dislike of any difficulty or scene. At the same time the presence of one unusual stranger in his hotel that evening was like a speck of dirt on something just cleaned. There was never any borderland or anteroom in the Vernon Hotel, no people waiting in the hall, no customers coming in on chance. There were fifteen waiters. There were twelve guests. It would be as startling to find a new guest in the hotel that night as to find a new brother taking breakfast or tea in one's own family. Moreover, the priest's appearance was second-rate and his clothes muddy; a mere glimpse of him afar off might precipitate a crisis in the club. Mr. Lever at last hit on a plan to cover, since he might not obliterate, the disgrace. When you enter (as you never will) the Vernon Hotel, you pass down a short passage decorated with a few dingy but important pictures, and come to the main vestibule and lounge which opens on your right into passages leading to the public rooms, and on your left to a similar passage pointing to the kitchens and offices of the hotel. Immediately on your left hand is the corner of a glass office, which abuts upon the lounge—a house within a house, so to speak, like the old hotel bar which probably once occupied its place.

In this office sat the representative of the proprietor (nobody in this place ever appeared in person if he could help it), and just beyond the office, on the way to the servants' quarters, was the gentlemen's cloak room, the last boundary of the gentlemen's domain. But between the office and the cloak room was a small private room without other outlet, sometimes used by the proprietor for delicate and important matters, such as lending a duke a thousand pounds or declining to lend him sixpence. It is a mark of the magnificent tolerance of Mr. Lever that he permitted this holy place to be for about half an hour profaned by a mere priest, scribbling away on a piece of paper. The story which Father Brown was writing down was very likely a much better story than this one, only it will never be known. I can merely state that it was very nearly as long, and that the last two or three paragraphs of it were the least exciting and absorbing.

For it was by the time that he had reached these that the priest began a little to allow his thoughts to wander and his animal senses, which were commonly keen, to awaken. The time of darkness and dinner was drawing on; his own forgotten little room was without a light, and perhaps the gathering gloom, as occasionally happens, sharpened the sense of sound. As Father Brown wrote the last and least essential part of his document, he caught himself writing to the rhythm of a recurrent noise outside, just as one sometimes thinks to the tune of a railway train. When he became conscious of the thing he found what it was: only the ordinary patter of feet passing the door, which in an hotel was no very unlikely matter. Nevertheless, he stared at the darkened ceiling, and listened to the sound. After he had listened for a few seconds dreamily, he got to his feet and listened intently, with his head a little on one side. Then he sat down again and buried his brow in his hands, now not merely listening, but listening and thinking also.

The footsteps outside at any given moment were such as one might hear in any hotel; and yet, taken as a whole, there was something very strange about them. There were no other footsteps. It was always a very silent house, for the few familiar guests went at once to their own apartments, and the well-trained waiters were told to be almost invisible until they were wanted. One could not conceive any place where there was less reason to apprehend anything irregular. But these footsteps were so odd that one could not decide to call them regular or irregular. Father Brown followed them with his finger on the edge of the table, like a man trying to learn a tune on the piano.

First, there came a long rush of rapid little steps, such as a light man might make in winning a walking race. At a certain point they stopped and changed to a sort of slow, swinging stamp, numbering not a quarter of the steps, but occupying about the same time. The moment the last echoing stamp had died away would come again the run or ripple of light, hurrying feet, and then again the thud of the heavier walking. It was certainly the same pair of boots, partly because (as has been said) there were no other boots about, and partly because they had a small but unmistakable creak in them. Father Brown had the kind of head that cannot help asking questions; and on this apparently trivial question his head almost split. He had seen men run in order to jump. He had seen men run in order to slide. But why on earth should a man run in order to walk? Or, again, why should he walk in order to run? Yet no other description would cover the antics of this invisible pair of legs. The man was either walking very fast down one-half of the corridor in order to walk very slow down the other half; or he was walking very slow at one end to have the rapture of walking fast at the other. Neither suggestion seemed to make much sense. His brain was growing darker and darker, like his room.

Yet, as he began to think steadily, the very blackness of his cell seemed to make his thoughts more vivid; he began to see as in a kind of vision the fantastic feet capering along the corridor in unnatural or symbolic attitudes. Was it a heathen religious dance? Or some entirely new kind of scientific exercise? Father Brown began to ask himself with more exactness what the steps suggested. Taking the slow step first: it certainly was not the step of the proprietor. Men of his type walk with a rapid waddle, or they sit still. It could not be any servant or messenger waiting for directions. It did not sound like it. The poorer orders (in an oligarchy) sometimes lurch about when they are slightly drunk, but generally, and especially in such gorgeous scenes, they stand or sit in constrained attitudes. No; that heavy yet springy step, with a kind of careless emphasis, not specially noisy, yet not caring what noise it made, belonged to only one of the animals of this earth. It was a gentleman of western Europe, and probably one who had never worked for his living.

Just as he came to this solid certainty, the step changed to the quicker one, and ran past the door as feverishly as a rat. The

208

listener remarked that though this step was much swifter, it was also much more noiseless, almost as if the man were walking on tiptoe. Yet it was not associated in his mind with secrecy, but with something else—something that he could not remember. He was maddened by one of those half-memories that make a man feel half-witted. Surely he had heard that strange, swift walking somewhere. Suddenly he sprang to his feet with a new idea in his head, and walked to the door. His room had no direct outlet on the passage, but let on one side into the glass office, and on the other into the cloakroom beyond. He tried the door into the office, and found it locked. Then he looked at the window, now a square pane full of purple cloud cleft by livid sunset, and for an instant he smelt evil as a dog smells rats.

The rational part of him (whether the wiser or not) regained its supremacy. He remembered that the proprietor had told him that he should lock the door, and would come later to release him. He told himself that twenty things he had not thought of might explain the eccentric sounds outside; he reminded himself that there was just enough light left to finish his own proper work. Bringing his paper to the window so as to catch the last stormy evening light, he resolutely plunged once more into the almost completed record. He had written for about twenty minutes, bending closer and closer to his paper in the lessening light; then suddenly he sat upright. He had heard the strange feet once more.

This time they had a third oddity. Previously the unknown man had walked, with levity indeed and lightning quickness, but he had walked. This time he ran. One could hear the swift, soft, bounding steps coming along the corridor, like the pads of a fleeing and leaping panther. Whoever was coming was a very strong, active man, in still yet tearing excitement. Yet, when the sound had swept up to the office like a sort of whispering whirlwind, it suddenly changed again to the old slow, swaggering stamp.

Father Brown flung down his paper and, knowing the office door to be locked, went at once into the cloakroom on the other side. The attendant of this place was temporarily absent, probably because the only guests were at dinner and his office was a sinecure. After groping through a gray forest of overcoats, he found that the dim cloak room opened on the lighted corridor in the form of a sort of counter or half-door, like most of the counters across which we have all handed umbrellas and received tickets. There was a light immediately above the semi-circular arch of this opening. It threw little illumination on Father Brown himself, who seemed a mere dark outline against the dim sunset window behind him. But it threw an almost theatrical light on the man who stood outside the cloak room in the corridor.

He was an elegant man in very plain evening dress; tall, but with an air of not taking up much room; one felt that he could have slid along like a shadow where many smaller men would have been obvious and obstructive. His face, now flung back in the lamplight, was swarthy and vivacious, the face of a foreigner. His figure was good, his manners good humored and confident; a critic could only say that his black coat was a shade below his figure and manners, and even bulged and bagged in an odd way. The moment he caught sight of Brown's black silhouette against the sunset, he tossed down a scrap of paper with a number and called out with amiable authority: "I want my hat and coat please; I find I have to go away at once."

Father Brown took the paper without a word, and obediently went to look for the coat; it was not the first menial work he had done in his life. He brought it and laid it on the counter; meanwhile, the strange gentleman who had been feeling in his waistcoat pocket, said, laughing: "I haven't got any silver; you can keep this." And he threw down half a sovereign, and caught up his coat.

Father Brown's figure remained quite dark and still; but in that instant he had lost his head. His head was always most valuable when he had lost it. In such moments he put two and two together and made four million. Often the Catholic Church (which is wedded to common sense) did not approve of it. Often he did not approve of it himself. But it was real inspiration—important at rare crises—when whosoever shall lose his head the same shall save it.

"I think, sir," he said civilly, "that you have some silver in your pocket."

The tall gentleman stared. "Hang it," he cried, "If I choose to give you gold, why should you complain?"

"Because silver is sometimes more valuable than gold," said the priest mildly; "that is, in large quantities."

The stranger looked at him curiously. Then he looked still more curiously up the passage towards the main entrance. Then he looked back at Brown again, and then he looked very carefully at the window beyond Brown's head, still colored with the afterglow of the storm. Then he seemed to make up his mind. He put one hand on the counter, vaulted over as easily as an acrobat and towered above the priest, putting one tremendous hand upon his collar.

"Stand still," he said, in a hacking whisper. "I don't want to threaten you, but—"

"I do want to threaten you," said Father Brown, in a voice like a rolling drum, "I want to threaten you with the worm that dieth not, and the fire that is not quenched."

"You're a rum sort of cloak-room clerk," said the other.

"I am a priest, Monsieur Flambeau," said Brown, "and I am ready to hear your confession."

The other stood gasping for a few moments, and then staggered back into a chair.

The first two courses of the dinner of The Twelve True Fishermen had proceeded with placid success. I do not possess a copy of the menu; and if I did it would not convey anything to anybody. It was written in a sort of super-French employed by cooks, but quite unintelligible to Frenchmen. There was a tradition in the club that the *hors d'oeuvres* should be various and manifold to the point of madness. They were taken seriously because they were avowedly useless extras, like the whole dinner and the whole club. There was also a tradition that the soup course should be light and unpretending—a sort of simple and austere vigil for the feast of fish that was to come. The talk was that strange, slight talk which governs the British Empire, which governs it in secret, and yet would scarcely enlighten an ordinary Englishman even if he could overhear it. Cabinet ministers on both sides were alluded to by their Christian names with a sort of bored benignity. The Radical Chancellor of the Exchequer, whom the whole Tory party was supposed to be cursing for his extortions, was praised for his minor poetry, or his saddle in the hunting field. The Tory leader, whom all Liberals were supposed to hate as a tyrant, was discussed and, on the whole, praised—as a Liberal. It seemed somehow that politicians were very important. And yet, anything seemed important about them except their politics. Mr. Audley, the chairman, was an amiable, elderly man who still wore Gladstone collars; he was a kind of symbol of all that phantasmal and yet fixed society. He had never done anything—not even anything wrong. He was not fast; he was not even particularly rich. He was simply in the thing; and there was an end of it. No party could ignore him, and if he had wished to be in the Cabinet he certainly would have been put there. The Duke of Chester, the vice-president, was a young and rising politician. That is to say, he was a pleasant youth with flat, fair hair and a freckled face, with moderate intelligence and enormous estates. In public his appearances were always successful and his principle was simple enough. When he thought of a joke he made it, and was called brilliant. When he could not think of a joke he said that this was no time for trifling, and was called able. In private, in a club of his own class, he was simply quite pleasantly frank and silly, like a schoolboy. Mr. Audley, never having been in politics, treated them a little more seriously. Sometimes he even embarrassed the company by phrases suggesting that there was some difference between a Liberal and a Conservative. He himself was a Conservative, even in private life. He had a roll of gray hair over the back of his collar, like certain old-fashioned statesmen, and seen from behind he looked like the man the Empire wants. Seen from the front he looked like a mild, self-indulgent bachelor, with rooms in the Albany—which he was.

As has been remarked, there were twenty-four seats at the terrace table, and only twelve members of the club. Thus they could occupy the terrace in the most luxurious style of all, being ranged along the inner side of the table, with no one opposite, commanding an uninterrupted view of the garden, the colors of which were still vivid, though evening was closing in somewhat luridly for the time of year. The chairman sat in the center of the line, and the vice-president at the righthand end of it. When the twelve guests first trooped into their seats it was the custom (for some unknown reason) for all the fifteen waiters to stand lining the wall like troops presenting arms to the king, while the fat proprietor stood and bowed to the club with radiant surprise, as if he had never heard of them before. But before the first chink of knife and fork this army of retainers had vanished, only the one or two required to collect and distribute the plates darting about in deathly silence. Mr. Lever, the proprietor, of course had disappeared in convulsions of courtesy long before. It would be exaggerative, indeed irreverent, to say that he ever positively appeared again. But when the important course, the fish course, was being brought on, there was—how shall I put it?—a vivid shadow, a projection of his personality, which told that he was hovering near. The sacred fish

212

course consisted (to the eyes of the vulgar) in a sort of monstrous pudding, about the size and shape of a wedding cake, in which some considerable number of interesting fishes had finally lost the shapes which God had given to them. The Twelve True Fishermen took up their celebrated fish knives and fish forks, and approached it as gravely as if every inch of the pudding cost as much as the silver fork it was eaten with. So it did, for all I know. This course was dealt with in eager and devouring silence; and it was only when his plate was nearly empty that the young duke made the ritual remark: "They can't do this anywhere but here."

"Nowhere," said Mr. Audley, in a deep bass voice, turning to the speaker and nodding his venerable head a number of times, "Nowhere, assuredly, except here. It was represented to me that the Café Anglais—"

Here he was interrupted and even agitated for a moment by the removal of his plate, but he recaptured the valuable thread of his thoughts. "It was represented to me that the same could be done at the Café Anglais. Nothing like it, sir," he said, shaking his head ruthlessly, like a hanging judge. "Nothing like it."

"Overrated place," said a certain Colonel Pound, speaking (by the look of him) for the first time for some months.

"Oh, I don't know," said the Duke of Chester, who was an optimist, "it's jolly good for some things, I think. You can't beat it at—"

A waiter came swiftly along the room, and then stopped dead. His stoppage was as silent as his tread; but all those vague and kindly gentlemen were so used to the utter smoothness of the unseen machinery which surrounded and supported their lives, that a waiter doing anything unexpected was a start and a jar. They felt as you and I would feel if the inanimate world disobeyed—if a chair ran away from us.

The waiter stood staring a few seconds, while there deepened on every face at the table a strange shame which is wholly the product of our time. It is the combination of modern humanitarianism with the horrible modern abyss between the souls of the rich and poor. A genuine historic aristocrat would have thrown things at the waiter, beginning with empty bottles, and very probably ending with money. A genuine democrat would have asked him, with a comrade-like clearness of speech, what the devil he was doing. But these modern plutocrats could not bear a poor man near to them, either as a slave or as a

213

friend. That something had gone wrong with the servants was merely a dull, hot embarrassment. They did not want to be brutal, and they dreaded the need to be benevolent. They wanted the thing, whatever it was, to be over. It was over. The waiter, after standing for some seconds rigid, like a cataleptic, turned round and ran madly out of the room.

When he reappeared in the room, or rather in the doorway, it was in company with another waiter, with whom he whispered and gesticulated with southern fierceness. Then the first waiter went away, leaving the second waiter, and reappeared with a third waiter. By the time a fourth waiter had joined this hurried synod, Mr. Audley felt it necessary to break the silence in the interest of Tact. He used a very loud cough, instead of a presidential hammer, and said: "Splendid work young Moocher's doing in Burma. Now, no other nation in the world could have—"

A fifth waiter had sped towards him like an arrow, and was whispering in his ear: "So sorry. Important! Might the proprietor speak to you?"

The chairman turned in disorder, and with a dazed stare saw Mr. Lever coming towards them with his lumbering quickness. The gait of the good proprietor was indeed his usual gait, but his face was by no means usual. Generally, it was a genial copper-brown; now it was a sickly yellow.

"You will pardon me, Mr. Audley," he said, with asthmatic breathlessness. "I have great apprehensions. Your fish-plates, they are cleared away with the knife and fork on them!"

"Well, I hope so," said the chairman, with some warmth.

"You see him?" panted the excited hotel keeper; "you see the waiter who took them away? You know him?"

"Know the waiter?" answered Mr. Audley indignantly. "Certainly not!"

Mr. Lever opened his hands with a gesture of agony. "I never send him," he said. "I know not when or why he come. I send my waiter to take away the plates, and he find them already away."

Mr. Audley still looked rather too bewildered to be really the man the Empire wants; none of the company could say anything except the man of wood—Colonel Pound—who seemed galvanized into an unnatural life. He rose rigidly from his chair, leaving all the rest sitting, screwed his eyeglass into his eye, and spoke in a raucous undertone as if he had half-

214

forgotten how to speak. "Do you mean," he said, "that some-body has stolen our silver fish service?"

The proprietor repeated the open-handed gesture with even greater helplessness; and in a flash all the men at the table were on their feet.

"Are all your waiters here?" demanded the colonel, in his low, harsh accent.

"Yes; they're all here. I noticed it myself," cried the young duke, pushing his boyish face into the inmost ring. "Always count 'em as I come in; they look so queer standing up against the wall."

"But surely one cannot exactly remember," began Mr. Audley, with heavy hesitation.

"I remember exactly, I tell you," cried the duke excitedly. "There never have been more than fifteen waiters at this place, and there were no more than fifteen tonight, I'll swear; no more and no less."

The proprietor turned upon him, quaking in a kind of palsy of surprise. "You say—you say," he stammered, "that you see all my fifteen waiters?"

"As usual," assented the duke. "What is the matter with that?"

"Nothing," said Lever, with a deepening accent, "only you did not. For one of zem is dead upstairs."

There was a shocking stillness for an instant in that room. It may be (so supernatural is the word death) that each of those idle men looked for a second at his soul, and saw it as a small dried pea. One of them—the duke, I think—even said with the idiotic kindness of wealth: "Is there anything we can do?"

"He has had a priest," said the Jew, not untouched.

Then, as to the clang of doom, they awoke to their own position. For a few weird seconds they had really felt as if the fifteenth waiter might be the ghost of the dead man upstairs. They had been dumb under that oppression, for ghosts were to them an embarrassment, like beggars. But the remembrance of the silver broke the spell of the miraculous; broke it abruptly and with a brutal reaction. The colonel flung over his chair and strode to the door. "If there was a fifteenth man here, friends," he said, "that fifteenth fellow was a thief. Down at once to the front and back doors and secure everything; then we'll talk. The twenty-four pearls of the club are worth recovering."

Mr. Audley seemed at first to hesitate about whether it was gentlemanly to be in such a hurry about anything; but, seeing the duke dash down the stairs with youthful energy, he followed with a more mature motion.

At the same instant a sixth waiter ran into the room, and declared that he had found the pile of fish plates on a sideboard, with no trace of the silver.

The crowd of diners and attendants that tumbled helter-skelter down the passages divided into two groups. Most of the Fishermen followed the proprietor to the front room to demand news of any exit. Colonel Pound, with the chairman, the vice-president, and one or two others darted down the corridor leading to the servants' quarters, as the more likely line of escape. As they did so they passed the dim alcove or cavern of the cloak room, and saw a short, black-coated figure, presumably an attendant, standing a little way back in the shadow of it.

"Hallo, there!" called out the duke. "Have you seen anyone pass?"

The short figure did not answer the question directly, but merely said: "Perhaps I have got what you are looking for, gentlemen."

They paused, wavering and wondering, while he quietly went to the back of the cloak room, and came back with both hands full of shining silver, which he laid out on the counter as calmly as a salesman. It took the form of a dozen quaintly shaped forks and knives.

"You—you—" began the colonel, quite thrown off his balance at last. Then he peered into the dim little room and saw two things: first, that the short, black-clad man was dressed like a clergyman; and, second, that the window of the room behind him was burst, as if someone had passed violently through.

"Valuable things to deposit in a cloak room, aren't they?" remarked the clergyman, with cheerful composure.

"Did—did you steal those things?" stammered Mr. Audley, with staring eyes.

"If I did," said the cleric pleasantly, "at least I am bringing them back again."

"But you didn't," said Colonel Pound, still staring at the broken window.

"To make a clean breast of it, I didn't," said the other, with some humor. And he seated himself quite gravely on a stool.

"But you know who did," said the colonel.

"I don't know his real name," said the priest placidly, "but I know something of his fighting weight, and a great deal about his spiritual difficulties. I formed the physical estimate when he was trying to throttle me, and the moral estimate when he repented."

"Oh, I say—repented!" cried young Chester, with a sort of crow of laughter.

Father Brown got to his feet, putting his hands behind him. "Odd, isn't it," he said, "that a thief and a vagabond should repent, when so many who are rich and secure remain hard and frivolous, and without fruit for God or man? But there, if you will excuse me, you trespass a little upon my province. If you doubt the penitence as a practical fact, there are your knives and forks. You are The Twelve True Fishers, and there are all your silver fish. But He has made me a fisher of men."

"Did you catch this man?" asked the colonel, frowning.

Father Brown looked him full in his frowning face. "Yes," he said, "I caught him, with an unseen hook and an invisible line which is long enough to let him wander to the ends of the world, and still to bring him back with a twitch upon the thread."

There was a long silence. All the other men present drifted away to carry the recovered silver to their comrades, or to consult the proprietor about the queer condition of affairs. But the grim-faced colonel still sat sideways on the counter, swinging his long, lank legs and biting his dark moustache.

At last he said quietly to the priest: "He must have been a clever fellow, but I think I know a cleverer."

"He was a clever fellow," answered the other, "but I am not quite sure of what other you mean."

"I mean you," said the colonel, with a short laugh. "I don't want to get the fellow jailed; make yourself easy about that. But I'd give a good many silver forks to know exactly how you fell into this affair, and how you got the stuff out of him. I reckon you're the most up-to-date devil of the present company."

Father Brown seemed rather to like the saturnine candor of the soldier. "Well," he said, smiling, "I mustn't tell you anything of the man's identity, or his own story, of course; but there's no particular reason why I shouldn't tell you of the mere outside facts which I found out for myself."

He hopped over the barrier with unexpected activity, and sat beside Colonel Pound, kicking his short legs like a little boy on a gate. He began to tell the story as easily as if he were telling it to an old friend by a Christmas fire.

"You see, Colonel," he said, "I was shut up in that small room there doing some writing, when I heard a pair of feet in this passage doing a dance that was as queer as the dance of death. First came quick, funny little steps, like a man walking on tiptoe for a wager; then came slow, careless, creaking steps, as of a big man walking about with a cigar. But they were both made by the same feet, I swear, and they came in rotation; first the run and then the walk, and then the run again. I wondered at first idly and then wildly why a man should act these two parts at once. One walk I knew; it was just like yours, colonel. It was the walk of a well-fed gentleman waiting for something, who strolls about rather because he is physically alert than because he is mentally impatient. I knew that I knew the other walk, too, but I could not remember what it was. What wild creature had I met on my travels that tore along on tiptoe in that extraordinary style? Then I heard a clink of plates somewhere; and the answer stood up as plain as St. Peter's. It was the walk of a waiter—that walk with the body slanted forward, the eyes looking down, the ball of the toe spurning away the ground, the coat tails and napkin flying. Then I thought for a minute and a half more. And I believe I saw the manner of the crime, as clearly as if I were going to commit it."

Colonel Pound looked at him keenly, but the speaker's mild gray eyes were fixed upon the ceiling with almost empty wistfulness.

"A crime," he said slowly, "is like any other work of art. Don't look surprised; crimes are by no means the only works of art that come from an infernal workshop. But every work or art, divine or diabolic, has one indispensable mark—I mean, that the center of it is simple, however much the fulfilment may be complicated. Thus, in *Hamlet,* let us say, the grotesqueness of the grave-digger, the flowers of the mad girl, the fantastic finery of Osric, the pallor of the ghost and the grin of the skull are all oddities in a sort of tangled wreath round one plain tragic figure of a man in black. Well, this also," he said, getting slowly down from his seat with a smile, "this also is the plain tragedy of a man in black. Yes," he went on, seeing the colonel look up in some wonder, "the whole of this tale turns on a black coat. In this, as in *Hamlet,* there are the rococo excrescences— yourselves, let us say. There is the dead waiter, who was there when he could not be there. There is the invisible hand that swept your table clear of silver and melted into air. But every clever crime is founded ultimately on some one quite simple fact—some fact that is not itself mysterious. The mystification comes in covering it up, in leading men's thoughts away from it. This large and subtle and (in the ordinary course) most profitable crime, was built on the plain fact that a gentleman's evening dress is the same as a waiter's. All the rest was acting, and thundering good acting, too."

"Still," said the Colonel, getting up and frowning at his boots, "I am not sure that I understand."

"Colonel," said Father Brown, "I tell you that this archangel of impudence who stole your forks walked up and down this passage twenty times in the blaze of all the lamps, in the glare of all the eyes. He did not go and hide in dim corners where suspicion might have searched for him. He kept constantly on the move in the lighted corridors, and everywhere that he went he seemed to be there by right. Don't ask me what he was like; you have seen him yourself six or seven times tonight. You were waiting with all the other grand people in the reception room at the end of the passage there, with the terrace just beyond. Whenever he came among you gentlemen, he came in the lightning style of a waiter, with bent head, flapping napkin and flying feet. He shot out on to the terrace, did something to the table cloth, and shot back again towards the office and the waiters' quarters. By the time he had come under the eye of the office clerk and the waiters he had become another man in every inch of his body, in every instinctive gesture. He strolled among the servants with the absent-minded insolence which they have all seen in their patrons. It was no new thing to them that a swell from the dinner party should pace all parts of the house like an animal at the Zoo; they know that nothing marks the Smart Set more than a habit of walking where one chooses. When he was magnificently weary of walking down that particular passage he would wheel round and pace back past the office; in the shadow of the arch just beyond he was altered as by a blast of magic, and went hurrying forward again among the Twelve Fishermen, an obsequious attendant. Why should the gentlemen look at a chance waiter? Why should the waiters suspect a first-rate gentleman? Once or twice he played the coolest tricks. In the proprietor's private quarters he called out breezily for a syphon of soda water, saying he was thirsty. He said that he would carry it himself, and he did; he carried it quickly and correctly through the thick of you, a waiter with an

219

obvious errand. Of course, it could not have been kept up long, but it only had to be kept up till the end of the fish course.

"His worst moment was when the waiters stood in a row; but then he contrived to lean against the wall just round the corner in such a way that for that important instant the waiters thought him a gentleman, while the gentlemen thought him a waiter. The rest went like winking. If any waiter caught him away from the table, that waiter caught a languid aristocrat. He had only to time himself two minutes before the fish was cleared, become a swift servant, and clear it himself. He put the plates down on a sideboard, stuffed the silver in his breast pocket, giving it a bulgy look, and ran like a hare (I heard him coming) till he came to the cloak room. There he had only to be a plutocrat again—a plutocrat called away suddenly on business. He had only to give his ticket to the cloak-room attendant, and go out again elegantly as he had come in. Only—only I happened to be the cloak-room attendant."

"What did you do to him?" cried the colonel, with unusual intensity. "What did he tell you?"

"I beg your pardon," said the priest immovably, "that is where the story ends."

"And the interesting story begins," muttered Pound. "I think I understand his professional trick. But I don't seem to have got hold of yours."

"I must be going," said Father Brown.

They walked together along the passage to the entrance hall, where they saw the fresh, freckled face of the Duke of Chester, who was bounding buoyantly along towards them.

"Come along, Pound," he cried breathlessly. "I've been looking for you everywhere. The dinner's going again in spanking style, and old Audley has got to make a speech in honor of the forks being saved. We want to start some new ceremony, don't you know, to commemorate the occasion. I say, you really got the goods back, what do you suggest?"

"Why," said the colonel, eyeing him with a certain sardonic approval, "I should suggest that henceforward we wear green coats, instead of black. One never knows what mistakes may arise when one looks so like a waiter."

"Oh, hang it all!" said the young man, " a gentleman never looks like a waiter."

"Nor a waiter like a gentleman, I suppose," said Colonel Pound, with the same lowering laughter on his face. "Reverend sir, your friend must have been very smart to act the gentleman."

Father Brown buttoned up his commonplace overcoat to the neck, for the night was stormy, and took his commonplace umbrella from the stand.

"Yes," he said, "it must be very hard work to be a gentleman; but, do you know, I have sometimes thought that it may be almost as laborious to be a waiter."

And saying "Good evening," he pushed open the heavy doors of that palace of pleasures. The golden gates closed behind him, and he went at a brisk walk through the damp, dark streets in search of a penny omnibus.

THE MYSTERIOUS DEATH IN PERCY STREET

BY BARONESS ORCZY

Emmuska, Baroness Orczy, was born in Tarna-Örs, Hungary, in 1865. Her family moved to England when she was eight years old, and her first career was as an artist, a profession she shared with her husband, Montagu Barstow. Several of her paintings were exhibited at the Royal Academy. Her fictional detectives included The Old Man in the Corner, the unscrupulous lawyer Patrick (Skin O' My Tooth) Mulligan, and Lady Molly Robertson Kirk of the "Female Department" of Scotland Yard. But her most famous fictional character is Sir Percy Blakeney, better known as the Scarlet Pimpernel. Baroness Orczy died in 1947.

MISS POLLY BURTON had had many an argument with Mr. Richard Frobisher about that old man in the corner, who seemed far more interesting and deucedly more mysterious than any of the crimes over which he philosophized.

Dick thought, moreover, that Miss Polly spent more of her leisure time now in that A.B.C. shop than she had done in his own company before, and told her so, with that delightful air of sheepish sulkiness which the male creature invariably wears when he feels jealous and will not admit it.

Polly liked Dick to be jealous, but she liked that old scarecrow in the A.B.C. shop very much too, and though she made sundry vague promises from time to time to Mr. Richard Frobisher, she nevertheless drifted back instinctively day after day to the tea shop in Norfolk Street, Strand, and stayed there sipping coffee for as long as the man in the corner chose to talk.

On this particular afternoon she went to the A.B.C. shop with a fixed purpose, that of making him give her his views of Mrs. Owen's mysterious death in Percy Street.

The facts had interested and puzzled her. She had had countless arguments with Mr. Richard Frobisher as to the three great possible solutions of the puzzle—"Accident, Suicide, Murder?"

"Undoubtedly neither accident nor suicide," the old man said drily.

Polly was not aware that she had spoken. What an uncanny habit that creature had of reading her thoughts!

"You incline to the idea, then, that Mrs. Owen was murdered. Do you know by whom?"

He laughed, and drew forth the piece of string he always fidgeted with when unraveling some mystery.

"You would like to know who murdered that old woman?"

"I would like to hear your views on the subject," Polly replied.

"I have no views," he said. "No one can know who murdered the woman, since no one ever saw the person who did it. No one can give the faintest description of the mysterious man who alone could have committed that clever deed, and the police are playing a game of blindman's buff."

"But you must have formed some theory of your own," she persisted.

It annoyed her that the funny creature was obstinate about this point, and she tried to nettle his vanity.

"I suppose that as a matter of fact your original remark that 'there are no such things as mysteries' does not apply universally. There is a mystery—that of the death in Percy Street, and you, like the police, are unable to fathom it."

He pulled up his eyebrows and looked at her for a minute or two.

"Confess that that murder was one of the cleverest bits of work accomplished outside Russian diplomacy," he said with a nervous laugh. "I must say that were I the judge, called upon to pronounce sentence of death on the man who conceived that murder, I could not bring myself to do it. I would politely request the gentleman to enter our Foreign Office—we have need of such men. The whole *mise en scène* was truly artistic, worthy of its *milieu*—the Rubens Studios in Percy Street, Tottenham Court Road.

"Have you ever noticed them? They are only studios by name, and are merely a set of rooms in a corner house, with the windows slightly enlarged, and the rents charged accordingly in consideration of that additional five inches of smoky daylight, filtering through dusty windows. On the ground floor there is the order office of some stained-glass works, with a workshop in the rear, and on the first-floor landing a small room allotted to the caretaker, with gas, coal, and fifteen shillings a week, for which princely income she is deputed to keep tidy and clean the general aspect of the house.

"Mrs. Owen, who was the caretaker there, was a quiet, respectable woman, who eked out her scanty wages by sundry—mostly very meager—tips doled out to her by impecunious artists in exchange for promiscuous domestic services in and about the respective studios.

"But if Mrs. Owen's earnings were not large, they were very regular, and she had no fastidious tastes. She and her cockatoo lived on her wages; and all the tips added up, and never spent, year after year, went to swell a very comfortable little account at interest in the Birkbeck Bank. This little account had mounted up to a very tidy sum, and the thrifty widow, or old maid—no one ever knew which she was—was generally referred to by the young artists of the Rubens Studios as a 'lady of means.' But this is a digression.

"No one slept on the premises except Mrs. Owen and her

cockatoo. The rule was that one by one as the tenants left their rooms in the evening they took their respective keys to the caretaker's room. She would then, in the early morning, tidy and dust the studios and the office downstairs, lay the fire, and carry up coals.

"The foreman of the glass works was the first to arrive in the morning. He had a latchkey, and let himself in, after which it was the custom of the house that he should leave the street door open for the benefit of the other tenants and their visitors.

"Usually, when he came at about nine o'clock, he found Mrs. Owen busy about the house doing her work, and he had often a brief chat with her about the weather, but on this particular morning of February second he neither saw nor heard her. However, as the shop had been tidied and the fire laid, he surmised that Mrs. Owen had finished her work earlier than usual, and thought no more about it. One by one the tenants of the studios turned up, and the day sped on without anyone's attention being drawn noticeably to the fact that the caretaker had not appeared upon the scene.

"It had been a bitterly cold night, and the day was even worse; a cutting northeasterly gale was blowing, there had been a great deal of snow during the night which lay quite thick on the ground, and at five o'clock in the afternoon, when the last glimmer of the pale winter daylight had disappeared, the confraternity of the brush put palette and easel aside and prepared to go home. The first to leave was Mr. Charles Pitt; he locked up his studio and, as usual, took his key into the caretaker's room.

"He had just opened the door when an icy blast literally struck him in the face; both the windows were wide open, and the snow and sleet were beating thickly into the room, forming already a white carpet upon the floor.

"The room was in semi-obscurity, and at first Mr. Pitt saw nothing, but instinctively realizing that something was wrong, he lit a match, and saw before him the spectacle of that awful and mysterious tragedy which has ever since puzzled both police and public. On the floor, already half covered by the drifting snow, lay the body of Mrs. Owen face downwards, in a nightgown, with feet and ankles bare, and these and her hands were of a deep purple color; while in a corner of the room, hunched up with the cold, the body of the cockatoo lay stark and stiff.

225

"At first there was only talk of a terrible accident, the result of some inexplicable carelessness which perhaps the evidence at the inquest would help to elucidate.

"Medical assistance came too late; the unfortunate woman was indeed dead, frozen to death, inside her own room. Further examination showed that she had received a severe blow at the back of the head, which must have stunned her and caused her to fall, helpless, beside the open window. Temperature at five degrees below zero had done the rest. Detective-Inspector Howell discovered close to the window a wrought-iron gas bracket, the height of which corresponded exactly with the bruise which was at the back of Mrs. Owen's head.

"Hardly however had a couple of days elapsed when public curiosity was whetted by a few startling headlines, such as the halfpenny evening papers alone know how to concoct.

" 'The mysterious death in Percy Street.' 'Is it Suicide or Murder?' 'Thrilling details—Strange developments.' 'Sensational Arrest.'

"What had happened was simply this:

"At the inquest a few very curious facts connected with Mrs. Owen's life had come to light, and this had led to the apprehension of a young man of very respectable parentage on a charge of being concerned in the tragic death of the unfortunate caretaker.

"To begin with, it happened that her life, which in an ordinary way should have been very monotonous and regular, seemed, at any rate latterly, to have been more than usually checkered and excited. Every witness who had known her in the past concurred in the statement that since October last a great change had come over the worthy and honest woman.

"I happen to have a photo of Mrs. Owen as she was before this great change occurred in her quiet and uneventful life, and which led, as far as the poor soul was concerned, to such disastrous results.

"Here she is to the life," added the funny creature, placing the photo before Polly—"as respectable, as stodgy, as uninteresting as it is possible for a member of your charming sex to be; not a face, you will admit, to lead any youngster to temptation or to induce him to commit a crime.

"Nevertheless, one day all the tenants of the Rubens Studios were surprised and shocked to see Mrs. Owen, quiet, respectable, Mrs. Owen, sallying forth at six o'clock in the afternoon, attired in an extravagant bonnet and a cloak trimmed with imitation astrakhan which—slightly open in front—displayed a gold locket and chain of astonishing proportions.

"Many were the comments, the hints, the bits of sarcasm leveled at the worthy woman by the frivolous confraternity of the brush.

"The plot thickened when from that day forth a complete change came over the worthy caretaker of the Rubens Studios. While she appeared day after day before the astonished gaze of the tenants and the scandalized looks of the neighbors, attired in new and extravagant dresses, her work was hopelessly neglected, and she was always 'out' when wanted.

"There was, of course, much talk and comment in various parts of the Rubens studios on the subject of Mrs. Owen's 'dissipations.' The tenants began to put two and two together, and after a very little while the general consensus of opinion became firmly established that the honest caretaker's demoralization coincided week for week, almost day for day, with young Greenhill's establishment in Number Eight Studio.

"Everyone had remarked that he stayed much later in the evening than anyone else, and yet no one presumed that he stayed for purposes of work. Suspicions soon rose to certainty when Mrs. Owen and Arthur Greenhill were seen by one of the glass workmen dining together at Gambia's Restaurant in Tottenham Court Road.

"The workman, who was having a cup of tea at the counter, noticed particularly that when the bill was paid,the money came out of Mrs. Owen's purse. The dinner had been sumptuous— veal cutlets, a cut from the joint, dessert, coffee, and liqueurs. Finally, the pair left the restaurant apparently very gay, young Greenhill smoking a choice cigar.

"Irregularities such as these were bound sooner or later to come to the ears and eyes of Mr. Allman, the landlord of the Rubens Studios; and a month after the New Year, without further warning, he gave her a week's notice to quit his house.

" 'Mrs. Owen did not seem the least bit upset when I gave her notice,' Mr. Allman declared in his evidence at the inquest; 'on the contrary, she told me that she had ample means, and had only worked recently for the sake of something to do. She added that she had plenty of friends who would look after her, for she had a nice little pile to leave to anyone who would know how to get the right side of her.'

"Nevertheless, in spite of this cheerful interview, Miss Bedford, the tenant of Number Six Studio, had stated that when she took her key to the caretaker's room at six thirty that afternoon, she found Mrs. Owen in tears. The caretaker refused to be comforted, nor would she speak of her trouble to Miss Bedford.

"Twenty-four hours later she was found dead.

"The coroner's jury returned an open verdict, and Detective-Inspector Jones was charged by the police to make some inquiries about young Mr. Greenhill, whose intimacy with the unfortunate woman had been universally commented upon.

"The detective, however, pushed his investigations as far as the Birkbeck Bank. There he discovered that after her interview with Mr. Allman, Mrs. Owen had withdrawn what money she had on deposit, some eight hundred pounds, the result of twenty-five years' savings and thrift.

"But the immediate result of Detective-Inspector Jones's labors was that Mr. Arthur Greenhill, lithographer, was brought before the magistrate at Bow Street on the charge of being concerned in the death of Mrs. Owen.

"Now, you know as well as I do how the attitude of the young prisoner impressed the magistrate and police so unfavorably that, with every new witness brought forward, his position became more and more unfortunate. Yet he was a good-looking, rather coarsely built young fellow, with one of those awful Cockney accents which literally make one jump. But he looked painfully nervous, stammered at every word spoken, and repeatedly gave answers entirely at random.

"His father acted as lawyer for him, a rough-looking elderly man, who had the appearance of a country attorney rather than of a London solicitor.

"The police had built up a fairly strong case against the lithographer. Medical evidence revealed nothing new: Mrs. Owen had died from exposure, the blow at the back of the head not being sufficiently serious to cause anything but temporary disablement. When the medical officer had been called in, death had intervened for some time; it was quite impossible to say how long, whether one hour, or five, or twelve.

"The appearance and state of the room, when the unfortunate woman was found by Mr. Charles Pitt, were again gone over in minute detail. Mrs. Owen's clothes, which she had worn during the day, were folded neatly on a chair. The key of her cupboard was in the pocket of her dress. The door had been slightly ajar, but both the windows were wide open; one of them, which had the sash-line broken, had been fastened up most scientifically with a piece of rope.

"Mrs. Owen had obviously undressed preparatory to going to bed, and the magistrate very naturally soon made the remark how untenable the theory of an accident must be. No one in their five senses would undress with a temperature at below zero, and the windows wide open.

"After these preliminary statements the cashier of the Birkbeck was called and he related the caretaker's visit at the bank.

" 'It was then about one o'clock,' he stated. 'Mrs. Owen called and presented a check to self for £827, the amount of her balance. She seemed exceedingly happy and cheerful, and talked about needing plenty of cash, as she was going abroad to join her nephew, for whom she would in future keep house. I warned her about being sufficiently careful with so large a sum, and parting from it injudiciously, as women of her class are very apt to do. She laughingly declared that not only was she careful of it in the present, but meant to be so for the far-off future, for she intended to go that very day to a lawyer's office and to make a will.'

"The cashier's evidence was certainly startling in the extreme, since in the widow's room no trace of any kind was found of any money; against that, two of the notes handed over by the bank to Mrs. Owen on that day were cashed by young Greenhill on the very morning of her mysterious death. One was handed in by him to the West End Clothiers Company, in payment for a suit of clothes, and the other he changed at the Post Office in Oxford Street.

"After that all the evidence had of necessity to be gone through again on the subject of young Greenhill's intimacy with Mrs. Owen. He listened to it all with an air of the most painful nervousness; his cheeks were positively green, his lips seemed dry and parched, for he repeatedly passed his tongue over them, and when Constable E 18 deposed that at two A.M. on the morning of February second he had seen the accused and spoken to him at the corner of Percy Street and Tottenham Court Road, young Greenhill all but fainted.

"The contention of the police was that the caretaker had been murdered and robbed during that night before she went to

229

bed, that young Greenhill had done the murder, seeing that he was the only person known to have been intimate with the woman, and that it was, moreover, proved unquestionably that he was in the immediate neighborhood of the Rubens Studios at an extraordinarily late hour of the night.

"His own account of himself, and of that same night, could certainly not be called very satisfactory. Mrs. Owen was a relative of his late mother's, he declared. He himself was a lithographer by trade, with a good deal of time and leisure on his hands. He certainly had employed some of that time in taking the old woman to various places of amusement. He had on more than one occasion suggested that she should give up menial work and come and live with him, but, unfortunately, she was a great deal imposed upon by her nephew, a man of the name of Owen, who exploited the good-natured woman in every possible way, and who had on more than one occasion made severe attacks upon her savings at the Birkbeck Bank.

"Severely cross-examined by the prosecuting counsel about this supposed relative of Mrs. Owen, Greenhill admitted that he did not know him—had, in fact, never seen him. He knew that his name was Owen, and that was all. His chief occupation consisted in sponging on the kind-hearted old woman, but he only went to see her in the evenings, when he presumably knew that she would be alone, and invariably after all the tenants of the Rubens Studios had left for the day.

"I don't know whether at this point it strikes you at all, as it did both magistrate and counsel, that there was a direct contradiction in this statement and the one made by the cashier of the Birkbeck on the subject of his last conversation with Mrs. Owen. 'I am going abroad to join my nephew, for whom I am going to keep house,' was what the unfortunate woman had said.

"Now Greenhill, in spite of his nervousness and at time contradictory answers, strictly adhered to his point, that there was a nephew in London who came frequently to see his aunt.

"Anyway, the sayings of the murdered woman could not be taken as evidence in law. Mr. Greenhill senior put the objection, adding: 'There may have been two nephews,' which the magistrate and the prosecution were bound to admit.

"With regard to the night immediately preceding Mrs. Owen's death, Greenhill stated that he had been with her to the theater, had seen her home, and had had some supper with her in her room. Before he left her, at two A.M., she had of her own accord made him a present of ten pounds, saying: 'I am a sort of aunt to you, Arthur, and if you don't have it, Bill is sure to get it.'

"She had seemed rather worried in the early part of the evening, but later on she cheered up.

" 'Did she speak at all about this nephew of hers or about her money affairs?' asked the magistrate.

"Again, the young man hesitated, but said, 'No, she did not mention either Owen or her money affairs.'

"If I remember rightly," added the old man in the corner, "for recollect I was not present, the case was here adjourned. But the magistrate would not grant bail. Greenhill was removed looking more dead than alive—though everyone remarked that Mr. Greenhill senior looked determined and not the least worried. In the course of his examination on behalf of his son, of the medical officer and one or two other witnesses, he had very ably tried to confuse them on the subject of the hour at which Mrs. Owen was last known to be alive.

"He made a very great point of the fact that the usual morning's work was done throughout the house when the inmates arrived. Was it conceivable, he argued, that a woman would do that kind of work overnight, especially as she was going to the theater, and therefore would wish to dress in her smarter clothes? It certainly was a very nice point leveled against the prosecution, who promptly retorted: Just as conceivable as that a woman in those circumstances of life should, having done her work, undress beside an open window at nine o'clock in the morning with the snow beating into the room.

"Now it seems that Mr. Greenhill senior could produce any amount of witnesses who could help to prove a conclusive alibi on behalf of his son, if only some time subsequent to that fatal two A.M. the murdered woman had been seen alive by some chance passerby. Mr. Greenhill senior was an able man and an earnest one, and I fancy the magistrate felt some sympathy for his strenuous endeavors on his son's behalf. He granted a week's adjournment, which seemed to satisfy Mr. Greenhill completely.

"In the meanwhile the papers had talked of and almost exhausted the subject of the mystery in Percy Street. There had been, as you no doubt know from personal experience, innumerable arguments on the puzzling alternatives:

231

"Accident?

"Suicide?

"Murder?

"A week went by, and then the case against young Greenhill was resumed. Of course, the court was crowded. It needed no great penetration to remark at once that the prisoner looked more hopeful, and his father quite elated.

"Again a great deal of minor evidence was taken, and then came the turn of the defense. Mr. Greenhill called Mrs. Hall, confectioner, of Percy Street, opposite the Rubens Studios. She deposed that at eight o'clock in the morning of February second, while she was tidying her shop window, she saw the caretaker of the Studios opposite, as usual, on her knees, her head and body wrapped in a shawl, cleaning her front steps. Her husband also saw Mrs. Owen, and Mrs. Hall remarked to her husband how thankful she was that her own shop had tiled steps, which did not need scrubbing on so cold a morning.

"Mr. Hall, confectioner, of the same address, corroborated this statement, and Mr. Greenhill, with absolute triumph, produced a third witness, Mrs. Martin, of Percy Street, who from her window on the second floor had, at seven thirty A.M., seen the caretaker shaking mats outside her front door. The description this witness gave of Mrs. Owen's getup, with the shawl round her head, coincided point by point with that given by Mr. and Mrs. Hall.

"After that Mr. Greenhill's task became an easy one; his son was at home having his breakfast at eight o'clock that morning—not only himself but his servants would testify to that.

"The weather had been so bitter that the whole of that day young Greenhill had not stirred from his own fireside. Mrs. Owen was murdered after eight A.M. on that day, since she was seen alive by three people at that hour, therefore his son could not have murdered Mrs. Owen. The police must find the criminal elsewhere, or else bow to the opinion originally expressed by the public that Mrs. Owen had met with a terrible untoward accident, or that perhaps she may have wilfully sought her own death in that extraordinary and tragic fashion.

"Before young Greenhill was finally discharged, one or two witnesses were again examined, chief among these being the foreman of the glassworks. He had turned up at Rubens Studios at nine o'clock, and been in business all day. He averred positively that he did not specially notice any suspicious-looking individual crossing the hall that day. 'But,' he remarked with a smile, 'I don't sit and watch everyone who goes up and down stairs. I am too busy for that. The street door is always left open; anyone can walk in, up or down, who knows the way.'

"That there was a mystery in connection with Mrs. Owen's death—of that the police have remained perfectly convinced; whether young Greenhill held the key of that mystery or not, they have never found out to this day.

"I could enlighten them as to the cause of the young lithographer's anxiety at the magisterial inquiry, but, I assure you, I do not care to do the work of the police for them. Why should I? Greenhill will never suffer from unjust suspicions. He and his father alone—besides myself—know in what a terribly tight corner he all but found himself.

"The young man did not reach home till nearly five o'clock that morning. His last train had gone; he had to walk, lost his way, and wandered about Hampstead for hours. Think what his position would have been if the worthy confectioners of Percy Street had not seen Mrs. Owen 'wrapped up in a shawl, on her knees, doing the front steps.'

"Moreover, Mr. Greenhill senior is a solicitor, who has a small office in John Street, Bedford Row. The afternoon before her death Mrs. Owen had been to that office and had there made a will by which she left all her savings to young Arthur Greenhill, lithographer. Had that will been in other than paternal hands, it would have been proved, in the natural course of such things, and one other link would have been added to the chain which nearly dragged Arthur Greenhill to the gallows—the link of a very strong motive.'

"Can you wonder that the young man turned livid, until such time as it was proved beyond a doubt that the murdered woman was alive hours after he had reached the shelter of his home?

"I saw you smile when I used the word 'murdered,'" continued the old man in the corner, growing quite excited now that he was approaching the dénouement of his story. "I know that the public, after the magistrate had discharged Arthur Greenhill, were quite satisfied to think that the mystery in Percy Street was a case of accident—or suicide."

"No," replied Polly, "there could be no question of suicide for two very distinct reasons."

He looked at her with some degree of astonishment. She

supposed that he was amazed at her venturing to form an opinion of her own.

"And may I ask what, in your opinion, these reasons are?" he asked very sarcastically.

"To begin with, the question of money," she said. "Has any more of it been traced so far?"

"Not another five-pound note," he said with a chuckle; "they were all cashed in Paris during the Exhibition, and you have no conception how easy a thing that is to do, at any of the hotels or smaller *agents de change*."

"That nephew was a clever blackguard," she commented.

"You believe, then, in the existence of that nephew?"

"Why should I doubt it? Someone must have existed who was sufficiently familiar with the house to go about in it in the middle of the day without attracting anyone's attention."

"In the middle of the day?" he said with a chuckle.

"Any time after eight thirty in the morning."

"So you, too, believe in the 'caretaker, wrapped up in a shawl,' cleaning her front steps?" he queried.

"But—"

"It never struck you, in spite of the training your interviews with me must have given you, that the person who carefully did all the work in the Rubens Studios, laid the fires, and carried up the coals, merely did it in order to gain time; in order that the bitter frost might really and effectually do its work, and Mrs. Owen not be missed until she was truly dead."

"But—" suggested Polly again.

"It never struck you that one of the greatest secrets of successful crime is to lead the police astray with regard to the *time* when the crime was committed.

"In this case the 'nephew,' since we admit his existence, would—even if he were ever found, which is doubtful—be able to prove as good an alibi as young Greenhill."

"But I don't understand—"

"How the murder was committed?" he said eagerly. "Surely you can see it all for yourself, since you admit the 'nephew'—a scamp, perhaps—who sponges on the good-natured woman. He terrorizes and threatens her, so much so that she fancies her money is no longer safe even in the Birkbeck Bank. Women of that class are apt at times to mistrust the Bank of England. Anyway, she withdraws her money. Who knows what she meant to do with it in the immediate future?

234

"In any case, she wishes to give it after her death to a young man whom she likes, and who has known how to win her good graces. That afternoon the nephew begs, entreats for more money; they have a row; the poor woman is in tears, and is only temporarily consoled by a pleasant visit at the theater.

"At two o'clock in the morning young Greenhill parts from her. Two minutes later the nephew knocks at the door. He comes with a plausible tale of having missed his last train, and asks for 'a shakedown' somewhere in the house. The good-natured woman suggests a sofa in one of the studios, and then quietly prepares to go to bed. The rest is very simple and elementary. The nephew sneaks into his aunt's room, finds her standing in her nightgown; he demands money with threats of violence; terrified, she staggers, knocks her head against the gas bracket, and falls on the floor stunned, while the nephew seeks for her keys and takes possession of the eight hundred-odd pounds. You will admit that the subsequent *mise en scène* is worthy of a genius.

"No struggle, not the usual hideous accessories round a crime. Only the open windows, the bitter northeasterly gale, and the heavily falling snow—two silent accomplices, as silent as the dead.

"After that the murderer, with perfect presence of mind, busies himself in the house, doing the work which will insure that Mrs. Owen shall not be missed, at any rate, for some time. He dusts and tidies; some few hours later he even slips on his aunt's skirt and bodice, wraps his head in a shawl, and boldly allows those neighbors who are astir to see what they believe to be Mrs. Owen. Then he goes back to her room, resumes his normal appearance, and quietly leaves the house."

"He may have been seen."

"He undoubtedly *was* seen by two or three people, but no one thought anything of seeing a man leave the house at that hour. It was very cold, the snow was falling thickly, and as he wore a muffler round the lower part of his face, those who saw him would not undertake to know him again."

"That man was never seen nor heard of again?" Polly asked slowly.

"He has disappeared off the face of the earth. The police are searching for him, and perhaps some day they will find him—then society will be rid of one of the most ingenious men of the age."

The old man had paused, absorbed in meditation. The young girl also was silent. Some memory too vague as yet to take a definite form was persistently haunting her; one thought was hammering away in her brain, and playing havoc with her nerves. That thought was the inexplicable feeling within her that there was something in connection with that hideous crime which she ought to recollect, something which—if she could only remember what it was—would give her the clue to the tragic mystery, and for once insure her triumph over this self-conceited and sarcastic scarecrow in the corner.

He was watching her through his great bone-rimmed spectacles, and she could see the knuckles of his bony hands, just above the top of the table, fidgeting, fidgeting, fidgeting, till she wondered if there existed another set of fingers in the world which would undo the knots his lean ones made in that tiresome piece of string.

Then suddenly—*à propos* of nothing, Polly *remembered*—the whole thing stood before her, short and clear like a vivid flash of lightning—Mrs. Owen lying dead in the snow beside her open window; one of them with a broken sash-line, tied up most scientifically with a piece of string. She remembered the speculative talk there had been at the time about this improvised sash-line.

That was after young Greenhill had been discharged, and the question of suicide had been voted out.

Polly remembered that in the illustrated papers photographs appeared of this wonderfully knotted piece of string, so contrived that the weight of the frame could but tighten the knots, and thus keep the window open. She remembered that people deduced many things from that improvised sash-line, chief among these deductions being that the murderer was a sailor—so wonderful, so complicated, so numerous were the knots which secured the window-frame.

But Polly knew better. In her mind's eye she saw those fingers rendered doubly nervous by the fearful cerebral excitement, grasping at first mechanically, even thoughtlessly, a bit of twine with which to secure the window; then the ruling habit strongest through all, the girl could see it; the lean and ingenious fingers fidgeting, fidgeting with that piece of string, tying knot after knot, more wonderful, more complicated, than any she had yet witnessed.

"If I were you," she said, without daring to look into that

236

corner where he sat, "I would break myself of the habit of perpetually making knots in a piece of string."

He did not reply, and at last Polly ventured to look up—the corner was empty, and through the glass door beyond the desk, where he had just deposited his few coppers, she saw the tails of his tweed coat, his extraordinary hat, his meager, shriveled-up personality, fast disappearing down the street.

Miss Polly Burton (of the *Evening Observer*) was married the other day to Mr. Richard Frobisher (of the *London Mail*). She has never set eyes on the old man in the corner from that day to this.

THE AFFAIR AT THE
SEMIRAMIS HOTEL

BY A. E. W. MASON

Alfred Edward Woodley Mason was born in London in
1865 and received an M. A. degree at Oxford. After a
brief acting career he began writing historical and adventure novels. His first novel, *A Romance of Wastdale*,
was published in 1895. *The Four Feathers* (1902) is
considered his masterpiece. A Member of Parliament
for four years, Mason was an enthusiastic sportsman and
traveler. He wrote novels of espionage, politics, and intrigue, often with exotic settings. Several of his Inspector Hanaud stories have been made into motion pictures. Mason died in 1948.

MR. RICARDO, WHEN THE excitements of the Villa Rose were done with, returned to Grosvenor Square and resumed the busy, unnecessary life of an amateur. But the studios had lost their savor, artists their attractiveness, and even the Russian opera seemed a trifle flat. Life was altogether a disappointment; Fate, like an actress at a restaurant, had taken the wooden pestle in her hand and stirred all the sparkle out of the champagne; Mr. Ricardo languished—until one unforgettable morning.

He was sitting disconsolately at his breakfast-table when the door was burst open and a square, stout man, with the blue, shaven face of a French comedian, flung himself into the room. Ricardo sprang up in delight. "My dear Hanaud!"

He seized his visitor by the arm, feeling it to make sure that here, in flesh and blood, stood the man who had introduced him to the acutest sensations of his life. He turned towards his butler, who was still beating expostulations in the doorway at Hanaud's unceremonious erruption.

"Another place, Burton, at once," he cried, and as soon as he and Hanaud were alone: "What good wind blows you to London?"

"Business, my friend. The disappearance of bullion somewhere on the line between Paris and London. But it is finished. Yes, I take a holiday."

A light had suddenly flashed in Mr. Ricardo's eyes, and was now no less suddenly extinguished. Hanaud paid no attention whatever to his friend's disappointment. He pounced upon a piece of silver which adorned the tablecloth and took it over to the window.

"Everything is as it should be, my friend," he exclaimed, with a grin. "Grosvenor Square, the *Times* open at the money column, and a false antique upon the table. Thus I have dreamed of you. All Mr. Ricardo is in that sentence."

Ricardo laughed nervously. Recollection made him wary of Hanaud's sarcasms. He was shy even to protest the genuineness of his silver. But, indeed, he had not the time. For the door opened again and once more the butler appeared. On this occasion, however, he was alone.

"Mr. Calladine would like to speak to you, sir," he said.

"Calladine!" cried Ricardo in an extreme surprise. "That is the most extraordinary thing." He looked at the clock upon his mantelpiece. Its hands stood at barely half-past eight. "At this hour, too?"

"Mr. Calladine is still wearing evening dress," the butler remarked.

Ricardo started in his chair. He began to dream of possibilities; and here was Hanaud miraculously at his side.

"Where is Mr. Calladine?" he asked.

"I have shown him into the library."

"Good," said Mr. Ricardo. "I will come to him."

But he was in no hurry. He sat and let his thoughts play with this incident of Calladine's early visit.

"It is very odd," he said. "I have not seen Calladine for months—no, nor has anyone. Yet, a little while ago, no one was more often seen."

He fell apparently into a muse, but he was merely seeking to provoke Hanaud's curiosity. In this attempt, however, he failed. Hanaud continued placidly to eat his breakfast, so that Mr. Ricardo was compelled to volunteer the story which he was burning to tell.

"Drink your coffee, Hanaud, and you shall hear about Calladine."

Hanaud grunted with resignation, and Mr. Ricardo flowed on:

"Calladine was one of England's young men. Everybody said so. He was going to do very wonderful things as soon as he had made up his mind exactly what sort of wonderful things he was going to do. Meanwhile, you met him in Scotland, at Newmarket, at Ascot, at Cowes, in the box of some great lady at the Opera, in any fine house where the candles that night happened to be lit. He went everywhere, and then a day came and he went nowhere. There was no scandal, no trouble, not a whisper against his good name. He simply vanished. For a little while a few people asked: 'What has become of Calladine?' But there never was any answer, and London has no time for unanswered questions. Other promising young men dined in his place. Calladine had joined the huge legion of the Come-to-nothings. No one even seemed to pass him in the street. Now unexpectedly, at half-past eight in the morning, and in evening dress, he calls upon me. 'Why?' I ask myself."

Mr. Ricardo sank once more into a reverie. Hanaud watched him with a broadening smile of pure enjoyment.

"And in time, I suppose," he remarked casually, "you will perhaps ask him?"

Mr. Ricardo sprang out of his pose to his feet.

"Before I discuss serious things with an acquaintance," he said with a scathing dignity, "I make it a rule to revive my impressions of his personality. The cigarettes are in the crystal box."

"They would be," said Hanaud, unabashed, as Ricardo stalked from the room. But in five minutes Mr. Ricardo came running back, all his composure gone.

"It is the greatest good fortune that you, my friend, should have chosen this morning to visit me," he cried, and Hanaud nodded with a little grimace of resignation.

"There goes my holiday. You shall command me now and always. I will make the acquaintance of your young friend."

He rose and followed Ricardo into his study, where a young man was nervously pacing the floor.

"Mr. Calladine," said Ricardo. "This is Mr. Hanaud."

The young man turned eagerly. He was tall, with a noticeable elegance and distinction, and the face which he showed to Hanaud was, in spite of its agitation, remarkably handsome.

"I am very glad," he said. "You are not an official of this country. You can advise—without yourself taking action."

Hanaud frowned. He bent his eyes uncompromisingly upon Calladine.

"What does that mean?" he asked, with a note of sternness in his voice.

"It means that I must tell someone," Calladine burst out in quivering tones, "that I don't know what to do. I am in a difficulty too big for me."

Hanaud looked at the young man keenly. It seemed to Ricardo that he took in every excited gesture, every twitching feature, in one comprehensive glance. Then he said in a friendlier voice:

"Sit down and tell me"—and he himself drew up a chair to the table.

"I was at the Semiramis last night," said Calladine, naming one of the great hotels upon the Embankment. "There was a fancy-dress ball."

All this happened, by the way, in those far-off days before the war when London, flinging aside its reticence, its shy self-consciousness, had become a city of carnivals and masquerades, rivaling its neighbors on the Continent in the spirit of its gaiety, and exceeding them by its stupendous luxury. "I went by the merest chance. My rooms are in the Adelphi Terrace."

"There!" cried Mr. Ricardo in surprise, and Hanaud lifted a hand to check his interruptions.

Calladine drew up a chair opposite to Hanaud and, seating himself, told, with many nervous starts and in troubled tones, a story which, to Mr. Ricardo's thinking, was as fabulous as any out of the "Arabian Nights."

"I had a ticket," he began, "but no domino. I was consequently stopped by an attendant in the lounge at the top of the staircase leading down to the ballroom.

" 'You can hire a domino in the cloakroom, Mr. Calladine,' he said to me. I had already begun to regret the impulse which had brought me, and I welcomed the excuse with which the absence of a costume provided me. I was, indeed, turning back to the door, when a girl who had at that moment run down from the stairs of the hotel into the lounge, cried gaily: 'That's not necessary'; and at the same moment she flung to me a long scarlet cloak which she had been wearing over her own dress. She was young, fair, rather tall, slim, and very pretty; her hair was drawn back from her face with a ribbon, and rippled down her shoulders in heavy curls; and she was dressed in a satin coat and knee-breeches of pale green and gold, with a white waistcoat and silk stockings and scarlet heels to her satin shoes. She was as straight-limbed as a boy, and exquisite like a figure in Dresden china. I caught the cloak and turned to thank her. But she did not wait. With a laugh she ran down the stairs, a supple and shining figure, and was lost in the throng at the doorway of the ballroom. I was stirred by the prospect of an adventure. I ran down after her. She was standing just inside the room alone, and she was gazing at the scene with parted lips and dancing eyes. She laughed again as she saw the cloak about my shoulders, and I said to her:

" 'May I dance with you?'

" 'Oh, do!' she cried, with a little jump, and clasping her hands. She was of a high and joyous spirit and not difficult in the matter of an introduction. 'This gentleman will do very well to present us,' she said, leading me in front of a bust of the God Pan which stood in a niche of the wall. 'I am, as you see, straight

242

out of an opera. My name is Celymène or anything with an eighteenth-century sound to it. You are—what you will. For this evening we are friends.'

" 'And for tomorrow?' I asked.

" 'I will tell you about that later on,' she replied, and she began to dance with a light step and a passion in her dancing which earned me many an envious glance from the other men. I was in luck, for Celymène knew no one, and though, of course, I saw the faces of a great many people whom I remembered, I kept them all at a distance. We had been dancing for about half an hour when the first queerish thing happened. She stopped suddenly in the midst of a sentence with a little gasp. I spoke to her, but she did not hear. She was gazing past me, her eyes wide open, and such a rapt look upon her face as I had never seen. She was lost in a miraculous vision. I followed the direction of her eyes and, to my astonishment, I saw nothing more than a stout, short, middle-aged woman, egregiously overdressed as Marie Antoinette.

" 'So you do know someone here?' I said, and I had to repeat the words sharply before my friend withdrew her eyes. But even then she was not aware of me. It was as if a voice had spoken to her while she was asleep and had disturbed, but not wakened her. Then she came to—there's really no other word I can think of—she came to with a deep sigh.

" 'No,' she answered. 'She is a Mrs. Blumen from Chicago, a widow with ambitions and a great deal of money. But I don't know her.'

" 'Yet you know all about her,' I remarked.

" 'She crossed in the same boat with me,' Celymène replied. 'Did I tell you that I landed at Liverpool this morning? She is staying at the Semiramis too. Oh, let us dance!'

" "She twitched my sleeve impatiently, and danced with a kind of violence and wildness as if she wished to banish some sinister thought. And she did undoubtedly banish it. We supped together and grew confidential, as under such conditions people will. She told me her real name. It was Joan Carew.

" 'I have come over to get an engagement if I can at Covent Garden. I am supposed to sing all right.'

" 'You have some letters of introduction, I suppose?' I asked.

" 'Oh, yes. One from my teacher in Milan. One from an American manager.'

"In my turn I told her my name and where I lived, and I gave

243

her my card. I thought, you see, that since I used to know a good many operatic people, I might be able to help her.

" 'Thank you,' she said, and at that moment Mrs. Blumen, followed by a party, came into the supper-room and took a table close to us. There was at once an end of all confidences— indeed, of all conversation. Joan Carew lost all the lightness of her spirit; she talked at random, and her eyes were drawn again and again to the grotesque slander on Marie Antoinette. Finally I became annoyed.

" 'Shall we go?' I suggested impatiently, and to my surprise she whispered passionately:

" 'Yes. Please! Let us go.'

"Her voice was actually shaking, her small hands clenched. We went back to the ballroom, but Joan Carew did not recover her gaiety, and half way through a dance, when we were near the door, she stopped abruptly.

" 'I shall go,' she said. 'I am tired.'

"I protested, but she made a little grimace.

" 'You'll hate me in half an hour. Let's be wise and stop now while we are friends,' she said, and while I removed the domino from my shoulders she stooped very quickly. It seemed to me that she picked up something which had lain hidden beneath the sole of her slipper. She certainly moved her foot, and I certainly saw something small and bright flash in the palm of her glove as she raised herself again.

" 'Yes, we'll go,' she said, and we went up the stairs into the lobby.

" 'But I shall meet you again?' I asked.

" 'Yes. I have your address. I'll write and fix a time when you will be sure to find me in. Good night, and a thousand thanks.'

"She was speaking lightly as she held out her hand, but her grip tightened a little and—clung.

" 'I am half inclined to ask you to stay, however dull I am; and dance with me till daylight—the safe daylight,' she said.

" 'Let us go back then!' I urged. She gave me an impression suddenly of someone quite forlorn. But Joan Carew recovered her courage, 'No, no,' she answered quickly. She snatched her hand away and ran lightly up the staircase, turning at the corner to wave her hand and smile. It was then half-past one in the morning."

"And when did you go home?" Hanaud asked of Calladine.

Calladine was not sure. His partner had left behind her the

strangest medley of sensations in his breast. He was puzzled, haunted, and charmed. He had to think about her; sleep was impossible. He wandered for awhile about the ballroom. Then he walked to his chambers along the echoing streets and sat at his window; and some time afterwards the hoot of a motor-horn broke the silence and a car stopped and whirred in the street below. A moment later his bell rang.

He ran down the stairs in a queer excitement, unlocked the street door, and opened it. Joan Carew, still in her masquerade dress with her scarlet cloak about her shoulders, slipped through the opening.

"Shut the door," she whispered.

Calladine latched the door. Above, in the well of the stairs, the light spread out from the open door of his flat. Down here all was dark. He could just see the glimmer of her white face, the glitter of her dress, but she drew her breath like one who has run far. They mounted the stairs cautiously. He did not say a word until they were both safely in his parlor; and even then it was in a low voice.

"What has happened?"

"You remember the woman I stared at? You didn't know why I stared, but any girl would have understood. She was wearing the loveliest pearls I ever saw in my life."

Joan was standing by the edge of the table. She was tracing with her finger a pattern on the cloth as she spoke. Calladine started with a horrible presentiment.

"Yes," she said. "I worship pearls. I always have done so. For one thing, they improve on me. I haven't got any, of course. I have no money. But friends of mine who do own pearls have sometimes given theirs to me to wear when they were going sick, and they have always got back their luster. I think that has had a little to do with my love of them. Oh, I have always longed for them."

She was speaking in a dull, monotonous voice. But Calladine recalled the ecstasy which had shone in her face when her eyes first had fallen on the pearls, the passion with which she had danced to throw the obsession off.

"And I never noticed them at all," he said.

"Yet they were wonderful. The color! The luster! All evening they tempted me. I was furious that a fat, coarse creature like that should have such such exquisite things. Oh, I was mad."

She covered her face suddenly with her hands and swayed.

245

Calladine sprang towards her. But she held out her hand.

"No, I am all right." And though he asked her to sit down she would not. "You remember when I stopped dancing suddenly?"

"Yes. You had something hidden under your foot?"

The girl nodded.

"Her key!" And under his breath Calladine uttered a startled cry.

"A little Yale key," the girl continued. "I saw Mrs. Blumen looking on the floor for something, and then I saw it shining on the very spot. Mrs. Blumen's suite was on the same floor as mine, and her maid slept above. All the maids do. I knew that. Oh, it seemed to me as if I had sold my soul and was being paid."

Now Calladine understood what she had meant by her strange phrase—"the safe daylight."

"I went up to my little suite," Joan Carew continued. "I sat there with the key burning through my glove until I had given her time enough to fall asleep. Then I crept out. The corridor was dimly lit. Far away below the music was throbbing. Up here it was as silent as the grave. I opened the door—her door. I found myself in a lobby. The suite, though bigger, was arranged like mine. I slipped in and closed the door behind me. I listened in the darkness. I couldn't hear a sound. I crept forward to the door in front of me. I stood with my fingers on the handle and my heart beating fast enough to choke me. I had still time to turn back. But I couldn't. There were those pearls in front of my eyes, lustrous and wonderful. I opened the door gently an inch or so—and then—it all happened in a second."

Joan Carew faltered. The night was too near to her, its memory too poignant with terror. She shut her eyes tightly and cowered down in a chair.

"Go on," Calladine said.

"I found myself inside the room with the door shut behind me. I had shut it myself in a spasm of terror. And I dared not turn round to open it. I was helpless."

"What do you mean? She was awake?"

Joan Carew shook her head.

"There were others in the room before me, and on the same errand—men!"

Calladine drew back, his eyes searching the girl's face.

"Yes?" he said slowly.

246

"I didn't see them at first. I didn't hear them. The room was quite dark except for one jet of fierce white light which beat upon the door of a safe. And as I shut the door the jet moved swiftly and the light reached me and stopped. I was blinded. I stood in the full glare of it, drawn up against the panels of the door, shivering, sick with fear. Then I heard a quiet laugh, and someone moved softly towards me. Oh, it was terrible! I recovered the use of my limbs; in a panic I turned to the door, but I was too late. While I fumbled with the handle I was seized; a hand covered my mouth. I was lifted to the center of the room. The jet went out, the electric lights were turned on. There were two men dressed as apaches in velvet trousers and red scarves, like a hundred others in the ballroom below, and both were masked. I struggled furiously; but, of course, I was like a child in their grasp. 'Tie her legs,' the man whispered who was holding me; 'she's making too much noise.' I kicked and fought, but the other man stooped and tied my ankles, and I fainted.

"When I came to, the lights were still burning, the door of the safe was open, the room empty; I had been flung onto a couch at the foot of the bed. I was lying there quite free."

"Was the safe empty?" asked Calladine.

"I didn't look," she answered. "Oh!"—and she covered her face spasmodically with her hands. "I looked at the bed. Someone was lying there—under a sheet and quite still. There was a clock ticking in the room; it was the only sound. I was terrified. If I didn't get out of the room at once I felt that I should scream and bring everyone to find me alone with—what was under the sheet in the bed. I ran to the door and looked out through a slit into the corridor. It was still quite empty, and below the music still throbbed in the ballroom. I crept down the stairs, meeting no one until I reached the hall. I looked into the ballroom as if I was searching for someone. I stayed long enough to show myself. Then I got a cab and came to you."

Calladine sat watching the girl in silence.

Then he asked, and his voice was hard:

"Is that all you have to tell me?"

"Yes."

Calladine rose to his feet and stood beside her.

"Then how do you come to be wearing this?" he asked, and he lifted a chain of platinum and diamonds which she was wearing about her shoulders. "You weren't wearing it when you danced with me."

Joan Carew stared at the chain.

"No. It's not mine. I have never seen it before." Then a light came into her eyes. "The two men—they must have thrown it over my head when I was on the couch—before they went." She looked at it more closely. "That's it. The chain's not very valuable. They could spare it, and—it would accuse me—of what they did."

"Yes, that's very good reasoning," said Calladine coldly.

Joan Carew looked quickly up into his face.

"Oh, you don't believe me," she cried. "You think—oh, it's impossible."

"But you went to steal, you know," he said gently.

"Yes, I did, but not this." And she held up the necklace. "Should I have stolen this, should I have come to you wearing it, if I had stolen the pearls, if I had"—and she stopped—"if my story were not true?"

Calladine weighed her argument.

"No, I think you wouldn't," he said frankly.

Calladine looked at the clock. It was nearly five o'clock in the morning, and though the music could still be heard from the ballroom in the Semiramis, the night had begun to wane upon the river.

"You must go back," he said. "I'll walk with you."

They crept silently down the stairs and into the street. They met no one until they reached the Strand. There many, like Joan Carew in masquerade, were standing about, or walking hither and thither in search of carriages and cabs.

"You can slip in unnoticed," said Calladine as he looked into the thronged courtyard. "I'll telephone to you in the morning."

"You will?" she cried eagerly.

"Yes, for certain," he replied. "Wait in until you hear from me. I'll think it over. I'll do what I can."

"Thank you," she said fervently.

He watched her scarlet cloak flitting here and there in the crowd until it vanished through the doorway. Then, for the second time, he walked back to his chambers, while the morning crept up the river from the sea.

This was the story which Calladine told in Mr. Ricardo's library. Mr. Ricardo heard it out with varying emotions. He began with a thrill of expectation, like a man on a dark threshold of great excitements. The setting of the story appealed to him, too, by a sort of brilliant bizarrerie which he found in it. But, as it went on, he grew puzzled and a trifle disheartened. There were flaws and chinks; he began to bubble with unspoken criticisms, then swift and clever thrusts which he dared not deliver. He looked upon the young man with disfavor, as upon one who had half opened a door upon a theater of great promise and shown him a spectacle not up to the mark. Hanaud, on the other hand, listened imperturbably, without an expression upon his face, until the end. Then he pointed a finger at Calladine and asked him what to Ricardo's mind was a most irrelevant question.

"You got back to your rooms, then, before five, Mr. Calladine, and it is now nine o'clock less a few minutes."

"Yes."

"Yet you have not changed your clothes. Explain to me that. What did you do between five and half-past eight?"

Calladine looked down at his rumpled shirt front.

"Upon my word, I never thought of it," he cried. "I was worried out of my mind. I couldn't decide what to do. Finally, I determined to talk to Mr. Ricardo, and after I had come to that conclusion I just waited impatiently until I could come round with decency."

Hanaud rose from his chair. His manner was grave, but conveyed no single hint of an opinion. He turned to Ricardo.

"Let us go round to your young friend's room in the Adelphi," he said; and the three men drove there at once.

Calladine lodged in a corner house and upon the first floor. His rooms, large and square and lofty, with Adam mantelpieces and a delicate tracery upon their ceilings, breathed the grace of the eighteenth century. Broad high windows, embrasured in thick walls, overlooked the river and took in all the sunshine and the air which the river had to give. And they were furnished fittingly. When the three men entered the parlor, Mr. Ricardo was astounded. He had expected the untidy litter of a man run to seed, the neglect and the dust of the recluse. But the room was as clean as the deck of a yacht; an Aubusson carpet made the floor luxurious underfoot; a few colored prints of real value decorated the walls; and the mahogany furniture was polished so that a lady could have used it as a mirror. There was even a china bowl full of fresh red roses.

"So you live here, Mr. Calladine?" said Hanaud.

"Yes."

"With your servants, of course?"

"They come in during the day," said Calladine, and Hanaud looked at him curiously.

"Do you mean that you sleep here alone?"

"Yes."

"But your valet?"

"I don't keep a valet," said Calladine; and again the curious look came into Hanaud's eyes.

"Yet," he suggested gently, "there are rooms enough in your set of chambers to house a family."

Calladine colored.

"I prefer at night not to be disturbed," he said, stumbling a little over the words.

Hanaud nodded his head with sympathy.

"Yes, yes. And it is a difficult thing to get—as difficult as my holiday," he said ruefully, with a smile for Mr. Ricardo. "However"—he turned towards Calladine—"no doubt, now that you are at home, you would like a bath and a change of clothes. And when you are dressed, perhaps you will telephone to the Semiramis and ask Miss Carew to come round here."

Hanaud shut the door upon Calladine, then crossed the room to Mr. Ricardo who, seated at the open window, was plunged deep in reflections.

"You have an idea, my friend," cried Hanaud.

Mr. Ricardo started out of an absorption which was altogether assumed.

"I was thinking," he said, with a faraway smile, "that you might disappear in the forests of Africa, and at once everyone would be very busy about your disappearance. You might leave your village in Leicestershire and live in the fogs of Glasgow, and within a week the whole village would know your postal address. But London—what a city! How different! How indifferent! Turn out of St. James's into the Adelphi Terrace and not a soul will say to you: 'Dr. Livingstone, I presume?' "

"But why should they," asked Hanaud, "if your name isn't Dr. Livingstone?"

Mr. Ricardo smiled indulgently.

"Scoffer!" he said. "You understand me very well," and he sought to turn the tables on his companion. "And you—does this room suggest nothing to you? Have you no ideas?" But he knew very well that Hanaud had. Ever since Hanaud had crossed the threshold he had been like a man stimulated by a drug.

"Yes," he said, "I have."

He was standing now by Ricardo's side with his hands in his pockets, looking out at the trees on the Embankment and the barges swinging down the river. In a moment or two he began to walk about the room with that curiously light step which Ricardo was never able to reconcile with his cumbersome figure. With the heaviness of a bear he still padded. He went from corner to corner, opened a cupboard here, a drawer of the bureau there.

"You are looking for something," Ricardo announced with sagacity.

"I am," replied Hanaud; and it seemed that in a second or two he found it. Yet—yet—he found it with his hands in his pockets, if he had found it. Mr. Ricardo saw him stop in that attitude in front of the mantelshelf, and heard him utter a long, low whistle. Upon the mantelshelf some photographs were arranged, a box of cigars stood at one end, a book or two lay between some delicate ornaments of china, and a small engraving in a thin gilt frame was propped at the back against the wall. Ricardo surveyed the shelf from his seat in the window, but he could not imagine which it was of these objects that so drew and held Hanaud's eyes.

Hanaud, however, stepped forward. He looked into a vase and turned it upside down. Then he removed the lid of a porcelain cup, and from the very look of his great shoulders Ricardo knew that he had discovered what he sought. He was holding something in his hands, turning it over, examining it. When he was satisfied he moved swiftly to the door and opened it cautiously. Both men could hear the splashing of water in a bath. Hanaud closed the door again with a nod of contentment and crossed once more to the window.

"Yes, it is all very strange and curious," he said, "and I do not regret that you dragged me into the affair. You were quite right, my friend, this morning. It is the personality of your young Mr. Calladine which is the interesting thing. For instance, here we are in London in the early summer. The trees out, freshly green, lilac and flowers in the gardens, and I don't know what tingle of hope and expectation in the sunlight and the air.

"Can you understand a young man with money, with fastid-

251

ious tastes, good-looking, hiding himself in a corner at such a time—except for some overpowering reason? No. Nor can I. There is another thing—I put a question or two to Calladine.

"He has no servants here at night. He is quite alone and—here is what I find interesting—he has no valet. That seems a small thing to you?" Hanaud asked at a movement from Ricardo. "Well, it is no doubt a trifle, but it's a significant trifle in the case of a young rich man. It is generally a sign that there is something strange, perhaps even something sinister, in his life. Mr. Calladine, some months ago, turned out of St. James's into the Adelphi. Can you tell me why?"

"No," replied Mr. Ricardo.

Hanaud stretched out a hand. In his open palm lay a small round hairy bulb about the size of a big button and of a color between green and brown.

"Look!" he said. "What is that?"

Mr. Ricardo took the bulb wonderingly.

"It looks to me like the fruit of some kind of cactus."

Hanaud nodded.

"It is. You will see some pots of it in the hothouses of any really good botanical gardens. They are labeled *Anhalonium Luinii*. But among the Indians of Yucatan the plant has a simpler name."

"What name?" asked Ricardo.

"Mescal."

Mr. Ricardo repeated the name. It conveyed nothing to him.

"Mescal is a drug."

Ricardo started.

"Yes, you are beginning to understand now," Hanaud continued, "why your young friend Calladine turned out of St. James's into the Adelphi Terrace."

Ricardo turned the little bulb over in his fingers.

"You make a decoction of it, I suppose?" he said.

"Or you can use it as the Indians do in Yucatan," replied Hanaud. "Mescal enters into their religious ceremonies. They sit at night in a circle about a fire built in the forest and chew it, while one of their number beats perpetually upon a drum."

Hanaud looked round the room and took notes of its luxurious carpet, its delicate appointments. Outside the window there was a clamor of voices. Boats went swiftly down the river on the ebb. Beyond the mass of the Semiramis rose the great gray-white dome of St. Paul's.

"It's a long way from the forests of Yucatan to the Adelphi Terrace of London," said Hanaud. "Yet here, I think, in these rooms, when the servants are all gone and the house is very quiet, there is a little corner of wild Mexico."

A look of pity came into Mr. Ricardo's face. He had seen more than one young man of great promise slacken his hold and let go, just for this reason.

"It's like bhang and kieff and the rest of the devilish things, I suppose," he said, indignantly tossing the button upon the table.

Hanaud picked it up.

"No," he replied. "It's not quite like any other drug. It has a quality of its own which just now is of particular importance to you and me. Yes, my friend, we must watch that we do not make the big fools of ourselves in this affair."

"There," Mr. Ricardo agreed with an ineffable air of wisdom, "I am entirely with you."

"Now, why?" Hanaud asked. Mr. Ricardo was at a loss for a reason, but Hanaud did not wait. "I will tell you. Mescal intoxicates, yes—but it does more—it gives to the man who eats of it color-dreams."

"Color-dreams?"

"Yes, strange heated charms, in which violent things happen vividly among bright colors. Color is the gift of this little prosaic brown button." He spun the bulb in the air like a coin, and catching it again, took it over to the mantelpiece and dropped it into the porcelain cup.

"Are you sure of this?" Ricardo cried excitedly, and Hanaud raised his hand in warning. He went to the door, opened it for an inch or so, and closed it again.

"I am quite sure," he returned. "I have for a friend a very learned chemist in the Collège de France. He is one of those enthusiasts who must experiment upon themselves. He tried this drug."

"Yes," Ricardo said in a quieter voice. "And what did he see then?"

"He had a vision of a wonderful garden bathed in sunlight, an old garden of gorgeous flowers and emerald lawns, ponds with golden lilies and thick yew hedges—a garden where peacocks stepped indolently and groups of gay people fantastically dressed quarreled and fought with swords. That is what he saw. And he saw it so vividly that, when the vapors of the drug passed from his brain and he waked, he seemed to be coming out of the real world into a world of shifting illusions."

"Out of the real world," Mr. Ricardo quoted, "I begin to see."

"Yes, you begin to see, my friend, that we must be very careful not to make the big fools of ourselves. My friend of the Collège de France saw a garden. But had he been sitting alone in the window-seat where you are, listening through a summer night to the music of the masquerade at the Semiramis, might he not have seen the ballroom, the dancers, the scarlet cloak, and the rest of this story?"

"You mean," cried Ricardo, now fairly startled, "that Calladine came to us with the fumes of mescal still working in his brain, that the false world was the real one still for him."

"I do not know," said Hanaud. "At present I only put questions. I ask them of you. I wish to hear how they sound. Let us reason this problem out. Calladine, let us say, takes a great deal more of the drug than my professor. It will have on him a more powerful effect while it lasts, and it will last longer. Fancy-dress balls are familiar things to Calladine. The music floating from the Semiramis will revive old memories. He sits here, the pageant takes shape before him, he sees himself taking his part in it. Oh, he is happier here sitting quietly in his window-seat than if he was actually at the Semiramis. For he *is* there more intensely, more vividly, more really, than if he had actually descended this staircase. He lives his story through, the story of a heated brain, the scene of it changes in the way dreams have, it becomes tragic and sinister, it oppresses him with horror, and in the morning, so obsessed with it that he does not think to change his clothes, he is knocking at your door."

Mr. Ricardo raised his eyebrows.

"Ah! You see a flaw in my argument," said Hanaud. But Mr. Ricardo was wary. Too often in other days he had been leaped upon and trounced for a careless remark.

"Let me hear the end of your argument," he said. "There was then to your thinking no temptation of jewels, no theft, no murder—in a word, no Celymène?"

"No!" cried Hanaud. "Come with me, my friend. I am not so sure that there was no Celymène."

With a smile upon his face, Hanaud led the way across the room. He had the dramatic instinct, and rejoiced in it. He was going to produce a surprise for his companion and, savoring the moment in advance, he managed his effects. He walked towards the mantelpiece and stopped a few paces away.

"Look!"

Mr. Ricardo looked and saw a broad Adam mantelpiece. He turned a bewildered face to his friend.

"You see nothing?" Hanaud asked.

"Nothing!"

"Look again! I am not sure—but is not Celymène posing before you?"

Mr. Ricardo looked again. There was nothing to fix his eyes. He saw a book or two, a cup, a vase or two, and nothing else except a very pretty and apparently valuable piece of—and suddenly Mr. Ricardo understood. Straight in front of him, in the very center of the mantelpiece, a figure in painted china was leaning against a china stile. It was the figure of a perfectly impossible courtier, feminine and exquisite, and appareled even to the scarlet heels, exactly as Calladine had described Joan Carew.

Hanaud chuckled with satisfaction when he saw the expression upon Mr. Ricardo's face.

"Ah, you understand," he said. "Do you dream, my friend? At times—yes, like the rest of us. Then recollect your dreams? Things, people which you have seen perhaps that day, perhaps months ago, pop in and out of them without making themselves prayed for. Thus, our friend here sits in the window, intoxicated by his drug, the music plays in the Semiramis, the curtain goes up in the heated theater of his brain. He sees himself step upon the stage, and who else meets him but the china figure from his mantelpiece?"

Mr. Ricardo for a moment was all enthusiasm. Then his doubt returned to him.

"What you say, my dear Hanaud, is very ingenious. The figure upon the mantelpiece is also extremely convincing. And I should be absolutely convinced but for one thing."

"Yes?" said Hanaud.

"I am—I may say it, I think—a man of the world. And I ask myself whether a young man who has given up his social ties, who has become a hermit, and still more who has become the slave of a drug, would retain that scrupulous carefulness of his body which is indicated by dressing for dinner when alone?"

Hanaud struck the table with the palm of his hand.

"Yes. That is the weak point in my theory. You have hit it. I knew it was there—that weak point, and I wondered whether

255

you would seize it. Yes, the consumers of drugs are careless, untidy—even unclean as a rule. But not always. We must be careful. We must wait."

"For what?" asked Ricardo.

"For the answer to a telephone message," replied Hanaud.

Both men waited impatiently until Calladine came into the room. He wore now a suit of blue serge, he had a clearer eye, his skin a healthier look; he was altogether a more reputable person. But he was plainly very ill at ease. He offered his visitors cigarettes, he proposed refreshments, he avoided entirely and awkwardly the object of their visit. Hanaud smiled. His theory was working out. Sobered by his bath, Calladine had realized the foolishness of which he had been guilty.

"You telephoned to the Semiramis, of course?" said Hanaud cheerfully.

Calladine grew red.

"Yes," he stammered.

"Yet I did not hear that volume of 'Hallos' which precedes telephonic connection in your country of leisure," Hanaud continued.

"I telephoned from my bedroom. You would not hear anything in this room."

"Yes, yes; the walls of these old houses are solid." Hanaud was playing with his victim. "And when may we expect Miss Carew?"

"I can't say," replied Calladine. "It's very strange. She is not in the hotel."

Mr. Ricardo and Hanaud exchanged a look. They were both satisfied now. There was no word of truth in Calladine's story.

"Then there is no reason for us to wait," said Hanaud. "I shall have my holiday after all." And while he was yet speaking the voice of a newsboy calling out the first edition of an evening paper became distantly audible. Hanaud broke off his farewell. For a moment he listened, with his head bent. Then the voice was heard again, confused, indistinct; Hanaud picked up his hat and cane and, without another word to Calladine, raced down the stairs. Mr. Ricardo followed him, but when he reached the pavement, Hanaud was half down the little street. At the corner, however, he stopped, and Ricardo joined him, coughing and out of breath.

"What's the matter?" he gasped.

"Listen," said Hanaud.

256

At the bottom of Duke Street, by Charing Cross Station, the newsboy was shouting his wares. Both men listened, and now the words came to them.

"*Mysterious crime at the Semiramis Hotel!*"

Ricardo stared at his companion.

"You were wrong, then!" he cried. "Calladine's story was true."

For once Hanaud was quite disconcerted.

But before he could move a taxicab turned into the Adelphi from the Strand, and wheeling in front of their faces, stopped at Calladine's door. From the cab a girl descended.

"Let us go back," said Hanaud.

Mr. Ricardo could no longer complain. It was half-past eight when Calladine had first disturbed the formalities of his house in Grosvenor Square. It was barely ten now, and during that short time he had been flung from surprise to surprise.

"I am alive once more," Mr. Ricardo thought as he turned back with Hanaud, and in his excitement he cried his thought aloud.

"Are you?" said Hanaud. "And what is life without a newspaper? If you will buy one from that remarkably raucous boy at the bottom of the street, I will keep an eye upon Calladine's house till you come back."

Mr. Ricardo sped down to Charing Cross and brought back a copy of the *Star*. He handed it to Hanaud, who stared at it doubtfully, folded as it was.

"Shall we see what it says?" Ricardo asked impatiently.

"By no means," Hanaud answered, waking from his reverie and tucking the paper briskly away into the tail pocket of his coat. "We will hear what Miss Joan Carew has to say, with our minds undisturbed by any discoveries."

They went quickly to Calladine's rooms. As they entered Mr. Ricardo saw a girl turn to them suddenly a white face of terror, and flinch as though already she felt the hand of a constable upon her shoulder. Calladine, on the other hand, uttered a cry of relief.

"These are my friends," he exclaimed to the girl, "the friends of whom I spoke to you;" and to Hanaud he said: "This is Miss Carew."

Hanaud bowed.

"You shall tell me your story, mademoiselle," he said very gently, and a little color returned to the girl's cheeks.

"But you have heard it," she answered.

"Not from you," said Hanaud.

So for a second time in that room she told the history of that night. She was just a very young and very pretty girl, telling in a low and remorseful voice of the tragic dilemma to which she had brought herself. Of Celymène all that remained was something exquisite and fragile in her beauty, in the slimness of her figure, in her daintiness of hand and foot—something almost of the hothouse. But the story she told was the same which Calladine had already related.

"Thank you," said Hanaud when she had done. "Now I must ask you two questions."

"I will answer them."

"You will forgive me, Miss Carew. But have you ever stolen before?"

Joan Carew turned upon Hanaud with spirit. Then a change swept over her face.

"You have a right to ask," she answered. "Never." She looked into his eyes as she answered. Hanaud did not move. He sat with a hand upon each knee and led to his second question.

"Early this morning, when you left this room, you told Mr. Calladine that you would wait at the Semiramis until he telephoned to you?"

"Yes."

"Yet when he telephoned, you had gone out?"

"Yes."

"Why?"

"I will tell you," said Joan Carew. "I could not bear to keep the little diamond chain in my room.

"I was terrified," continued Joan Carew. "I kept thinking: 'They must have found out by now. They will search everywhere.' I didn't reason. I lay in bed expecting to hear every moment a loud knocking on the door. Besides—the chain itself being there in my bedroom—her chain—the dead woman's chain—no, I couldn't endure it. I felt as if I had stolen it."

Joan Carew explained how she had risen, dressed, wrapped the chain in a pad of cotton-wool and enclosed it in an envelope. The envelope had not the stamp of the hotel upon it. It was a rather large envelope, one of a packet which she had bought in a crowded shop in Oxford Street on her way from Euston to the Semiramis. She had bought the envelopes of that particular size in order that when she sent her letter of intro-

258

duction to the Director of the Opera at Covent Garden she might enclose with it a photograph.

"And to whom did you send it?" asked Mr. Ricardo.

"To Mrs. Blumen at the Semiramis. I printed the address carefully. Then I went out and posted it."

"Where?" Hanaud inquired.

"In the big letter-box of the Post Office at the corner of Trafalgar Square."

Hanaud looked at the girl sharply.

"You had your wits about you, I see," he said.

"What if the envelope gets lost?" said Ricardo.

Hanaud laughed grimly.

"If one envelope is delivered at its address in London today, it will be that one," he said. "The news of the crime is published, you see," and he swung round to Joan. "Did you know that, Miss Carew?"

"No," she answered in an awestricken voice.

"Well, then, it is. Let us see what the special investigator has to say about it." And Hanaud, with a deliberation which Mr. Ricardo found quite excruciating, spread out the newspaper on the table.

There was only one new fact in the couple of columns devoted to the mystery. Mrs. Blumen had died from chloroform poisoning. She was of a stout habit, and the thieves were not skilled in the administration of the anesthetic.

"It's murder none the less," said Hanaud, and he gazed straight at Joan, asking her by the direct summons of his eyes what she was going to do.

"I must tell my story to the police," she replied, painfully and slowly.

Hanaud neither agreed nor differed. His face was blank, and when he spoke there was no cordiality in his voice. "Well," he asked, "and what is it that you have to say to the police, miss? That you went into the room to steal, and that you were attacked by two strangers, dressed as Apaches, and masked? That is all?"

"Yes."

"And how many men at the Semiramis ball were dressed as Apaches and wore masks? Come! Make a guess. A hundred at the least?"

"I should think so."

"Then what will your confession do beyond—I quote your

259

expressive English idiom—putting you in the coach?"

"Yet I think I must tell the police," she repeated, looking up and dropping her eyes again. Mr. Ricardo noticed that her eyelashes were very long. For the first time Hanaud's face relaxed.

"And I think you are quite right," he cried heartily, to Mr. Ricardo's surprise. "Tell them the truth before they suspect it, and they will help you out of the affair if they can. Not a doubt of it. Come, I will go with you myself to Scotland Yard."

"Thank you," said Joan, and the pair drove away in a cab together.

Hanaud returned to Grosvenor Square alone and lunched with Ricardo.

"It was all right," he said. "The police were very kind. Miss Joan Carew told her story to them as she had told it to us. Fortunately, the envelope with the platinum chain had already been delivered, and was in their hands. They were much mystified about it, but Miss Joan's story gave them a reasonable explanation. I think they are inclined to believe her; and if she is speaking the truth, they will keep her out of the witness-box if they can."

"She is to stay here in London, then?" asked Ricardo.

"Oh, yes; she is not to go. She will present her letters at the Opera House and secure an engagement, if she can. The criminals might be lulled thereby into a belief that the girl had kept the whole strange incident to herself, and that there was nowhere even a knowledge of the disguise which they had used." Hanaud spoke as carelessly as if the matter was not very important; and Ricardo, with an unusual flash of shrewdness, said:

"It is clear, my friend, that you do not think those two men will ever be caught at all."

Hanaud shrugged his shoulders.

"But," exclaimed Ricardo, "those pearls were of great value, and pearls of great value are known; so, when they come upon the market—"

"That is true," Hanaud interrupted imperturbably. "But how are they known?"

"By their weight," said Mr. Ricardo.

"Exactly," replied Hanaud. "But did you not know that pearls can be peeled like an onion? No? It is true. Remove a skin, two skins, the weight is altered, the pearl is a trifle smaller. It has lost a little of its value, yes—but you can no longer identify it as the so-and-so pearl which belonged to this or that sultan, was stolen by the vizier, bought by Messrs. Lustre and Steinopolis, of Hatton Garden, and subsequently sold to the wealthy Mrs. Blumen. No, your pearl has vanished altogether. There is a new pearl which can be traded." He looked at Ricardo. "Who shall say that those pearls are not already in one of the queer little back streets of Amsterdam, undergoing their transformation?"

The days flew by. It was London's play-time. The green and gold of early summer deepened and darkened. Hanaud made acquaintance with the wooded reaches of the Thames; Joan Carew sang *Louise* at Covent Garden with notable success; and the affair of the Semiramis Hotel, in the minds of the few who remembered it, was already added to the long list of unfathomed mysteries.

But towards the end of May there occurred a startling development. Joan Carew wrote to Mr. Ricardo that she would call upon him in the afternoon, and she begged him to secure the presence of Hanaud. She came as the clock struck; she was pale and agitated; and in the room where Calladine had first told the story of her visit she told another story which, to Mr. Ricardo's thinking, was yet more strange.

"It has been going on for some time," she began. "I thought of coming to you at once. Then I wondered whether, if I waited—oh, you'll never believe me!"

"Let us hear," said Hanaud.

"I began to dream of that room, the two men disguised and masked, the still figure in the bed. Night after night! I was terrified to go to sleep. I felt the hand upon my mouth. I used to catch myself falling asleep, and walk about the room with all the lights up to keep myself awake. Oh, my nights were horrible until"—she paused and looked at her companions doubtfully— "until one night the mask slipped."

"What—?" cried Hanaud.

"It is true, the mask slipped on the face of one of the men—of the man who held me. Only a little way; it just left his forehead visible."

"Well?" asked Hanaud.

"I waked up," the girl continued, "in the darkness, and for a moment the whole scene remained vividly with me—for just

261

long enough for me to fix clearly in my mind the figure of the Apache with the white forehead showing above the mask."

"When was that?"asked Ricardo.

"A fortnight ago."

"Why didn't you come with your story then?"

"I waited," said Joan. "What I had to tell wasn't yet helpful. I thought that another night the mask might slip lower still. Besides, I—it is difficult to describe just what I felt. I felt it important just to keep that photograph in my mind, not to think about it, not to talk about it, not even to look at it too often lest I should begin to imagine the rest of the face and find something familiar in the man's carriage and shape when there was nothing really familiar to me at all. Do you understand that?"

"Yes," replied Hanaud.

"I thought there was a chance now—the strangest chance— that the truth might be reached. I did not wish to spoil it," and she turned eagerly to Ricardo, as if, having persuaded Hanaud, she would now turn her batteries on his companion. "My whole point of view was changed. I was no longer afraid of falling asleep lest I should dream. I wished to dream, but—"

"But you could not," suggested Hanaud.

"No, that is the truth," replied Joan Carew. "Whereas before I was anxious to keep awake and yet must sleep from sheer fatigue, now that I tried consciously to put myself to sleep I remained awake all through the night, and only towards morning, when the light was coming through the blinds, dropped off into a heavy, dreamless slumber.

"Then came my rehearsals," Joan Carew continued, "and that wonderful opera drove everything else out of my head. I had such a chance, if only I could make use of it! When I went to bed now, I went with that haunting music in my ears—the call of Paris—oh, you must remember it. But can you realize what it must mean to a girl who is going to sing it for the first time in Covent Garden?"

Mr. Ricardo saw his opportunity. He, the connoisseur, could answer that question.

"It is true, my friend," he informed Hanaud with quiet authority. "The great march of events leaves the artist cold. He lives aloof. While the tumbrils thunder in the streets he adds a delicate tint to the picture he is engaged upon or recalls his triumph in his last great art."

262

"Thank you," said Hanaud gravely. "And now Miss Carew may perhaps resume her story."

"It was the very night of my début," she continued. "I had supper with some friends. A great artist, Carmen Valeri, honored me with her presence. I went home excited, and that night I dreamed again."

"Yes?"

"This time the chin, the lips, the eyes were visible. There was only a black strip across the middle of the face. And I thought—nay, I was sure—that if that strip vanished I should know the man."

"And it did vanish?"

"Three nights afterwards."

"And you did know the man?"

The girl's face became troubled.

"I knew the face, that was all," she answered. "I was disappointed. I had never spoken to the man. I am sure of that still. But somewhere I have seen him."

"You don't even remember when?" asked Hanaud.

"No." Joan Carew reflected for a moment with her eyes upon the carpet, and then flung up her head with a gesture of despair. "No. I try all the time to remember. But it is no good."

"How did you pass the evening of that night when you first dreamed complete the face of your assailant?"

Joan Carew reflected. Then her face cleared.

"I know," she exclaimed. "I was at the opera."

"And what was being given?"

"The Jewels of the Madonna."

Hanaud nodded his head. To Ricardo it seemed that he had expected precisely that answer.

"Now," he continued, "you are sure that you have seen this man?"

"Yes."

"Very well," said Hanaud. "There is a game you play at children's parties—is there not?—animal, vegetable, or mineral, and always you get the answer. Let us play that game for a few minutes, you and I."

Joan Carew drew up her chair to the table and sat with her chin propped upon her hands and her eyes fixed on Hanaud's face. As he put each question she pondered on it and answered.

"You crossed on the *Lucania* from New York?"

"Yes."

"Picture to yourself the dining-room, the tables. You have the picture quite clear?"

"Yes."

"Was it at breakfast that you saw him?"

"No."

"At luncheon?"

"No."

"At dinner?"

"No."

"In the library, when you were writing letters, did you not one day lift your head and see him?"

"No."

"On the promenade deck? Did he pass you when you sat in your deck-chair?"

"No."

Step by step Hanaud took her back to New York to her hotel, to journeys in the train. Then he carried her to Milan where she had studied. It was extraordinary to Ricardo to realize how much Hanaud knew of the curriculum of a student aspiring to grand opera. From Milan he brought her again to New York, and at the last, with a start of joy, she cried: "Yes, it was there."

Hanaud took his handkerchief from his pocket and wiped his forehead.

"Ouf!" he grunted. "To concentrate the mind on a day like this, it makes one hot, I can tell you. Now, Miss Carew, let us hear."

It was at a concert at the house of a Mrs. Starlingshield on Fifth Avenue and in the afternoon. Joan Carew sang. She was a stranger to New York and very nervous. She saw nothing but a mist of faces while she sang, but when she had finished, the mist cleared, and as she left the improvised stage she saw the man. He was standing against the wall in a line of men. There was no particular reason why her eyes should single him out, except that he was paying no attention to her singing, and, indeed, she forgot him altogether afterwards.

"I just happened to see him clearly and distinctly," she said. "He was tall, clean-shaven, rather dark, not particularly young—thirty-five or so, I should say—a man with a heavy face and beginning to grow stout. He moved away while I was bowing to the audience, and I noticed him afterwards talking to people."

"Do you remember to whom?"

264

"No."

"Did he notice you, do you think?"

"I am sure he didn't," the girl replied emphatically.

She gave, so far as she could remember, the names of such guests and singers as she knew at that party. "And that is all," she said.

"Thank you," said Hanaud. "It is perhaps a good deal."

"You will let me hear from you?" she cried, as she rose to her feet.

"Miss Carew, I am at your service," he returned. She gave him her hand timidly and he took it cordially. For Mr. Ricardo she had merely a bow, a bow which recognized that he distrusted her and that she had no right to be offended. Then she went, and Hanaud smiled across the table at Ricardo.

"Yes," he said, "all that you are thinking is true enough. A man who slips out of society to indulge a passion for a drug in greater peace, a girl who, on her own confession, tried to steal, and, to crown all, this fantastic story. It is natural to disbelieve every word of it. But we disbelieved before, when we left Calladine's lodging in the Adelphi, and we were wrong."

"You have an idea?" exclaimed Ricardo.

"Perhaps!" said Hanaud. And he looked down the theater column of the *Times*. "Let us distract ourselves by going to the theater."

"You are the most irritating man!" Mr. Ricardo broke out impulsively. "If I had to paint your portrait, I should paint you with your finger against the side of your nose, saying mysteriously: 'I know,' when you know nothing at all."

Hanaud made a schoolboy's grimace. "We will go and sit in your box at the opera tonight," he said.

They reached Covent Garden before the curtain rose. Mr. Ricardo's box was on the lowest tier and next to the omnibus box.

"We are near the stage," said Hanaud, as he took his seat in the corner and so arranged the curtain that he could see and yet was hidden from view. "I like that."

The theater was full; stalls and boxes shimmered with jewels and satin, and all that was famous that season for beauty and distinction had made its tryst there that night.

"Yes, this is wonderful," said Hanaud. "What opera do they play?" He glanced at his program and cried, with a little start of surprise: "We are in luck. It is *The Jewels of the Madonna.*"

"Do you believe in omens?" Mr. Ricardo asked coldly. He had not yet recovered from his rebuff of the afternoon.

"No, but I believe that Carmen Valeri is at her best in this part," said Hanaud.

Mr. Ricardo belonged to that body of critics which must needs spoil your enjoyment by comparisons and recollections of other great artists. He was at a disadvantage certainly tonight, for the opera was new. But he did his best. He imagined others in the part, and when the great scene came at the end of the second act, and Carmen Valeri, on obtaining from her lover the jewels stolen from the sacred image, gave such a display of passion as fairly enthralled that audience, Mr. Ricardo sighed quietly and patiently.

"How Calvé would have brought out the psychological value of that scene!" he murmured; and he was quite vexed with Hanaud, who sat with his opera glasses held to his eyes, and every sense apparently concentrated on the stage. The curtains rose and rose again when the act was concluded, and still Hanaud sat motionless as the Sphinx, staring through his glasses.

"That is all," said Ricardo when the curtains fell for the fifth time.

"They will come out," said Hanaud. "Wait!" And from between the curtains Carmen Valeri was led out into the full glare of the footlights. Then at last Hanaud put down his glasses and turned to Ricardo with a look of exultation and genuine delight.

"What a night!" said Hanaud. "What a wonderful night!" And he applauded until he split his gloves. At the end of the opera he cried: "We will go and take supper at the Semiramis. Yes, my friend, we will finish our evening like gallant gentlemen. Come!"

In spite of his boast, however, Hanaud hardly touched his supper, and he played with, rather than drank, his brandy and soda. He sat with his back to the wall watching the groups which poured in. Suddenly his face lighted up.

"Here is Carmen Valeri!" he cried. "Once more we are in luck. Is it not that she is beautiful?"

Mr. Ricardo turned languidly about in his chair and put up his eyeglass.

"So-so," he said.

266

"Ah!" returned Hanaud. "Then her companion will interest you still more. For he is the man who murdered Mrs. Blumen."

Mr. Ricardo jumped so that his eyeglass fell and tinkled on its cord against the buttons of his waistcoat.

"What!" he exclaimed. "It's impossible!" He looked again. "Certainly the man fits Joan Carew's description. But—" He turned back to Hanaud utterly astounded. And as he looked at the Frenchman all his earlier recollections of him, of his swift deductions, of the subtle imagination which his heavy body so well concealed, crowded in upon Ricardo and convinced him.

"How long have you known?" he asked in a whisper of awe.

"Since ten o'clock tonight."

"But you will have to find the necklace before you can prove it."

"The necklace!" said Hanaud carelessly. "That is already found."

Mr. Ricardo had been longing for a thrill. He had it now.

"It's found?" he said in a startled whisper.

"Yes."

Ricardo turned again, with as much indifference as he could assume, towards the couple who were settling down at their table, the man with a surly indifference, Carmen Valeri with the radiance of a woman who has just achieved a triumph and is now free to enjoy the fruits of it. Confusedly, recollections returned to Ricardo of questions put that afternoon by Hanaud to Joan Carew—subtle questions into which the name of Carmen Valeri was continually entering. She was a woman of thirty, certainly beautiful, with a clear, pale face and eyes like the night.

"Then she is implicated too!" he said. What a change for her, he thought, from the stage of Covent Garden to the felon's cell.

"She!" exclaimed Hanaud; and in his passion for the contrasts of drama Ricardo was almost disappointed. "She has nothing whatever to do with it. She knows nothing. André Favart there—yes. But Carmen Valeri! She's as stupid as an owl, and loves him beyond words. Do you want to know how stupid she is? You shall know. I asked Mr. Clements, the director of the opera house, to take supper with us, and here he is."

Hanaud stood up and shook hands with the director. He was of the world of business rather than of art, and long experience of the ways of tenors and primadonnas had given him a good-humored cynicism.

"They are spoilt children, all tantrums and vanity," he said, "and they would ruin you to keep a rival out of the theater."

He told them anecdote upon anecdote.

"And Carmen Valeri," Hanaud asked in a pause. "Is she troublesome this season?"

"Has been," replied Clements dryly. "At present she is playing at being good. But she gave me a turn some weeks ago." He turned to Ricardo. "Superstition's her trouble, and André Favart knows it. She left him behind in America this spring."

"America!" suddenly cried Ricardo; so suddenly that Clements looked at him in surprise.

"She was singing in New York, of course, during the winter," he returned. "Well, she left him behind, and I was shaking hands with myself when he began to deal the cards over there. She came to me in a panic. She had just had a cable. She couldn't sing on Friday night. There was a black knave next to the nine of diamonds. She wouldn't sing for worlds. And it was the first night of *The Jewels of the Madonna!* Imagine the fix I was in!"

"What did you do?" asked Ricardo.

"The only thing there was to do," replied Clements with a shrug of the shoulders. "I cabled Favart some money and he dealt the cards again. She came to me beaming. Oh, she had been so distressed to put me in the cart! But what could she do? Now there was a red queen next to the ace of hearts, so she could sing without a scruple so long, of course, as she didn't pass a funeral on the way down to the opera house. Luckily she didn't. But my money brought Favart over here, and now I'm living on a volcano. For he's the greatest scoundrel unhung. He never has a farthing, however much she gives him; he's a blackmailer, a swindler, has no manners and no graces, looks like a butcher and treats her as if she were dirt, never goes near the opera except when she is singing in this part, and she worships the ground he walks on. Well, I suppose it's time to go."

The lights had been turned off, the great room was emptying. Mr. Ricardo and his friends rose to go, but at the door Hanaud detained Mr. Clements, and they talked together alone for some little while, greatly to Mr. Ricardo's annoyance. Hanaud's good humor, however, when he rejoined his friend, was enough for two.

"I apologize, my friend, with my hand on my heart. But it was for your sake that I stayed behind. You have a meretricious taste for melodrama which I deeply deplore, but which I mean to gratify. I ought to leave for Paris tomorrow, but I shall not. I shall stay until Thursday."

Mr. Ricardo bubbled with questions, but he knew his man. He would get no answer to any of them tonight. So he worked out the problem for himself as he lay awake in his bed, and he came down to breakfast next morning fatigued but triumphant. Hanaud was already chipping off the top of his egg at the table.

"So I see you have found it all out, my friend," he said.

"Not all," replied Ricardo modestly, "and you will not mind, I am sure, if I follow the usual custom and wish you a good morning."

"Not at all," said Hanaud. "I am all for good manners myself. But I am longing to hear the line of your reasoning."

Mr. Ricardo did not need much pressing.

"Joan Carew saw André Favart at Mrs. Starlingshield's party, and saw him with Carmen Valeri. For Carmen Valeri was there. I remember that you asked Joan for the names of the artists who sang, and Carmen Valeri was among them."

Hanaud nodded his head.

"No doubt Joan Carew noticed Carmen Valeri particularly, and so took unconsciously into her mind an impression of the man who was with her, André Favart—of his build, of his walk, of his type."

Again Hanaud agreed.

"She forgets the man altogether, but the picture remains latent in her mind—an undeveloped film.

"Then came the tragic night at the Semiramis. She does not consciously recognize her assailant, but she dreams the scene again and again, and by a process of unconscious cerebration the figure of the man becomes familiar. Finally she makes her début, is entertained at supper afterwards, and meets once more Carmen Valeri."

"Yes, for the first time since Mrs. Starlingshield's party," interjected Hanaud.

"She dreams again, she remembers asleep more than she remembers when awake. The presence of Carmen Valeri at her supper-party has its effect. By a process of association she recalls Favart, and the mask slips on the face of her assailant. Some days later she goes to the opera. She hears Carmen Valeri sing in *The Jewels of the Madonna*. No doubt the passion of her acting, which I am more prepared to acknowledge this morning than I was last night, affects Joan Carew powerfully, emotionally. She goes to bed with her head full of Carmen Valeri, and she dreams not of Carmen Valeri, but of the man who is unconsciously associated with Carmen Valeri in her thoughts. The mask vanishes altogether. She sees her assailant now, has his portrait limned in her mind."

"Yes," said Hanaud. "It is curious, the brain working while the body sleeps, the dream revealing what thought cannot recall."

Mr. Ricardo was delighted. He was taken seriously.

"But of course," he said, "I could not have worked the problem out but for you. You knew of André Favart and the kind of man he was."

Hanaud laughed.

"Yes. That is always my one little advantage. I know all the cosmopolitan blackguards of Europe." His laughter ceased suddenly, and he brought his clenched fist heavily down upon the table. "Here is one of them who will be very well out of the world, my friend," he said very quietly.

For a few moments there was silence. Then Ricardo asked: "But have you evidence enough?"

"Yes."

"Your two chief witnesses, Calladine and Joan Carew—you said it yourself—there are facts to discredit them. Will they be believed?"

"But they won't appear in the case at all," Hanaud said. "Wait, wait!" and once more he smiled. "By the way, what is the number of Calladine's house?"

Ricardo gave it, and Hanaud thereupon wrote a letter. "It is all for your sake, my friend," he chuckled.

"Nonsense," said Ricardo. "You have the spirit of the theater in your bones."

"Well, I shall not deny it," said Hanaud, and he sent out the letter to the nearest pillar-box.

Mr. Ricardo waited in a fever of impatience until Thursday came. At breakfast Hanaud would talk of nothing but the news of the day. At luncheon he was no better. The affair of the Semiramis Hotel seemed a thousand miles from his thoughts. But at five o'clock he said as he drank his tea:

"You know, of course, that we go to the opera tonight?"

"Yes. Do we?"

"Yes. Your young friend Calladine, by the way, will join us in your box."

270

"That is very kind of him, I am sure," said Mr. Ricardo.

The two men arrived before the rising of the curtain, and in the crowded lobby a stranger spoke a few words to Hanaud, but what he said Ricardo could not hear. They took their seats in the box, and Hanaud looked at his program.

"Ah! It is *Il Ballo de Maschera* tonight. We always seem to hit upon something appropriate, don't we?"

Then he raised his eyebrows.

"Oh-o! Do you see that our pretty young friend, Joan Carew, is singing in the rôle of the page? It is a showy part. There is a particular melody with a long-sustained trill in it. By the way, I should let Calladine find it all out for himself."

Mr. Ricardo nodded sagely.

"Yes. That is wise. I had thought of it myself." But he had done nothing of the kind. He was only aware that the elaborate stage-management in which Hanaud delighted was working out to the desired climax, whatever that climax might be. Calladine entered the box a few minutes later and shook hands with them awkwardly.

"It was kind of you to invite me," he said and, very ill at ease, he took a seat between them.

"There's the overture," said Hanaud. The curtains divided and were festooned on either side of the stage. The singers came on in their turn; the page appeared to a burst of delicate applause (Joan Carew had made a small name for herself that season), and with a stifled cry Calladine shot back in the box as if he had been struck. Even then Mr. Ricardo did not understand. He only realized that Joan Carew was looking extraordinarily trim and smart in her boy's dress. He had to look from his program to the stage and back again several times before the reason of Calladine's exclamation dawned on him. When it did, he was horrified. Hanaud, in his craving for dramatic effects, must have lost his head altogether. Joan Carew was wearing, from the ribbon in her hair to the scarlet heels of her buckled satin shoes, the same dress as she had worn on the tragic night at the Semiramis Hotel. He leaned forward in his agitation to Hanaud.

"You must be mad. Suppose Favart is in the theater and sees her. He'll be over on the Continent by one in the morning."

"No, he won't," replied Hanaud. "For one thing, he never comes to Covent Garden unless one opera, with Carmen Valeri in the chief part, is being played, as you heard the other night at supper. For a second thing, he isn't in the house. I know where he is. He is gambling in Dean Street, Soho. For a third thing, my friend, he couldn't leave by the nine o'clock train for the Continent if he wanted to. Arrangements have been made. For a fourth thing, he wouldn't wish to. He has really remarkable reasons for desiring to stay in London. But he will come to the theater later. Clements will send him an urgent message, with the result that he will go straight to Clements's office. Meanwhile, we can enjoy ourselves, eh?"

Never was the difference between the amateur dilettante and the genuine professional more clearly exhibited than by the behavior of the two men during the rest of the performance. Mr. Ricardo might have been sitting on a coal fire from his jumps and twistings; Hanaud stolidly enjoyed the music, and when Joan Carew sang her famous solo his hands clamored for an encore. Certainly, whether excitement was keeping her up or no, Joan Carew had never sung better in her life. Her voice was clear and fresh as a bird's—a bird with a soul inspiring its song. Even Calladine drew his chair forward again and sat with his eyes fixed upon the stage and quite carried out of himself. He drew a deep breath at the end.

"She is wonderful," he said.

"We will go round to the back of the stage," said Hanaud.

They passed through the iron door and across the stage to a long corridor with a row of doors on one side. There were two or three men standing about in evening dress, as if waiting for friends in the dressing-rooms. At the third door Hanaud stopped and knocked. The door was opened by Joan Carew, still dressed in her green and gold. Her face was troubled, her eyes afraid.

"Courage, little one," said Hanaud, and he slipped past her into the room. "It is as well that my ugly, familiar face should not be seen too soon."

The door closed and one of the strangers loitered along the corridor and spoke to a call-boy. The call-boy ran off. For five minutes more Mr. Ricardo waited with a beating heart. He had the joy of a man in the center of things. All those people driving homewards in their motor-cars along the Strand—how he pitied them! Then, at the end of the corridor, he saw Clements and André Favart. They approached, discussing the possibility of Carmen Valeri's appearance in London opera during the next season.

272

"We have to look ahead, my dear friend," said Clements, "and though I should be extremely sorry—"

At that moment they were exactly opposite Joan Carew's door. It opened, she came out; with a nervous movement she shut the door behind her. At the sound André Favart turned, and he saw up against the panels of the door, with a look of terror in her face, the same gay figure which had interrupted him in Mrs. Blumen's bedroom.

Favart stared and uttered an oath. His face turned white; he staggered back, as if he had seen a ghost. Then he made a wild dash along the corridor, and was seized and held by two of the men in evening dress. Favart recovered his wits. He ceased to struggle.

"What does this outrage mean?" he asked, and one of the men drew a warrant and notebook from his pocket.

"You are arrested for the murder of Mrs. Blumen in the Semiramis Hotel," he said, "and I have to warn you that anything you may say will be taken down and may be used in evidence against you."

"Preposterous!" exclaimed Favart. "There's a mistake. We will go along to the police and put it right. Where's your evidence against me?"

Hanaud stepped out of the doorway of the dressing-room.

"In the property-room of the theater," he said.

At the sight of him Favart uttered a violent cry of rage. "You are here, too, are you?" and he sprang at Hanaud's throat. Hanaud stepped lightly aside. Favart was borne down to the ground, and when he stood up again the handcuffs were on him.

Favart was led away, and Hanaud turned to Ricardo and Clements.

"Let us go to the property-room," he said. They passed along the corridor, and Ricardo noticed that Calladine was no longer with them. He turned and saw him standing outside Joan Carew's dressing-room. In the property-room there was already a detective in plainclothes.

"What is it you really want, sir?" the property-master asked of the director.

"Only the jewels of the Madonna," Hanaud answered.

The property-master unlocked a cupboard and took from it the sparkling cuirass. Hanaud pointed to it, and there, lost among the huge glittering stones of paste and false pearls, Mrs. Blumen's necklace was entwined.

273

"Then that is why Favart came always to Covent Garden when *The Jewels of the Madonna* was being performed!" exclaimed Ricardo.

Hanaud nodded.

"He came to watch over his treasure."

Ricardo was piecing together the sections of the puzzle.

"No doubt he knew of the necklace in America. No doubt he followed it to England."

"But to hide them here!" cried Mr. Clements. "He must have been mad."

"Why?" asked Hanaud. "Can you imagine a safer hiding place? Who is going to burgle the property-room of Covent Garden? Who is going to look for a priceless string of pearls among the stage jewels of an opera house?"

"You did," said Mr. Ricardo.

"I?" replied Hanaud, shrugging his shoulders. "Joan Carew's dreams led me to André Favart. The first time we came here and saw the pearls of the Madonna, I was on the lookout, naturally. I noticed those pearls through my opera glasses."

"At the end of the second act?" cried Ricardo suddenly. "I remember now."

"Yes," replied Hanaud. "But for that second act the pearls would have stayed comfortably here all through the season. Carmen Valeri—a fool as I told you—would have tossed them about in her dressing-room without a notion of their value, and at the end of July, when the murder at the Semiramis Hotel had been forgotten, Favart would have taken them to Amsterdam and made his bargain."

They left the theater together and walked down to the grill-room of the Semiramis. But as Hanaud looked through the glass door he turned and drew back.

"We will not go in, I think, eh?"

"Why?" asked Ricardo.

Hanaud pointed to a table. Calladine and Joan Carew were seated at it taking their supper.

"Perhaps," said Hanaud with a smile, "perhaps, my friend—what? Who shall say that the rooms in the Adelphi will not be given up?"

They turned away from the hotel. But Hanaud was right, and before the season was over Mr. Ricardo had to put his hand in his pocket for a wedding present.

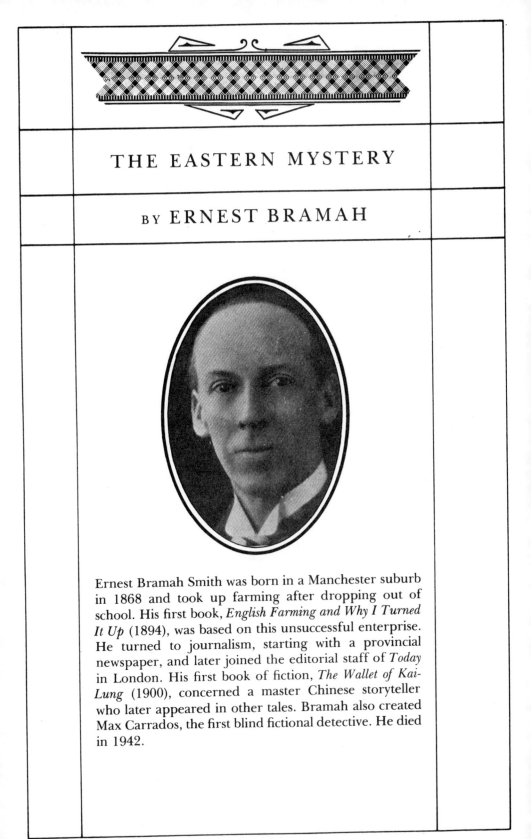

THE EASTERN MYSTERY

BY ERNEST BRAMAH

Ernest Bramah Smith was born in a Manchester suburb in 1868 and took up farming after dropping out of school. His first book, *English Farming and Why I Turned It Up* (1894), was based on this unsuccessful enterprise. He turned to journalism, starting with a provincial newspaper, and later joined the editorial staff of *Today* in London. His first book of fiction, *The Wallet of Kai-Lung* (1900), concerned a master Chinese storyteller who later appeared in other tales. Bramah also created Max Carrados, the first blind fictional detective. He died in 1942.

IT COULD SCARCELY BE CALLED Harris's fault, whatever the driver next behind might say in the momentary bitterness of his heart. In the two-fifths of a second of grace at his disposal Mr. Max Carrado's chauffeur had done all that was possible and the bunt that his radiator gave the stair-guard of the London General in the front was insignificant. Then a Railway Express Delivery skated on its dead weight into his luggage platform and a Pickford, turning adroitly out of the mêlée, slewed a stationary Gearless round by its hand-rail stanchion to spread terror and great confusion in the other line of traffic.

The most unconcerned person, to all appearance, was the driver of the London General, the vehicle whose sudden stoppage had initiated the riot of confusion. He had seen a man, engrossed to the absolute exclusion of his surroundings by something that took his eye on the opposite footpath, dash into the road and then, brought up suddenly by a realization of his position, attempt to retrace his steps. He had pulled up so expertly that the man had escaped, so smoothly that not a passenger was jarred, and now he sat with a dazed and vacant expression on his face, leaning forward on his steering wheel, while caustic inquiry and retort winged unheeded up and down the line behind him.

It was not until the indispensable ceremony of everyone taking everyone else's name and number had been observed under the authority of the tutelary constable that the single occupant of the private car stirred to show any interest in the proceedings.

"Parkinson," he called quietly, summoning his attendant to the window.

"Ask Mr. Tulloch if he will come round here when he has finished with the policeman."

"Mr. Tulloch, sir?"

"Yes; you remember Dr. Tulloch of Netherhempsfield? He is out in front there."

A moment later Jim Tulloch, as genial as of old, but his exuberance temporarily damped by the cross-bickering in which he had just been involved, thrust his head and arm through the sash.

"Lord, it really is you, then, Wynn,* old man?" he cried. "When your Parkinson came up I simply couldn't believe it. The world grows smaller, I declare."

"At all events this car does," responded Carrados, wringing the hearty outstretched hand. "They've got us two inches less than the makers ever intended. Is it your doing, Jim?"

"Did ever you hear such a thing?" protested Tulloch. "And yet that walleyed atrocity yonder has kidded the copper that if he hadn't stopped dead—well, I should."

"Was it a near thing?" asked Carrados confidentially.

"Well, strictly between ourselves. I don't mind admitting that it might have been something of a shave," confessed Tulloch, with a cheerful grin. "But, Lord bless you, Wynn, the streets of London are paved with 'em nowadays. You don't merely take your life in your hands if you want to get about; you carry it on each foot."

"Look here," said Carrados. "You never let me know that you were up in town, Tulloch. What are you doing today?"

"I beg your pardon, sir," interrupted Parkinson's respectable voice, "but the policeman wishes to speak with you, sir."

"With me?" queried Tulloch restlessly. "Oh, good Lord, have we to go into all that again?"

"It's only the bus-driver, sir," apologized the constable with the tactful deference that the circumstances seemed to demand. "As you are a doctor—I think there's something the matter with him."

"I'm sure there is," assented Tulloch. "All right, I'm coming. Are you in a hurry, Wynn?"

"I'll wait," was the reply.

The doctor found his patient propped up on a doorstep. Having, as he expressed it afterwards, "run the rule over him," he prescribed a glass of water and an hour's rest. The man was shaken, that was all.

"Nerves, Wynn," he announced when he returned to his friend. "I don't quite understand his emotion, but the shock of not having run over me seems to have upset the poor fellow."

"I was asking you whether you were doing anything today," said Carrados. "Can you come back with me to Richmond?"

"I'm not doing anything as far as that goes," admitted Tulloch. "In fact," he added ruefully, "that's the plague of it. I'm

---

*Max Carrados's original surname.

277

waiting to hear from a man who's waiting to hear from another man, and *he's* depending on something that may or mayn't, you understand."

"Then you can come along now. Get in."

"If it's dinner you mean, I can't come straight away, you know," protested Tulloch. "Look at me togs"—he stood back to display a serviceable Norfolk suit—"all right for the six-thirty sharp of a Bloomsbury boarding house, but—eh, what?"

"Don't be an ass, Jim," said the blind man amiably. "I can't see your silly togs."

"No ladies or any of your tony friends?"

"Not a soul."

"The fact is," confided Tulloch, taking his place in the car, "I've been out of things for a bit, Wynn, and I'm finding civilization a shade cast-iron now. I've been down in the wilds since you were with me."

"I wondered where you were. I wrote to you about six months ago and the letter came back."

"Did it actually? Now that must have been almighty careless of someone, Wynn. I'm sorry; I'm a bit of a rolling stone, I suppose. When Darrish came back to Netherhempsfield my job was done there. I felt uncommonly restless. I hadn't much chance of buying a practice or dropping into a partnership worth having and I jibbed at setting up in some Godforsaken backwater and slipping into middle age 'building up a connection.' Lord, Carrados, the tragic monotony of your elderly professional nonentity! I've known men who whispered to me between the pulls at confidential pipes that they've come to hate the streets and the houses and the same old everlasting silly faces that they met day after day until they began to think very queer thoughts of how they might get away from it all."

"Yes," said Carrados.

"Anyway, 'Not yet,' I promised myself, and when I got the chance of a temporary thing on a Red Cable liner I took it like a shot. That was something. If there was a mighty sameness about it after a bit, it wasn't the sameness I'd been accustomed to. Then, as luck of one sort or another would have it, I got laid out with a broken ankle on a Bombay quay."

Carrados voiced commiseration.

"But you made a very good mend of it," he said. "It's the left, of course. I don't suppose anyone ever notices it."

"I took care of that," replied Tulloch. "But it was a slow

278

business and threw all my plans out. I was on a very loose end when one day, outside the Secretariat, as they call it, I ran up against a man called Fraser whom I'd known building a viaduct or something of that sort in the Black Country.

" 'What on earth are *you* doing here?' we naturally said at once and he was the first to reply.

" 'I'm just off to repair an irrigation "bund" a thousand miles more or less away, and I'm looking for a doctor who can speak six words of Hindustani, and doesn't mind things as they are. What are you doing?'

" 'Good Lord, old man,' I said, 'I was looking for you!' "

It only required an occasional word to keep Tulloch going, and Carrados supplied it. He heard much that did not interest him—of the journey inland, of the face of the country, the surprising weather, the great work of irrigation, and the other impressive wonders of man and nature. These things could be got from books, but among the weightier cargo Tulloch now and again touched off some inimitable phase of life or told an uninventable anecdote of native character.

Yet the buoyant doctor had something on his mind, for several times he stopped abruptly on the edge of a reminiscence, as though he were doubtful, if not of the matter, at least of the manner in which he should begin. These indications were not lost on his friend, but Carrados made no attempt to press him, being very well assured that sooner or later the ingenuous Jim would find himself beyond retreat. The occasion came just after dinner. There had been a reference to the language.

"I often wish that I was a better stick at it," said Tulloch. "I'd picked up a bit in Bombay and of course I threw myself into it when Fraser got me to the post. I managed pretty well with the coolies in the camp, but when I tried to have a word with the ryots living round—little twopenny ha'penny farmers, you know—I could make no show of it. A lot of queer fish you come across out there, in one way or another, you take my word. You never know whether a man's a professional saint of extreme holiness or a hereditary body-snatcher whose shadow would make a begging leper consider himself unclean until he had walked seventy miles to drink a cupful of filthy water out of a stinking pond that a pockmarked ascetic had been sitting in for three years in order to contemplate quietly."

"Possibly he really was unclean—in consequence or otherwise," suggested Carrados.

"Help!" exclaimed Tulloch tragically. "There are things that have to be seen. But then so was the sanctified image, so that there's nothing for an outsider to go by. And then all the different little lots with their own particular little heavens and their own one exclusive way of getting there, and their social frills and furbelows—Jats and Jains and Thugs and Mairs and Gonds and Bhills and Toms, Dicks, and Harrys—suburban society is nothing to it, Wynn, nothing at all. There was a strange old joker I've been in mind to tell you about, though it was no joke for him in the end. God alone knows where he came from, but he was in the camp one evening juggling for stray coppers in a bowl. Pretty good juggling too it seemed to be, of the usual Indian kind—growing a plant out of a pumpkin seed, turning a stick into a live snake, and the old sword and basket trick that every Eastern conjurer keeps up his sleeve; but all done out in the open, with people squatting round and a simplicity of appliance that would have taken all the curl out of one of your music-hall magicians. With him he had a boy, his son, a misshapen, monkey-like anatomy of about ten, but there was no doubt that the man was desperately fond of his offspring.

"That night this ungainly urchin, taking a cooler in one of the big irrigation canals, got laid hold of by an alligator and raised the most unearthly screech anything human ever got out. I seemed to have had something prominent to do with the damp job of getting as much of him away from the creature as we could, and old Calico—that's what we anglicized the juggler's name into—had some sort of idea of being grateful in consequence. Although I don't doubt that he'd have put much more faith in a local wizard if one had been available, he let us take the boy into the hospital tent and do what we could for him. It wasn't much, and I told my assistant to break it to poor old Calico that he must be prepared for the worst. A handy man, that assistant, Wynn. He was a half-breed 'Portugoose,' as they say in Bombay, with the name of Vasque d'Almeydo, and I understood that he'd had some training. When we got out there he said that it was all the same to him, but he admitted quite blandly that he was really a cook and nothing more. What about his excellent testimonials? I asked him, and he replied with cheerful impenitence that he had bought them in the open market for one rupee eight, adding feelingly that he would willingly have given twice as much to qualify for my honorable service. In the end he did pretty much as he liked, and as he could speak five languages and scramble through seven dialects, I was glad to have him about on any terms. I don't quite know how he broke it, but when I saw him later he said that Calico was a 'great damn fool.' He was a conjurer and knew how tricks were done and yet he had set out at once for some place thirty miles away to procure a charm of some sort, the Portuguese would swear from a hint he had got. Vasque laughed pleasantly as he commented on native credulity. The next day the boy died and an hour later poor Calico came reeling in. He'd got a nasty cut over the eye and a map of the route drawn over him in thorns and blisters and sand-burns, but he'd got something wrapped in a bit of rag carried in the left armpit, and I felt for the poor old heathen. When he understood, he borrowed a spade and, taking up the child just as he was, he went off into the pagan solitude to bury him. I'd got used to these simple ways by that time.

"I thought that I'd seen the end of the incident, but late that night I heard the sentry outside challenge someone—we'd had so many tools and things looted by 'friendlies' that they'd lent us half a company of Sikhs from Kharikhas—and a moment later Calico was salaaming at the tent door. As it happened, Vasque was away at a village, trafficking for some ducks, and I had to grapple with the conversation as best I could—no joke, I may tell you, for the juggler's grasp on conventional Urdu was about as slender as my own. And the first thing he did was to put his paws on my astonished feet, then up to his forehead, and to prostrate himself to the ground.

" 'Sahib,' he protested earnestly, 'I am thy slave and docile elephant for that which thou hast done for the man-child of my house.'

"Now you know, Wynn, I simply can't stand that sort of thing. It makes me feel like such a colossal ass. So I tried, ungraciously enough, to cut him short. But it couldn't be done. Poor old Calico had come to discharge what weighed on him as a formidable obligation and my 'Don't mention it, old chap,' was quite out of the picture. Finally, from some obscure fold of his outfit, he produced a little screw of cloth and began to unwrap it.

" 'Take it, O sahib, and treasure it as you would a cup of water in the desert, for it has great virtue of the hidden kind. Condescend to accept it, for it is all I have worthy of so great a burden.'

281

" 'I couldn't think of it, Khaligar,' I said, trying to give his name a romantic twist, for the other sounded like guying him. 'I've done nothing, you know, and in any case this is much more likely to work with you than with me—an unbeliever. What is it, anyway?'

" 'It is the sacred tooth of the ape-god Hanuman and it protects from harm,' he replied, reverently displaying what looked to me like an old rusty nail. 'Had I but been able to touch so much as the hem of the garment of my manlet with it before the hour of his outgoing he would assuredly have recovered.'

" 'Then keep it for your own protection,' I urged. 'I expect that you run more risks than I do.'

" 'When the flame has been extinguished from a candle the smoke lingers but a moment before it also fades away,' he replied. 'Thy servant has no wish to live now that the light of his eyes has gone out, nor does he seek to avert by magic that which is written on his forehead.'

" 'Then it is witchcraft?' I said, pointing to the amulet.

" 'I know not,' he answered, 'but if it be witchcraft it is of the honorable sort and not the goety of Shaitan. For this cause it is only of avail to one who acquires it without treachery or guile. Take it, sahib, but do not suffer it to become known even to those of your own table.'

" 'Why not?' I asked.

" 'Who should boast of pearls in a camp of armed bandits?' he replied evasively. 'A word spoken in a locked closet becomes a beacon on the hilltop for men to see. Yet have no fear; harm cannot come to you, for your hand is free from complicity.'

"I hadn't wanted the thing before, but that settled me. I very much doubted how the conjurer had gotten possession of it and I had no wish to be mixed up in an affair of any sort. I told him definitely that while I appreciated his motives I shouldn't deprive him of so great a treasure. He seemed really concerned, and Fraser told me afterwards that for one of the tribe to be under what he regarded as an unrequited obligation was a dishonor. I should probably have had some trouble to get him off, only just then we heard Vasque returning. Calico hastily wrapped up the relic, stowed it away among his wardrobe, and, with his most ceremonious salaam, disappeared.

" 'Do you know anything about the tooth of the ape-god Hanuman, Vasque?' I asked him some time later. The 'Portugoose' seemed to know a little about everything and in conse-

282

quence of my dependence on him he strayed into a rather more free and easy manner than might have passed under other conditions. But I'm not ceremonious, you know, Wynn."

And Carrados laughed and agreed.

" 'The sacred tooth of Sira Hanuman, sir?' said Vasque. 'Oh, that's all great tom dam foolery. There are a hundred million of them. The most notable one was worshipped at the Mountain of Adam in Ceylon until it was captured by my ancestor, the illustrious Admiral d'Almeydo, who sent it with much pomp and circumstance to Goa. Then the Princes of Malabar offered a ransom of rupees, forty lakhs, for it, which the Bishop of Goa refused.'

" 'What became of it?' I asked, but Vasque didn't know. He was somewhat of a liar, in fact, and I daresay that he'd made it all up to show off his knowledge."

"No," objected Carrados; "I think that Baldaeus, the Dutch historian, has a similar tale. What happened to Calico?"

"That was the worst of it. Some of our men found his body lying among the tamarisk scrub two days later. There was no doubt that he'd been murdered, and not content with that, the ghouls had mutilated him shamefully afterwards. Even his cheeks were slashed open. So, you see, the tooth of Hanuman had not protected him."

"No," assented Carrados, "it had certainly not protected him. Was anything done—anyone arrested?"

"I don't think so. You know what the natives are in a case like that; no one knows anything, even if they have been looking on at the time. I suppose a report would be sent up, but I never heard anything more. I always had a suspicion that Calico, with his blend of simple faith and gypsy blood, had violated a temple, or looted a shrine, to try to save his son's life, and that the guardians of the relic tracked him and revenged the outrage. Anyway, I was glad that I hadn't accepted it after that, for I had enough excitement without."

"What was that, Jim?"

"Oh, I don't know, but I always seemed to be running up against something about that time. Twice my tent was turned inside out in my absence, once my clothes were spirited away while I was bathing, and the night before we broke up the camp I was within an ace of being murdered."

"You bear a charmed life," said Carrados suggestively, but Tulloch did not rise to the suggestion.

"It was a bit of luck. Those dacoits are as quiet as death, but for some reason I woke suddenly with the idea that the devilment was brewing. I slipped on the first few things that came to hand and went to reconnoiter. As I passed through the canvas I came face to face with a native, and two others were only a few yards behind. Without any ceremony the near man let drive at my throat with one of those beastly wavy daggers they go in for. I suppose I managed to dodge in the fraction of a second, for he missed me. I gave a yell for assistance, landed the leader one in the eye, and backed into my tent for a weapon. By the time I was out again our fellows were running up, but the precious trio had disappeared."

"That was the last you saw of them?" asked Carrados tentatively.

"No, queerly enough. The day I sailed I encountered the one whose eye I had touched up. It was down by the water—the Apollo Bander—at Bombay, and I was so taken aback, never thinking but that the fellow was hundreds of miles away, that I did nothing but stare. But I promised myself that in the unlikely event of ever seeing him again I would follow him up pretty sharply."

"Not under the wheels of a London General again, I hope!"

Tulloch's brown fist came down upon the table with a crash.

"The devil, Carrados!" he exclaimed. "How did you know?"

"Parkinson was just describing to me a rather exotic figure. Then the rest followed."

"Well, you were right. There was the man in Holborn, and of all the fantastic things in the world for a bloodthirsty thug from the back wilds of Hindustan, I believe that he was selling picture postcards!"

"Possibly a very natural thing to be doing in the circumstances."

"What circumstances, Wynn?"

"Those you are telling me of. Go on."

"That's about all there is. When I saw the man I was so excited, I suppose, that I started to dash across without another thought. You know the result. Of course he had vanished by the time I could look round."

"You are quite sure he is the same?"

"There's always the possibility of a mistake, I admit," considered Tulloch, "but, speaking in ordinary terms, I should say that it's a moral certainty. On the first occasion it was bright

284

moonlight and the sensational attack left a very vivid photograph in my mind. In Bombay I had no suspicion of doubt about the man, and he was still carrying traces of my fist. Here, it is true, I had less chance of observing him, but recognition was equally instantaneous and complete. Then consider that each time he has slipped away at once. No, I am not mistaken. What is he after, Wynn?"

"I am very much afraid that he is after you, my friend," replied Carrados, with some concern lurking behind the half-amused voice.

"After me!" exclaimed Tulloch with righteous indignation. "Why, confound his nerve, it ought to be the other way about. What's he after me for?"

"India is a conservative land. The gods do not change. A relic that was appraised at seven hundred thousand ducats in the days of Queen Elizabeth is worth following up today—apart, of course, from the merit thereby acquired by a devotee."

"You mean that Calico's charm was the real original thing that Vasque spoke of?"

"It is quite possible; or it may be claimed for it even if it is not. Goa has passed through many vicissitudes; its churches and palaces are now in ruins. What is more credible—"

"But in any case I haven't got the thing. Surely the old ass needn't murder me to find out that."

The face he appealed to betrayed nothing of the thoughts behind it. But Carrados's mind was busy with every detail of the story he had heard, and the more he looked into it the less he felt at ease for his impetuous friend's safety.

"On the contrary," he replied, "from the pious believer's point of view, the simplest and most effective way of ascertaining it was to try to murder you, and your providential escape has only convinced them that you are now the holder of the charm."

"The deuce!" said Tulloch ruefully. "Then I have dropped into an imbroglio after all. What's to be done?"

"I wonder," mused the blind man speculatively, "I wonder what really became of the thing."

"You mean after Calico's death?"

"No, before that. I don't imagine that your entertaining friend had it at the end. He had nothing to look forward to, you remember; he did not wish to live. His assassins were those who were concerned in the recovery of the relic, for why else was he

285

mutilated but in order to discover whether he had concealed it with more than superficial craft—perhaps even swallowed it? They found nothing or you would not have engaged their attention. As it was, they were baffled and had to investigate further. Then they doubtless learned that you had put this man under an undying obligation, possibly they even knew that he had visited you the last thing before he left the camp."

"It seems likely enough in an incredible sort of way," admitted the doctor. "But I don't see why this old sport should be occupying himself as he is in the streets of London."

"That remains to be looked into. It may be some propitiatory form of self-abasement that is so potent in the Oriental system. But it may equally well be something quite different. If the man is of high priestly authority there are hundreds of his co-religionists here at hand whose lives he could command in such a service. He may be in communication with some, or contriving to make himself quite readily accessible. Are there any Indians at your boarding house?"

"I have seen a couple recently."

"Recently! Then they came after you did?"

"I don't know about that. I haven't had much to do with the place."

"I don't like it, Jim," said Carrados, with more gravity than he was accustomed to put into the consideration of his own risks.

"Well, for that matter, I'm not exactly pining for trouble," replied his friend. "But I can take care of myself anyway."

"But you can't," retorted Carrados. "That's just the danger. If you were blind it would be all right, but your credulous, self-opinionated eyes will land you in some mess. . . . Tomorrow, at all events, Carlyle shall put a watch on this enterprising Hindu and we shall at least find out what his movements are."

Tulloch would have declined the attention, but Carrados was insistent.

"You must let me have my way in such an emergency, Tulloch," he declared. "Of course you would say that it's out of your power to prevent me, but among friends one acquiesces to a certain code. I say this because I may even find it necessary to put a man on you as well. This business attracts me resistlessly. There's something more in it than we have got at yet, something that lies beyond the senses and strives to communicate itself through the unknown dimension that we have all stood just upon the threshold of, only to find that we have lost the key. It's more elusive than Macbeth's dagger: 'I have thee not and yet I see thee still'—always just out of reach. What is it, Jim; can't you help us? Don't you feel something portentous in the air, or is it only my blind eyes that can see beyond?"

"Not a bit of it," laughed Tulloch cheerfully. "I only feel that a blighted old heathen is leading himself a rotten dance through his pig-headed obstinacy. Well, Wynn, why can't he be rounded up and have it explained that he's on the wrong tack?"

"He would not believe." Carrados was pacing the room in one of his rare periods of mental tension. Instinct, judgment, experience, and a subtler prescience that enveloped reason seemed at variance in his mind. Then he swung round and faced his visitor.

"Look here, Tulloch, stay with me for the present," he urged. "You can go there for your things tomorrow and I can fix you up in the meantime. It's safer; I feel it will be safer."

"Safer! Good Lord! What could you have safer than a stodgy second-rate boarding house in Hapsburg Square? The place drones respectability. Miss Vole, the landlady, is related to an archdeacon and nearly all the people there are on half-pay. The two Indians are tame baboos. Besides, if I get this thing I told you of, I shall be off to South America in a few days, and that ought to shake off this old man of the tooth."

"Of course it won't; nothing will shake him off if he's made the vow. Well, have it your own way. One can't expect a doctor of robust habit to take any reasonable precautions, I know. How is your room situated?"

"Pretty high up. Next to the attic, I imagine. It must be, because there is a little trap-door in the ceiling leading there."

"A trap door leading to the attic! Well, at all events there is no four-post bed with a canopy that slides up and down; nor a revolving wardrobe before a secret passage?"

"Get on with you," retorted Tulloch. "It's just the ordinary contrivance that you find in every roof when the attic isn't made into rooms. There's nothing in it."

"Possibly; but there may be. Anyway, drive a tack in and hang up a tin can or something that must clatter down if the door is raised an inch. You have a weapon, I suppose?"

"Now you're talking, Wynn. I do put some faith in that. I have a grand little revolver in my bag and I can sleep like a feather when I want."

"Little? What size does it take?"

"Oh, well it's a three-twenty, if it comes to that. I prefer a moderate bore myself."

Carrados opened a drawer of his desk and picked up half a dozen brass cartridges.

"When you get back, throw out the old ones and reload with these to oblige me," he said. "Don't forget."

"Right," assented Tulloch, examining them with interest; "but they look just like mine. What are they?—something new?"

"Not at all; but we know that they are charged and you can rely on them going off if they are fired."

"What a chap you are," declared Tulloch with something of the admiring pity that summed up the general attitude towards Max Carrados. "Well, I must be going off myself, old man. I'm hoping for a letter about that little job and if it comes I want to answer it tonight. You've given me a fine time and we've had a great talk."

"I'm glad we met. And if you go away suddenly don't leave it to chance the next time you are back." He did not seek to detain his guest, for he knew that Tulloch was building somewhat on the South American appointment. "Shall Harris run you home?"

"Not a bit of it. I'll enjoy a walk to the station, and these Tubes of yours'll land me within me loose-box by eleven. It's a fine place, this London, after all."

They had reached the front door, opened it, and were standing for a moment looking towards the yellow cloud that arched the west end of the city like the mirage of a dawn.

"Well, goodbye, old man," said Tulloch heartily, and they shook hands. At the touch an extraordinary impulse swept over Carrados to drag his friend back into the house, to implore him to remain the night, or to do something to upset the arranged order of things for the next few hours. With the cessation of physical contact the vehemence of the possession dwindled away, but the experience, short as it was, left Carrados white and shaken. He could not trust himself to speak; he waved his hand, and, turning quickly, went back to the room where they had sat together to analyze the situation and to determine how to act. Presently he rang for his man.

"Some notes were taken after that little touch in Holborn this afternoon, Parkinson," he said. "Have you the address of the leading motor-bus driver among them?"

"The London General, sir?"

"Yes; the man who was the first to stop."

Parkinson produced the memorandum book and referred to the latest of its entries.

"He gave his private residence as fourteen Cogg's Lane, Brentford, sir."

"Brentford! That is fortunate. I am going to see him tonight if possible. You will come with me, Parkinson. Tell Harris to get out the car. What is the time?"

"Ten seventeen, sir."

"We will start in fifteen minutes. In the meanwhile just hand me the large book labeled 'Xavier' from the top shelf there."

"Yes, sir. Very well, sir. I will convey your instructions to Harris, sir."

It was perhaps rather late for a casual evening call, but not, apparently, too late for Cogg's Lane, Brentford. Mr. Fitzwilliam—Parkinson had infused a faint note of protest into his voice when he mentioned the bus-driver's name—Mr. Fitzwilliam was out, but Mrs. Fitzwilliam received the visitor with conspicuous felicity and explained the circumstances. Fitzwilliam was of a genial, even playful, disposition, but he had come home brooding and depressed. Mrs. Fitzwilliam had not taken any notice of it—she put it down to his feet—but by cajolery and innuendo she had persuaded him to go to the picture palace to be cheered up, and as it was now on the turn of eleven he might be expected back at any moment. In the meantime, the lady had a favorite niece who was suffering—as the doctor himself confessed—from a very severe and unusual form of adenoids. Carrados disclosed the fact that the subject of adenoids was one that interested him deeply. He knew, indeed, of a case that was thought by the patient's parents to be something out of the way, but even it, he admitted, was commonplace by the side of the favorite niece. The minutes winged.

"That's Fred," said Mrs. Fitzwilliam, as the iron gate beyond the little plot of beaten earth that had once been a garden gave its individual note. "Seems strange that they should be so ignorant at a hospital, doesn't it?"

"Hallo, what's now?" demanded Mr. Fitzwilliam, entering.

Mrs. Fitzwilliam made a sufficient introduction and waited for the interest to develop. So far the point of Carrados' visit had not appeared.

"I believe that you know something about motors?" inquired the blind man.

"Well, what if I do?" retorted the busdriver. His attitude was protective rather than intentionally offensive.

"If you do, I should be glad if you would look at the engine of my car. It got shaken, I fancy, in a slight accident that we had in Holborn this afternoon."

"Oh!" The driver looked hard at Carrados, but failed to get behind an expression of mild urbanity. "Why didn't you say so at first?" he grumbled. "All right; I'll trot round with you. Shan't be long, missis."

He led the way out and closed the door behind them, not ceasing to regard his visitor with a distrustful curiosity. At the gate he stopped, having by that time brought his mind round to the requirements of the situation, and faced Carrados. "Look here," he said, "what's up? You don't want me to look at no bloomin' engine, you know. I don't half like the whole bally business, let me tell you. What's the game?"

"It's a very simple game for you if you play it straighfor-wardly," answered Carrados. "I want to know just how much you had to do with saving that man's life in Holborn today."

Fitzwilliam instinctively fell back a step and his gaze on Carrados quickened in its tensity.

"What d'yer mean?" he demanded with a quality of apprehension in his voice.

"That is complicating the game," replied Carrados mildly. "You know exactly what I mean."

"And what if I do?" demanded the driver. "What have you got to do with it?"

"I happened to be in the car following you. We were scraped, but I am not making any claim for damages. I am satisfied that you did very well indeed in the circumstances, and if a letter to your people—I know one of the directors—saying as much as would be of any use to you—"

"Now we're getting on, sir," was the mollified admission. "You mustn't mind a bit of freshness, so to speak. You took me by surprise, that's what it was, and I've been wound up ever since that happened." He hesitated, and then flung out the question almost with a passionate directness: "What was it, sir? In God's name, what was it?"

"What was it?" repeated the blind man's level voice persuasively.

"It wasn't me. I couldn't have done nothing. I didn't see the man, not in time to have an earthly. Then we stopped. Good

Lord, I've never felt a stop like that before. It was as though a rubber band had tightened and pulled us up against ten yards squoze into one, so that you didn't hardly know it. I hadn't nothing to do with it. Not a brake was on, and the throttle open and the engine running. There we were. And me half silly."

"You did very well," said Carrados soothingly.

"I did nothing. If it had been left to me there'd have been an inquest. You seemed to have noticed something, sir. How do you work it out?"

Carrados parried the question with a disingenuous allusion to the laws of chance. He had not yet worked it out, but he was not disposed to lay his astonishing conclusions, so far as they went, before the busdriver's crude discrimination. He had learned what he wanted. With a liberal acknowledgment of the service, he bade Mr. Fitzwilliam good night and returned to his waiting car.

"Back home, Harris," he directed. He had gone out with some intention of including Hapsburg Square in his peregrination. He was now assured that his anxiety was groundless.

But the next morning all his confidence was shattered in a moment. It was his custom before and during breakfast to read by touch the headings of the various items in the newspapers and to mark for Greatorex's later reading such paragraphs as claimed his interest. Generally he could, with some inconvenience, distinguish even the ordinary type by the same faculty, but sometimes the inequality of pressure made this a laborious process. There was no difficulty about the larger types, however, and with a terrible misgiving, fingertip and brain had grasped the significance of a prominent heading:

FATAL GAS EXPLOSION

HAPSBURG SQUARE
BOARDING HOUSE IN FLAMES

"Are you there, Parkinson?" he called.

Parkinson could scarcely believe his well-ordered ears. Not since the early days of his affliction had Carrados found it necessary to ask such a question.

"Yes, sir, I'm here," he almost stammered in reply. "I hope you are not unwell, sir?"

"I'm all right, thanks," responded his master. "I was mentally elsewhere. I want you to read me this paragraph. It deeply concerns me."

"The one about Dr. Tulloch, sir?" The name had caught the man's eye at once. "Dear me, sir."

"Yes; go on," said Carrados, with his nearest approach to impatience.

" 'During the early hours of this morning,' " read Parkinson, " 'Fifty-two Hapsburg Square was the scene of a gas explosion which was unhappily attended by loss of life. Shortly after midnight the neighborhood was alarmed by the noise of a considerable explosion which appeared to blow out the window and front wall of one of the upper bedrooms, but as the part in question was almost immediately involved in flames it is uncertain what really happened. The residents of the house, which is a boarding establishment carried on by Miss Vole (a relative, we are informed, of Archdeacon Vole of Worpsley), were quickly made aware of their danger and escaped. The engines arrived within a few minutes of the alarm and soon averted any danger of the fire spreading. When it was possible to penetrate into the upper part of the house it was discovered that the occupant of the bedroom where the explosion took place, a Dr. Tulloch who had only recently returned to this country from India, had perished. Owing to the charred state of the body it is impossible to judge how he died, but in all probability he was mercifully killed or at least rendered unconscious by the force of the explosion.' That is all, sir."

"I ought to have kept him," muttered Carrados reproachfully. "I ought to have insisted. The thing has been full of mistakes." He could discover very little further interest in his breakfast and turned to the other papers for possible enlargement of the details. "We shall have to go down," he said. "Tell Harris."

"Very well, sir."

Greatorex, just arrived for the day, put his head in at the door.

"Morning, sir," he nodded. "Tulloch's here and wants to see you. Came in with me. Hullo, Parkinson, seen a ghost?"

"He hasn't yet," volunteered his master. "But we both expect to. Yes, send him in here. Only one mistake the more, you see," he added to his servant. "And one the less," he added to himself.

"I might just as well have stayed, you know," was Tulloch's greeting, and going across to his friend he dropped a weighty hand upon his shoulder.

" 'There are more things in heaven and earth than in your philosophy, Horatio,' " he barbarously misquoted with significance. "There, you see, Wynn, I can apply Shakespeare to the situation as well as you."

"Quite so," assented Carrados. "In the meanwhile, will you have some breakfast?"

"It's what I came in the hopes of," admitted the doctor. "That and being burned out of hearth and home. I thought that I might as well quarter myself on you for a couple of days. You've seen the papers?"

His friend indicated the still-open front page.

"Ah, that one. *The Morning Reporter* gave me a better obituary. I often had a sort of morbid fancy to know what they'd say about me afterwards. It seemed unattainable, but, like most things, it's a sad disappointment when it comes. Six lines is the longest, Wynn, and they've got me degree wrong."

"Whose was the body?" asked Carrados.

Gravity descended upon Tulloch at the question. He looked round to make sure that Parkinson had left the room.

"No one will ever know, I'm hoping," he replied. "He was charred beyond recognition. But you know, Wynn, and I know, and we can hold our tongues."

"The Indian avenger, of course?"

"Yes. I went round there early this morning expecting nothing and found the place a wreck. One can only guess now what happened, but the gas-bracket is just beneath that trap-door I told you of and there's a light kept burning in the passage outside. One of the half-pay men brought me a nasty wavy dagger that had been picked up in the road. 'One of your Indian curiosities, I suppose, Dr. Tulloch?' he remarked. I let it pass at that, for I was becoming cautious midst so much devilment. 'I'm afraid that there's nothing else of yours left,' he went on, 'and there wouldn't have been this if it hadn't been blown through the window.' He was quite right. I haven't a thing left in the world but this Norfolk suit that I stand up in, and, as matters are, I'm jolly well glad you didn't give me time to change yesterday."

"Ah," assented Carrados thoughtfully. "Still the Norfolk suit, of course. Tell me, Jim, you had it in India?"

"To be sure I had. It was new then. You know, one doesn't always go about there in white drill and a cork helmet, as your artists here seem to imagine. It's cold sometimes, I can tell you.

293

This coat is warm; I got very fond of it. You can't understand one getting fond of a mere suit, you with your fifty changes."

"Of course I can. I have a favorite jacket that I would not part from for rubies, and it's considerably more of an antique than yours. That's still a serviceable suit, Jim. Come and let me have a look at it."

"What d'ye mean?" said Tulloch, complying reluctantly. "You're making fun of me little suit and it's the only thing in the world that stands between me and the entire."

"Come here," repeated Carrados, "I am not in the least guying. I'm far too serious. I am more serious, I think, than I have ever been in my life before." He placed the wondering doctor before him and proceeded to run a light hand about the details of his garments, turning the doctor round until the process was complete. "You wore these clothes when the native you call Calico came to you that night?"

"It's more than likely. The nights were cold."

Carrados seemed strangely moved. He got up, walked to the window, as his custom was, for enlightenment, and then, after wandering about the room, touching here and there an object indecisively, he unlocked a cabinet and slid out a tray of silver coins.

"You've never seen these, have you?" he asked.

"No, what are they?" responded Tulloch, looking on.

"Pagan art at its highest. The worship of the strong and beautiful."

"Worth a bit?" suggested Tulloch knowingly.

"Not what they cost." Carrados shot back the tray and paced the room again. "You haven't told me yet how you were preserved."

"How—?"

"Last night. You know that once more you escaped death."

"I suppose I did. Yes. . . . And do you know why I have been hesitating to tell you?"

"Why?"

"Because you won't believe me."

Carrados permitted himself to smile.

"Try," he said laconically.

"Well, of course, I quite intended to. . . . The sober truth is, Wynn, that I forgot the address and could not get there. It was the silliest and simplest thing in the world. I walked to the station here, booked for Russell Square, and took a train. When I got out I started off and suddenly pulled up. Where was I going? My mind, on that one point, had developed a perfect blank. All the facts had vanished. Drum my encephalon how I might, I could not recall Miss Vole, Fifty-two, or Hapsburg Square. Mark you, it wasn't loss of memory in the ordinary sense. I remembered everything else; I knew who I was and what I wanted well enough. Of course the first thing I did was to turn out my pockets. I had letters, certainly, but none to that address and nothing else to help me. 'Very well,' I said, 'It's a silly game, but I'll walk round till I find it.' Had again! I walked for half an hour, but I saw nothing the faintest degree familiar. Then I saw 'London Directory Taken Here' in a pub window. 'Good,' I thought. 'When I see the name it will all come back again.' I went in, had something, and looked through the 'Streets' section from beginning to end." He shook his head shrewdly. "It didn't work."

"Did it occur to you to ring me up? You'd given me the address."

"It did; and then I thought, 'No, it's midnight now'—it was by then—'and he may have turned in early and been asleep.' Well, things had got to such a pass that it seemed the simplest move to walk into the first moderate hotel I came to, pay for my bed, and tell them to wake me at six, and that's what I did. Now what do you make of that?"

"That depends," replied Carrados slowly. "The scientist would perhaps hint at a telepathic premonition operating subconsciously through receptive nerve centers. The sceptic would call it a lucky coincidence. The devoutly religious person would claim another miracle."

"Oh, come now!" protested Tulloch.

"Yes, come now," struck in Carrados, rising with decision and moving towards the door. "Come to my room and then you shall judge for yourself. It's too much for any one man to contemplate alone. Come on." He walked quietly across the hall to his study, dismissing Greatorex elsewhere with a word, and motioned the mystified doctor to a chair. Then he locked the door and sat down himself.

"I want you to carry your mind back to that night in your tent when the native Khaligar, towards whom you had done an imperishable service, presented himself before you. By the inexorable ruling of his class he was your bondsman in service until he had repaid you in kind. This, Jim, you failed to understand. You would not be repaid, and yet he wished to die."

The doctor nodded. "I daresay it comes to that," he said.

295

"He could not die with this debt undischarged. And so, in the obscurity of your tent, beneath your unsuspecting eyes, this conjurer did, as he was satisfied, requite you. You thought you saw him wrap the relic in its covering. You did not. You thought he put it back in his own clothes. He did not. Instead, he slipped it dexterously between the lining and the cloth of your own coat. You had seen him do much cleverer things even in the open sunlight."

"You don't say," exclaimed Tulloch, springing to his feet, "that even now—"

"Wait!" cried the blind man warningly. "Don't seek it yet. You have to face a more stupendous problem."

"What is that?"

"Three times at least your life has been—as we may say—miraculously preserved. It was not your doing, your expertness, my friend. . . . What is this sacred relic that once was in its jeweled shrine on the high altar of the great cathedral at Goa, that opulent archbishopric of the East to which Portugal in the Sixteenth Century sent all that was most effective of treasure, brain, and muscle to conquer the body and soul of India?"

"You suggested that it might be the original relic to which Vasque had referred."

"The natives may have thought so. What would be more natural than that an ignorant despoiler should assume the thing which he found the most closely guarded and the most richly casketed to be the object for which he himself would have the deepest veneration?"

"Then I don't follow you," said Tulloch.

"Because I have the advantage of having turned to the local and historical records bearing on the circumstances since you first started me," Carrados replied. "For instance, in the year 1582 Akbar, who was a philosopher and a humorist as well as a model ruler, sent an invitation to the 'wise men among the Franks' at Goa to journey to Agra, there to meet in public controversy before him a picked band of Mohammedan mullas and prove the superiority of their faith. The challenge was accepted. Abu-l-Fazl records the curious business and adds a very significant detail. These priests, to cut the matter short in the spirit of the age, offered to walk through a fiery furnace in the defense of their belief. It came to nothing, because the other side backed out, but the challenge is suggestive because, however fond the priesthood of those times may have been of putting other people to the ordeal of fire and water, its members were singulary modest about submitting to such tests themselves. What mystery was there here, Tulloch? What had those priests of Goa that made them so self-confident?"

"This relic you suggest?"

"Yes, I do. But, now, what is the relic? A monkey's or an ape-god's tooth, an iron-stained belemnite, the fragment of a pagan idol—you and I can smile at that. We are Christians. No matter how unorthodox, no matter how noncommital our attitude may have grown, there is upon us the unconscious and hereditary influence of century after century of blind and implicit faith. To you and to me, to everyone who has listened to the story as a little child, it is only conceivable that if miraculous virtues reside in anything inanimate it must preeminently be in the close accessories of that great world's tragedy, when, as even secular and unfriendly historians have been driven to admit, something out of the order of Nature did shake the heavens."

"But this," articulated Tulloch with dry throat, leaning instinctively forward from the pressure of his coat, "this—what is it, then?"

"You described it as looking like a nail," responded Carrados. "It is a nail. Rusty, you said, and it could not well be otherwise than red with rust. And old. More than nineteen hundred years old."

Tulloch came unsteadily to his feet and slowly slipping off his coat he put it gently away on a table apart from where they sat.

"Is it possible?" he asked in an awestruck whisper. "Wynn, is it—is it really possible?"

"It is not only possible," he heard the blind man's more composed voice replying, "but in one aspect it is even very natural. Physically, we are dealing with an historical fact. Somewhere on the face of the earth these things must be enduring; scattered, buried, lost perhaps, but still existent. And among the thousands of relics that the different churches have made claim to, it would be remarkable indeed if some at least were not authentic. That is the material aspect."

"Yes," assented Tulloch anxiously, "yes, that is simple, natural. But the other side, Carrados—the things that we know have happened—what of that?"

"That," replied Carrados, "is for each man to judge according to his light."

"But you?" persisted Tulloch. "Are you convinced?"

"I am offered a solution that explains everything when no other theory will," replied the blind man evasively. Then on the top of Tulloch's unsatisfied "Ah!" he added, "But there is something else that confronts you. What are you going to do?" and his face was towards the table across the room.

"Have you thought of that?"

"It has occurred to me. I wondered how you would act."

It was some time before either spoke again. Then Tulloch broke the silence.

"You can lend me some things?" he asked.

"Of course."

"Then I will decide," he announced with resolution. "Whatever we may think, whatever might be urged, I cannot touch this thing; I dare not even look on it. It has become too solemn, too awful, in my mind, to be seen by any man again. To display it, to submit it to the test of what would be called 'scientific proof,' to have it photographed and 'written up' —impossible, incredible! On the other hand, to keep it safely to myself—no, I cannot do that either. You feel that with me?"

The blind man nodded.

"There is another seemly, reverent way. The opportunity offers. I found a letter at the house this morning. I meant to tell you of it. I have got the appointment that I told you of and in three days I start for South America. I will take the coat just as it is, weight it beyond the possibility of recovery, and sink it out of the world in the deepest part of the Atlantic; beyond controversy, and safe from falling to any ignoble use. You can supply me with a box and lead. You approve of that?"

"I will help you," said Carrados.

THE BLOOMSBURY WONDER

BY THOMAS BURKE

Thomas Burke was born in London in 1886 and worked in a secondhand bookshop and a literary agency before producing his first book, a series of London sketches commissioned by a publisher. His first and best crime book, *Limehouse Nights,* is a series of violent, highly colored tales about London's Chinatown. Other collections include *Whispering Windows, The Bloomsbury Wonder,* and *Dark Nights.* His short story, "The Hands of Mr. Ottermole" (1931), was voted by Ellery Queen and eleven other critics as the best detective short story of all time. The D. W. Griffith film, *Broken Blossoms,* was based on one of Burke's short stories. He died in 1945.

I

AS THAT SEPTEMBER MORNING came to birth in trembling silver and took life in the hue of dusty gold, I swore.

I had risen somewhat early and was standing at the bathroom window of my Bloomsbury flat shaving. I first said something like "Ooch!" and then I said something more intense. The cause of these ejaculations was that I had given myself the peculiarly nasty kind of cut that you can only get from a safety-razor, and the cause of the cut was a sudden movement of the right elbow, and the cause of that was something I had seen from my window.

Through that gracious gold, which seemed almost like a living presence blessing the continent of London, moved a man I knew. But a man I knew transformed into a man I did not know. He was not hurrying, which was his usual gait. He wasn't even walking. He was sailing. I never saw such a schoolgirl step in a man. I never saw such rapture in the lift of a head.

He was not tall, but he was so thin, and his clothes fitted so tightly, that he gave an illusion of height. He wore a black double-breasted overcoat, buttoned at the neck, black trousers and nondescript hat. He held his arms behind him, the right hand clasping the elbow of the left arm. His slender trunk was upright, and his head thrown back and lifted.

In the dusty sunlight he made a silhouette. I saw him in the flat only. And I realized then that I always had seen him in the flat; never all round him. The figure he cut in that sunlight made me want to see round him, though what I should find I did not know and could not guess. And to this day I don't know and can't guess.

II

In conventional society, I suppose, he would have been labeled a queer creature, this Stephen Trink; but the inner quarters of London hold so many queer creatures, and I have so wide an aquaintance among them, that Trink was just one of my crowd. I forget how I came to know him, but for about two years we had been seeing each other once or twice a week; sometimes oftener. I liked him almost at once, and the liking grew. Although I was always aware in his company of a slight unease, I took every opportunity of meeting him. He charmed me. The charm was not the open, easy charm of one's intimate friend, for we never reached that full contact. It was more spell than charm; the attraction of opposites, perhaps. His only marked characteristic was a deep melancholy, and now that I try to recall him I find that that is the one clear thing that I can recall. He was one of those men nobody ever really knows.

Stephen Trink would have been passed over in any company, and at my place always was. Only when I directed my friends' attention to him, did they recollect having met him and examine their recollection; and then they were baffled. I once asked five friends in turn what they thought of him, and I was given pictures of five totally different men, none of whom I had myself seen in Trink. Each of them, I noted, had to hesitate on my question, and stroke his hair, and say: " 'M . . . Trink. We-el, he's just an ordinary sort of chap—I mean—he's a—sort of—" Then, although he had been with us ten minutes ago, they would go on to draw a picture as from hazy memory. They seemed to be describing a man whom they weren't sure they had seen. Their very detail was the fumbling detail of men who are uncertain what they did see, and try to assure themselves by elaboration that they did at any rate see *something*. It was as though he had stood before the camera for his photograph, and the developed plate had come out blank.

In appearance, as I say, he was insignificant, and, with his lean, questing face and frail body, would have passed anywhere as an insipid clerk. He stressed his insipidity by certain physical habits. He had a trick of standing in little-girl attitudes—hands behind back, one foot crooked round the other—and of demurely dropping his eyes if you looked suddenly at him; and, when speaking to you, looking up at you as though you were his headmaster. He had, too, a smile that, though it sounds odd when used of a man, I can only describe as winsome. The mouth was sharp-cut, rather than firm, and drooped at the corners. The lower jaw was drawn back. His hair was honey-colored and plastered down. His voice was thin, touched with the east wind; and it was strange to hear him saying the warm, generous things he did say about people in the sleety tone that goes with spite. To everything he said that tone seemed to add the words: *Isn't it disgusting?* His eyes, behind spectacles, were mild and pale blue. Only when the spectacles were removed did one perceive character; then, one could see that the eyes held curious experience and pain.

Wherever he might be, he never seemed to be wholly *there.* He had an air of seeming to be listening to some noise outside the room. He would sit about in attitudes that, since Rodin's Penseur, we have come to accept as attitudes of thought; but if you looked at his face you'd say it was empty. He was not thinking; he was brooding. Though indoors he was languid and lounge-y, and his movements were the movements of the sleepwalker, in the street his walk was agitated and precipitous. He seemed to be flying from pursuit. One other notable point about him was that, quiet, insignificant, withdrawn as he was, he could be a most disturbing presence. Even when relaxed in an armchair he somehow sent spears and waves of discomfort through the air, sucking and drying the spirit of the room and giving me that edge of unease.

What his trouble was—if his melancholy arose from a trouble—he never told me. Often, when I urged him, flippantly, to Cheer Up, he spoke of This Awful Burden, but I dismissed it as the usual expression of that intellectual weariness of living which we call "modern."

He had private means by which he could have lived in something more than comfort, but he seemed contented with three rooms in the forlorn quarter where Bloomsbury meets Marylebone—well-furnished rooms that one entered with surprise from the dinge of Fitzroy Square. He was a member of two of the more serious clubs, but used them scarcely twice a year. His time he employed in the Bloomsbury and Marylebone fashion—as an aimless intellectual. He occupied himself writing metallic studies for all sorts of hole-and-corner Reviews; and all the time he was doing it he affected to despise himself for doing it and to despise the breed with whom he mixed. He attended all their clique and coterie gatherings—teas, dinners, Bloomsbury salons, private views—and took part in all the frugal follies of the Cheyne Walk Bohemia. You saw him, as they say, everywhere. Yet, at all these affairs, though he looked younger than most of the crowd, he had always the attitude of the amused grownup overlooking the antics of the nursery. I can't think how even their pallid wits didn't perceive that embodied sneer at them and their doings.

Although not physically strong he had immense vitality, which he exhibited in long night walks through London. This was a habit which I shared with him and which, begun in childhood, gave me my peculiar and comprehensive knowledge of the hinterland of this continent of London. I believe that it was on one of these night wanderings that we first really met, though there must have been a perfunctory introduction in somebody's flat. Knowing that I was an early riser, he would sometimes, at the end of one of these rambles, knock me up at half-past seven for breakfast, and then go to sleep on my settee. Glad as I always was to have his company, he was a difficult guest. He had a disorderly mind and Japanese ideas of time. A "look-in" often meant that he would stay for four or five hours, and an arrangement to dine and spend the evening often meant that he would look-in for ten minutes and then abruptly disappear without a word about dinner. He had a habit of using in casual conversation what is called bad language—a certain sign of uneasy minds—and his talk was constantly agitated with purposeless use of "blasted," and "bloody" and "bastard." In all other matters he was gentle and thoughtful. He would not, as they say, do anything for anybody, but for a few people his time and labor and influence were available in full measure. He was so kind of spirit, so generous of affection, that sometimes I thought that his melancholy arose from a yearning to love and be loved. At other times this would be contradicted by his self-sufficiency.

And that, I think, is all I can tell you about him. He eludes me on paper as he eluded me in life. So with this light sketch I pass on to the real matter of this story—to his friends, the Roakes; for it was by his friendship with them that I was brought into contact with horror.

Another of our points in common was a wide range of friendships. Most men find their acquaintance among their own "sort" or their own "set," and never adventure beyond people of like education, like tastes, and like social circumstances. I have never been able to do that, nor Trink. We made our friends wherever we found them, and we found them in queer places. An assembly of all our friends at one meeting in our rooms would have surprised (and dismayed) those of them who knew us only as writers in such-and-such circumstances. I had, of course, a number of close friends among fellow-authors and among musicians, but my most intimate friend at that time, who knew more about me than any other creature, was an old disciple of Madame Blavatsky, who devoted his spare time to original research on the lost Atlantis. Trink's was a shop-keeper; a man who kept what is called a "general" shop at the northern end of Great Talleyrand Street.

Despite my own assorted friendships, I could never quite understand *this* friendship, for the man had no oddities, no character, no corner where he even grazed the amused observation of Trink. It may have been, of course—and this fact explains many ill-assorted friendships—that they liked the same kind of funny story, or walked at the same pace in the streets. I don't know. Friendships *are* bound by slender things like that. Or it may have been—and I think this is what it was—that they were bound by love. I am sure there was more in it than mere liking of each other's talk and company, for Trink, being what he was, could have found no pleasure in the pale copy-book talk of Horace Roake. I thought I could perceive on either side an essence or aura of devotion, and if the devotion were at all stronger on one side, it was on the side of the culti-vated man of brains rather than the tired, brainless shop-keeper. I spent many evenings in their company, either at Trink's flat or in the shop-parlor, and I noted their content in long silences, when they merely sat together and smoked, and their quick, voiceless greeting when they met. Trink seemed to be happier in Roake's shabby room than anywhere. *Why* was one of his mysteries.

Although the public spoke of Roake's shop as a General Shop, he did not himself recognize that style. There are tradi-tions in these matters. In trade-lists there are no drapers, or milkmen, or greengrocers, or ironmongers. The man we style milkman styles himself dairyman, though he may never have seen a dairy. The greengrocer is a pea and potato salesman. The bookmaker is a commission agent. Drapers and iron-mongers are haberdashers and dealers in hardware. The butcher is a purveyor of meat, the publican a licensed victualler. So Mr. Roake, who kept no pastas or Chianti, or Bolognas or Garlic, styled himself Italian warehouseman. His shop stood, as I say, at the northern end of Great Talleyrand Street, between Woburn Place and Gray's Inn Road.

This is a district of long, meaningless streets and disinherited houses. Once, these houses were the homes of the prosperous; today they have only faded memories. They lie, these streets and houses, in an uneasy coma, oppressed by a miasma of the secondhand and the outmoded—secondhand shops, secondhand goods, secondhand lodgings, filled with secondhand furniture, and used by secondhand people breathing secondhand denatured air.

When Roake set up his shop here, he blunderingly chose the apt setting for himself and his family. They belonged there. They were typical of a thousand decent, hardworking, but stagnant families of our cities. For four generations the family had not moved its social level. A faint desire to rise they must have had, but rising means adventure, and they feared adventure. On the wife's side and the husband's side the strain was the same—lukewarm and lackadaisical. There they had stood, these many years, like rootless twigs in the waste patch between the stones and the pastures; and there, since the only alternative was risk and struggle, they were content to stand. Roake himself, if I saw him truly, had the instincts of the aristocrat hidden in the habits of the peasant. One of life's misfits. He had the fine feature and clean eye of that type, but though he looked like what is called a gentleman, nobody would have mistaken him for one. His refinement of feature and manner came really, not from the breeding of pure strains, but from undernourishment in childhood. He had a mind of wide, if aimless, interests, and a certain rough culture acquired by miscellaneous reading.

His wife was largely of his sort, but without the culture. Her life had been a life of pain and trial, and it had taught her nothing. Her large, soft face was expressionless. The thousand experiences of life had left not even a fingerprint there, and she still received the disappointments and blows of fortune with indignation and querulous collapse.

There were two boys and a girl. The girl had something of her father's physical refinement. Her head and face were beautiful; so beautiful that people turned to glance at her as she passed in the streets. Her manners and voice were—well, dreadful. She would often respond to those admiring glances by putting out her tongue. She was wholly unconscious of her beauty, not because she was less vain than her sex, but because her beauty was not to her own taste. She admired and envied girls of florid complexion and large blue eyes and masses of hair and dimpled mouths—chocolate-box beauties—and her own beauty was a glorious gift thrown to the dogs. To see that grave dark head and those deep-pool Madonna eyes set against those sprawling manners and graceless talk gave one a shudder.

Of the two boys, one might say that they saw life as nothing but a program of getting up, going to work, working, eating, going to bed. Only it wouldn't be true. They saw life no more than a three-months' old baby sees life. They were clods.

These were the people Trink had chosen as friends, and by all of them he was, not adored, for they were incapable of that, but liked to the fullest extent of their liking. He was their honored guest, and on his side he gave them affection and respect. The two boys worked together in a boot and shoe factory, and the shop was run by Mr. and Mrs. Roake and the girl, Olive. Olive knew enough about the business to do her bit without any mental strain, and she had a flow of smiles and empty chatter that in such a shop was useful.

These General Shops—often spoken of as "little gold-mines"—are usually set, like this one, in side streets. It is by their isolated setting that they flourish. The main streets are not their territory, and such a shop in a main street would certainly fail, for these streets hold branches of the multiple stores as well as shops devoted singly to this or that household necessity. Your successful General Shop, then, chooses a situation as far from competition as possible, but in the center of a thicket of houses. In that situation it wins its prosperity from the housewife's slips of memory. She arrives home from her High Street shopping, and finds that she has forgotten salt or custard-powder or bacon, and to save a mile walk she sends one of the children to the General Shop. It is for this that it exists; not for regular supply but as convenience in emergency. Unhampered by other shops and encircled by hundreds of forgetful households, the well-conducted General is certain of success, and many of these shops have a weekly turnover, made up of pennyworths of this and ounces of that, near two hundred pounds.

So the Roakes were doing well. Indeed, they were very comfortable and could have been more than comfortable; but they were so inept, and knew so little of the art of useful spending, that their profits showed little result in the home. If they could not be given the positive description of a happy family, at least they lived in that sluggish sympathy which characters only faintly aware of themselves give each other; and that was the feeling of the home—lymphatic and never *quite*. The wireless set worked, but it was never in perfect tone. The sitting-room fire would light, but only after it had been coaxed by those who knew its "ways." The hot water in the bathroom was never more than very warm. The flowers in the back garden were never completely and unmistakably blossoms. The shop-door would shut, but only after three sharp pressures—the third a bad-tempered one. They bought expensive and warranted clocks, and the clocks took the note of the family, and were never "right." New and better pieces of furniture were frequently bought for the sitting room, but it never succeeded in looking furnished. If you saw the house, you could imagine the family; if you met the family, you could imagine the house.

Hardly a family, one would think, marked out for tragedy, or even for disaster; yet it was upon these lusterless, half-living people that a blind fury of annihilation rushed from nowhere and fell, whirling them from obscurity and fixing their names and habits in the scarlet immortality of the Talleyrand Street Shop Murder.

It was about the time when those gangs called "The Boys" were getting too cocksure of their invulnerability, and were extending their attentions from rival gangs and publicans to the general public, that the catastrophe came by which Stephen Trink lost his one close friend. Beginning with sub-Post Offices, the gangs passed to the little isolated shops. From all parts of London came reports of raids on these shops. The approach was almost a formula. "Give us a coupler quid. Come on," or "We want a fiver. Quick. Gonna 'and over or gonna 'ave yer place smashed up?" Given the alternative the little shop-keeper could do nothing but pay. He *might* have refused, and have had his place smashed up, and he might have been lucky enough to get the police along in time to catch two or three of the gang and get them six months or twelve months each. But that wouldn't have hurt *them,* since their brutal and perilous ways of life make them utterly fearless; and he would still be left with a smashed shop, pounds' worth of damaged and un-saleable goods, the loss of three or four days' custom during repairs, and no hope of compensation from anybody. So, as a matter of common sense, he first paid up, and then reported the matter to the police; and serious citizens took up his griev-ance, and wrote to the papers and asked what we supported a police force for, etc., etc.

Then, sharply on top of a dozen of these shop-raids, came the murder of the Roakes.

307

III

Marvellous and impenetrable is the potency of words. Hear the faint spirit-echo of *Shelley*; the cold Englishness of *Shakespeare*; the homespun strength of *John Bunyan*. And so it is with ideas; and so, particularly, with that idea for which sign and sound is MURDER.

Now, by long association, murder is linked in our minds with midnight, or at least, with dark; and these two conceptions of the cloaked side of nature combine in dreadfulness to make deeper dread. Again, poetic justice. But harmonious combinations of dreadfulness, though they intensify each other, are dreadfulness only, and are therefore less potent to pluck at the heart than dreadfulness in discord with its setting; for there comes in the monstrous. Rape of womanhood is dreadful but understandable. Rape of childhood goes beyond the dreadful into depths that the mind recoils from sounding. Murder at midnight, though it will shock as it has shocked through centuries of civilization, is a shock in its apt setting. But murder in sunlight is a thought that freezes and appals. It bares our souls to the satanic shudder of blood on primroses.

One can catch, then, the bitter savor of a certain moment of a sunny afternoon in Great Talleyrand Street. From the few horrified words of a neighbor I am able to reconstruct the whole scene.

IV

It was just after three o'clock of a September afternoon—a September of unusual heat; hotter than the summer had been. The heat made a blanket over the city, and in the sidestreets life was in arrest, bound in slumber and steam and dust. In Great Talleyrand Street carts and cars stood outside shops and houses as though they would never move again. Even the shops had half-closed their eyes. Errand boys and workless laborers lounged or lay near the shops, sharing jealously every yard of the shade afforded by the shop-blinds. The faded Regency houses stewed and threw up a frowst. Through its dun length, from its beginning near Gray's Inn to its nebulous end somewhere in St. Pancras, the heat played in a fetid shimmer and shrouded either end in an illusion of infinity. The gritty odors of vegetable stalls, mixed with the acrid fumes of the cast-off-clothes shops, were drawn up in the sun's path to float in the air and fret the noses of the loungers. The ice-cream cart, zones with the Italian colors, made a cool center for the idle young. A woman was offering chrysanthemums from a barrow piled high with that flower. Her barrow and her apron made a patch of living gold against the parched brown of the street.

Then, into this purring hour, came a figure and a voice. From the upper end of the street it came, crying one word; and the blunt syllables of that word went through the heat and dust, and struck the ears of those within hearing with the impact of cold iron. The street did not stir into life. It exploded.

Those nearest scrambled up, crying—not saying; such is the power of that word that it will always be answered with a cry—crying: "Where? Where?" "In there—there—three-ninety-two." And the man ran on to Tenterden Street, still crying, "Murder!" and those who had heard the word ran in a trail to number 392.

The shop with its battling odors of bacon, cheese, paraffin, spice, biscuits, bread, pickles, was empty. The runners looked beyond it. A small door led from the shop to the back parlor. The upper half of the door was of glass, and this half was veiled by a soiled lace curtain. Its purpose was to screen the folk in the parlor—where they sat at intervals between trade rushes—from the eyes of customers, while those in the parlor could, by the greater light of the shop, see all comers. But since the curtain served a purely workaday office—the private sitting-room was upstairs—it had been allowed to over-serve its time, and frequent washings had left it with so many holes that its purpose was defeated. People in the shop could, by those holes, see straight and clearly into the parlor; could see the little desk with account-books and bills, and could often see the cashbox and hear the rattle of accountancy. It was proved by experiment that a man on the threshold of the shop could, without peering, see what was going on in the shop-parlor.

The leaders of the crowd looked hastily about the shop and behind the two small counters; then, through those holes, they had the first glimpse of what they had come to see.

The sun was at the back. It shone through the garden window, and made a blurred shaft of dancing motes across the worn carpet and across the bloody body of Horace Roake. He lay beside his desk. The back of his head was cleanly broken. By the door leading to the inner passage lay the body of Mrs.

309

Roake. She lay with hands up, as though praying. Her head was flung violently back, disjointed. Of the two boys, who had been spending the last day of their holidays at home, the younger, Bert, lay in a corner by the window, almost in a sitting posture. His head hung horridly sideways, showing a dark suffusion under the left ear. The leaders looked and saw; then someone said "The girl!" They pulled open the door leading to passage and kitchen. In the sun-flushed passage lay the twisted body of Olive Roake. Her head, too, was thrown back in contortion. One glance at the dark excoriations on her neck told them how she had met her death. Three glances told them of the dreadful group that must have made entrance here; one to kill with a knife, one with a blow, and one to strangle with the hands.

For some seconds those inside could not speak; but as the crowd from the street pushed into the shop, and those in the shop were pushed into the parlor, those inside turned to push them back; and one of them, finding voice, cried uselessly, as in the way in dark moments: "Why? Why? all this—these nice people—just for a pound or two? It's—it's *unnecessary!*"

He was right, and this was felt more strongly when it was found that this thing had not been done for a pound or two. The desk was locked, and the cashbox and the two tills in the shop were intact. Clearly this was not haphazard killing for robbery. There was a grotesquerie about the scene that hinted at more than killing: an afterthought of the devilish. These people, who had led their ignoble but decent lives in ignoble back streets, were made still more ignoble in death. The battered head of Roake, the crumpled bulk of Mrs. Roake, the macabre mutilation of the gracious symmetry of youth and maidenhood, were more than death. Not only were they dead, but the peace that touches the most ugly and malign to dignity, the one moment of majesty that is granted at last to us all, was denied them. The temple of the Holy Ghost was riven and left in the derisive aspect of a dead cat in a gutter.

So they lay in the floating sunshine of that afternoon, and so the crowd stood and stared down at them until the police came. Who had done this thing? How did they do it in an open shop? How did they get away?

Then someone who knew the family cried, "Where's Artie?" And some went upstairs and some went into the little garden. But all that they found was an open bedroom window and signs of a flight. No Artie.

V

It was between three o'clock and half past of the day when I had given myself that nasty cut that Trink made one of his "drop-in" calls. I was accustomed to these calls. He would come in, potter about, turn over any new books or periodicals I had, make a few remarks about nothing, disturb the atmosphere generally, and then slide away. But this afternoon he didn't disturb the atmosphere. He seemed lighter and brighter than usual. Something of that morning mood that I had seen in him seemed to be still with him. Tired and pale he certainly was—the result of his night-walk, I guessed—but there was a serenity about him that was both new and pleasing. For almost the first time I felt fully at ease with him; no longer conscious of the something that I had never been able to name. In that quarter of an hour I seemed to be nearer to him and to know him better than I had ever known him. To put it into a crude colloquialism, he seemed *more human.* He stayed but a short time, not fidgeting, but sitting restfully on the settee in that complete ease that one knows after long physical exercise. I remarked on this. I told him that I had seen him from my window, bouncing through the square, and told him that the bouncing and his present mood proved that plenty of exercise was what he needed, and that he would probably find, as George Borrow found, that it was a potent agent for the conquest of accidie— or, I added, liver. He smiled; dismissed the diagnosis of his trouble, and soon afterwards went, or, rather, faded away, so that when I resumed work I was barely certain that he had been with me at all.

About an hour later I became aware that I was disturbed, and when, half-consciously and still at work, I located it as something coming from the street; a sound that came at first from below the afternoon din, then rose to its level and spilled over it. It was the cry of newspaper boys.

As my flat is three floors up (no lift) I did not send out for a paper, but I rang up a friend on the *Evening Mercury* and asked what the big story was. He gave me the story so far as it had then come in.

After the first shock, my first thought was of what it would mean to Trink. Terrible as the fate of that family was, they meant little to me, and I could only feel for them the detached and fleeting pity that we feel at any reported disaster. For you

311

will have noted, as a kink of human nature, that nobody ever does feel sympathy for a murdered man. All our interest—yes, and a perverse, half-guilty sympathy—is on the murderer. But for Trink, their friend, it would be a blow, and a keener blow since it came with such ghastly irony on top of his happy, swinging mood of that day. He had just, it seemed, found some respite from his customary gloom, only to be brutally flung back into it, and deeper. I thought at first of going round to him, and then I thought not. He would want no intruders.

Meantime, the papers were publishing rush extras, and as the news had withdrawn me from work, and I could not return to it, I went out and bought the three evening papers, and sat in a tea-shop reading them.

There was no doubt that the affair, following on the large publicity and discussion given to the shop-raids, had stirred the press and alarmed the public. I saw it on the faces of the home-going crowd and heard it reflected in the casual remarks of stranger to stranger in the tea-shop and around the 'buses. All that evening and night the word Murder beat and fluttered about the streets and alleys and suburban avenues, and wherever it brushed it left a smear of disquiet. Accustomed as London is to murder, and lightly, even flippantly as it takes all disturbances, the details of this one moved them, for clearly it was no ordinary murder of anger or revenge, or for the removal of inconvenient people for gain. How could these little people have offended? Who would want them out of the way? If it was the work of "The Boys," it might be anybody's turn next. It it wasn't the work of "The Boys," then, said the press, it must have been the work of wandering lunatics of gorilla's strength and ferocity. And if they were loose, nobody would be safe. Private houses and people in the streets would be wholly at the mercy of such fearless and furious creatures as these appeared to be. In the meantime they *were* loose; even now, perhaps, prowling about and contemplating another stroke; sitting by your side in the train or 'bus, or marking your home or shop for their next visit. They were loose, and while they were loose they spread their dreadful essence as no artist or prophet can hope to spread *his*. Scores of mothers from the streets about Talleyrand Street, hearing the news and seizing on the Press conjecture of wandering madmen, ran to schools in the district to meet their children. They were always aware of peril from the filth that hovers about playground gates; today

312

they were made aware of a more material and annihilating peril.

Through all the thousand little streets of the near and far suburbs went the howl of the newsboy, and its virulent accents went tingling through the nerves of happy households. To people sitting late in their gardens, veiled from the world, came at twilight a sudden trembling and sweeping of the veil as the wandering Chorus stained the summer night with: *Shawking Murd' 'n Blooms-bree—' Pur!' London Fam'ly Mur-der—' purr'!* It broke into the bedrooms of wakeful children, and into the study of the scholar, and into the sick room and across quiet supper tables and wherever it fell it left a wound. The Press, having given the wound, went on to probe and exacerbate it with the minutiae of horror; ending with the disturbing advice to householders to see to their bolts and fastenings that night. It was the "splash" story of the day, and each paper had a narrative from neighbors and from those who were near the shop at the time of the discovery. At late evening the story was this.

Artie Roake had been quickly found and interviewed. He frankly explained his absence by the regrettable fact that he had run away. Some information he was able to give, but none that in any way helped the search for the murderers.

As that day was the last day of his holidays, he had, he said, been taking things easy, and after the midday dinner had gone upstairs to lie down. He left his brother in the garden. His father and sister were in the shop-parlor, and his mother was in the shop. From two o'clock to five o'clock was a slack time with them. Most of the business came before twelve or from five o'clock to closing time; the afternoon brought mere straggles of custom. He remembered lying down on his bed, with coat and waistcoat off, and remembered nothing more until he suddenly awoke, and found himself, he said, all of a sweat. His head and hands were quite wet. He jumped up from the bed and stood uncertainly for a few moments, thinking he was going to be ill. And well he might have been ill, seeing what foul force was then sweeping through the air of that little house. Out of the sunlight something from the neglected corners of hell had come creeping upon it, to charge its rooms with poison and to fire it with the black lightning of sudden death. At the moment he awoke this creeping corruption must then have been in the house, and in its presence not the thickest and most wooden organism could have slept; for by some old sense of forest

313

forefathers we are made aware of such presences. We can perceive evil in our neighborhood through every channel of perception; can even *see* it through the skin. The potency of its vapors, then, must have worked upon the skin and the senses of this lad, as the potency of the unseen reptile works upon the nerves of birds, and he awoke because an alien and threatening presence had called him to awake. It must have been that, and not a cry or a blow, that awoke him, because he said that, during the few seconds when he stood half-awake and sweating, he heard his mother's voice in a conversational murmur. It was some seconds after *that* that the sweat froze on his face at the sound of his father's voice in three plodding syllables—"Oh . . . my . . . God!—and then of a noise such as a coalman makes when he drops an empty sack on the pavement. And then, almost simultaneously with the sack sound, he heard a little squeak that ended in a gurgle; and over-riding the gurgle an "Oh!" of surprise from his brother, and soft, choking tones of terror saying "No—no—no!" And then silence. And then he heard two sharp clicks, as of opening and shutting a door; and then a moment's pause; and then swift feet on the stairs. Had he had the courage to go down on his father's first cry, his courage, one may guess, would have been wasted. Hands would have been waiting for him, and he too would have ended on a gurgle. But if he had had the courage to wait before he fled until the figure or figures on the stairs had come high enough to give him one glimpse, he might have had the clue to one of the men that would have helped the police to the others. But he didn't wait. He bolted. He offered the reporters no feeble excuse of going to raise the alarm or get help. He said that those sounds and the sort of feeling in the house so affected him with their hint of some unseen horror that he didn't think of anybody or anything; only of getting out. Peering from his door, he said, just as the sound of the feet came, he could see part of the staircase, and the sunlight through the glazed door between shop-passage and garden threw a shadow, or it might have been two shadows, halfway up the stairs. He could hear heavy panting. In the moment of his looking, the shadow began to swell and to move. He saw no more. In awkward phrases (so one of the reports stated) he tried to say that he felt in that shadow something more than assault ending in killing; he felt something horrible. From later information I understood this. It *was* horrible; so horrible that even this vegetable soul had responded to it. So, driven by he knew not what, and made, for the first time in his life, to hurry, he turned from the house of dusty sunshine and death to the open world of sky and shops and people. He bolted through the upper window and over the backyard, and did not stop or call for help until he was four streets away; at which point the cry of Murder led to a pursuit and capture of him.

He made his confession sadly but without shame. He *knew*, he said, that it was all over; that he could be of no use; that they were all dead. But when they pressed him *how* he knew, he relapsed from that moment of assertion into his customary cow-like thickness, and they could get no more from him than a mechanical, "I dunno. I just knew."

He was detained by the police for further questioning, and it appeared later that the questioning had been severe. But though there was at first an edge of official and public suspicion of him, he was able to satisfy the police that he knew nothing, and was allowed to go home to an uncle's.

No weapons were found, no fingerprints, no useful foot-prints. Nor had any suspicious characters been seen hanging about; at least, none markedly suspicious to the district; for in these misty byways queer characters of a sort were a regular feature, and its houses were accustomed at all hours of day and night to receiving furtive strangers. Taking it, at first sight, as gang work, the police, it was said, were pursuing enquiries in that direction, which meant that for the next few days all known members of North London and West End gangs were rounded up and harried out of their wits by detentions, questionings and shadowings. Already, at that early hour, reports had come in of the detention of unpleasant characters at points on the roads from London—Highgate, Ealing, Tooting. Communications had been made with all lunatic asylums in and near London, but none could report any absentees. All those on the police list who might have been concerned in it—the shop and till special-ists—were being visited and questioned, and many, knowing that they would be visited anyway, were voluntarily coming in to give satisfactory accounts of themselves.

One bright "special" had put his mind to the case and lighted the darkness of the police with a possible culprit. He learned that Horace Roake was fifty-five, and from his study of "our medical correspondent" he knew that fifty-five was the male climacteric, the age when men of formerly sober life—

315

particularly quiet men of Roake's type—go off the rails into all sorts of jungles of unnamable adventure. Was it not worth asking, he said, whether Mr. Roake might not have been doing badly in business, and being at that age had . . . ? But a rival paper, in the later issue, took this torch and extinguished it by bank evidence that Roake was not doing badly in business, and by private police-surgeon information that neither Roake nor any other of the victims could possibly have died by suicide.

There, that evening, it was left. Next morning there were further details, but nothing pointing towards an arrest. From some of these details it was clear that the affair, if planned at all, had been most cunningly planned and timed, and swiftly done; for the people were seen alive a minute and a half before the cry of Murder had been raised. The more likely conjecture, though, was that it was the impulsive act of a wandering gang.

A woman volunteered that she had visited the shop just after three—about ten minutes after—and had been served by Mrs. Roake. Nobody else was in shop. She left the shop and went a little way down the street to leave a message with a friend, and having left the message she re-passed the Roakes' shop, and saw a man whom she did not closely notice standing at the counter rattling some coins and calling "Shop!" Her own home was twelve doors from the shop. She had scarcely opened and closed her door, was, indeed, still on the mat, setting down her shopping basket, when she heard the cry of Murder. In the immediate instant of silence following that cry she heard a church clock strike the quarter past three, which meant that only three minutes had passed from the time of her being served by Mrs. Roake, and one minute from the time of her seeing the man.

Another statement came from a man whose house backed on to the Roakes'. He was on a night-shift at the docks, and went on at four o'clock. By daily use he knew exactly how to time himself to get there punctually from his home in Frostick Street; the time was fifty minutes; and he left home regularly at ten minutes past three. He was putting on his boots, he said, when, happening to glance through the window, he saw Mr. and Mrs. Roake in the shop-parlor doing—well, as he put it, clearly without any intent of flippancy, carrying-on and canoodling. They must then have remembered that they were open to curious eyes, for they immediately moved away from the window into the darker part of the room. At half-past four the even paper came into the docks, and he saw that the family had been discovered dead five minutes after he had seen this little husband-and-wife moment.

One of the morning papers gave me a particular irritation. There was a solemn youth named Osbert Freyne (recently down from Cambridge) who used to come into my place at odd times, though I never made him welcome. He used to sit and blither—talk one could not call it. I don't know why he continued to come, because I was always as rude to him as I can allow myself to be to anybody; but he did come and he did meet Trink, and he knew of Trink's acquaintance with the Roakes.

Well, one of the papers had an appendix to the Talleyrand "story"—an appendix by this solemn youth. Like most of his unbalanced kind, though he affected to despise modern writing, he wasn't above making money out of it when he could. The fellow had had a talk (or blither) with Trink, and had sold it to the paper as an interview with "an intimate friend of the unfortunate family." The result was that Trink had been visited and questioned by the police on the family's history and habits and their friends, and other journalists had followed the police, and altogether the poor fellow's miserable day had been made additionally miserable.

I knew what he must be feeling about it, for I myself began to be moved by it, though quite unwarrantably. I had scarcely any interest in those people, yet whenever I thought about the affair I suffered a distinct chill, as though I personally were in some way touched by it; an entirely unreasonable chill which I could not shake off because common sense could not reach it.

Among the first to be examined were the witnesses who were in the street at the time the alarm was given. This again brought nothing useful; indeed, the result was only confusion on confusion. Seventeen people who had been near the spot were asked—Who was the man who rushed from the shop crying Murder? None of them knew him. They were then asked— What sort of man was he? Not one could make a clear answer. Eleven were so surprised that they didn't look at him. The other six—who, if they had looked at him, hadn't seen him but wouldn't admit it—gave six different descriptions. One saw a tall firmly-built man with red face. One saw a short man in a mackintosh. One saw a man in shirt and trousers only— obviously a confusion with the fleeing boy, Artie. One saw a fat man in a gray suit and a bowler hat. One saw a medium-sized man in cloth cap and the strapped corduroys of the navy. One saw a black man.

It seemed fairly certain, though, that the man who cried Murder could not have been the murderer, for two witnesses had seen members of the family alive within less than two minutes of the murders; and one man could not have been responsible for that wholesale slaughter in that space of time. The man who ran out must have been the man who had been seen by the woman witness standing there and shouting "Shop!" and as that was only one minute before the alarm, clearly *he* could not have been the murderer. He had not come forward, but then, there might be many innocent explanations of that. He might have been a man of nervous type who had received such a shock from what he had seen that he wished to avoid all association with the matter. Or he might have been a quiet, shy fellow who would hate to be mixed up in any sensational public affair. Having given the alarm, and having no useful information to offer beyond what the crowd saw for themselves, he might have considered he had done his duty.

Generally, it was felt that it must have been the work of a gang—either a gang of thieves who were disturbed by the alarm before they could get at the cash, or, as suggested, a gang of drunken or drugged Negroes—and the gang must have entered from the back, or someone in the street would have noted them. It was the Negro suggestion that caught the public, chiefly because it seemed obvious and because it afforded a pious opportunity of shaking what they liked to think was an un-English crime on to those who were un-English. In talk around the streets the police were criticized for not concentrating on the Negro quarter. It was all very well to say that all the Negroes questioned had accounted for their movements. If the public were in the police's place, the public would know what to do, and so on.

The evening papers of that day brought more news, but none of it led anywhere. More suspicious characters on the outskirts of London had been detained, and two men—one a soldier at Sheerness, the other a tramp at Gerard's Cross—had given themselves up for the murder, only to be thrown out an hour later. People in the neighborhood now began to remember strange and significant happenings centering on the Roakes, which they hadn't remembered the day before. Queer visitors, letters by every post, sudden outgoings, late home-comings—all the scores of commonplace family happenings which, when isolated and focused and limelit by tragedy and publicity, assume an air of the sinister and portentous.

Day by day the story mounted, and all fact that was thin was fortified by flagrant conjecture and by "sidelights" and comparison with similar crimes.

The police were following a clue at Bristol. A broken and stained bicycle pump had been found behind the mangle in the scullery and was being examined by the Home Office experts. Three of the leading Yard men had left London for a destination unknown. The writer of an anonymous letter, received at Bow Street the day after the murders, was asked to communicate with any police station under a pledge of the fullest protection from all consequences. The Flying Squad had spent a whole day combing the road from Stoke Newington to Waltham Cross. Watch was being kept at Gravesend, Queenboro', Harwich, Grimsby, Hull and Newcastle for two men, believed to be Norwegians. The police were anxious to get in touch with these men. Blandly and hopefully they invited these two men to visit the Yard. But despite these invitations, despite official rewards and newspaper rewards running into many hundreds of pounds, no outside help was secured, no "splits"—those ever-present helps in baffling crimes—came forward to give their pals away.

Then, at the end of the week, the Sunday papers had a plum. All these minor diversions were canceled and the men called off. The new story was that the District Inspector, with a detachment of officers in an armored police car, had left for Nottingham; and the story was given out with such a note of assurance that the thing appeared to be settled. And it was. Press and public waited eagerly on the result of this expedition. And they waited. After two days, as the result of waiting, the Press was proudly silent on Nottingham. There was no report on the Nottingham expedition, but in its place a calm ignoring of it, as though it had never been. Nottingham was still on the map of England but it was out of the news. The public heard nothing. Not a word. Somewhere between London and Nottingham the Great Talleyrand Murder Mystery faded away; crept into the valley of undiscovered crimes, and died as mysteriously as the Roake family had died.

Thereafter public and press interest declined. From being a "splash" story it came to an ordinary column; then, from the main page it passed to the secondary news page; then it fell to half a column, and at the end of three weeks it had no space at all. The mystery that had been the subject of talk in offices, shops, trains, restaurants and homes, was forgotten. The best brains had been at work upon it and had failed; and although I, in common with other amateurs, had my theories about it, not one of them bore steady examination.

Today I know the solution, but I did not arrive at it by my own thought or by thought based on the experts' labors. We were all looking for madmen, or, if we dismissed madmen, then for some possible motive; and in looking for motives we were looking for the ordinary human motives that we could appreciate, and that appear again and again in murder. None of us thought of inventing a *new* motive; and that was where the solution lay. It was not the experts, but Stephen Trink, the dabbler, who showed me where to look; who took my eyes off a gang, and showed me how all this death and disaster and stretching of police wits could have been the work of two hands belonging to one man. He even pointed to the man.

VI

It was about a month after the affair had died down that I found among the morning mail on my tea-tray a letter from Trink. It was dated from a hotel in the New Forest, and was an unusually long letter from one who scarcely ever addressed more than a postcard. And a queer letter. I read it in bed, and for some long time—an hour, I should think—I could not bring myself to get up and face the day. When at last I did, I found work impossible. All that day and night I was haunted by a specter of forbidden knowledge, and I went perfunctorily about my occasions with a creeping of the flesh, as when one discovers a baby playing with a boiling kettle, or touches something furry in the dark. I knew then what it was that the boy Artie was trying to say.

But as the letter requires no editing or pointing, I give it *verbatim*.

Dear T.B.,
As we haven't met for some time I thought you might like a word from Stephen Trink. I've been down here for a week or so among the pines, seeking a little open-air massage for jangled

nerves. You understand. It was a dreadful business, and I didn't want to see anybody, especially friends. I'm here doing nothing and seeing nothing—just breathing and drowsing.

I suppose they've got no farther with it. Strange that the police, so astonishingly clever in making up really baffling and complicated cases, are so often beaten by a simple case. But you, as an artist, know how often a subtle piece of work which the public imagine to have been achieved by laborious and delicate process, was in fact done with perfect ease; and how often the simple piece of work has meant months of planning and revision. I don't know if you've thought about it at all, but it seems to me that they've been misled all along by the matter of time. They assumed that that little time, for such a business, must imply a gang. No sound reason why it should, though. As Samuel Nicks established an alibi by accomplishing the believed impossible—committing a crime at Gad's Hill, Kent, early one morning and being seen at York at seven o'clock the same evening, so this man deceived public opinion. The public of the seventeenth century held that it was not possible for a man to be in Kent in the morning and at York in the evening; all the horses in the kingdom couldn't carry him that distance in that time. Therefore, it hadn't been done, and Sam Nicks hadn't been in Kent that day. But it *was* done. And so here. Four murders by different means had been accomplished in a few seconds over a minute. Therefore, say the public (the experts, too), arguing from the general, it must have been the work of a gang. They were satisfied that no one man could do it, and if no one man could do it, then no one man *had* done it. But public opinion is always saying It Can't Be Done, and is always eating its words. You and I know that what any one man can *conceive,* some other man can *do.* I can imagine that this could be the work of one man, and I'm satisfied that it *was* the work of one man. It was done by the exception to the rule, and I'll show you how he could have done it, and how he got away. As to getting away, of course he got away by running away. If you say that a running man at such a moment would attract attention, well, we know that he did attract attention. He was clever enough to know that in successfully running away, it depends how you run. He covered his appearance and his running by drawing the whole street's attention to himself. He knew enough about things to know that his cry would blind everybody. They might be looking, but they wouldn't be seeing—as we know they weren't. All their senses would gather to reinforce the sense of hearing. As soon as he was round a corner he could slip his hat in his pocket and put on a cap. Nothing makes a sharper edge on the memory, or more effectually changes a man's appearance, than the hat. Then he could fling his coat over his arm, and go back and join the crowd.

The affair had to the public, as we know, the air of being the work of a brilliant and invincible gang of schemers, who weren't playing by any means their first stroke: or else of a gang of crafty madmen. It was this that increased its horror. But it was no planned affair, and no gang affair. It was the work of a man momentarily careless of results. Being careless, he made no mistakes. As often happens, he, the inexpert, achieved casually what trained minds arrive at step by step.

Now as to how. Really very simple. The core of the mystery is this: he was a man of unbelievable swiftness of act and motion. That's all.

People don't seem to realize that taking human life is a very simple matter. They seem to think that it involves thought, planning, struggle and mess. Nothing of the kind. It can be done as easily as the slaughter of a rabbit—more easily than the slaughter of a hen. A pressure with two fingers on a certain spot, or one sharp flick on a point at the back of the neck, and the business is done. It's part of the irony that plays about the creature, Man, that the neck, which supports his noblest part, should be his weakest part. You could do it without fuss in the club, on top of the 'bus, at Lord's, or at the theater, or in your own home or your victim's. You remember that morning when you were showing me your collection of Eastern weapons? Among them you had a case of Burmese poison darts. You took these out of their cylinder and showed them to me. I was leaning forward with my hands on your desk, and you were turning them about between finger and thumb. One minute movement of a minute muscle of your forefinger, and the point would have touched my hand, and Trink would have been out. Supposing you'd been not feeling very well—liverish—and my face or my voice had irritated you to the point of blind exasperation. A wonderful chance. Accidents often happen when things like that are being shown round. You may have seen the chance. If you did, only common good nature can have restrained you—supposing that you were irritated by me—as nothing but good nature restrains me from slapping a bald head in front of me at the theater. One second would have done it, where shooting and throat-cutting not only take time but often cause disorder and fuss, besides involving extravagant use of means. One stroke of a finger directed by a firm wrist achieves the result without any stress or display. Many people are killed by four or five stabs of a knife, or by a piece of lead shot from an instrument that has to be loaded, and in which a lever has to be released, causing a loud bang. Unnecessary, and possibly wasted. Because no result can be achieved unless that piece of lead goes to a certain spot. And there's nothing that that piece of lead can do that four fingers can't do. You could have six friends in your room looking over your curios, and with merely the movement of the arm that an orchestral conductor makes in directing a three-four bar, you could, holding one of those Burmese darts, touch the hands of those friends. In five minutes you would have changed your warm gossipy room into a sepulchre. And yet people still think of murder as implying revolvers, knives, arsenic; and murderers still take five minutes over throttling from the front with both hands, when two seconds with the side of one hand will do it from the back. It is because of this that the unintelligent conceive murder as terrific, demanding time and energy; and still think that all murder must leave obvious traces of murder. Not at all. For every one murder that is known to be a murder, I am certain that six other people, who meet Accidental Death or are Found Drowned, lose their lives by murder.

This man, as I say, was swifter than most of us. He strolled into the shop. Calling "Shop!" he went to the parlor door. There he met Roake. One movement. Mrs. Roake would turn. Another movement. The girl was coming through the door leading to the passage. Two steps and another movement. The boy comes through the garden to the shop. A fourth movement. One movement with a knife on the back of Roake's head. One pressure with the thumb to Mrs. Roake. One movement with both hands to the girl. One sharp touch on the boy's neck. And the foul thing was done in a matter of seconds. A movement overhead. The other boy stirring. He waits for him to come down. The boy doesn't come. He hears the noise of his flight. Then he makes his own by running full tilt into the faces of a score of people and crying his crime.

That's all.

Looking over this, I'm afraid it reads as though I'm writing with levity. But I'm not. I'm just analyzing the situation and the probable attitude of the man. The whole thing is too frightful for me to treat it as seriously as I naturally feel about it; or, rather, in trying to treat it as a problem, I've forgotten that these poor people were my friends.

Now as to why any man not a natural criminal or lunatic should have created this horror of destruction—this isn't going to be so easy. Here I'm on dangerous and delicate ground, and before I can present what looks to me like a reasonable explanation I must ask you to empty your mind of your reason and of all that knowledge of human nature on which people base their judgment of human motive and human behavior. It should never be said that "people don't do these things" or that such and such a thing is contrary to human nature; because people do anything and are always going contrary to our accepted notions of human nature. You must see it as clearly as one sees a new scientific idea—without reference to past knowledge or belief. It means trespassing into the forbidden, though I think you've peeped into more secret corners of the mind than the ordinary man. Or not peeped, perhaps, I think you've always known without peeping.

It's difficult to put the presentation of it into assured and assuring phrasing. But I'll try.

What I offer is this. This man had a motive for this wanton slaughter. But not a motive that would pass with common understanding. Neither hate nor lust nor the morbid vanity that sometimes leads stupid people to the committal of enormous crimes. Nothing of that sort. And he wasn't a madman without responsibility for his actions. He knew fully what he was doing and he did it deliberately. He committed more than a crime; he committed a sin. And meant to. Most men think that sin is the ultimate depth to which man can sink from his gods; but this man didn't sink. He rose, by sin, out of something fouler than sin. That something is the spirit of unexpressed, potential evil; something that corrodes not only the soul of the man in whom it dwells, but the souls of men near him and the beautiful world about him. This evil doesn't always—indeed, seldom does—live in what we call wicked people. Almost always in the good. In comparison with such people the wicked are healthy. For these people, the germ-carriers, are more dangerous to the soul of man than a million criminals or a thousand sinners. They can penetrate everywhere. We have no armor against their miasma. They do no evil, but they're little hives of evil. Just as some people can spread infection without themselves taking the disease, so these good people can, without sinning, spread among the innocent the infection of sin. They lead stainless lives. Their talk is pure. Yet wherever they go they leave a gray trail that pollutes all that is noble and honest. They diffuse evil as some lonely places—themselves beautiful—diffuse evil. You must have met people of this sort—good people—and have been faintly conscious, after an hour of their company, of some emanation that makes you want to open spiritual windows. Happy for them, poor creatures, if they can discover and prove themselves before death for what they are. Some do. For those who don't, who only discover the foulness of their souls after death, God knows what awaits them.

There's something in these people. Some awful essence of the world's beginnings. Some possession that can only be cast out in one way—a dreadful way. Where it began one cannot say. Perhaps strange sins, projected in the cold hearts of creatures centuries-dead, projected but never given substance, take on a ghost-essence and wander through the hearts of men as cells of evil. And wander from heart to heart, poisoning as they go, until at last they come to life in a positive sin, and, having lived, can die. Nobody knows. But that's my explanation of these people—they're possessed. Possessed by some radioactive essence of evil, and before they can be saved they must sin. Just as poison is necessary to some physical natures and, denied it, they die, so sin may be necessary to these spiritual natures. They must express and release that clotted evil, and they can no more be cleansed of it before it's expressed than a man can be cleansed of a fever before it's reached its climacteric. Once expressed, it can be met and punished and pardoned; but abstract evil can't be met. Even God can't conquer Satan. There's nothing to conquer. Satan lives in these million fragments of potential evil, and until that evil is crystallized in an act, all the powers of good are powerless.

Let's suppose that this man was one of these, consciously possessed of this intangible essence of evil, conscious of it as a blight upon him and upon those about him; tortured by it like a man with a snake in his bosom, and for many years fighting its desire for expression and release until the fight became unbearable. There's only one way of escape for him—to sin and to sin deeply. Always he's haunted by the temptation to sin. His whole life's been clouded by visions and lures of unnameable sins, and by agonizing combats to escape them. Always he fights this temptation, and so, continuing to shelter the evil, he gives it time to

325

grow and to make his own emanations stronger. When his only real hope of conquering it lies in giving it life.

And then at last he yields. There comes, one day, the eruptive, whirlwind moment of temptation, stronger than any he has known. All his powers of resistance go down in an avalanche. With a sigh of relief he yields. And suddenly, with the disappearance of resistance, and with the resolve to sin, he would find, I think, the serenity of resignation filling his whole being, and setting his pulse in tune with erring humanity. He would walk the streets with a lighter step than he has known since childhood. All his temptations would have been towards the foulest sin he could conceive, the lowest depth; and at last, driven by the importunate fiend, it's this sin that he commits. It may be that he was led farther than he meant to go. He may have intended to murder only one, but in committing the one murder, his fiend broke out in full power, and led him deeper and deeper into maniac slaughter. That's how it looks. But the thing was done, the sin committed, and in the Satanic moment he frees himself forever from his fiend, not by binding it, but by releasing it. Like a long-embalmed body exposed to the air, it has one minute of life; the next it crumbles into dust, and he is free.

That's my theory. This man, without sin, would have died here and hereafter, for his soul didn't belong to him at all. Indeed, he was a man without a soul. Now he's a man with a stained soul which can be purified. He has seen himself as he is, on this earth, in time to prepare himself for his next stage. By that sin he can now, as a fulfilled and erring soul, work out his penance and his redemption.

I guess I've said enough. You may dismiss this as a far-fetched and ludicrous fancy. But it isn't a fancy; it's a statement. You may say that no man could, under the most overwhelming temptation, do this appalling act of murdering, not an enemy, but a friend; or having done it, could live under its burden. I can't argue with you as to what man can and can't do. I only see what is done. It's useless to tell me that this couldn't have happened. I can only say that it did.

Whatever you may know as to the reactions of humanity to this or that situation, I know that, after years of torment, I'm now, for the first time, at peace.

Yours,

S.T.

BICKMORE DEALS WITH THE DUCHESS

BY J. S. FLETCHER

Joseph Smith Fletcher was born in 1863 in Yorkshire, England, and worked as a journalist in London for several years. He produced more than 100 volumes of poetry, biography, historical fiction, nonfiction, and mysteries. He was relatively unknown in the United States until President Woodrow Wilson read and praised *The Middle Temple Murders* (1918). His best-known fictional detectives are Roger Camberwell (*The Ebony Box,* 1934; *The Eleventh Hour,* 1935), Archer Dawe, and Paul Campenhaye. Fletcher died in Dorking, Surrey, in 1935.

WHEN BICKMORE, WHO DEALT in antique furniture, old pictures, and the like at a gloomy old shop in the High Market at Norcaster, set out one morning to attend the sale by auction of the effects of a resident of the town who had recently died, he had no idea that any romance or sensational development would result from whatever he might do that day. Neither was foreign to his trade; in his time he had known both. More than once romance had sprung from his acquisition of some ancient cabinet; now and then the clue to a crime had been found in a bit of furniture casually purchased and set aside to be examined at leisure; on one occasion a missing will had been discovered hidden away in a frowsy old book which Bickmore had bought for five shillings and would cheerfully have sold for twenty. But these events and developments were rare; they were accidents, like the sudden and unexpected turnings-up of a perfect and complete and undoubtedly genuine set of Chippendale chairs in a house where you would never have thought to find such a thing, or the discovery of an unquestionable Gainsborough or a gem of a Reynolds in the garret of a countryman's cottage. And nobody expects accidents, and Bickmore expected nothing more that morning than that he was going to buy two or three or four lots of the old stuff which Mr. Septimus Walkinshaw had left on departing this life.

The late Mr. Walkinshaw, in his time, had been a well-to-do chartered accountant in the town, a man of considerable means. But he was also known as an antiquary, and as an occasional collector who knew good things when he saw them. Bickmore, who had once or twice visited the old gentleman's quiet house in the Friaries, knew that several articles of ancient furniture were now to be offered for sale by auction which were specially worth buying. In the preliminary stages of the proceedings he bought two or three such things, but he was never really interested until there was put up an old bureau of great age at which he himself had seen its late owner writing. It was a beautiful bit of work, in excellent preservation: oddly enough, there was no great competition for it, and Bickmore acquired it for fifty guineas, and later in the day had it transferred to his warehouse with his other purchases. For the rest of that afternoon and evening, however, being otherwise busied, he gave no more thought to it. And he was not even thinking about it next morning when, soon after Norcaster had awakened to another day's business, into his shop came bustling the auctioneer under whose hammer the bureau had fallen, and who now carried in his hand the buff envelope of a telegram.

"Morning, Bickmore!" said the auctioneer, who was on familiar terms with every tradesman in the town. "Fine morning! Look here!—this came while I was at breakfast. Here—read it for yourself. It concerns you more than me—as it's a day too late."

Bickmore, who was a man of few words, took the telegram and read:

> *To* Strymer, Auctioneer, Norcaster, England.
> Just heard of Walkinshaw's sale. Buy in for me old bureau that stood in his library. Go to any price.
> *From* Duchess of Norcaster, Hotel de Paris, Monte Carlo.

"Of course you'll sell," remarked Strymer, as Bickmore silently handed back the flimsy scrap of paper. "I expect the Duchess saw the advertisement of old Walkinshaw's sale in the *Times*, and made a mistake in the actual date. Anyway, I didn't get that until this morning—too late for me to act for her. However, if you'll say what you want, I'll wire at once to her Grace. Fifty guineas you gave, eh, Bickmore? Well? What's your price for your bargain?"

But Bickmore was rubbing his chin.

"Um!" he answered after a long pause, during which Strymer began to look at him wonderingly. "Afraid I can't say, Mr. Strymer, just now. You see—the fact is, I've a customer in view."

"Oh, come!" expostulated the auctioneer. "Her Grace, now! You can't refuse her! And look at your chance! See what she says: 'Go to any price.' Come now!—name your figure. I don't want to disappoint her Grace."

But Bickmore shook his head.

"No," he said, "not at present, anyway. The—the other party has an option on it. I can't do anything this morning, Mr. Strymer."

"Come—come!" urged Strymer. "Look here!—say a hundred and fifty! She'll go to that. And that's a hundred clear profit!"

"No," replied Bickmore. "Sorry, but I can't do it."

Strymer tried five minutes' more coaxing, but it was useless. At the end of his fruitless endeavor he went away, grumbling, and Bickmore rubbed his chin still more as he watched him go. And then Bickmore asked himself a question in plain words: Why did the Duchess of Norcaster, who was certainly not a collector, and didn't know a bit of Sheraton from the product of a local cabinetmaker, want Walkinshaw's bureau?—want it so much that she was willing to pay just about any price for it? Why?

The more Bickmore put this question to himself, the more he failed to find any likely answer to it. He knew the Duchess— everybody knew her—as wife of one of the great local magnates. She was still on the right side of forty; she was good-looking; she was popular. She came of an old sporting family, and if she was not on the racecourse, or a puppy-walking show, or at something else connected with dogs or horses, she was at Deauville or at Monte Carlo—as in the present instance—or, if at home, at the bridge-table. Sport, cards, games of chance— that was the Duchess. And she was wanting to buy Walkinshaw's bureau at any price!—she, whose natural tastes would much more likely have run to something brand-new and conspicuously vulgar out of Tottenham Court Road or Kensington. If she had been some relation of old Walkinshaw's, now, and was cherishing a sentimental affection for a piece of furniture regularly associated with him, there might have been something in it, said Bickmore; but she wasn't. Bickmore, though ignorant of Debrett or Burke, was not unacquainted with the Duchess's pedigree. She came of a race of hard-living, hard-riding, hard-drinking country squires, and she had been a bit of a hoyden before the Duke married her and transformed her into a Duchess. But then, reflected Bickmore, everybody in the neighborhood knew that the Duke was about as big an ass as they made 'em, and that his spouse did pretty much as she liked. And after all, the present question was—Why did she want that bureau at any price?

When Bickmore had eaten his midday dinner that day, he went back to his place of business and locked himself in the room in which the Walkinshaw bureau had been temporarily stored. He spent a few minutes in looking at it, very thoughtfully; a few more in walking around it and inspecting it from every possible point of view. This over, he began to tap and prod it, as if it had been a prize ox at a cattle show and he was estimating its condition and solidity. And eventually, having unlocked it, he began to examine it within, inch by inch. There was nothing unusual in its appearance, interiorly, but Bickmore was not the man to be deceived by appearances. When he had let down the flap which served as a writing-desk and saw the usual neat little pigeonholes, compartments, and miniature drawers all finished with the exquisite perfection of detail peculiar to the old furniture makers, he only saw what he had expected to see. And he did not trouble to open the larger drawers beneath the flap—three of them; good, roomy drawers: Bickmore's concern was with the smaller apparatus at the top. For he had a conviction which had first arisen in his mind when Strymer handed him the Duchess's telegram and had grown stronger ever since—the conviction that somewhere in old Walkinshaw's bureau there was a secret receptacle, and in it was deposited something which the Duchess of Norcaster was extremely anxious to recover.

It took Bickmore, for all his knowledge of old furniture and the ways of its ingenious makers, the better part of an hour to find what he felt certain, all along, was there. But in the end, after a vast amount of measuring with a pocket foot-rule, and reckoning up measurements with a bit of pencil and scrap of paper, he came suddenly on what he wanted—a small secret drawer, most cunningly contrived. The cleverness of its contrivance was all the more remarkable because, once you knew the secret, it was as easy to bring that drawer to light as it was to open any of the other drawers and compartments about which there was no secret. But there it was, a small, coffin-shaped receptacle, about a quarter the dimensions of a cigar box. And in it lay an oblong parcel, done up in soft tissue paper, and carelessly tied about with a bit of ordinary string, ending in a double knot.

It was characteristic of Bickmore that instead of cutting the string with his penknife he carefully and slowly untied the double knot which secured it; characteristic, too, that he laid the string aside with as much care as if it had been gold cord. It was with similar care that he took off the tissue paper—to reveal an inner wrapping of soft white leather. When that had been unrolled, Bickmore found himself staring at a magnificent diamond necklace—and at a folded half-sheet of notepaper,

331

the only other contents of the mysterious parcel, and the only other contents of the secret drawer.

Bickmore gave his first attention to the half-sheet of notepaper. When he had unfolded it, he saw that a couple of lines of writing ran across it—the stiff, crabbed writing of old Walkinshaw, every letter perfectly formed, every t crossed, and every i dotted. This is what he read:

Received from Mr. Septimus Walkinshaw as a loan the sum of five thousand pounds.

Mirabelle Norcaster

Bickmore began to understand things. The Duchess of Norcaster had borrowed five thousand pounds from Mr. Walkinshaw and had deposited with him as security a diamond necklace. But what interested Bickmore was a question which immediately sprang into his mind—Was this *the* necklace which formed a part of the famous Norcaster Diamonds? Everybody had heard of the Norcaster Diamonds—they were an heirloom in the family, going with title and estate. And of course there was local tradition about them; it was commonly believed that they were kept in a sealed box in the strong room of some London bank, and were never taken out except to be worn by the Duchess of the time being at some unusually great event—a Coronation, or a State banquet or ball, or coming-of-age festivity, or ducal reception of Royalty, or something equally grand. From an inspection of the stones and their setting, Bickmore was certain that this was *the* necklace. And it was very evident that the Duchess had raised five thousand pounds on it from Mr. Walkinshaw, and had seen him place it and her receipt for his money in that secret drawer—good reason why she wanted to buy the bureau! In fact, Bickmore now believed that he saw through the whole thing. The transaction had been an absolutely secret one, between Walkinshaw and the Duchess. Soon after it had taken place, Walkinshaw had died, very suddenly; the sale of his effects had soon followed; the Duchess wanted to get hold of the bureau in order that she might repossess herself of her diamonds without repaying the loan to Walkinshaw's residuary legatee. And who was *he*? Bickmore did not know; that was a detail . . . the thing to be done at present was . . .

What Bickmore did was to wrap up the parcel again, replace

it in the secret drawer, and have the bureau transferred to a private room, the key of which he put in his pocket. That done he asked himself a question—How soon should he see the Duchess?

Bickmore knew the Duchess would come. She was sure to come. He felt positive that if Strymer had telegraphed to her that he had been unable to secure the bureau, as he probably had, she would hurry home from Monte Carlo as fast as she could travel. Oh, yes, she would be walking into his shop before many days were over—as sure as his name was Daniel Bickmore. Very good!—but before he was honored with her Grace's visit, Bickmore was going to know a thing or two.

But before Bickmore progressed far in his pursuit of knowledge, Strymer appeared again—next day. Once more he carried a telegram in his hand. And in his eye there was the expression of a man who feels that though he has been repulsed once, he will certainly not be baffled twice.

"Hullo, Bickmore!" he exclaimed, unceremoniously. "That bureau, now. Here's another wire from the Duchess. Of course, I wired to her yesterday, after seeing you, and told her that her first telegram had come too late for me to execute her commission, and that you'd bought that particular bit of stuff at Walkinshaw's sale. Here's her reply."

Bickmore, with no show of interest, took the paper which Strymer shoved into his hand, and read what was written thereon.

See Bickmore at once. Give any price he likes. Must have bureau.

"Of course you'll sell, after that?" said Strymer. "Come now!—what's the figure?"

Bickmore handed back the telegram and turned to what he had been doing when the auctioneer came in.

"Can't name any figure, Mr. Strymer," he replied calmly. "I told you yesterday—somebody else has an option on it."

"Just so!—but can't you get rid of him, or her, or whoever it is?" persisted Strymer. "I reckon you'll not get out of him or her what you'll get out of the Duchess! See what she says?—'Give any price he likes'! Look here, now!—name your price, and I'll go so far as to settle here and now! Can't say fairer than that, Bickmore, can I? Come!"

"No," answered Bickmore. "Business is business. I'm not in a position to treat. All I've got to say is—if, when the Duchess comes home, I still have the bureau to sell, she shall have the first refusal. Can't do more."

Strymer looked at him wonderingly.

"Hanged if I understand this!" he exclaimed. "What is there that's particularly fetching about the thing? Nice bit of old stuff, to be sure—but I've had far nicer through my hands. Fifty guineas didn't you give, eh? And you mean to tell me that whoever it is that's got an option on the bureau will give you so much that you think it worth while to refuse my offer on her Grace's behalf? Cash down, Bickmore! Write you a check this minute—if we agree on a price."

"Can't do it," said Bickmore. "Said all I've got to say."

Bickmore's first step was to go across to the post office and dispatch a telegram. That telegram was to a man whom he knew in London—a man who had extensive dealings in precious stones, and was of great repute as an expert. Bickmore had had business transactions with him on various occasions, and knew that he could trust him. And when, in response to the telegram, the man turned up in Norcaster that evening, Bickmore took him home to his private house, gave him a good dinner, and later, when they were alone with their cigars and their glasses, suddenly produced the diamond necklace from his pocket, and handing it to his guest asked him laconically what he thought of it.

The expert let the necklace slide through his fingers— lovingly. He made a soft, purring sound as if he had been caressing something for which he had a sentimental affection. But suddenly he rose smartly from his chair, crossed over to a point immediately beneath an electric light, and looked closer, and still closer. And with equal suddenness he turned on his host, and taking his cigar from his lips with one hand, waved the necklace at him with the other, and snapped out a single word:

"*Paste!*"

Bickmore's face remained as immovable as that of a marble bust which looked down on him and his guest from a bracket in the corner. He nodded over the rim of his glass, which he was just then raising to his lips.

"Paste, eh?" he remarked, indifferently. "You're certain?"

The guest, who was a bluff and hearty sort of person,

laughed, threw the necklace on the table, and picking up his own glass took a long pull at its contents.

"As ever they make 'em, my boy!" he answered. "Stake my professional reputation on it—oh, yes—paste! Bee-u-tiful work, my boy—I've a pretty good idea whose work, too!"

"Whose, then?" demanded Bickmore.

"Parisian, my boy—excellent work done there in the imitation-gem line. I should say, if I were asked, as you ask me, my boy, it was done by Legros and Folquet—I've seen a lot of work of theirs. Of course it's a very fine, beautiful, perfectly executed replica of some famous necklace—I daresay I could trace that necklace, if necessary. But—a replica! Not an original. Not diamonds. No, my boy—paste!"

"What's a thing like that worth—as paste?" inquired Bickmore.

The expert rubbed his plump hands together, and drew inspiration from his big cigar.

"Well, my boy, it depends. It's the workmanship, d'ye see? The stuff—pooh! And the setting—not much. It's the imitating of the real thing—the exquisite artistry of the workmanship, my boy! And that's a lovely bit of work—oh, lovely! A few hundred pounds, my boy, at least."

"And the original?" suggested Bickmore. "What about its worth?"

The expert's round face grew grave. He waved his cigar at Bickmore.

"Ah, my boy!" he said. "Now you ask me a very serious question—a question of the first magnitude! You mean, my boy, that supposing that little toy was made of real diamonds it would be worth—so much?"

"That's just about it," assented Bickmore. "What would the original—diamonds the size and so on of those things—be worth?"

"There's other things than size, my boy," said the expert solemnly. "There's all sorts of things to be taken into consideration in estimating the value of diamonds. But I should say, my boy, that the original of that replica, if the stones are of the first quality, is worth nearer forty than thirty thousand! You might say thirty-five thousand of the best, my boy."

"Very nice figure," observed Bickmore, dryly. "And you haven't the slightest hesitation in saying that this is—paste?"

"Oh, not the slightest, my boy!" affirmed the expert.

"Then oblige me by sitting down at that desk and writing out a certificate to that effect," said Bickmore. "I will need it."

Next morning Bickmore replaced the necklace in the secret drawer of the bureau, but the little parcel of soft leather and tissue paper in which it was enclosed now contained another document in addition to the receipt—the expert's certificate. That done, Bickmore locked up the bureau and the room in which he had stored it. This, he was well aware, was the waiting stage. And he was the sort of man who could wait patiently.

But one day he knew that he would not have to wait long. Turning over the morning papers at his club, his eye caught the Duchess of Norcaster's name. Her Grace had just returned from the Riviera to her town house in London. Bickmore smiled—and from that moment began to expect the Duchess at any instant. Many instants went by, however, and many hours, and many days and still no Duchess appeared. Bickmore kept his ears open at that center of local gossip, the club; it would soon be known there if the Duchess came down to the ducal seat just outside the town. But he heard nothing of her arrival there. Yet one item of interest he did hear, and that was that her Grace had fallen upon great good luck at the tables at Monte Carlo. That made Bickmore all the more certain that she would come to see him—and with a full purse.

Instead of the Duchess, there walked, one afternoon, into his shop an elegantly-attired, handsome, middle-aged lady who, when Bickmore first became aware of her distinguished presence, was calmly surveying the various contents of the establishment through a gold-mounted lorgnette. She deigned to see Bickmore at last, and surveyed him from top to toe as if he had been a five-foot cupboard.

"Oh—ah—you are Mr. Bickmore, I suppose?" she suggested, in a condescending, high-pitched voice.

"At your service, ma'am," assented Bickmore, with his best bow.

"Just so! I—ah—I am thinking of taking a house near the town, and I should like to look round your stock, don't you know, with the idea of seeing if you have anything—anything particularly good, you know—that would attract me," said the lady. "So much more convenient, you see, if one can find a few things close at hand, don't you know? I hear you sometimes have some exceptionally good pieces of old furniture?"

"Somewhat noted for that, ma'am," replied Bickmore. "I have at times some of the finest old work that you could get anywhere in England, but it's very soon picked up. If you will allow me to show you round . . ."

The visitor was only too willing to be shown round, and Bickmore proceeded to act as guide to his collection. But he was suddenly much more interested in his caller as a personality than as a possible customer. Taking a closer inspection of her as she stood examining certain vases, Bickmore knew that he had seen her before. And just as suddenly he remembered where. About a year previously there had been a great open-air fête in the Duke of Norcaster's park, and Bickmore, in company with several hundreds of his fellow-townsmen and their wives, had attended it. There had been a large house party at the Duke's at the time, and its members had moved freely about the grounds. Bickmore now remembered that he had seen this morning's caller strolling around with the Duchess. And having settled that point, he lost all interest in her as a customer, and began to watch her as something else—a spy.

But Bickmore was careful to keep playing his own part. He took his visitor from room to room, showing her things that were of note and value; finally, well knowing what he was doing, he unlocked the door of the room in which he had stored the Walkinshaw bureau, and ushered her in with the remark that there were a few choice articles there which were well worth inspection. Watching his companion narrowly, he saw that she spotted the bureau as soon as she crossed the threshold; he knew, too, that she would not draw his attention to it until she had affected to inspect the other things. When at last she came to the corner in which it stood, she pretended to pass it by as an object of no particular interest; then paused.

"Rather a quaint old thing!" she remarked patronizingly. "Nothing very exceptional about it, though, is there?"

"An excellent example of its period, ma'am," replied Bickmore, "and in splendid preservation. It belonged to the late Mr. Walkinshaw of this town, who was a collector of repute."

The lady showed more interest.

"Dear me!" she said. "What is it like—inside?"

Bickmore produced a key from his pocket, and unlocked and let down the flap. And keeping his watchful eye on his companion he saw her go straight to a certain part of the top half of the revealed interior—where, as Bickmore well knew, there was a spring that released the secret drawer. But he showed no trace of having seen—instead, he began to expatiate on the beauties of the bureau. Suddenly, his visitor dropped into a chair, close by.

"I—oh, dear me!" she gasped, "I feel—faint! Can—can you get me a glass of water?"

It was a long way up from that upstairs room to the regions below, where drinking water was likely to be kept. But Bickmore laughed inwardly at being able to checkmate this very obvious move. The room in which they stood was one that he used as a sort of private office, and there was a corner cupboard in it from which he immediately produced a carafe of water and a glass. And as he crossed the floor with them he spoke, and unless his pretended customer was unusually obtuse she must have noted a slight touch of sarcasm in his tone.

"I have both brandy and whisky here, ma'am," said Bickmore. "And soda water. If you would prefer—?"

"Oh, no, thank you!" exclaimed the lady.

She took the glass and sipped a little of the water, murmuring something about a weak heart, always affected by climbing stairs; presently she made a quick recovery, and setting down the glass, smiled on Bickmore for the first time since she had entered the establishment. It was one of those smiles which are best described by the word wheedling.

"And how much do you want for this old bureau, Mr. Bickmore?" she asked in dulcet tones. "Do you know, I've taken quite a fancy to it."

"That bureau, ma'am, is not for sale," he replied, quietly. "Another person has an option on it."

That evening, looking in at the club for an hour or two, Bickmore ran into Strymer. Strymer made a face at him.

"Well?" inquired Bickmore. "And what have I done?"

"Got me a very hot quarter of an hour this morning!" answered Strymer. "That's what you've done! The Duchess turned up at my office, just before noon —she's come down here for a few days. Wanted to know what the so-and-so I meant by not carrying out her commission. Of course, I threw all the blame on you!"

"Very kind of you, I'm sure," replied Bickmore. "I daresay I can stand it. But I should think it would have been much more pertinent if the Duchess had told you why she was so anxious to get hold of that particular piece of furniture."

"She did!" exclaimed Strymer. "She says it was once in her family. Belonged to her grandfather, on the maternal side—old Squire Camp—ages ago."

"Who told her that?"

"Old Walkinshaw, she says. Had to see him on some charitable business or other, not long before she went off to the Riviera, and he pointed out this bureau to her, and told her its history. What's more, she says that old Walkinshaw promised to leave the bureau to her when he died. See?"

"Well, he didn't."

"Of course he didn't!" agreed Strymer. "May have meant to, though. But he popped off on the sudden. By the way, heard about his will?"

"Not a word," replied Bickmore. "Interesting?"

Strymer rubbed his hands.

"Left everything he had to the town!" he answered joyously. "A lot of it to the established charities, some to create new trusts, a certain amount for improvements, and that sort of thing. Very sporting of the old chap. But then, of course, he'd neither kith nor kin, as they say, and he'd certainly made his money here. Yes, that's it—all to the town. Postlethwaite, in Market Street, is sole executor, but they say he's little to do except to hand over the money to the Mayor and Corporation as trustees."

"Oh!" remarked Bickmore.

Strymer tapped the side of his nose and went to play bridge, and Bickmore turned into the reading room and looked at the newspapers.

"She'll come herself tomorrow!" he muttered. "Dead certain!"

And at eleven o'clock next morning the Duchess came.

The Duchess came openly, in her smartest car. Bickmore, catching sight of its grandeur, resolved to play his part like a man, and hurried to his door; the Duchess, handsome and debonaire, smiled broadly at him.

"Well, Mr. Bickmore!" she said, jollily, "I've come to see you about that old bureau. Lot of bother you've given me, too! Or it's given me!—"

"The latter supposition is more correct, your Grace," replied Bickmore. "I should be sorry to give your Grace any trouble."

"Oh, well, I suppose it was my own fault for mistaking the date of Mr. Walkinshaw's sale," said the Duchess graciously. "I always did get hopelessly mixed about dates, and when one's far away from home, you know, eh? Of course, if Mr. Strymer had got my telegram in time, there'd have been no bother at all— he'd have bought the thing in for me. But now look here, Mr. Bickmore, what's this Mr. Strymer tells me?—that somebody has an option on the bureau?"

"The option has not been taken up," replied Bickmore.

"Oh, I'm so glad!" she exclaimed. "That's lucky—for me, isn't it? Then of course you'll sell it to me?"

"Perhaps your Grace would like to see the bureau?" suggested Bickmore.

He led the Duchess through the shop and up various flights of stairs to the room in which the much-desired piece of furniture was housed. Once inside, with the door closed, he waved his hand towards the corner by his desk.

"Your Grace recognizes it?"

The Duchess smiled at the bureau as a mother might have smiled on a long-lost and just-recovered child.

"Oh, of course!" she exclaimed. "Delightful old thing, isn't it? Used to belong to my grandfather, you know. And Mr. Walkinshaw promised to leave it to me."

"But he didn't."

"Well, the poor man died so suddenly," said the Duchess. "Otherwise— but come now, Mr. Bickmore, I'm so pleased that the other person didn't take up his option! Now, how much?"

"Your Grace is extremely anxious to secure possession," said Bickmore, with a look at the Duchess which made her start, and glance with sudden attention at him. "But I am in possession— and sometimes I buy things which I don't care to part with. I, too, am a bit of a collector. And collectors, your Grace, have their—eccentricities. Fads, you know. Now—why, frankly, is your Grace so very desirous of buying this bureau?"

The Duchess gave Bickmore another look. It expressed a good deal—and it suddenly became transformed into an expression of ingenuous candor that would have suited a stage milkmaid.

"Mr. Bickmore!" she exclaimed. "I'll tell you! Between ourselves! There's something in that bureau that belongs to me!"

"Yes," said Bickmore, quietly, "There is also something that belongs to—somebody else!"

"To—somebody else? To—whom?" she inquired anxiously.

"To the late Mr. Walkinshaw's executor," said Bickmore. "Listen, your Grace. Suppose I tell you what is in that bureau. There is a secret drawer, and in the secret drawer there is a small parcel, done up in tissue paper and soft leather. Within it is what looks like a diamond necklace. There is also a document signed by your Grace acknowledging the receipt of five thousand pounds borrowed by your Grace from Mr. Walkinshaw. With the existence and whereabouts of these things your Grace is familiar. But your Grace is not aware that there is also in that parcel a certificate signed by one of the leading jewel experts of London, in which he testifies that the alleged diamonds of the necklace are not diamonds at all, but—paste!"

The Duchess, an eminently healthy and vigorous specimen of femininity, had collapsed into a convenient elbow chair by that time. She sat drumming her fingers on its arms and staring at Bickmore, silently. And Bickmore nodded at her.

"Cold, plain truth, your Grace!" he said icily. "Unpleasant fact!"

The Duchess found her tongue at last.

"What—what do you want?"

"I gave fifty guineas for the bureau, at the Walkinshaw sale," replied Bickmore. "As your Grace is so anxious to have it, I will take sixty guineas for it. But," he added, as the Duchess sprang to her feet, "on condition!"

"Condition?" exclaimed the Duchess. "What condition?"

"Mr. Postlethwaite, whose offices are just round the corner, is sole executor of the late Mr. Walkinshaw's will," continued Bickmore. "If your Grace will be good enough to go there and see him, and bring back to me a receipt showing that your Grace has paid him five thousand pounds, the bureau and its contents—"

The Duchess's eyes flashed.

"Otherwise," concluded Bickmore, slowly, "otherwise, much as I should regret it—"

The Duchess went.

THE AGE OF MIRACLES

BY MELVILLE DAVISSON POST

Melville Davisson Post was born in Romines Mills, West
Virginia, on April 19, 1871, and received a B.A. and an
LL. B. from West Virginia University. He practiced
criminal and corporate law for eleven years and was
active in local politics. His short stories appeared in
many magazines and introduced such characters as
Uncle Abner and the (at first) unscrupulous lawyer
Randolph Mason. His other series characters include Sir
Henry Marquis of Scotland Yard, Monsieur Jonquelle,
Prefect of Police of Paris, and Walker of the Secret Serv-
ice. A master of the short story, Post never wrote a
novel-length mystery. He died on June 23, 1930.

THE GIRL WAS STANDING APART from the crowd in the great avenue of the poplars that led up to the house. She seemed embarrassed and uncertain what to do, a thing of April emerging into Summer.

Abner and Randolph marked her as they entered along the gravel road.

They had left their horses at the gate, but she had brought hers inside, as though from some habit unconsciously upon her.

But halfway to the house she had remembered and got down. And she stood now against the horse's shoulder. It was a black hunter, big and old, but age marred no beauty of his lines. He was like a horse of ebony, enchanted out of the earth by some Arabian magic, but not yet by that magic awakened into life.

The girl wore a long, dark riding skirt, after the fashion of the time, and a coat of hunter's pink. Her dark hair was in a great wrist-thick plait. Her eyes, too, were big and dark, and her body firm and lithe from the out-of-doors.

"Ah!" cried Randolph, making his characteristic gesture, "Prospero has been piping in this grove. Here is a daughter of the immortal morning! We grow old, Abner, and it is youth that the gods love."

My uncle, his hands behind him, his eyes on the gravel road, looked up at the bewitching picture.

"Poor child," he said. "The gods that love her must be gods of the valleys and not gods of the hills."

"Ruth amid the alien corn! Is it a better figure, Abner? Well, she has a finer inheritance than these lands—she has youth!"

"She ought to have both," replied my uncle. "It was sheer robbery to take her inheritance."

"It was a proceeding at law," replied the Justice. "It was the law that did the thing, and we cannot hold the law in disrespect."

"But the man who uses the law to accomplish a wrong, we can so hold," said my Uncle Abner. "He is an outlaw, as the highwayman and the pirate are."

He extended his arm toward the great house sitting at the end of the avenue.

"In spite of the sanction of the law I hold this dead man for a robber. And I would have wrested these lands from him, if I could. But your law, Randolph, stood before him."

"Well," replied the Justice, "he takes no gain from it. He lies yonder waiting for the grave."

"But his brother takes," said Abner, "and this child loses."

The Justice, elegant in the costume of the time, turned his ebony stick in his fingers.

"One should forgive the dead," he commented in a facetious tone. "It is a mandate of the Scripture."

"I am not concerned about the dead," replied Abner. "The dead are in God's hands. It is the living who concern me."

"Then," cried the Justice, "you should forgive the brother who takes."

"And I shall forgive him," replied Abner, "when he returns what he has taken."

"Returns what he has taken!" Randolph laughed. "Why, Abner, the devil could not filch a coin out of the clutches of old Benton Wolf."

"The devil," said my uncle, "is not an authority that I depend on."

"A miracle of Heaven, then," said the Justice. "But, alas, it is not the age of miracles."

"Perhaps," replied Abner, "but I am not so certain."

They had come now to where the girl stood, her back against the black shoulder of the horse. The morning air moved the yellow leaves about her feet. She darted out to meet them, her face aglow.

"Damme!" cried Randolph. "William of Avon knew only witches of the second order! How do you do, Julia? I have hardly seen you since you were no taller than my stick, and told me that your name was 'Pete-George,' and that you were a circus horse, and offered to do tricks for me."

A shadow crossed the girl's face.

"I remember," she said, "it was up there on the porch!"

"Egad!" cried Randolph, embarassed. "And so it was."

He kissed the girl's fingers and the shadow in her face fled for a moment.

For the man's heart was good, and he had the manner of a gentleman. But it was Uncle Abner whom she turned to in her dilemma.

"I forgot," she said," and almost rode into the house. Do you think I could leave the horse here? He will stand if I drop the rein."

Then she went on to make her explanation. She wanted to see the old house that had been so long her home. This was the only opportunity, today, when all the countryside came to the dead man's burial. She thought she might come, too, although her motive was no tribute of respect.

She put her hand through Abner's arm and he looked down upon her, grave, and troubled.

"My child," he said, "leave the horse where he stands and come with me—for my motive, also, is no tribute of respect; and you go with a better right than I do."

"I suppose," the girl hesitated, "that one ought to respect the dead, but this man—these men—I cannot."

"Nor can I," replied my uncle. "If I do not respect a man when he is living, I shall not pretend to when he is dead. One does not make a claim upon my honor by going out of life."

They went up the avenue among the yellow poplar leaves and the ragweed and fennel springing up along the unkept gravel.

It was a crisp and glorious morning. The frost lay on the rail fence. The spider webs stretched here and there across the high grasses of the meadows in intricate and bewildering lacework. The sun was clear and bright, but it carried no oppressive heat as it drew on in its course toward noon.

The countryside had gathered to see Adam Wolf buried. It was a company of tenants, the idle and worthless mostly, drawn by curiosity. For in life the two old men who had seized upon this property by virtue of a defective acknowledgement to a deed permitted no invasion of their boundary.

Everywhere the lands were posted; no urchin fished and no schoolboy hunted. The green perch, fattened in the deep creek that threaded the rich bottom lands, no man disturbed. But the quail, the pheasant, the robin, and the meadow lark, old Adam pursued with his fowling piece.

He had tramped about with it in all seasons. One would have believed that all the birds of heaven had done the man some unending harm and in revenge he had declared a war. And so the accident by which he met his death was a jeopardy of the old man's habits, and to be looked for when one lived with a fowling piece in one's hands and grew careless in its use.

The two men lived alone and thus all sorts of mystery sprang

345

up around them, elaborated by fancy and gaining in grim detail at every storyteller's hand. It had the charm and thrilling interest of an adventure, then, for the countryside to get this entry.

The brothers lived in striking contrast. Adam was violent, and his cries and curses, his hard and brutal manner were the terror of those who passed at night that way, or the urchin overtaken by darkness on his road home. But Benton got about his affairs in silence, with a certain humility of manner, and a mild concern for the opinion of his fellows.

Still, somehow, the traveler and the urchin held him in a great terror. Perhaps because he had got his coffin made and kept in his house, together with his clothes for burial. It seemed uncanny thus to prepare against his dissolution and to bargain for the outfit, with anxiety to have his shilling's worth.

And yet, with this gruesome furniture at hand, the old man, it would seem, was in no contemplation of his death. He spoke sometimes with a marked savor and an unctuous kneading of the hands of that time when he should own the land, for he was the younger and by rule should have the expectancy of life.

There was a crowd about the door and filling the hall inside, a crowd that elbowed and jostled, taken with a quivering interest, and there to feed its maw of curiosity with every item.

The girl wished to remain on the portico, where she could see the ancient garden and the orchard and all the paths and byways that had been her wonderland of youth, but Abner asked her to go in.

Randolph turned away, but my uncle and the girl remained some time by the coffin. The rim of the dead man's forehead and his jaw were riddled with bird shot, but his eyes and an area of his face below them, where the thin nose came down and with its lines and furrows made up the main identity of features, were not disfigured. And these preserved the hard stamp of his violent nature, untouched by the accident that had dispossessed him of his life.

He lay in the burial clothes and the coffin that Benton Wolf had provided for himself, all except the gloves upon his hands. These Benton had forgotten to provide in advance. And now when he came to prepare his brother for a public burial, for no other had touched the man, he must needs take what he could find out about the house—a pair of old knit gloves with every rent and moth hole carefully darned, as though the man had

346

sat down there with pains to give his brother the best appearance that he could.

This little touch affected the girl to tears, so strange is a woman's heart. "Poor thing!" she said. And for this triviality she would forget the injury that the dead man and his brother had done to her, forget the loss they had inflicted, and her long distress.

She took a closer hold upon Abner's arm, and dabbed her eyes with a tiny handkerchief.

"I am sorry for him," she said, "for the living brother. It is so pathetic."

And she indicated the old, coarse gloves so crudely darned and patched together.

But my uncle looked down at her, strangely, and with a cold, inexorable face.

"My child," he said, "there is a curious virtue in this thing that moves you. Perhaps it will also move the man whose handiwork it is. Let us go up and see him."

Then he called the Justice.

"Randolph, come with us."

The Justice turned about. "Where do you go?" he asked.

"Why, sir," Abner answered, "this child is weeping at the sight of the dead man's gloves, and I thought, perhaps, that old Benton might weep at them too, and in the softened mood return what he has stolen."

The Justice looked upon Abner as upon one gone mad.

"And be sorry for his sins! And pluck out his eye and give it to you for a bauble! Why, Abner, where is your common sense. This thing would take a miracle of God."

My uncle was undisturbed.

"Well," he said, "come with me, Randolph, and help me to perform that miracle."

He went out into the hall, and up the wide old stairway, with the girl, in tears, upon his arm. And the Justice followed, like one who goes upon a patent and ridiculous fool's errand.

They came into an upper chamber, where a great bulk of a man sat in a padded chair looking down upon his avenue of trees. He looked with satisfaction. He turned his head about when the three came in and then his eyes widened among the folds of fat.

"Abner and Mr. Randolph and Miss Julia Clayborne!" he gurgled. "You come to do honor to the dead!"

347

"No, Wolf," replied my uncle, "we come to do justice to the living."

The room was big and empty but for chairs and an open secretary of some English make. The pictures on the wall had been turned about as though from lack of interest in the tenant. But there hung in a frame above the secretary—with its sheets of foolscap, its iron ink-pot and quill pens—a map in detail, and the written deed for the estate that these men had taken in their lawsuit. It was not the skill of any painter that gave pleasure to this mountain of a man; not fields or groves imagined or copied for their charm, but the fields and groves that he now possessed and mastered.

The old man's eyelids fluttered an instant as with some indecision, then he replied, "It was kind to have this thought of me. I have been long neglected. A little justice of recognition, even now, does much to soften the sorrow at my brother's death."

Randolph caught at his jaw to keep in the laughter. And the huge old man, his head crouched into his billowy shoulders, his little reptilian eye shining like glass, went on with his speech.

"I am the greater moved," he said, "because you have been aloof and distant with me. You, Abner, have not visited my house, nor you, Randolph, although you live at no great distance. It is not thus that one gentleman should treat another. And especially when I and my dead brother, Adam, were from distant parts and came among you without a friend to take us by the hand and bring us to your door."

He sighed and put the fingers of his hands together.

"Ah, Abner," he went on, "it was a cruel negligence, and one from which I and my brother Adam suffered. You, who have a hand and a word at every turning, can feel no longing for this human comfort. But to the stranger alone, and without the land of his nativity, it is a bitter lack."

He indicated the chairs about him.

"I beg you to be seated, gentlemen and Miss Clayborne. And overlook that I do not rise. I am shaken at Adam's death."

Randolph remained planted on his feet, his face now under control. But Abner put the child into a chair and stood behind it, as though he were some close and masterful familiar.

"Wolf," he said,"I am glad that your heart is softened."

"My heart—softened!" cried the man. "Why, Abner, I have the tenderest heart of any of God's creatures. I cannot endure to kill a sparrow. My brother Adam was not like that. He would be for hunting the wild creatures to their death with firearms. But I took no pleasure in it."

"Well," said Randolph, "the creatures of the air got their revenge of him. It was a foolish accident to die by."

"Randolph," replied the man, "it was the very end and the extreme of carelessness. To look into a fowling piece, a finger on the hammer, a left hand holding the barrel halfway up to see if it was empty. It was a foolish and simple habit of my brother, and one that I abhorred and begged him to forgo, again and again, when I have seen him do it.

"But he had no fear of any firearms, as though by use and habit he had got their spirit tamed—as trainers, I am told, grow careless of wild beasts, and jugglers of the fangs and poison of their reptiles. He was growing old and would forget if they were loaded."

He spoke to Randolph, but he looked at Julia Clayborne and Abner behind her chair.

The girl sat straight and composed, in silence. The body of my uncle was to her a great protecting presence. He stood with his broad shoulders above her, his hands on the back of the chair, his face lifted. And he was big and dominant, as painters are accustomed to draw Michael in Satan's wars.

The pose held the old man's eye, and he moved in his chair; then he went on, speaking to the girl.

"It was kind of you, Abner, and you, Randolph, to come in to see me in my distress, but it was fine and noble in Miss Julia Clayborne. Men will understand the justice of the law and by what right it gives and takes. But a child will hardly understand that. It would be in nature for Miss Clayborne, in her youth, to hold the issue of this lawsuit against me and my brother Adam, to feel that we had wronged her; had by some unfairness taken what her father bequeathed to her at his death, and always regarded as his own. A child would not see how the title had never vested, as our judges do. How possession is one thing, and the title in fee simple another and distinct. And so I am touched by this consideration."

Abner spoke then.

"Wolf," he said, "I am glad to find you in this mood, for now Randolph can write his deed, with consideration of love and affection instead of the real one I came with."

The old man's beady eye glimmered and slipped about.

349

"I do not understand, Abner. What deed?"

"The one Randolph came to write," replied my uncle.

"But, Abner," interrupted the Justice, "I did not come to write a deed." And he looked at my uncle in amazement.

"Oh, yes," returned Abner, "that is precisely what you came to do."

He indicated the open secretary with his hand.

"And the grantor, as it happens, has got everything ready for you. Here are foolscap and quill pens and ink. And here, exhibited for your convenience, is a map of the lands with all the metes and bounds. And here," he pointed to the wall, "in a frame, as though it were a work of art with charm, is the court's deed. Sit down, Randolph, and write."

And such virtue is there in a dominant command that the Justice sat down before the secretary and began to select a goose quill. Then he realized the absurdity of the direction and turned about.

"What do you mean, Abner?" he cried.

"I mean precisely what I say," replied my uncle. "I want you to write a deed."

"But what sort of deed," cried the astonished Justice, "and by what grantor, and to whom, and for what lands?"

"You will draw a conveyance," replied Abner, "in form, with covenants of general warranty for the manor and lands set out in the deed before you and given in the plat. The grantor will be Benton Wolf, Esquire, and the grantee, Julia Clayborne, and mark you, Randolph, the consideration will be love and affection, with a dollar added for the form."

Old man Benton was amazed. His head, bedded into his huge shoulders, swung about; his pudgy features worked; his expression and his manner changed; his reptilian eyes hardened; he puffed with his breath in gusts.

"Not so fast, my fine gentlemen!" he gurgled. "There will be no such deed."

"Go on, Randolph," said my uncle, as though there had been no interruption, "get this business over."

"But, Abner," returned the justice, "it is fool's work—the grantor will not sign."

"He will sign," said my uncle, "when you have finished, and seal and acknowledge—go on!"

And such authority was in the man to impose his will that the bewildered Justice spread out his sheet of foolscap, dipped his quill into the ink, and began to draw the instrument. And while he wrote, Abner turned back to the gross old man.

"Wolf," he said, "must I persuade you to sign the deed?"

"Abner," cried the man, "do you take me for a fool?"

"I do not," replied my uncle, "and therefore I think that you will sign."

The obese old man spat violently on the floor, his face a horror of great folds.

"Sign!" he sputtered. "Idiot, madman! Why should I sign away my lands?"

"There are many reasons," replied Abner calmly. "The property is not yours. You got it by a legal trick—the judge who heard you was bound by the technicalities of language. But you are old, Wolf, and the next Judge will go beyond the record. He will be hard to face. He has expressed himself on these affairs. 'If the widow and the orphan cry to me, I will surely hear their cry.' Sinister words, Wolf, for one who comes with a case like yours into the Court of Final Equity."

"Abner," cried the old man, "begone with your sermons!"

My uncle's big fingers tightened on the back of the chair.

"Then, Wolf," he said, "if that does not move you, let me urge the esteem of men and this child's sorrow, and our high regard."

The old man's jaw chattered and he snapped his fingers.

"I would not give that for the things you name," he cried, and he set off a tiny measure of his index finger with the thumb. "Why, sir, my whim, idle and ridiculous, is a greater power to move me than this drivel."

Abner did not move, but his voice took on depth and volume.

"Wolf," he said," a whim is sometimes a great lever to move a man. Now, I am taken with a whim myself. I have a fancy, Wolf, that your brother Adam ought to go out of the world barehanded as he came into it."

The old man twisted his great head, as though he would get Abner wholly within the sweep of his reptilian eye.

"What?" he gurgled. "What is that?"

"Why, this," replied my uncle. "I have a whim—'idle and ridiculous,' did you say, Wolf? Well, then, idle and ridiculous, if you like, that your brother ought not to be buried in his gloves."

Abner looked hard at the man and, although he did not move, the threat and menace of his presence seemed somehow to advance him. And the effect on the huge old man was like

351

some work of sorcery. The whole mountain of him began to quiver and the folds of his face seemed spread over him with thin oil. He sat piled up in the chair and the oily sweat gathered and thickened on him. His jaw jerked and fell into a baggy gaping and the great expanse of him worked as with an ague.

Finally, out of the pudgy, undulating mass, a voice issued, thin and shaken.

"Abner," it said, " has any other man this fancy?"

"No," replied my uncle, "but I hold it, Wolf, at your decision."

"And, Abner," his thin voice trebled, "you will let my brother be buried as he is?"

"If you sign!" said my uncle.

The man reeked with the terror on him, and one thought that his billowy body would never again be at peace. "Randolph," he quavered, "bring me the deed."

Outside, the girl sobbed in Abner's arms. She asked for no explanation. She wished to believe her fortune a miracle of God, forever—to the end of all things. But Randolph turned on my uncle when she was gone.

"Abner! Abner!" he cried. "Why in the name of the Eternal was the old creature so shaken at the gloves?"

"Because he saw the hangman behind them," replied my uncle. "Did you notice how the rim of the dead man's face was riddled by the bird shot and the center of it clean? How could that happen, Randolph?"

"It was a curious accident of gunfire," replied the Justice.

"It was no accident at all," said Abner. "That area of the man's face is clean because it was *protected*. Because the dead man put up his hands to cover his face when he saw that his brother was about to shoot him. The backs of old Adam's hands, hidden by the gloves, will be riddled with bird shot like the rim of his face."

Top Secret

Top Secret

The Truth behind Today's Pop Mysticisms

ROBERT M. PRICE

Foreword by Julia Sweeney

 **Prometheus Books**

59 John Glenn Drive
Amherst, New York 14228–2119

Published 2008 by Prometheus Books

Inquiries should be addressed to
Prometheus Books
59 John Glenn Drive
Amherst, New York 14228–2119
VOICE: 716–691–0133, ext. 210
FAX: 716–691–0137
WWW.PROMETHEUSBOOKS.COM

12 11 10 09 08   5 4 3 2 1

Library of Congress Cataloging-in-Publication Data

Price, Robert M., 1954–
    Top secret : the truth behind today's pop mysticisms / by Robert M. Price
        p. cm.
    Includes bibliography and index.
    ISBN 978–1–59102–608–2
    1. Mysticism—Comparative studies. I. Title.

BL625.P73 2008
204—dc22

2007051803

Printed in the United States of America on acid-free paper

To Catherine Groves,
longtime friend and beloved fellow-seeker

Contents

CONTENTS

Foreword

*D*o you have any idea how few people out there are like Robert Price? Well, you could say that obviously there is only one of him. And yes, that is true. But that is a sad thing. People like him, who have the scholarship about religion and then experience inside religion—who have a skeptic's eye but a compassionate heart, mixed with brutal and dead-on humor—well, those people are rare people. I mean, really rare. You see, most critics of mysticism are only critics, and most believers are only believers, but Robert Price understands it from all sides. He has the vast knowledge and wit to deliver accurate overviews and analysis of all the latest contemporary spiritual approaches that have infiltrated the marketplace of ideas.

When Oprah did two entire shows about *The Secret*, I was flabbergasted. I mean, I like to think of Oprah as a voracious reader and a champion of women as intelligent people who can think critically. Someone who wouldn't be taken in by something so blatantly aimed at commercializing spirituality. A book that takes simple ideas and cloaks them in mystery for the purpose of selling more books. People were coming up to me right and left asking if I had read *The Secret*. Copies of *The Secret* were littered around the edges of the sitcom set where I was working when it was first released. I tried to tell people what I thought, what crap I thought it was. But they wouldn't listen. And Robert Price describes why— and I mean why it was crap AND why they wouldn't listen. He even describes what about the book is actually good! And y'know, he is right; people *are* spiritually hungry. And books like *The Secret* actually do give them something—a little tiny something—but something to quell their appetite for something deeper—a perspective worth investigating. And Robert Price gets that. It's not simply a dismissal, it's an analysis, an appreciation; he puts these books and authors and their ideas in context.

This book will be a good resource for years to come. I am so glad he wrote this book. I make no secret of that.

Julia Sweeney
Saturday Night Live star and
author of *God Said, "Ha!"*
and *My Beautiful Loss of Faith Story*

Introduction

Sheep without a Shepherd

*I*n Mark 6:34 we read how Jesus found himself unexpectedly mobbed by a crowd of seekers. He was already overworked and in fact was hoping for a rare interval of relaxation. But here they were. "And he had compassion on them, because they were like sheep without a shepherd; and he began to teach them many things." I have long thought that the metaphor used here describes our generation of Americans when it comes to religion like nothing else does. Everywhere one looks, there are the spiritually hungry, lining up at the doors of megachurches, yoga classes, and chanting workshops like the Depression poor waiting to get into the soup kitchen. Lately one sees a huge number of the chronically hungry at the checkout buying copies of a book called *The Secret* by Rhonda Byrne.

And since, if you look closely, you will notice many of them leaving one church, class, or workshop and going to try another, you have to wonder if they are being served anything very nourishing. But even if they go on to the next open religious door and the next, this proves their hunger is real and growing. I have learned to look at the plight of such seekers from several standpoints at

INTRODUCTION

once. I have been a parish minister, with a congregation eager to consider new theological alternatives. I have been a happy parishioner at a more staid, traditional Episcopal church. I am a scholar of religion, having earned one PhD degree in theology and another, a dozen years later, in New Testament studies. I have taught world religions to college students for many years. And I am both a writer and an editor of fantasy fiction. All these perspectives have proven quite illuminating for me as I strive to understand the spiritual condition of my contemporaries. For one thing, my long years of studying and teaching both the Bible and the religions have enabled me to identify the ancient sources, sometimes hidden, of the new spiritualities. Since some of them are presented in novelistic, story form, my skills as a writer and a critic come into play. It is important, after all, to detect where spurious rhetoric and verbal fireworks are substituting for sound argument sense.

Most scholars who do have a genuine grasp of technical religious lore do not bother to try to straighten out these manifold confusions. Having perhaps escaped from such hokum in their own youth, they want to waste no more time on it. But then who else is likely to do the job? If we have "put away childish things," who but we are in a position to try to point to a better way? I think that is the way of the compassionate Christ, as well as of the kindly condescending bodhisattva. If we have learned anything from our advanced religious studies, we ought to have learned our obligation to serve those sheep. If not to feed them ourselves, our task is at least to guide them away from poison pasturage. We must not absorb the terrible elitism of Jesus' foes who regarded the laity as "an accursed multitude that knoweth not the Law" (John 7:49).

It is by now evident that I shall have a number of criticisms to aim at several contemporary spiritual approaches. My motive is not to fault the various spiritual teachers as failing to meet some standard of orthodoxy that I have defined. I am more concerned with whether the doctrines appear to be healthy and wise, especially when compared to the ancient traditions they draw from. Many of the doctrines and therapies discussed here are based on older traditions, but some are poorer, watered-down versions. And because of that, those who try them find themselves only half satisfied as with junk food that is momentarily tasty but lacks real nourishment. I cannot help thinking that the historic treasures of Buddhism, Christianity, Hinduism, the Kabbalah, and so on, would do people more good. There is no shortcut to enlightenment if one embarks on any of these paths.

But, on the other hand, our seekers are *half* satisfied! Their glass is half full! A completely negative assessment, a snobbish condemnation of today's mystical paths, overlooks this fact. It fails to take all the evidence into account. In *Top Secret*, I should like to sift through the facts, the claims, the doctrines, in order to separate the wheat from the chaff. I approach each option on the menu hoping for some wheat, not expecting there to be only chaff. And I am usually right. I have learned much from doing this research. And I don't just mean I have cataloged a few more facts to exhibit in my intellectual museum. I have grown personally, as I hope you will through reading this book, as well as the books I discuss. But I cannot allow what virtues I find to cause me to cover a multitude of sins. What is still wrong may be dangerously wrong. I believe my approach is unique, its attempt at objectivity (and an attempt is the best one can ask) uniquely successful. Sometimes one cannot pronounce a verdict of unambiguous positive or negative on a particular spiritual system. That itself is a helpful finding. When reality is ambiguous, we might as well know it.

So, you see, my subtitle, *The Truth behind Popular Mysticisms*, means two things. First, the secret of Byrne's *The Secret* and many more books like it is that their derivative nature and misleading, sometimes dangerous, claims often leave the sincere seeker ever and again embittered. That is a sad truth. Second, there is a glad truth to match it: these mystical approaches, at least several of them, do manage to capture and convey genuine insights many of us could afford to learn. We only cheat ourselves if we ignore those insights because of faults we find in the messengers. That is the truth that lies packaged, sometimes buried, amid the wild claims of New Age and New Thought gurus. Their credulous fans would be well advised to be a little more skeptical. The rest of us might profit from taking a second look at what we too easily dismiss.

The spiritual currents I am endeavoring to chart in this book can be grouped naturally under a few headings. First, we have Rhonda Byrne's best seller *The Secret*, the latest standard-bearer for the New Thought movement, historically represented by the Unity School of Christianity, the Church of Religious Science, and Science of Mind. Byrne admittedly synthesized the similar teachings of numerous motivational gurus and life coaches, all of whom promote New Thought. Indeed, inside and outside of *The Secret* itself, there is a whole group of New Thought writers to consider. Some are associated with the New Age movement and combine the beliefs of that movement with the optimistic determination of New Thought (as represented, e.g., by the Unity School of Christianity). I would place Wayne W. Dyer and Shakti Gawain among New Age/New Thought writers. They come in for exposition and examination on the heels of older New Thought exponents like James Allen, Venice J. Bloodworth, and Jack Ensign Addington. I will ask in that chapter if either subgroup's metaphysics are necessary to the basic New Thought attitude, or indeed whether it presupposes any philosophical commitment at all.

Second, one can scarcely ignore the prolific Deepak Chopra, who turns out to be an apostle of Hindu Vedanta, though he first presents it as if it is simply the implications of the New Physics. In Dr. Chopra's case, certain astonishing claims have raised suspicions about his sincerity. Not being a mind reader, I cannot hope to settle such a question, but it does require a brief treatment, since the question of charlatanry and showmanship is nothing new in this field, and critics have perhaps been too hasty to throw the baby out with the bathwater. The history of religions tells us something common sense does not: sometimes hoaxers may also be genuine spiritual teachers. They are playing the role of a Sacred Trickster. In this chapter I have decided to focus on one important Chopra volume that seems to me central: *How to Know God*.

Third comes neo-Buddhism, the Vajradhatu tradition begun by the controversial Chögyam Trungpa, a master of the Tibetan Kagyü and Nyingma School, and carried on after his death by his student Pema Chödrön. I will discuss their books, Trungpa's *Cutting Through Spiritual Materialism*, justly considered a modern classic, and Chödrön's *Awakening Loving Kindness*, a collection of her retreat sermons. In the case of both lamas, there is again the question of hypocrisy or imposture, and again both defy stereotypes and help us modify, maybe even discard, our either-or oppositions (a very Buddhist thing to do in any case).

Our fourth focus is Eckhart Tolle, he whose name fortuitously combines the last names of two great German mystics of earlier centuries. Though not "officially" representing any one tradition, Tolle's spiritual path consistently reminds me of Buddhism, Zen in particular, but as he has his own version and appears to have arrived at it by his own path, it seems right not to subsume him in the chapter on Buddhism.

INTRODUCTION

Next I mean to give a chapter to each of three new scriptures: Helen Schucman's *A Course in Miracles*, Neale Donald Walsch's *Conversations with God*, and James Redfield's *The Celestine Prophecy*. Between *A Course in Miracles* and *Conversations with God* I insert a chapter on Marianne Williamson and her book *Return to Love*, a popularization of the already popular *Course in Miracles*. Williamson is enough of a phenomenon by herself as to deserve more than a few paragraphs parasitic on her inspiration. For one thing, she combines the insights of the *Course* with elements of New Thought. It is fascinating that both she and her predecessor Helen Schucman are Jews, though neither had professed Judaism as a creed before awakening to the revelations of the *Course*. Once they did, they found themselves proponents of a kind of New Age Christianity. Other debtors to the *Course in Miracles* are Donald Walsch, Wayne W. Dyer, Eckhart Tolle, and David R. Hawkins (*Power vs. Force: The Hidden Determinants of Human Behavior*), but I deal with them separately, in other chapters along with other writers with whom they share even more.

By the way, I know Redfield's book is an admitted fiction, but that really makes little difference; among its devout and enthusiastic readers the novel itself has absorbed the aura and authority of the ancient document that lends it its title. The other two scriptures are more in the nature of supposedly channeled revelations. Each of these new bibles deserves a chapter unto itself, as I'm sure the adherents of each would agree.

Like Hinduism and Buddhism, Gnosticism is an ancient faith, but unlike the others (with whom it shares key similarities) Gnosticism did not manage to survive the ages intact. Though there were occasional, spontaneous reinventions of the Gnostic wheel over the centuries, Gnosticism was a delicate flame that blew out or was snuffed out again and again. In our day its candle has been lit again, beginning with Sigmund Freud's disciple Carl Jung, who saw in Basilides and other ancient Gnostic mystagogues the first practicing psychoanalysts. He found that their insights both paralleled and instructed his own project of psychic exploration. Stephan A. Hoeller was entranced by Jung's privately circulated pamphlet, *The Seven Sermons to the Dead*, in which Jung prophesied in the persona, like a present-day channeler, of Basilides. Hoeller began a project of demythologizing Gnosticism along the lines set down by Jung. On the basis of it, Hoeller has founded his own Gnostic denomination today. Timothy Freke and Peter Gandy have done the same thing, following up a trilogy of books on Gnostic myth and the problem of the historical Jesus with a series of traveling seminars on what they consider to be modern Gnosticism. So the ninth chapter in our survey treats of the work of all these gentlemen.

The tenth chapter deals with another ancient tradition, almost as esoteric and certainly as controversial as Gnosticism, that of the Jewish Kabbalah. This tradition reached the height of both its sophistication and its popularity in the sixteenth century with the teaching of Galilean rabbi Isaac Luria. It fell into disrepute because of its association with certain failed messianic movements that brought shame and ridicule upon European Jewry. The Kabbalah has retreated from common view but has never died out. Gaining popular strength again among Hasidic Jews, it is today spreading more widely even among non-Jews. An apostle of Lurianic Kabbalah to the modern world is Rabbi Michael Berg. I discuss his book *The Way: Using the Kabbalah for Spiritual Transformation and Fulfillment*.

So far the reader may be wondering at the conspicuous absence of evangelical Christianity among the topics in this book. I have saved it for last. I do not discuss the American evangelical tradition in anything like a comprehensive manner. That would be beside the point of the present book, where I am treating only new variations on classical traditions. I have recently dealt with one popular contemporary version of evangelicalism, Rick Warren and his ubiquitous book *The Purpose-Driven Life*, in my rejoinder, *The Reason-Driven Life*. But here I focus on another hugely popular megachurch minister, Joel Osteen, author of *Your Best Life Now*. It will be my contention that Osteen might as well have been placed in the New Thought chapter, and that his references to God and the Bible are essentially vestigial and superfluous. Nor is this a criticism of his gospel, only an attempt to understand it as a transitional form in an evolving religious trajectory.

Is humor compatible with the discussion of serious, even eternal themes? May occasional sarcasm be tolerated amid religious discussion? I find it helpful in writing and teaching about these great matters. A bit of humor saves us from taking our own opinions too seriously and gives us perspective on deadly serious issues whose gravity might otherwise intimidate and overwhelm us. So I hope you will receive my occasional wisecracks, as well as my blunt criticisms, in the spirit in which I offer them: as an index of how much love I have for the material and how little I relish its trivialization. Besides, if the old Zen masters could be acerbic curmudgeons, why can't I?

Robert M. Price
Lammas, 2006

Chapter 1

Secret Identity

Rhonda Byrne's *The Secret*, Wayne W. Dyer, Shakti Gawain, et al.

THE NEW CURIOSITY SHOPPE

*C*artoonist Walt Kelly's canny muskrat Pogo once confessed that this "nuclear" stuff with which everybody seemed so preoccupied confused him. Said Pogo, "It ain't so new, and it ain't so clear." The same might be said of the spiritual tidal wave called *The Secret*, both DVD and book, written by Rhonda Byrne and espoused by Oprah Winfrey. Just as Billy Graham became a household name once William Randolph Hearst took an interest in the aspiring young evangelist and issued the order to his papers to "puff Graham," Rhonda Byrne became a living legend (at least for fifteen minutes) thanks to Oprah's heraldic promotion. You know what Jesus said: "There is nothing hidden except to be revealed later on." In this case, as in so many, the appeal the "ancient secrecy" is merely a ploy to hype a product. When we claim that something is a secret, our goal is of course not to keep that secret, but to blab it. Otherwise we should just keep mum about it, right? And it seems more likely than not that what is about to be hawked as a newly revealed secret was never any such thing. One thinks of newspaper ads announcing a "sale" with the same old—if not higher—prices.

It is probably no accident that *The Secret* bears a striking resemblance to the mega-phenomenon *The Da Vinci Code* by Dan Brown. In that novel, Brown imagined a secret safeguarded by an esoteric order called the Priory of Sion, a society reaching back in time to the medieval Knights Templar and listing among its "Grand Masters" just about every significant historical figure Brown (and his source Michael Baigent) could think of, notably Leonardo da Vinci. The secret was the knowledge that Jesus of Nazareth had fathered a daughter with Mary Magdalene, and that she was mother to the Merovingian Dynasty of France. Byrne's "secret" is nothing like this, but she claims the same sort of bogus pedigree, listing among the venerable possessors of her elite information "Plato, Shakespeare, Newton, [Victor] Hugo, Beethoven, Lincoln, Emerson, Edison, Einstein" (p. ix). "Abraham, Isaac, Jacob, Joseph, Moses, and Jesus were not only prosperity teachers, but also millionaires themselves, with more affluent lifestyles than many present-day millionaires could conceive of" (p. 109). Yet she provides no documentation for these wild claims. All Byrne seems to mean is that she has found isolated sentences or insights in their work that seem to her to be handy illustrations, even if taken out of context. But it is safe to venture that few of these Grand Masters of the Secret would sign on to the particular system Byrne is preaching.

That system is what is commonly called "New Thought." The "secret" is how Byrne could have remained ignorant of New Thought for as long as she did if she is, in fact, an expert on the subject. Not only is the content of every page—no exaggeration—pretty much right out of previous New Thought works, but even the title is borrowed from Robert Collier's *The Secret of the Ages*

(1926). But her sources go back farther than that. New Thought began, as far as we are concerned, in nineteenth-century America with Phineas Parkhurst Quimby and Mary Baker Eddy, inspired in some measure by Ralph Waldo Emerson, but even then, as its proponents were the first to point out, it possessed much more ancient antecedents. But everything old becomes new again, so the title "New Thought" need cause no one any annoyance, any more than referring to "New York" does.

But not everything old is wise. How well thought out is the doctrine? We will explore that question here. And we will need to try to keep certain distinctions in mind. I recall attending a New Age expo in Raleigh, North Carolina, a couple of years ago and finding among the booths one representing something called the Center for Creative Living. It was a local congregation allied with the Church of Religious Science. The group's pamphlets were swift to explain to the casual reader that it did not really belong there amid crystal gazers and channelers; it represented not so much *New Age* belief as *New Thought* metaphysics. Oh, it wasn't an opportunistic fraud, like finding among the exhibits at a peace rally a table of apolitical fundamentalists promoting Jesus as the secret to "real peace." No, the New Thoughters had every reason to be there. For New Age and New Thought ideas quite naturally attract the same audience. But it is important, in order to understand either one, to distinguish between the two, since they do not stand or fall together.

And just as one may embrace New Thought belief without accepting the larger worldview of the New Age (including pyramids, reincarnation, sunken continents, crystals, channeling, flying saucers, etc.), so may one learn much from New Thought without imbibing the philosophical assumptions its advocates have used to support it. As always, the investigator of new notions coming to birth must take care not to eject the baby with the bathwater. So in the present survey, we will try to observe all these distinctions. And in so doing, I think we will find a consistent pattern whereby *The Secret*, in company with most recent New Thought preachers (including Wayne Dyer, Shakti Gawain, and Marianne Williamson), tends to clothe the central insights of the older generation of New Thought teachers (e.g., Thomas Troward, James Allen, Jack Ensign Addington, and Venice J. Bloodworth) in the stardust of the New Age movement. Though this metaphysical retooling sweetens the mix for many of today's readers, I think it has placed unnecessary stumbling blocks in the path of some who might otherwise gain from the New Thought approach but just cannot bring themselves to stomach what appears to them bubble-headed pseudoscience and pseudophilosophy. So it will be worthwhile to distinguish the various layers encasing New Thought as we read it in venues like *The Secret*. It is not so much a case of comparing apples with oranges as it is returning to the metaphor of infant care, of peeling away a dirty diaper from a squalling baby: when you have done so, the infant may cease being so annoying.

THE LAWS OF THOUGHT

The Secret posits a nondualist metaphysics, sometimes tilting toward pantheism, other times toward monism. These are closely related worldviews, the difference being a matter of what grade of reality one ascribes to the perceived diversity of the world. If one discounts the particulars around one as illusions, *masks* of the One, one qualifies as a monist. If one makes all the appearances into *faces* of the One, one is a pantheist. But this difference is academic for our discussion: New Thought beliefs are easily compatible with either monism or pantheism. We find in all types of New Thought the belief that God and all "creatures" are one, whether the type of New Thought is primarily derived from philosophical reasoning or from Christian mysticism. "This great fact is that pure spirit continually subsists in the absolute, whether in a corporeal body or not; and from it all the phenomena of being flow, whether on the mental plane or the physical" (Troward, p. 19).

Sometimes the New Thought God-concept, inherited by Rhonda Byrne and Team *Secret* (I refer to Rhonda Byrne with the host of gurus whose one-note teachings she synthesizes), sounds strikingly like Yogacara Buddhism with its Mind-Only doctrine: "The One Mind is all intelligence, all wisdom, and all perfection, and it is everything and everywhere at the same time. If everything is the One Universal Mind, and the whole of it exists everywhere, then it is all in You!" (Byrne, pp. 160–61). "Mind is all there is" (Addington, p. 1). "Man has been made co-creator with the Universal Mind in the area of his own life" (Addington, p. 3). "This Life that we are expressing is one with all Life; therefore, there is no separation between God and man, or man and man. We are all One in Mind" (Addington, p. 81). "Mind and matter are one; there is no matter for all is one, the visible and the invisible energy; the inner picture and the outer picture are one and the same. The outer reflects the inner" (Addington, p. 122). "Thought is the only reality" (Bloodworth, p. 17). "Some have personalized this power and call it God" (Bloodworth, p. 26). "The real 'I' of you is eternal and is one with the Universal Mind" (Bloodworth, p. 27). "When you find yourself being overwhelmed by any evidence of the five senses, remember that everything is made from the invisible substance all about you" (Bloodworth, p. 110). "The foundation for life in the new world is built on the understanding that there is a higher intelligence, a fundamental creative power, or energy, in the universe which is the source and substance of all existence" (Gawain, *Creative Visualization*, p. 7). "There's a universal intelligence subsisting throughout nature inherent in every one of its manifestations. You are one of those manifestations. You are a piece of this universal intelligence—a slice of God, if you will. . . . You are God manifested" (Dyer, p. 44). "You realize, perhaps for the first time, that you and your Source are one when you let go of the ego-mind, which has convinced you that you're separate from the power of intention" (Dyer, p. 218). "There's nothing 'out there,' other than consciousness itself" (Hawkins, p. 245).

The utility of such a metaphysic is to provide access to this larger reality, enabling individuals to draw upon the noumenal, unseen world, or to manipulate it, so as to make changes in the phenomenal world. That, of course, is the very essence of *The Secret*. Its fans constitute what sociologists call, first, an "audience cult," since there is no live-in commune and no one looking over your shoulder; you support it like Deadheads traveling wherever they have to for the next concert. Second, it is a "thaumaturgical" or manipulationist cult, teaching an ostensible wonder-working technique. The goal is not, as in many cults and religions—say, for instance, the Unification Church—so much to change *the* world as to change *my* world. It does me little good to say that the whole universe is mine in the abstract sense that I am one with it, if I cannot cash it in here and now. One of the great New Thought handbooks of an earlier generation bears the title *The Magic of Believing*, and the title is apt, for this sort of thinking marks a return to magic in the classic sense, namely, magic as "occult science," a method for drawing upon unseen realities in roughly the same manner one draws upon electricity by plugging an appliance into a wall. Only in this case the power envisioned is more comprehensive, the power to reshape reality and to materialize desired circumstances. I do not mean to discount *The Secret* or New Thought by using words like "magic" or by characterizing it this way. Indeed, one must say in its behalf, and on behalf of all ancient magic, that it represents a more "scientific" approach than religion's alternative: prayer.

Ancient magic, for example, rain dances, sought to manipulate nature. But it didn't work very often. The shaman might go back again and again to the drawing board, trying to eliminate more and more variables, but nothing really improved the success rate. Prayer gradually replaced magic, not because it yielded better results, but only because it "saved the appearances." It made a soft claim up front that would not be debunked by the lack of results. Magic posited a process of straight cause and effect. Thus, if it failed, one's methods were shown up as false. But the one who seeks favors from the gods, who are personal wills like himself, goes into the bargain with eyes wide open to the fact that he may return empty-handed. The gods may not feel inclined to help, or they may know better. Then why bother? It may be that the gods will never provide their aid if we do not at least ask them for it, so we ask. It might help. Of course, consistent with the same results is the possibility that there are no gods: the results would be the same. So the premise of prayer cannot be debunked.

Team *Secret*, with other recent New Thought theorists, is not satisfied with such a system. *Secret*'s proponents seek a return to a scientific model: the manipulation of "laws," laws of thought, laws of reality, and the two are the same if reality is ultimately a Unity in which knowledge and being are one.

TOP SECRET

HELP ME, RHONDA

Though at the turn of the twentieth century we already find Thomas Troward explicating New Thought with the aid of "up-to-date science" (p. 3), it seems mainly to be the newer generation of New Thoughters who have confused the issue by supplementing, as they think, idealist metaphysics with pseudoscience. Rhonda Byrne and company are among the most egregious. Byrne recalls in *The Secret*: "I never studied science or physics at school, and yet when I read complex books on quantum physics I understood them perfectly because I wanted to understand them" (p. 156). This is why we don't let students grade their own papers. You don't need Heisenberg's uncertainty principle to doubt seriously whether Ms. Byrne has grasped the first thing about quantum physics—or, for that matter, *any* kind of physics. "Thoughts are magnetic, and thoughts have a frequency . . . they magnetically attract all *like* things that are on the same frequency" (p. 10). "When you think about what you want, and you emit that frequency, you cause the energy of what you want to vibrate at that frequency and you bring it to You! As you focus on what you want, you are changing the vibration of the atoms of that thing, and you are causing it to vibrate to You" (pp. 156–57). Well, that is just silly. Yes, we can read the signals of a thought's electrochemical discharge along the synapses. But we can do this only because we insert electrodes into people's gray matter. The fact that we have to do this implies that the brain is not, as per Team *Secret*, a TV transmitter tower broadcasting thoughts like the trademark of the old RKO Radio Pictures. And can any of the "personal transformation specialists" and "trainers in the field of mind potential" whose names and quotes sprinkle the pages of *The Secret* please explain how that new job or car I am visualizing has a "frequency"?

My nerve endings may be vibrating as I drool over some object that I want, but in what sense is that object returning my "vibes"? If Rhonda Byrne really believes that Albert Einstein taught *this*, one might suggest she take another look at those physics books, maybe starting with *Quantum Physics for Dummies*.

Listen to Shakti Gawain: "Physicists are now discovering what metaphysicians have claimed for thousands of years: seemingly solid physical matter is, in reality, made of energy. If we look through a powerful microscope at anything 'solid,' we see an infinite number of little, vibrating particles. If we closely examine one of these particles, we discover that it is made of even smaller particles, and so on. The fact is that everything physical is made of 'energy'—which we can also call 'spirit' or 'the universe.' So modern science supports the ancient metaphysical truth that form is created out of spirit" (*Creative Visualization*, pp. 35–36). Perhaps Ms. Gawain is not to be blamed for not being sophisticated enough in scientific theory to make such a category leap. She does not claim to be a scientist. (But then she ought to refrain from issuing such pontifications.) At any rate, we have here the same sort of medicine-show physics we are used to hearing from Deepak Chopra. We haven't seen the last of it. But our concern here is how such claims fit into the New Thought premise of manipulating the forces and fabric of reality.

The Secret, in company with Transcendental Meditation (TM) adepts (Maharishi Mahesh Yogi, Deepak Chopra, John Hagelin) and New Age New Thoughters (like Shakti Gawain and Wayne Dyer), tries to establish access to a trough from which we may drink cosmic power. And certain features of contemporary scientific theorizing seem to provide the necessary building blocks. Like the talking heads in the fantasy movie *What the Bleep Do We Know?* Team *Secret* capitalizes, first, on Heisenberg's uncertainty principle, trying to break down any strict cause-and-effect nexus, as if to reinstate an element of magical spontaneity into the fabric of existence. This indeterminacy is supposed to make miracles possible, since there would then be no ironclad "natural laws" to violate. Their next step is to exploit Michael Polanyi's insight in *Personal Knowledge*, apparently corroborated by experiments, that the mere presence, as well as the shifting perspective, of the observer affects the outcome of any experiment. These conundrums, which ought indeed to make us reexamine any scientific dogmas we may embrace, they take as proof of other New Age dogmas, almost in the manner of Immanuel Velikovsky using Exodus to verify his astronomical theories—and vice versa. As H. P. Lovecraft warned, "Don't let the Einstein-twisters catch you here!" (to Frank Belknap Long, February 20, 1929, in Derleth, p. 265).

What the New Age New Thoughters are trying to do is to use the New Physics to provide an evidential basis for the more slippery New Thought talk of "Godstuff" and "intentionality" and "invisible substance." But they may be lengthening the line of defense rather than shortening it. A more promising avenue might lie with philosophical speculation, perhaps a modification of Immanuel Kant. Kant was trying to explain how we know what we know. He reasoned that reason alone cannot tell us what things are like beyond the senses. It requires sense data to process. But can we know for sure that the senses are accurately conveying to us the way things really are? He concluded that we cannot know what the "Thing in Itself," out there, beyond the senses, is like. He referred to it with intentional vagueness as the "Undifferentiated Manifold of Perception." Awareness of this filters into the brain via what Kant called "categories of perception" and "logical functions of judgment." This is an array of brain functions that process sensory input and feed it to the brain in a way that makes sense to it. These categories and functions would include cause and effect, time, and space (though Kant named many more). Where do we derive our certainty, for instance, that every time we pick a pair of apples out of this basket and another pair from that basket we will end up with four apples? Ultimately it may not be as neat and simple as what we seem to be seeing, but we can never "see around" those categories and functions, so we might as well resign ourselves to the certainty we do feel this way. We know the categories will yield predictable results each time, and that other observers will perceive the same things the same way we do, because we all are equipped with the same machinery. Well, a New Thoughter might be understood as arguing, in effect, that one can gain conscious control over the categories of perception and logical functions of judgment, thus changing or adjusting what one perceives/receives through the senses from the Undifferentiated Manifold of Perception beyond us. As far as I know, Kant himself never thought of such a thing, but who knows?

Wayne Dyer seems everywhere to confuse metaphor with metaphysics. "The impact of higher and faster frequencies on lower and slower frequencies can be measured, and it's in this regard that you can make a huge impact on eradicating the energy factors in your life that are obstructing your connection to intention. The purpose of moving up the frequency ladder is to change your vibratory level of energy so that you're at the higher and faster frequencies where your energy levels match up with the highest frequency level of all: the energy of the all-creating Spirit of intention itself" (p. 68). All this techno-gibberish has exactly the same value and function as that in *Ghostbusters* or *Star Trek*, namely, to flummox the reader and make him think Dyer has mastered some "technology of transformation," which he has not. It is not that he is not in possession of some real wisdom, but he seems to think it needs the support of smoke and mirrors. One wonders if Dyer has ever bothered to check a fact in his life. He appears to swallow the Carlos Castaneda novels as literally true. Once he "explained" how the word *sorcerer* means "one in touch with the Source." Of course it does not. *Sorcery* comes from the Latin *sortiarius*, meaning "one who practices divination by casting lots." The root is *sors*, "lots." But what does Dyer care?

Surely the most outrageous piece of pseudoscientific claptrap awaits us in David R. Hawkins's *Power vs. Force: The Hidden Determinants of Human Behavior*, which Wayne Dyer calls "perhaps the most important and significant book I've read in the past ten years" (cover blurb). One can scarcely imagine a more comical descent into terminal silliness than that undertaken by Hawkins and, with him, the totally credulous Dyer, who makes quite the big deal of it in his "Power of Intention" lectures. You see, Hawkins has discovered an infallible epistemological "wormhole" between the macrocosm and the microcosm, a technique that allows us completely to circumvent the hard work of intellectual analysis and discernment. Instead, we may cut to the chase, discovering the truth of any proposition via the simple test of *kinesiology*. Yes, you read that right, the science of muscle tension and tone. Hawkins has "discovered" that if one gets a test subject to stand still with his arm at right angles to his body and then makes a statement to him, the degree of truth in the proposition can be indexed by the amount of resistance the subject's arm offers when the tester tries manually to lower it, like pushing down the handle of an old-time water pump. The harder it is to push that arm down, the more truth there is in the proposition (and this whether the test subject understands the proposition or not). But there are other versions of this kinesiological divining tool, presumably easier to perform while wearing one's straitjacket:

> A profoundly telling exercise may be performed by evaluating the books in one's library. Simply hold them over your solar plexus, and have somebody test your muscle strength. As you do so, your books will end up in two piles; reflection on the differences between the two can produce a revelation. (p. 124)

No, simply reading them isn't as good. Why?

> The extreme negativity of many popular works of pseudophilosophy, for example, is obvious if one tests these books. But even being forewarned can't defend us against unwitting entrainment [*sic*] by invisible energy fields that activate when these works are read. One may think that he can maintain his psychic independence by refuting the work intellectually, but mere exposure to the material has a profound negative effect that continues even after the material is intellectually rejected. It's as though, within those negative influences, there's a hidden virus whose invasion of our psyches goes unnoticed. (p. 287)

Ah, could it be . . . *Satan*? For Hawkins, and one must suppose Dyer, "reason, so vulnerable to loss of perspective through self-absorption, has in the long run never provided man with any solid moral, or even intellectual certainty. . . . In a world of mass confusion, we desperately need a reliable, accurate, objectively verifiable yardstick to measure truth with" (p. 281). And that tool? Why, muscle flexing of course! One must question the sanity of anyone offering such a proposal and, equally, the intellectual seriousness of anyone who accepts it.

TOP SECRET

The metaphysics of old Judge Troward start looking pretty good after this digression into the Twilight Zone. Troward certainly evidenced a degree of intellectual rigor utterly alien to the folksy ramblings of Wayne Dyer. Dyer gets up in front of an audience and makes apodictic assertions about the nature of Reality as if his pantheism were self-evident, needing no justification. He is simply preaching a gospel as if he were Jim Bakker, only one suspects government-funded public television would probably not give Bakker free airtime to do his preaching, as they do Wayne Dyer.

Anyhow, Troward attempts to argue (in depth and detail that I cannot reproduce here) that the life-giving essence from which all things proceed is Thought, and that, along the lines of René Descartes, Thought has no extension in space and therefore none in time either. This means that we ourselves participate, at least potentially, in a universal, illimitable Now. Furthermore, we may access this dimension through the subconscious mind which, as Jung also says, has no time dimension. "Time is just an illusion. . . . If you can understand that there is no time, and accept that concept, then you will see that whatever you want in the future already exists" (Byrne, p. 62). "The subconscious is that marvelous phase of your mind that brings things into existence by the sheer power of thought. It is the spiritual part of us and through it we are connected to the Divine and brought into relation with Infinite constructive forces of the universe" (Bloodworth, p. 22).

Troward posited a realm of rational-spiritual forms or prototypes, as in Plato, which "inhabit" this spaceless, timeless realm and which are temporarily copied by matter here in the conditioned, relative realm of mundane reality. We may manipulate the conditioned realm around us by the expedient of fashioning a new, specific prototypical form in the invisible realm. Such a form will begin to attract to itself a material instantiation on the material plane. "The creative Force of the universe is working through you. . . . You have only to provide the mold in which it is to take shape, and that mold is formed by your thoughts" (Robert Collier, quoted in Addington, p. 34). *The Secret* agrees: "It means that *every possibility already exists*. All knowledge, all discoveries, and all inventions of the future, are in the Universal Mind as possibilities, waiting for the human mind to draw them out" (p. 161).

VISUALIZATION AND MANIFESTATION

Or, in terms more familiar from *The Secret* and other New Thought writers, one "visualizes" what one wants and it will "manifest" itself in the world of experience. "Whatever we think about gradually becomes a subconscious pattern always tending to manifest itself in our experience" (Ernest Holmes, quoted in Addington, p. 22). "Once we are able to visualize the new concept in our minds, to accept it and believe in it, something happens in our experience and we find that we are able to leave behind us some of the failure patterns that we have longed to be rid of" (Addington, pp. 121–22). "Imagine things, not as they are, but as you would have them. Create a place for yourself in your imagination and hold it steadily. If you want a certain position, claim it as your own and '*see*' yourself doing it" (Bloodworth, p. 60). "In creative visualization you use your imagination to create a clear image of something you wish to manifest. Then you continue to focus on the idea or picture regularly, giving it positive energy until it becomes objective reality . . . in other words, until you actually achieve what you have been visualizing" (Gawain, *Creative Visualization*, pp. 2–3). "Remain confident that, through continued reliance on your imagination, your assumptions are materializing into reality" (Dyer, p. 41).

In order to plant such a seed, one must lift, as far as possible, the veil of normal consciousness separating the conscious from the subconscious mind. Meditation is the key, meditation as a kind of self-hypnosis to decentralize the ego and its bottleneck of consciousness. And yet one is hypnotizing not only oneself but also the great field of life force. This is possible because, while too vast and great to be limited to the confines of individual personality, that field is yet intelligent, like a computer program might be said to be. It must be for it to function as a logos-structure providing proportion and balance to the universe. It is not a personal deity who might speak to you. But it is a kind of listening ear for human voices whose direction it will take, precisely as the individual subconscious mind takes direction implicitly from the suggestion of a hypnotist.

> As you see the picture in your mind and feel it, you are bringing yourself to a place of believing you have it now. You are also implementing trust and faith in the Universe, because you are focusing on the end result and experiencing the feeling of that, without giving any attention whatsoever to "how" it will come about. Your picture in your mind is seeing it as done. Your feelings are seeing it as done. Your mind and your entire state of being are seeing it as *already* [having] *happened*. That is the art of visualization. (Byrne, p. 85)

> In actual practice the process consists in first forming a clear conception in the objective [i.e., conscious] mind of the idea we wish to convey to the subjective [i.e., subconscious] mind: then, when this has been firmly grasped, endeavour to lose sight of all other

facts connected with the external personality except the one in question, and then mentally address the subjective mind as though it were an independent entity and impress upon it what you want it to do or to believe. (Troward, p. 96)

The only effective way to use creative visualization is in the spirit of the way of the Tao—"going with the flow." That means you don't have to "effort" [*sic*] to get where you want to go; you simply put it out clearly to the universe where you would like to go, and then patiently and harmoniously follow the flow of the river of life until it takes you there. (Gawain, *Creative Visualization*, p. 42)

The metaphor of plant cultivation is important to New Thought, for one is advised to continue to meditate upon one's envisioned goal, feeding it with positive mental energy. "Like all the laws of nature, there is utter perfection in this law. You create your life. Whatever you sow, you reap! Your thoughts are seeds, and the harvest you reap will depend on the seeds you plant" (Byrne, p. 17). "When you sow seed thoughts for some special purpose, hold it in mind until you have acquired your desire in objective form. You cannot fail if you want anything hard enough to make the proper mental effort to impress your desire on your subconscious mind" (Bloodworth, p. 49). "So the more positive energy we put into imaging what we want, the more it begins to manifest in our lives" (Gawain, *Creative Visualization*, p. 7). Negative mental energy, by contrast, would be constituted by doubt and pessimism, dwelling on difficulties lying in the path of one's dream's realization. "To dwell upon old negative patterns is to bring more of their fruits into our experience. It is time we cast out the old thoughts of lack and failure and replaced them with mental equivalents of abundant success"

(Addington, p. 123). "While you are using affirmations, try to temporarily suspend any doubts or disbelief you may have, at least for the moment, and practice getting the feeling that that which you desire is very real and possible" (Gawain, *Creative Visualization*, p. 17). "If you worry about having negative thoughts, you will attract more worrying about your having negative thoughts" (Byrne, p. 22).

One repeats various "affirmations" which, as the etymology suggests, "firm up" the goal one seeks (Gawain, *Creative Visualization*, p. 21), drawing it closer and closer to realization, to manifestation. But there is another aspect to it: the repetition of one's affirmations serves as a technique for reconditioning oneself, building new and healthier mental habits. "When you repeat this affirmation, you are impressing your subconscious mind with just those qualities as a basis for the new character you are building, and this character will attract to itself conditions that correspond to it in kind and quality" (Bloodworth, p. 41). "Repeat these words, or create your [own] arrangements of words, which continually inundate your thoughts during your waking hours, with a new belief of being successful and abundant. When you've activated these thoughts enough times, they'll become your habitual way of thinking, and you will have taken the steps to eliminating your resistance to allowing" (Dyer, p. 178). "How do you get yourself to the point of believing? Start make-believing. Be like a child and make-believe. Act as if you have it already. As you make-believe, you will begin to *believe* you have received" (Byrne, p. 50).

Another type or technique of affirmation (and visualization) is *gratitude*: "When you give thanks as though you have already received what you want, you are emitting a powerful signal to the Universe. That signal is saying that you have received it already because you are feeling gratitude for it now" (Byrne, p. 80).

By now the reader may expect me to attack and deride such assurances, but I will not. This much is simply creative psychology. If repeated contemplation of a scientific formula, a historical fact, a new friend's name, or a sports score will eventually wear a groove in the gray matter of the brain, it is not hard to imagine that one's habits of expectation may be changed by the faithful repetition of an affirmation or a scriptural text. And this is a hint to which we shall return: it appears that much of New Thought's belief in visualization and manifestation does not really depend upon dubious metaphysics but may perhaps be backed up by recourse to more mundane, psychological conditions.

It is the belief of New Thought that the cosmos is a storehouse of abundance, rightfully to be enjoyed by everyone. "The Universe is the Universal supply and supplier of everything. . . . Think of the law of attraction as the law of supply" (Byrne, p. 163). "I'm suggesting that we can have everything the world has to offer—all the relationships, wealth, beauty, power, and fun we might want" (Gawain, *Living in the Light*, p. 21). "The face of abundance has absolutely no limits. . . . You were created from this very same unlimited abundance. The power of intention is everywhere. It is what allows everything to manifest, to increase, and to supply infinitely" (Dyer, p. 30). The reason we do not enjoy its bounty is that we suffer from "scarcity consciousness," a crippling belief in limitation, whether of available resources or of personal potential, and this belief becomes a self-fulfilling prophecy. One will hardly pursue what one believes does not exist. Troward writes, "Belief in limitation is the one and only thing that causes limitation, because we thus impress limitation upon the creative principle; and in proportion as we lay that belief aside our boundaries will expand, and increasing life and more abundant blessing will be ours" (Troward,

p. 105). "Be abundant . . . any attitude you have that reflects a scarcity consciousness will hold you back" (Dyer, p. 53).

THAT ATTRACTIVE LAW

All this may be summed up in the mantra-like slogan of *The Secret*: "the law of attraction." Rhonda Byrne says, "If you can think about what you want in your mind, and make that your dominant thought, you *will* it into your life" (p. 9). "The law of attraction says *like attracts like*, so when you think a thought, you are also attracting like thoughts to you. . . . As you think thoughts, they are sent out into the Universe, and they magnetically attract all like things that are on the same frequency" (p. 25). "If there is any reason for unhappiness, resolutely put it out of your mind, for *like attracts like*, and the more you think of discordant conditions, the more such conditions will manifest for you. *Concentrate on what you want.* When you do that, you are impressing that desire on your subconscious mind; *never* let your thoughts dwell on what you *do not want*" (Bloodworth, p. 34). "Always phrase affirmations in the most positive way that you can. Affirm what you *do* want, not what you *don't* want" (Gawain, *Creative Visualization*, p. 24).

Venice Bloodworth teaches, "The law is that 'like attracts like'" (p. 47), so that events will fall into line with our preoccupations. James Allen says, "The soul attracts that which it secretly harbors, that which it loves, and also that which it fears . . . and circumstances are the means by which the soul receives its own" (pp. 23–24). Jack Addington echoes: "the law of life gives back to us with undeviating accuracy exactly what we believe we can attain, exactly what we are able to accept for ourselves in our minds—no more, no less." Some call that "the law of attraction" (pp. 119–20). Shakti Gawain: "Our mental commentary influences and colors our feelings and perceptions about what's going on in our lives, and it is these thought forms that ultimately attract and create everything that happens to us" (*Creative Visualization*, p. 21). Wayne Dyer, a confessed believer in Jungian synchronicity, speaks of "attractor energy patterns" (p. 94). "Now those forces begin to work on everyone in your environment. The right people magically appear. The right materials show up. The phone rings and someone gives you information you've been wanting for months" (p. 95).

But is all this a matter of shaping what *happens*, or what we *notice*? No one will deny that a fixation on a goal will alert us to opportunities and possibilities we should never otherwise have noticed. Positivity and determination inspire very different reactions from others than apathy and pessimism do. It is no idle fancy to expect that life and the world will work differently for those who insist on pursuing betterment and achievement. Creating and focusing on a goal *does* seem to bring it into reality.

The psychology of New Thought writings, though often informal, is also often quite shrewd. With the sagacity of a Screwtape, New Thought writers warn us, in all our affirming, not to affirm that we are *going to* get what we want, since that places fulfillment in the future and reinforces the fact that you are still waiting for it, and *do not have it*.

> You must act, speak, and think, as though you are receiving it *now*. Why? The Universe is a mirror, and the law of attraction is mirroring back to you your dominant thoughts. . . . If your thoughts contain noticing you do not have it yet, you will continue to attract not having it yet. (Byrne, p. 49)

TOP SECRET

If you tell [the subconscious mind] that you wish to accomplish something at some time in the future, it will keep your desire "on ice" for you—always in the future. The direction that we give to the inner Self, our Self-Direction, should always be given in the now. The result, or the out-picturing of our direction may seem to come at a future date because the manifestation must necessarily be expressed in the relative, the world of relative time and space. In order to have our direction followed at all it must be given in the now, and it must be accepted now. (Addington, p. 131)

You should think of it in the present tense as *already* existing the way you want it to be. . . . Always phrase affirmations in the present tense, not in the future. It's important to create it as if it *already exists*. Don't say, "I will get a wonderful new job," but rather, "I now have a wonderful new job." This is not lying to yourself; it is acknowledging the fact that everything is created *first* on the mental plane, before it can manifest in objective reality." (Gawain, *Creative Visualization*, pp. 16, 24)

INVICTUS

Team *Secret,* like previous New Thought advocates, make what anyone would have to regard as a sound psychological observation. I like the way Jack Addington put it: "We limit ourselves by what our experience has been" (p. 126). In fact, isn't that the essence of neurosis according to Freud? Nursing an old wound, we come to feel that the future must necessarily be a replay of the past, that it will never turn out better, and that past experience is a destiny we are doomed forever to repeat. "The ego bases its perception of reality on what has happened in the past, carries those perceptions into the present and thus creates a future like the past. If we felt that we were lacking in our past, our thoughts about the future are based on those perceptions. We then enter the present in an effort to compensate for the past. Since that perception is our core belief, we recreate its conditions in the future" (Williamson, pp. 64–65). To this the remedy is simple, at least in principle: to realize that, as you change and mature, your options change. People will react to the newest version of you in a way they didn't and couldn't to the old edition. Hence the need to put some mental effort into reprogramming oneself, whether by affirmations or by basic openness to the future, a future different from the past. You are watching the television screen of your life. On one channel is a new episode; on the other there is a syndicated rerun. Which will you choose to watch? "When your inner speech focuses on the way things have always been, you act upon your thoughts of what has always been, and the universal all-creating force continues to deliver what has always been" (Dyer, p. 65).

Here we approach one of the most controversial aspects of both New Thought and New Age belief: the notion that one *creates one's own reality*, inadvertently if not by conscious will. "Your life is a mirror of the dominant thoughts you think" (Byrne, p. 20). "The world without is merely a reflection of what you have acknowledged as true in your world within, so if the state of your health or finances is not all that you desire, you must look within yourself for the cause" (Bloodworth, p. 12). This understanding meets us in two forms: the strong version fits more naturally with New Age metaphysics, which often includes a belief in reincarnation (e.g., Dyer, p. 225) or conscious preexistence of the soul (e.g., Gawain, *Living in the Light*, pp. 36, 119). Here we are told that we selected the conditions of our birth and life while cooling our heels in the intermediate *Bardo* zone between incarnations. This appears to be a mythologized version of the standard Hindu-Buddhist doctrine of karma which stipulates that all future circumstances are set in motion as repercussions, rewards, and punishments for actions in the previous life. Only in that version, nobody is shopping for a next life as if buying a time-share vacation spot. (Eckhart Tolle goes further than that, to a kind of solipsism, but that will have to wait for another chapter.)

The weak version seems more psychological than metaphysical in character. Shakti Gawain, even though she sounds like she espouses the strong, New Age version, finally seems to be describing the weak version: "The physical world is our creation: we each create our own version of the world, our particular reality, our unique life experience" (*Living in the Light*, p. 26). What does she mean? "I assume that *everything* in my life is my reflection, my creation; there are no accidents or events that are unrelated to me. If I see or feel something, if it has an impact on me, then my being has attracted or created it to show me something. If it didn't mirror some part of myself I wouldn't even be able to see it" (*Living in the Light*, pp. 26–27). This, it seems to me, is not that spooky. What is the selection principle by which your mind decides what you will perceive? Mainly, it chooses what is relevant to you and depicts it in familiar categories you can understand. This is why we often misread people, filtering their words and acts through our own agendas, fears, or hopes. Even the cosmos-voyaging Dyer says, "You must learn to assume responsibility for the circumstances of your life without any accompanying guilt. The circumstances of your life aren't the way they are because of karmic debt or because you're being punished. The circumstances of your life, including your health, are yours. Somehow they showed up in your life, so just assume that you participated in all of it" (p. 65). Fair enough. Schopenhauer thought so, too. And as Lovecraft said, "Ol' Art Schopenhauer had the straight goods" (Lovecraft, letter to James Ferdinand Morton, April 1, 1930, in Devleth).

> In all the universe there can be no such things as luck or fate; every action, every thought is governed by law. Behind every bit of good fortune lie the causes that we ourselves have sometime, somewhere set in motion. Behind all ill fortune we will find the energy we, ourselves, have generated. Every cause must have a certain definite effect, there is no dodging the results, we reap what we sow with exact mathematical precision. (Bloodworth, p. 9)

> That to which we give our attention grows. As we give our attention to the good, the positive, and the right, these will become our experience. (Addington, p. 201)

> The outer world of circumstances shapes itself to the inner world of thought, and both pleasant and unpleasant external conditions are factors which make for the ultimate good of the individual. (Allen, p. 24)

> These sources of your expectations are largely based on the beliefs of limitation, scarcity, and pessimism about what's possible for you. If these beliefs are the basis for how you look at life, then this perception of the world is what you expect for yourself. Attracting abundance, prosperity, and success from these limiting viewpoints is an impossibility. (Dyer, p. 174)

The commonsensical nature of New Thought becomes clear in Venice Bloodworth's observation on "lucky" and "unlucky" individuals (pp. 63–64). Are they the bearers of unseen auras of *mana-force*? Have they been cursed or blessed by gods of fortune? Of course not. One hears the endless whining of the *schlemiel* and observes the confidence of the winner, and one shortly realizes that their attitudes are not the *results* but the *causes* of their respective fortunes. Admittedly, we usually cannot trace specific acts, words, facial gestures, tones of voice, and so on, that influence our circumstances and outcomes. But that hardly means that to believe in such subtle effects is superstition. Our inability to account for every straw that is on its way to breaking the camel's back doesn't mean it's not breaking. The proposition here is no different in this respect from the claim of behaviorist psychology that, if we could identify and trace every factor that shapes and conditions our behavior, we could infallibly predict what we would do next. We cannot infallibly predict our own behavior or that of others, but that is not because there is no causal process. It is only due to our ignorance of factors below the level of awareness. And the same holds true for the New Thought belief that we subtly shape things to come out as we expect them to.

WORLD OF PAIN

Again, it is because they confuse a wise rule of thumb with an overarching system of metaphysics that people like Rhonda Byrne wind up heartlessly blaming the victim. "Often when people first hear this part of *The Secret* they recall events in history where masses of lives were lost, and they find it incomprehensible that so many people could have attracted themselves to the event. By the law of attraction, they had to be on the same frequency as the event" (p. 28). Or course she has in mind the Nazi Holocaust. Too bad those Jews didn't think happier thoughts, huh? And because they didn't, well, they asked for it! This is veering perilously close to the racist canard, still so commonly and blithely ventured, that Jews lacked the gumption to resist the Nazis and so had themselves to blame for their suffering. Why can't Byrne and Team *Secret* afford to admit that human beings can do terrible things to one another, and that some people wind up as the innocent prey of others, or else ground beneath the heel of impersonal catastrophe? Because such admissions of the patently obvious would explode the desired illusion that the individual controls his or her own universe. If they were to admit the obvious, that "the law of attraction" and "visualization and manifestation" are simply rules of thumb for achieving one's goals and not a totalizing explanation for all events, they could not make their grandiose promises to all and sundry. There would be no more blank check. And that doesn't sufficiently "empower" certain individuals who will accept nothing less than a comprehensive placebo.

Take the miserable skeletons of Darfur, prey both to starvation and to genocidal pogroms engineered by their fanatical Muslim overlords. Their own fault? Why don't they just "visualize" happiness, safety, and prosperity and wait for them to "manifest"? It is black comedy even to say that sarcastically. And the case is another that disproves the law of attraction *insofar as its proponents make it a comprehensive blueprint of reality.* But just as obvious as the gross inapplicability of the schema to the misery of Darfur is the great success people have experienced through New Thought insights. How do we understand these two facts: why this "secret" works when it does and doesn't when it doesn't?

Actually, there is no inconsistency. We just need to choose the appropriate larger context into which both phenomena fit. And that, I think, is Abraham Maslow's hierarchy of needs. Everyone has certain basic needs for food, shelter, sleep, and security. Until these are satisfied, people cannot afford the time to occupy themselves with hobbies, politics, sports, religion, or the arts. Food before meaning. This is why rescue missions dip out soup before preaching the gospel. More ethereal needs (spiritual and esthetic ones, etc.) can be sensed, much less met, only once one has gotten the more urgent business out of the way. In the same way, philosopher Josef Pieper (*Leisure the Basis of Culture*) showed how cultural achievements are possible only once a society (or a creative element within it, usually among the richest) can get others to do the labor, so they themselves can explore "free time pursuits." Maslow and Pieper have our answer: *The Secret*, New Thought, is a personal self-cultivation formula relevant only once one attains the higher levels of need satisfaction. It addresses the felt needs of those experiencing "relative deprivation," not absolute. It presupposes a framework of decisions, opportunities, and mental leisure in which one may select the best thoughts as from a gourmet menu. There's just not much time for that when you're dodging bullets or picking through a garbage can to feed your baby. Just as the starving do not have the luxury to theorize about morals and ethics (see William Golding's *Lord of the Flies* or Ingmar Bergman's *The Shame*), neither do the persecuted have the leisure to send out vibes to increase their chances of "success" by a standard that would be laughable in their circumstances. That would really be fiddling while Rome burns. And yet there is no need to belittle the needs felt by the affluent, including virtually all readers of this book or Rhonda Byrne's. Those are real needs, too. The wretches of Darfur would love to be fretting over these matters with us. Let's hope one day they get the chance, and we can all work on our middle-class suburban neuroses together.

SECRET WEAPON

And yet once again *The Secret* almost gets it right. In fact, it seems possible to imagine that "mind games" might indeed mitigate the horrors of the concentration camp. Victor Frankl found himself cooling his heels there, and he quickly devised a plan for keeping hope as well as sanity alive. He decided he would view the whole horrible experience as a participant-observer experiment in social psychology: how did his fellow inmates hold up? It worked, and when Frankl was released, he had conceived what he would call Logotherapy, a therapeutic approach centering on making *sense* of the apparent chaos of one's life. He wrote *Man's Search for Meaning*. Here is a man projecting "vibes" of rationality, albeit into a void of horror and doom. There was no "friendly universe" waiting, like a cooperative genie (as Byrne thinks, pp. 40, 46) to grant every whim Frankl might order up. Frankl had to be his own genie, casting spells of meaning to illuminate the darkness that ever threatened to close like an iron portcullis over his own sanity. As jailed mobster John Gotti put it: "It's mind over matter; if you don't mind, it don't matter."

The Secret has invited a storm of justified criticism because of its embrace of, indeed its harping on, bogus physics to make what is essentially a sound and clever psychological point. If only Byrne and her adherents would drop the pseudoscience! All this talk of "frequencies" and "sending out vibrations" must be recognized, and thus respected, as *metaphor*. Interpersonal influence is often and validly expressed in terms of contagious fire, fluid, or energy, as when we speak of "personal magnetism" or "charisma" (which means "anointing with oil"). In such cases we do not imagine we are actually emitting quantifiable energy waves or whatever. Nor do we need to formulate and defend a system of phony physics of "charisma," as if somehow the metaphors were not enough. We know that the phenomenon of personal magnetism is very real (look at Adolf Hitler), however it works. We don't have to understand the phenomenon down to the last detail to know it's dangerous and to watch out for it. Likewise we don't have to know exactly how it works when we send out subtle signals that shape what we get back—it just seems to work that way. Wise people realize that and try to live accordingly. Schopenhauer and Freud wanted them to.

NO MORE SECRETS

By now it has become clear, I hope, that, just as the newest crop of New Thought teachers have mixed up those teachings with superfluous New Age beliefs, so did the original New Thought believers hang the validity of their "practical spirituality" upon an idealist, pantheistic metaphysic which it can easily do without. Their error was to identify "the laws of thought" (or "the laws of life") with "the laws of the universe." By positing a magical universe whereby one may manipulate the macrocosm by fiddling with the microcosm, New Thoughters risked bringing into disrepute a helpful and incisive set of psychological observations that require neither divine revelation nor nondualist metaphysics. The New Thought notion of our creating our own reality through the choices we make and the mental habits we cultivate stems "merely" from the accumulated wisdom of humankind. The truth of this counsel cannot be verified in a laboratory but rather is based on anecdotal observation of the way people live life, successfully and unsuccessfully. Perhaps that is the difference between science and wisdom, neither of which is to be despised. And that is the truth behind *The Secret*.

Chapter 2
Karma Chameleon
Deepak Chopra, *How to Know God*

THE FOOL ON THE HILL

*I*n the beginning was Gaudapada, founder of Advaita Vedanta Hinduism. Gaudapada, so to speak, begat Shankara. Shankara, way down the line, begat the Maharishi Mahesh Yogi, who packaged nondualism for sale to Americans. Perhaps he thought, "If they'll meditate to improve their golf game, then that's how we'll promote it to them." Transcendental Meditation (TM) was born. There has always been something of a sleazy tinge to TM in the United States. TM was offered in public schools for credit, disavowing its religious identity. The Supreme Court recognized the (really overtly) religious nature of the ritual and the practice and threw it out of public schools. It's being ostensibly nonreligious (or as some said, "not a religion") was plainly sneaky disinformation, what some cults call "heavenly deception."

TM also invited disdain for its pseudoscientific claims such as its practicers being able to levitate, something they would, however, not allow any outsiders to witness. Alleged photos appeared to just catch people in a lotus position bouncing off a trampoline. TM also created its own dubiously scientific diet regimen allegedly derived from the Yajur Veda, one of the four Vedas of ancient Hinduism, but it is only loosely inspired by it.

What does any of this have to do with Dr. Deepak Chopra? Simply that he is just a TM salesman who decided to break away and hang out his own shingle. He makes the same pseudoscientific claims about a "Field of Creative Intelligence" which he claims is supported by quantum physics. (This is one more version of a concept we also find in New Thought and its modern "store brand" competitors like Wayne Dyer. To get ahead of the game, let me just say that I accept such a notion as a phenomenological description without begging any metaphysical questions.)

Deepak Chopra makes the same dangerous "alternative medicine" sort of assertions, also claiming to be able to diagnose ailments by feeling one's pulse. In this manner he once told a seeker that her cancer had evaporated, only to have her die from it soon afterward.

Chopra also claims to have levitated some eight feet through the air, even to have walked through walls like Jacob Marley. I'm sorry, but one simply cannot credit such claims. It is difficult even to give Chopra the benefit of the doubt that he was perhaps hallucinating while in a trance state. This is just medicine-show imposture.

To listen to (or read) Chopra without sufficient background knowledge, one would naturally infer that he is sharing the results of brand-new scientific research with exciting implications for both physical health and mind-over-matter wish fulfillment. His first choice is always to put his claims in scientific terms. But again and again he comes back to the unsung basis for all his claims: Advaita Vedanta Hinduism. How striking a "coincidence" that his supposed "science" invariably ended up at the same place his inherited Hindu doctrines led him anyway.

I do not mean to deny that Hindu doctrines are true, as they may well be for all I know. But I mean to point out that Chopra is essentially stooping to the standard TM ruse for evangelizing worldly Westerners, trying to convince them of Hindu doctrine by means of a misleading (pseudo)scientific idiom. We see the same in the TM-propaganda flick *What the Bleep Do We Know?*

WHAT THE BLEEP DOES HE KNOW?

Chopra and his fellow travelers are doing nothing essentially different from the tactics of Scientific Creationists and Intelligent Design advocates who seek to translate religious dogma derived from scripture into cosmetic, seemingly "scientific" terms so as to smuggle dogma into science classes, or at least to win for it the prestige due to science. He even performs the same switcheroo familiar from creationist propaganda, trying to equate science with religion, claiming it is a religion so as to claim equal rights or at least regard for other contested religions: "This is a bold claim, but it is corroborated by the fact that science—our most credible modern religion—also traces creation back to light" (p. 18).

The fact that Chopra's basis for belief is actually faith in Hinduism—despite his professed empiricism, "After centuries of knowing God through faith, we are now ready to understand divine intelligence directly" (p. 2)—explains the dogmatic manner in which he pontificates on matters that any scientist would only guess at in the most tentative, provisional terms. "Our whole notion of reality has actually been topsy-turvy. Instead of God being a vast, imaginary projection, he turns out to be the only thing that is real, and the whole universe, despite its immensity and solidity, is a projection of God's nature" (p. 2). This language suggests that we are lucky enough to have the veil of ignorance at last ripped away via some sort of discovery. It sounds as if we at last know the contours of the dark side of the moon now that the Apollo space program enabled astronauts to map it. But the great disclosure Chopra is talking about is simply that of religious conversion to nondualist Vedanta (he finally uses the term only on page 177, after he's got the reader "in the mood"). Once we accept by faith that it is true, then certain implications about God and the world will follow. That doesn't mean they are thus proven to be true. We do not "know" any such thing by scientific means any more than Shankara did, who used to argue his points with pretechnological metaphors like brooms and dustpans, monkeys and bananas. Quantum physics, with all its headache-inducing surprises, does not prove there is a divine Field of Creative Intelligence like the Force in *Star Wars*.

Chopra soon reveals that he is not serious about what scientists would call science. It turns out he can only win the game if he is allowed to change the rules: "[I]f we stubbornly cling to material reality as the only way to know anything, skepticism about God is totally justified. Miracles and angels defy reason, and even though holy visions may be catalogued time after time, the rational mind remains defiant, defending its sure grip on the material plane" (p. 4). What Chopra calls myopia is actually a clarification of vision. For thousands of years humankind languished in gross superstition, practicing the same sort of root bag medicine he advocates precisely because no one saw the need to adopt the scientific method, the only way to test claims. And then one simply must have something more substantial than "vibes" to put into the test tube. One might think long and hard before kissing science good-bye in order to welcome the sheer assertions of dangerous quacks with their pious Russian roulette approach to healing without medicine.

Thus it is no surprise that Chopra himself revels in gullibility. He applauds "the psychic surgeons of the Philippines, who seem to penetrate a patient's body with their hands and pull out all manner of bloody tissue, none of it anything that would be seen inside a body at autopsy" (p. 140). Usually what they show to the crowd is a bunch of chicken innards. These quacks are mere sleight-of-hand artists bilking their tragic victims as has been amply demonstrated. Chopra's choice of company says much about him.

Let's put this another way: there may perhaps be an invisible kind of reality that is "spiritual" if anyone knows how to define that in other terms than a psychological description of behavior and character. But then one must also provide some methodology to weigh and assess claims for that realm. I don't see that Chopra (or any of his congeners) has arrived at any such criterion. With him, it is always sheer assertion. The closest thing he has to evidence is anecdotes, some of them likely urban legends, from which he hastily generalizes to form axioms of the imagination.

METHOD VERSUS MADNESS

A major aspect of the scientific method is its criterion of impartial repeatability: if a researcher has done his experiment right, any colleague ought to be able to follow that same procedure and obtain the same results. That is important, because I want to be able to rely on the likelihood that when I plug the lamp in again, it will glow like it did when the salesman demonstrated it in the store. I want to be sure the medicine will work for me as it did for someone else with my affliction. Science is based on the method of repeatability, replication of results, or no scientific conclusions are possible. If you claim to have fused hydrogen atoms in your lab but I cannot get the same result with the same method, we simply cannot claim we have discovered a nuclear fusion technique. But little things like that do not trouble "Doctor" Chopra's blissed-out composure. He reveals more than he intends with this anecdote:

> Schlitz announced the success of her experiment, only to find that another researcher who tried to duplicate it failed miserably. He used exactly the same methods, but in his laboratory almost no one responded with second sight; they couldn't tell the difference between being watched and not being watched. Schlitz was baffled but confident enough to invite the second researcher to come to her lab. The two of them ran the experiment again, choosing subjects at the last moment to ensure that there was no tampering.
>
> Again Schlitz obtained her results, but when she consulted her colleague, he had obtained nothing. This was an extraordinary moment. How could two people run the same objective test with such dramatically different results? The only viable answer, as Schlitz saw it, must lie in the researcher himself. The outcome depended on *who you are*. As far as I know, this is as close as anyone has come to verifying that observer and observation can collapse into one. This fusion lies at the heart of the sacred response, because in unity all separation ends. (p. 162)

Well, that may pass for science in the ivied halls of Maharishi University, but it's not science everyplace else. Do you see what

Chopra is trying to do here? Results need no longer be replicable for us to accept them as "true." "Truth" varies with the eye of the beholder, because all is *maya*. Only that is to dignify it. It is to give a venerable, metaphysical name to quack science. Besides, Chopra's own drawing one single and normative conclusion from the experiment, that is, that there is no objectivity, is itself posing as an objective "finding" that he presumes the sympathetic reader will accept on the basis of this anecdote.

Chopra fibs to us that physicists would join him in carving reality into three levels. There is, first, "material reality, the world of objects and events"; second, "quantum reality, a transition zone where energy turns into matter"; and, third, "virtual reality, the place beyond time and space, the origin of the universe" (p. 11). And of course Chopra teaches that anyone may cross over from one level to the others. When we pray or meditate, we are sending out "intentions" from the material level into the quantum level, through the medium of which they set in motion repercussions from the virtual world, ripples that will rebound and return to our shore of the pond, fulfilling our wishes. The material world is thus malleable since quantum physics allegedly proves that there is no solid material world under our feet after all. Rather, we are told that seemingly solid objects like tables and the fists that smash down upon them are alike composed of subatomic particles farther from one another proportionately than Pluto is from the Sun. And these particles are really more like packets, bundles ("quanta") of energy, anyhow. Thus everything ultimately comes down to mostly empty space and some sparks of light.

But to all this mumbo jumbo one may offer the very same rejoinder that Samuel Johnson offered to the "Immaterialism" philosophy of Bishop George Berkeley when he kicked a stone and declared, "Thus I refute him!" You see, Deepak Chopra and his fellow dancing Wu Li masters have failed to learn a basic lesson about scientific description and theorizing. B. F. Skinner put it succinctly: "A theory about a thing does not change the thing the theory is about." Every theory seeks to account for the perceived reality of our experience. If the resultant theory implies something radically incongruous with the data it is trying to explain, something has gone badly awry. If I seek to explain why a rose is red and my proposal winds up implying the rose is really green, my proposal is to be rejected. The goal of any explanatory hypothesis, which is what quantum physics is supposed to be, is to "save the appearances." That is, the scientist wants to explain how things wind up as they are. He or she does not try to produce magic formulas we may use to transform things into what they are not. One may *also* try to transform things, by, for example, gene splicing or inducing mutation through exposure to radiation or a change of diet. But that is not the same sort of endeavor. Chopra and his fellow pseudoscientists are treating quantum physics like the "Syllogismobile" in the Harold Shea stories of L. Sprague de Camp and Fletcher Pratt. In these tales, scientist Shea discovered an equation that he need only run through his mind, and he would travel through time. Comic book superhero Johnny Quick similarly had only to repeat a certain arcane physics formula in order to gain superhuman speed. But in the real world it doesn't work that way.

Chopra, along with many New Thought and New Age gurus, believes that once one becomes aware of a subtle causal field (Dyer calls it "the field of intention"; Johnnie Colemon calls it "God-stuff"), one can manipulate it to bring into being whatever one desires. I do not mean to poke fun at it. Indeed, further on, I will defend something like it. But for the moment we must admit that such an understanding marks New Thought, Chopraism, and so on, as belonging to what sociologist Bryan Wilson calls a "Thaumaturgical" sect. Such a movement believes it can offer an occult means of manipulating reality for pretty much personal benefit. No doubt Chopra knows good and well that such conjuring is frowned upon by genuine spiritual adepts in India as a distraction from the real business of enlightenment. I am guessing that Chopra continues to uphold the public relations policy of TM: sell the Western rubes a gimmick to enhance their golf game, and eventually they may go the rest of the way to cosmic consciousness.

I want to pursue this business of miracles in a moment, to place them in their proper yogic context, but let me point out that in doing so I will be beginning a rundown of major features of Hinduism that Deepak Chopra initially soft-peddles, though he does eventually reveal the label on the bottle. In what follows, I do not wish to be read as "exposing" Chopra's teaching as bad or heretical or even as unreliable simply because I am indicating the Hindu origin and character of it. On the contrary, as a student of world religions I regard the teaching of Hinduism as both venerable and profound. Here is my gripe. Chopra says, "I have steered clear of dogma, knowing full well that Christians do not automatically accept an Eastern belief such as karma" (p. 190). In fact, he has done no such thing. The whole book *How to Know God* presents an unadulterated, if popularized, catechism of Advaita Vedanta Hinduism shading over into Mahayana Buddhism. Again, don't get me wrong: I can see the utility of trying to communicate these ideas in an idiom that might prove more natural and more palatable to Western readers, who might get scared off for no good reason if the author said, right up front, "I want to show you the advantages of believing in Nondualist Hinduism!" I believe it is a wise pedagog-

Chopra's thinking they seem to have a broader function. He is not impatient to have his *chelas* (us, his readers) storm the castle of enlightenment. For him, miracles (he prefers to use the Western, biblical term) are more important. They are signs and evidence of the interplay between the virtual and material realms by way of the quantum realm.

In company with traditional nondualist philosophers, Chopra understands the world of appearances, the so-called material world, to be largely illusory, even magical in the sense of a stage illusion. For Chopra, borrowing the paraphernalia of modern physics, the world boils down to a seething soup of "virtual photons" that manifest on the plane of sense perception in accord with either the (passive, unenlightened) expectations or the (active, enlightened) commands of the perceiver. The perceiver has power over what outcomes will manifest in his or her life. His or her intentions press this or that button, calling forth certain vibrations in this quantum ether: "The brain is shaping virtual photons into a pattern of experience" (p. 123). This is how miracle healings are done: "What [the medicine man] is trying to alter are the energy patterns that have become distorted, thus causing the disease. A rotten tooth, a tumor, or a detached retina are all a cluster of photons, a warped image made of light" (p. 141). "Things are real in the quantum world if you *make* them real, and that is done by manipulating light" (p. 144).

At times he seems to approach an almost Kantian perspective: "The whole universe is as we are, because without the human mind, there would be only quantum soup, billions of random sensory impressions. Yet thanks to the mind/brain, we recognize that encoded into the swirling cosmos are the most valued things in existence: form, meaning, beauty, truth, love. These are the realities the brain is reaching for" (p. 19).

In quantum terms, one cannot be certain about the line between hallucinations and reality. There are no definite events, no river of time that flows from past to present to future. What exists in its place is a rich matrix of possible outcomes. There are infinite choices within every event, and we determine which select few are going to manifest. At the depths of the mind field, where all things exist in seed form as virtual events, it hardly matters which ones eventually sprout. They are no more real than the seeds that didn't. (p. 262)

Here we seem to recognize Kant's undifferentiated manifold of perception out there in the noumenal world beyond the senses. Perceptions of that manifold can never be grasped with the eye of flesh (like Krishna, till he grants Arjuna a supernal eye with which to gaze upon his thousand-faced, million-armed outline). Rather, they must be filtered through the various "categories of perception" and "logical functions of judgment" before they can make sense to the brain. That Kant should come to mind is no real surprise, given that the early student of the Upanishads, Paul Deussen, already grasped the striking parallels between Hindu nondualism and Kantian epistemology.

The thought referred to, common to India, Plato, and Kant, that the entire universe is only appearance and not reality, forms not only the special and most important theme of all philosophy, but is also the presumption and *condition sine qua non* of all religion. All great religious teachers therefore, whether in earlier or later times . . . are alike unconsciously followers of Kant. (pp. 44–45)

Kant's apparatus of categories and functions corresponds to the *upadis*, or "limiting conditions," which refract the pure brilliance of the Brahman into false semblances, false because fragmentary, amenable to the feeble human mind. Where does Deepak Chopra contribute anything new? Unlike Kant, or the Upanishads for that matter (though echoing perhaps magical Vajrayana Buddhism), Chopra says that once we come to know of the filtering capacity of the mind, we can adjust its lenses to produce preferred effects. It is a tempting concept, though of course Kant would repudiate it. It is precisely the unalterable fixity of the categories and the functions, and their equal and identical sharing by all human perceivers, that account for the certainty we feel in the case of what Kant called synthetic a priori judgments. It is how we "know" that seven plus five will equal twelve every time, though there is nothing in the definition of either number that would necessitate it. For Chopra, for whom identical experiments may yield contradictory results for simultaneous experimenters, no such uniformity would be expected.

How miraculous does Deepak Chopra expect things to get? Like many writers in this field, he lays great store by meaningful coincidences, understood along the lines of Carl Jung's acausal principle of synchronicity. That is, striking coincidences are taken to illumine momentarily an overarching structure of meaning linking the microcosm (the human observer) with the macrocosm (the universe at large). One learns to read and to trust such intuitive signs in plotting one's life direction:

> [Y]ou begin to see that events form patterns; you see that they also hold lessons or messages or signs—the outer world somehow is trying to communicate—and then you see that these outer events are actually symbols for inner events. . . . The ripples flow out from the center, getting wider and wider, until you begin to see that the "invisible hand" has a mind behind it, as well as great wisdom in what it does. (Chopra, p. 109)

TOP SECRET

Though strict rationalists (I flatter myself to imagine I am num-
bered among them) may be tempted to dismiss all this as superstition, a mass of delusions of reference, remember that Arthur
Schopenhauer believed much the same thing, only he said the
guiding hand is one's own, operating with a wisdom one scarcely
suspected oneself of possessing. One need not follow Chopra all
the way toward Vedanta to suspect he may be on to something here.

Chopra sometimes sounds as if he believes, like the most credulous fundamentalist, that Jesus performed supernatural feats and
that more recent yogis have repeated them (pp. 33–34, 123 ["When
Jesus turned water into wine . . . he obliterated the arbitrary line
between imaginary results and real ones"], 132). But there is the
recurrent, unsettling suggestion that he knows better. "The real
point was to see that our senses aren't trustworthy at all. The incurable leper only appears that way, the few loaves and fishes are only
an illusion, the storm on the sea of Galilee can be calmed by a mere
act of will" (p. 33). New Thought practitioners follow Phineas
Parkhurst Quimby and Mary Baker Eddy in believing that Jesus
healed diseases because he saw their illusory (merely psychogenic
and psychosomatic) nature and drove home the same realization in
his patients. But Chopra seems to mean more than this. He seems
to mean that as genuine a miracle as one might hope to see, even
the turning of water into wine, would merely underline the "trick"
nature of "reality." It would not suspend or violate natural law but
rather expose the lack of any real natural law (no dharmas, insub-
stantiality, as Buddhists say).

But then one wonders if the same belief entitles Chopra to
employ fakery and imposture to teach his own doctrinal lessons.
After all, if there is finally no line separating reality from illusion,
an illusion is just as good as a "real" miracle and counts as one. "As

long as you don't know the secret, the illusion is a miracle" (p. 155). Here he is speaking of stage magic, but his point seems to be that the relevant factor in making something into a miracle is whether or not it promotes holiness (p. 155). "Since miracles are required to prove that a saint is real (at least in Catholicism), there is a tremendous temptation to make one up" (p. 154). Legends have the same symbolic import: "Such legends convey the tremendous effect of waking up to a new level of reality. That this reality arose in the mind sounds too abstract and prosaic. There needs to be a more dramatic event, such as a heaven that suddenly opens up, or divine messengers that descend from on high" (p. 209). Might not another such example be Chopra's own claim to have floated through the air while meditating? Again, as in the case of coy TM aeronauts, don't expect Dr. Chopra to let you see him doing it: "[T]he miracle worker has a limited range of ability. It is even said that having too many people in the room can defeat the phenomenon" (p. 141). Now, *that's* convenient! It is a classic dodge utilized by clairvoyants and other pseudopsychics. I can't help thinking of the character Invisible Boy in the comedy movie *Mystery Men*: he can only turn invisible when no one is looking at him! There is a more public experiment whereby we may hope to test Dr. Chopra's miracle claims. He contends that someone as tuned in as he is need not age physically! It's what you might call a longitudinal study, but eventually time will tell.

At one point our author muses:

These legends are now articles of faith, and for anyone to speculate that Muhammad might not have seen an angel or that Satan did not literally offer Jesus kingship over the earth would be risking blasphemy. However, it isn't necessary to believe or disbelieve the literal version of the Night of Qadr or the forty days in the wilderness. The essential point is that our minds can open to the sudden inrush of light. (p. 210)

By the same token, I wonder if it is supposed to be necessary for us to believe that Deepak Chopra himself levitated through the air once upon a time.

GOD BEYOND GOD

Chopra's book *How to Know God* is organized around seven God-concepts concomitant with seven levels of spiritual development of the individual. The religious psychology is often quite astute, whether or not one accepts the accompanying metaphysical claims. For his part, Chopra seems to me to step back and forth between the nondualist position of Shankara and the immanent-humanistic position of Patanjali (as interpreted by Mircea Eliade).

Shankara posited a distinction between levels of higher and lower knowledge. Compared to the higher level, the lower counted as mere ignorance. But in its own right, it was real knowledge (and knowledge of real truth) as far as it went. Lower knowledge professes a piety adoring a personal deity (*Isvara*, "the Lord," or Brahma the creator, or *Saguna Brahman*, Brahman with qualities), a creator and savior worthy of praise and with whom the soul seeks fellowship. And on that level of apprehension, there "exists" such a deity, though, as with everything on that penultimate plane of existence, it is less real than what is above it in the ontological hierarchy, and this latter is *Nirguna Brahman*, Brahman without qualities. When, through meditation, the adept makes the jump into higher knowledge, he puts away childish things and no more worships a deity he now knows is equal and identical to himself. TM outlines such higher rungs of the ladder to its advanced students, dropping the earlier pretenses: one reaches cosmic consciousness, then God consciousness, then Brahma consciousness. "That thou art." Even so, Deepak Chopra tells us that once we reach the highest stage of our projected development, we will know ourselves as God.

Patanjali, on the other hand, was the founder of Rajah yoga, a seven-stage path corresponding conspicuously to Chopra's seven stages of growth, each with a different God-concept. He seems to have believed that the gods were contained within the meditator as his own latent psychic powers, to be gradually awakened through meditation, as the Kundalini, the sleeping serpent of knowledge, ascends the spinal cord, illuminating each chakra in turn. *Chakras* ("wheels," "circles") are psychic energy nodes ranged up and down the spine: at the coccyx, behind the genitals, behind the navel (hence meditation as "navel gazing"), in the heart, in the throat, just above and between the eyes ("the third eye"), and atop the crown of the head. A different god indwells each, asleep and waiting to be awakened. But Patanjali did not believe there were extrahuman gods, much less a parallel, etheric spinal cord. According to Eliade, all this was simply a set of symbols that enabled the meditator to focus consciousness, very much in the manner of colors and sounds used in today's biofeedback training. "So now we have the outline for the entire spiritual journey in our hands: the unfolding of God is a process made possible by the brain's ability to unfold its own potential. . . . From the womb of the brain springs a new and useful God. Or to be precise, seven variations of God" (Chopra, p. 25). "In stage six all gods and goddesses are aspects of oneself expressed as fine energy states" (p. 145). As stage seven is realization of oneself as Brahman, we must suppose Chopra regards Patanjali's yoga as a preliminary level of "lower knowledge," useful as a stepping-stone.

Shankara took a great deal of heat for claiming to have transcended the need for worship. Many viewed him with great hostility as the enemy of religion, though of course he was not. But there can be charged feelings on both sides of this divide. Those embracing conventional theism will abhor the mystic's claims to union with the Godhead as blasphemous self-exaltation, while the mystic pities the "weaker brethren" as stubborn idolaters, worshiping the creation of their own imaginations. Each side may even view the other as atheists, denying the God their detractors believe in. This peculiar stalemate is of interest also to those not playing on either team. Self-proclaimed atheists, sitting in the stands, so to speak, may find themselves cheering alternately for both teams! Atheists may agree with each side's criticisms of the other. And it is just here that some of Deepak Chopra's statements about various levels of belief, and their concomitant God-concepts, become especially interesting.

Chopra is perhaps at his most acute when describing the limitations of immature God-concepts best left behind, whether one is off in the direction of mysticism or of secular atheism.

> In religious terms, some believers are content to love God and fear him at the same time. This duality in no way involves any condemnation of the deity. He is still "perfect" (meaning that he is always right) because those he punishes must always be wrong. . . .
>
> In this case faith depends on a value system that is preordained. If some ill befalls me, I must have committed a sin, even if I

didn't have any awareness of it. My task is to look deep enough until I find myself, and then I will see the perfect judgment God has rendered. To someone outside the system, however, it appears that an abused child is figuring out, through convoluted logic, how to make himself wrong so that the cruel parent remains right. In stage one, God has to be right. If he isn't, the world becomes too dangerous to live in. (pp. 62–63)

He has hit the nail right on the head. He is referring to the price to be paid by members of a cultural system for whom a sovereign God functions as a symbol to cushion the blows of injustice, adversity, and ignorance, as anthropologist Clifford L. Geertz put it. Nobody seems to take much comfort in the prospect of a morally neutral universe in which hapless humans are subject to the hammer blows of blind fate. We desperately want to believe there is justice, even if we must wait till the next life or enter some invisible heavenly realm in order for justice to be served. That may be cold comfort, but justice delayed is better than justice denied, since it would be just too terrifying to face the prospect of the mindless wrath of a hostile universe. We will do anything to protect the illusion of justice, or a just and sovereign order to the universe—even if we must become the scapegoats in the manner Chopra describes, taking the blame for imagined sin so as not to have to blame God for being unjust (or, worse, nonexistent!). This is also why we blame the victims. We hate to scapegoat them, but it is better to do so, we imagine, than to admit they are suffering for no reason. No, they *must* have deserved it, or there is no justice in the world, and then I will have to be afraid of the world.

Parenthetically, it is worth asking whether Chopra's own belief in karma is not subject to the very same objection. Does it, too, not entail blaming oneself as the victim in order to save face for cosmic justice? I *must* have deserved it! Even if it was for something I did in a previous, unremembered life! Yes, it all works out a bit too neatly, with me left holding the bag. But that is all right; Chopra accepts karma and reincarnation as only provisional, another product of *maya*, the shared illusion of the unenlightened. Reincarnation is an exact counterpart to the inferior "lower knowledge" version of God. It will likewise fade away when nondualist enlightenment dawns.

The immature God-concept Chopra describes here is a source of double binds and mixed signals: "In spiritual terms, God's protection is valued only by denying that he is also the source of the threat. In the end, nothing is outside the deity, so asking him to protect you from storms, famine, disease, and misfortune is the same as asking the perpetrator" (p. 66). To follow up Chopra's analogy of the desperate rationalizations of the abused child, we may recall what results from a home situation in which the child receives impossibly contradictory demands from a parent or parents: schizophrenia. One must be simultaneously all over the ballpark to be able to catch all the balls hit in every direction. There is an analogous result in religious growth: such piety becomes unworkable. One grows servile and self-punishing. Eventually one comes to the crossroads of rejecting such a God-concept if one is to have any prospect of spiritual maturity: "as long as the deity inspires awe, the way to him is through blind obedience" (p. 75)—and, again, through morbid introspection: "the fanatic must purify his very thoughts. Complete control over the mind is unachievable, but this doesn't prevent him from imposing ever stricter vigilance on 'crooked thoughts.'" Such a one, to advance any farther, "must find an inner life, which will never happen as long as he is policing his own desires. Vigilance kills all spontaneity in the end" (p. 83). (We will see later on how the type of Buddhism espoused by Pema Chödrön involves a rather different sort of careful, but nonbullying, introspection.) I call Deepak Chopra's insight at this point profound: a retrograde, essentially superstitious God-concept, though valued for the security it seems to give, must retard spiritual-emotional growth. One must either affirm the death of such a tyrant deity or transcend it on the way toward a "God beyond God." The two prospects may ultimately coincide if one believes, as Chopra does, that God and the true self are one.

Nondualist Vedanta does identify true self and true deity, only after sloughing off illusory concepts of both. We have seen how the demiurgic creator who issues commandments and promises salvation is not the ultimate God. What is? "The God of stage seven is so intangible that he can be defined by no qualities. Nothing remains to hold on to. In the ancient tradition, they define this aspect of spirit only by negation" (p. 160): *Neti, neti* ("Not this! Not that!" No-thing). But the same is true of the inmost self. It is the unchanging Atman. "The soul is as mysterious as God . . . it is not really as personal as people believe. The soul doesn't feel or move; it doesn't travel with you as you go about your life, nor does it endure birth, death, and decay. . . . It is pure spirit, made of the same essence as God. Atman cannot change in any way. It never reaches God because it never left in the first place. No matter how good or bad your life, your Atman remains constant; in fact, the worst criminal and the holiest saint have the same quantity of soul when it is this aspect that is in question" (pp. 275–76).

The Atman is unconditioned, unaffected by any karma you may generate, good or bad. But *something* is affected. Something accumulates karma and is reborn in order to answer for it by way of reward or punishment. What is that? It is the Jiva, or ego, the illusory psychological self. It is illusory because it possesses no abiding essence and is merely a collection of changing, shifting components, called *skandhas*. Think of Grandpa's ax. It is an heirloom in a farm family, passed down so long that it has required replacement of the handle twice and of the head three times. Is it still the "same" ax? No, it is a channel of change, a trajectory of impermanence, an empty riverbed. And so is the ego. Enlightenment is a matter of realizing that the composite, unstable ego is not oneself and ceasing to identify with either it or the desires that propel it toward new and pointless deeds. Jesus says, "A man's soul/life/self [Greek: *psuche*] does not consist in the abundance of his possessions" (Luke 12:15). He might have added that it equally does not consist in the sum total of his accomplishments, desires, thoughts, or even his rap sheet.

I must admit that the Hindu/Buddhist understanding of the psychological self as a phantom makes a lot of sense to me. I have sometimes caught a glimpse, or felt that I did, *behind* the edifice of the thoughts I had or the desire I felt or the argument I was making at the moment, and I had the strange impression *there was nothing there*. Nor is such a realization incompatible with secular rationalism, if one cares. After all, did not David Hume say pretty much the same thing?

IT AIN'T IN THE BIBLE BUT IT OUGHTA BE!

Like virtually all of today's spiritual teachers, Deepak Chopra tries to draw upon all religious traditions. No one, it seems, is able to imagine that great names of the past were not wise enough to agree with him, so to speak, in advance. But the uniformity of religious teachings is not actually so complete. Some traditions and scriptures cannot be pressed into Chopra's mold without a good bit of squeezing. So in conclusion, I will ask how faithfully Deepak Chopra represents the Bible in his *How to Know God.*

"The image [of God as a patriarch in a white robe seated on his throne] appears only once, in the Book of Daniel, whereas we are told many times in the books of Moses [Genesis through Deuteronomy] that God is without human form" (p. 31). Alas, we are told just the opposite. God(s) made human beings in his (their) own image and likeness, male and female, implying that there are male and female gods in human form, just as in all other ancient religions. The notion that the "image of God" in man refers to rationality or creativity or some such abstraction is a miserable rationalization by much later theologians embarrassed at the anthropomorphic faith of earlier Bible writers. Moses is told that he may not see God's face, for that would be too much for any living man, but he may see the receding figure of his broad back as God covers Moses with his hand (Exod. 33:22–23), which certainly implies a humanoid body. And so does Exodus 24:9–11 in which Moses, Aaron, Nadab, Abihu, and the elders of Israel climb the mountain to feast before God. "And they saw the God of Israel; and there was under his feet as it were a pavement of sapphire, like the very heaven for clearness" (Exod. 24:10).

"In the Bible one finds such verses as 'Seek ye the kingdom of heaven within'" (p. 92). Or does one? Chopra is thinking of Matthew 6:33, "But seek first his kingdom and his righteousness, and all these things shall be yours as well," and Luke 17:21, "for behold, the kingdom of God is within you."

"In one phrase—'As you sow, so shall you reap'—Jesus stated

the law of karma quite succinctly" (p. 114), except that it was not Jesus but *Paul* who said, "Do not be deceived; God is not mocked, for whatever a man sows, that he will also reap" (Gal. 6:7).

"Inspiration, as the Bible says, is an act of grace, a blessing" (p. 130). Er, not that I know of. Is there such a verse?

"Jesus was born into a world of magicians and miracles. . . . In those episodes where he drives out demons or defeats the sorcerer known as Simon Magus, Jesus draws a line between God's way and other ways" (p. 132). Oops! It was *Peter* who squared off with Simon Magus (in Acts 8), not Jesus.

Chopra ventures that, after the Book of Job, "God never again speaks in the Bible" (p. 283), but of course he does, including during the baptism and transfiguration scenes in Matthew, Mark, and Luke. Maybe Chopra just didn't bother to read any farther.

Incidentally, Chopra's casual treatment of the Bible, based apparently on loosely memorized quotations that it did not occur to him to check, illustrates exactly the sort of process form critics claim went on during the formation of the early, oral Jesus tradition. People seem to have combined the wording of similar sayings. They tended to unwittingly attribute sayings from other sages to Jesus, the fountain of wisdom. ("Sounds good! Jesus must have said it!") And they sometimes took stories featuring other miracle workers (Apollonius of Tyana, Pythagoras, Asclepius) and made Jesus the hero instead, just as Chopra innocently pits Jesus, instead of Peter, against Simon Magus.

Finally, Chopra's opportunistic and selective use of biblical data (certainly a common "sin") is a clue to how he also uses the data of physics and nutrition. In all these cases, when trying to decide whether to take the diagnosis of Dr. Chopra, I would seek a second opinion!

Chapter 3

Dharma Bums

Pema Chödrön and Chögyam Trungpa

SHE'S NOT CHINESE!

Once I was reading an interview in the *Sun*, an interrogation of the Buddhist pundit Pema Chödrön, whose name, face, and quotes I see often in some of the slick Buddhist magazines we subscribe to. There was a mini-article introducing her, and this was surprisingly revealing, pointing up a lingering uneasiness I had long felt regarding the sage in question. It seems that Pema Chödrön was a student of the enigmatic Tibetan master Chögyam Trungpa. One thing about this holy man: he died of cirrhosis of the liver, just like Pentecostal healer A. A. Allen did, only Trungpa drank himself under at the premature age of forty-four years. He used to speak portentously of the Buddhist doctrine of craving while swilling a can of Colt 45. He was addicted to "love affairs," that is, being a sexual predator among those tender souls who made the mistake of trusting him. Yeah, this guy is the very epitome of a spiritual guide! Do you think that the hip readers of mags like this would exercise anything like the anticipated degree of tolerance if they were talking about Jimmy Swaggart or Jim Bakker? Because this is like claiming apostolic succession from one of them. The latter portion of this chapter will deal with Trungpa. But first, what about the venerable Pema Chödrön herself? Her name means "Lotus Torch of the Dharma." One might expect its bearer to be a wizened lady reminiscent of Kwan Yin, an Asian counterpart to Mother Teresa. Not a chance. The apple-faced guru was born Deirdre Blomfield-Brown. Does that matter?

I thought immediately of a *Seinfeld* episode in which George Costanza's mother was persuaded not to divorce her husband by the wise words of Jerry's current girlfriend, Donna Chang, whose advice Estelle Costanza had absorbed over the phone. Grateful, Estelle invited Jerry and Donna over for dinner. It was only then that she realized Donna was a blonde Jew whose family name had been shortened from Changstein. Confronted with the reality of her counselor, Estelle yelled, "She's not Chinese! I thought she was Chinese! That changes everything!"

It was funny because, as George pointed out, the advice should have been as good no matter the ethnicity of the advisor. But you could see Estelle's point of view. She had been subtly cajoled into accepting Donna's wisdom by the exotic charisma of her Asian mystique. It had been the sugar that helped the medicine go down. Jerry saw the same thing and accused Donna of being a fraud, trying to trade on an illusory Chinese link to hype up her persona. And I thought that maybe Pema Chödrön was another Donna Chang. How much of the gravity of her teaching stems from a phony Tibetan mystique?

Was Pema much different from a channeler in my local Borders bookstore who claimed to channel the spirit of a Tibetan Buddhist monk? When she transited into her stage presence, she started speaking with a fake Chinese (not Tibetan) accent: "Likee soupee?" Her nonsense would have been nakedly exposed as nonsense without the trumpery, which it should have been anyway.

The larger issue here is another long-standing suspicion I have harbored concerning the integrity of many Americans' professions of Buddhist identity. "I'm a Buddhist," I will hear some people say. And then I will consider it a moment and think, "No, you're not." They'd like to think they are. They'd like others to think they are. But I'm not convinced. Harvey Cox, in his 1977 book, *Turning East*, suggested that the evidence was leading him to believe that Americans had hijacked Buddhism, the discipline of extirpating self and ego, and turned it into one more pop self-*realization* therapy. That's the impression I get, too. Especially when you see in American magazines an article about extinguishing materialistic desire cheek by Hoti jowl with numerous ads for all sorts of Buddhist materialistic goodies, including expensive statues, meditation mats, robes, and so on. Elizabeth Claire Prophet may have the balls to print the name "Gautama Buddha" on a paperback volume of her channeled bullshit, but that doesn't entitle or oblige me to consider it Buddhism.

Pema Chödrön might be entitled to the name if she had assimilated herself into the Buddhist cultural context. I teach Buddhism, too, in a Western academic setting. I need to be neither an Asian nor a Buddhist to do that. But I do not offer Buddhist spiritual counsel, nor am I competent to do so. When I learn that someone positioning herself as a Buddhist sage with the name Pema Chödrön is really Deirdre Blomfield-Brown, I think of the too-prolific paperback author Lobsang Rampa, actually Irish plumber Cyril Henry Hoskin. Why the stage name unless it's a schtick?

Especially when, in the *Sun* interview, we read that our guru

TOP SECRET

Pema "do[es]n't use Buddhist terminology much." This remark is a transparent bit of cheap rhetoric whereby one claims to transcend, with masterful nonchalance, the very tradition one pretends to derive one's authority from. How much credibility would you have in New Age circles if you billed yourself as the Bodhisattva Blomfield-Brown? But maybe there is after all more than meets the third eye here. In this chapter I want to compare Pema Chödrön's teaching (and that of her mentor Trungpa) with certain aspects of the Buddhist tradition. So it might not be a bad idea to summarize traditional Buddhist doctrine (dharma) first.

BUDDHIST EVOLUTION

The earliest Buddhism we know (thriving today in streamlined form as Theravada, "The Way of the Elders," Buddhism) taught that existence is characterized by three basic factors, the three marks of existence. The first is *anicca* (impermanence) or *kshanika* (flux): nothing is unchanging or permanent. Later this leads Buddhist philosophers to posit that things have no dharmas, no abiding natures, no substantial being. All is *maya* (illusion). The second mark is *anatta*: there is no soul, no self. This is the application of *anicca* to the individual. Of course there *seems* to be a self, an ego, the psychological self we measure on personality inventory tests. What Buddhists mean to deny is the eternal spark of the divine (the *Atman*) that Hindu philosophers distinguished from the ego-self (or *jiva*). The ego-self is not permanent or unchanging, so it is no real self (*Atman*). And there is no eternal individual self or soul beyond it. There are only the five *skandhas* (aggregates, component parts) of the ego-self: feelings, perceptions, body, instincts, thoughts.

These are not eternal or unchanging, but continue to change through one incarnation after another until liberation.

The third mark of existence derives from the first two: *dukkha* (suffering)—all life is suffering, and no wonder! We're inevitably frustrated as long as we seek abiding satisfaction in a shifting world (samsara) which itself does not abide and thus cannot provide abiding satisfaction. In fact, according to Buddhism (and Samkhya Hinduism, which may have influenced it), we return for life after life, gluttons for punishment, only because we *desire* to do so! We keep thinking, "If I could only take another stab at it . . . !" So we do! And it never turns out any better. But we never seem to learn. The satisfaction we seek, if we only knew it, is the extinguishing of the raging fever of desire. That satisfaction, accordingly, is called *Nirvana,* which means "extinction" as of a flame, the flames of desire and pain. One attains Nirvana, but one does not "go there," for it is not a place. It is rather a state of mind, and it may, and should, be attained within this life. One who does attain it is beyond the illusion of ego, beyond desire and suffering. There will be no further lives, for one has cut the nerve of samsaric returning by ceasing to desire. Desire, not karma, was what kept the merry-go-round going.

The central doctrine, the way of salvation, in Theravada Buddhism is *the Four Noble Truths.* The first truth is formally like a medical diagnosis: what is ailing you? *Life is suffering.* Buddhism does not put forth the ridiculous claim that everyone is in unremitting misery twenty-four hours a day. To say that life is suffering is more like Schopenhauer's dim view of life as a never-ending pendulum swing between frustration (I lack something and suffer for lacking it) and disappointment (I get it and quickly cease to appreciate it). Every moment of joy or triumph is tainted by the awareness of how fleeting it is. Second comes the etiology, or tracing of the symptoms to the root cause: *Suffering is caused by desire*. Third is the discovery of the antidote: *The cessation of suffering comes by the cessation of desire*. It only hurts when you desire? Then stop desiring! Fourth is the prescription: how do I actually treat the condition? *The cessation of desire comes by the Eightfold Path.*

The first stage of the Eightfold Path is *right knowledge*, acceptance of the Buddhist dharma. Second comes *right aspiration*, the determination to do what must be done, a decision of conversion or repentance. Third is *right speech*, a commitment to truth-telling, or at least to inoffensive speech, the balance between the two being hard to find in any given case. Fourth comes *right behavior*, referring to the basic Five Commandments that form the moral minimum even for Buddhist laity, namely, no lying, no killing of any animal life (Buddhists are vegetarians), no intoxicants, no sex outside marriage, no stealing. Fifth is *right livelihood*, the entrance upon monastic or convent life, since secular life, while not immoral, is nonetheless too distracting to allow the spiritual concentration required for becoming an adept. Sixth is *right effort*, or perseverance upon a toilsome way. Seventh is *right mindfulness*, which refers to a cultivation of full presence of mind in whatever one is doing. This practice will one day give birth to the Zen exercises of the Tea Ceremony, Sacred Archery, and the Drawing of the Sword, all efforts to identify oneself with one's action and to be fully present in it. It also appears to be related to the universal yogic attitude of "mere witness," an impartial, compassionate concern with the world around one, renouncing all vested interests, so that one's good deeds accrue no karma, since that would lead to further rebirths just as evil deeds would. Again, right mindfulness may be taken as denoting the initial stage of meditation, where one's consciousness has not yet transcended the worldly specifics of *namarupa* ("name and form"). Finally, the eighth stage is *right absorption*, the transcendence of name and form. The one who accomplishes this discipline is an Arhat, having attained Nirvana in this lifetime, and will not return for more incarnations.

Mahayana Buddhism has more adherents, extending throughout all of North Asia. *Mahayana* means either/both "greater vehicle" and "greater career." By contrast, Mahayana Buddhists have dubbed Southern, Theravada Buddhists the Hinayana Buddhists, or the "lesser vehicle" or "lesser career." One sometimes hears that "greater vehicle" or "greater raft" means that Mahayana Buddhism is more of a people's faith, less elitist than Theravada, which can be pursued rightly only by monks and nuns. But this is not the point of difference. Both *sanghas* (communities) maintain a two-tier system in which the laity, not yet ready to embark on the rigorous path undertaken by the monks, provide for them and worship the Buddha(s), which service contributes toward their future salvation. The difference here is that Theravada Buddhism promises only reincarnation in one of the heavens as one's reward, not Nirvana. Remember, because liberation is a change of mind and disposition, no one can simply hand it to you as a reward. A free ticket to heaven is another matter, however, and that is in fact available. It is not quite salvation, though. In Mahayana Buddhism, similar adherence to the holy men can bring a much greater return: a head start or even a free ticket to full Buddhahood. Why this difference?

This is just where the "greater career" business comes in. For Mahayana Buddhists came to believe it was the worst of ironies for Buddhists to seek Arhatship, the final attainment of Nirvana for themselves as individuals. How can that be, when the individual self is an illusion? So the goal became much loftier: in Mahayana, the proper goal is not to *be saved* but to *become a savior*, because no one can be saved until everyone is. The implication of this is that all the many Buddhas of the past, including Gautama, have deferred their own entry into Nirvanic bliss and are lingering in their own heavenly worlds to aid seekers, answering prayers, and so on. They are like glorified saints in the Roman Catholic Church, as opposed to the empty heavens of "Protestant" Theravada Buddhism. In Mahayana Buddhism, the elite, the first rank, whom the laity support, may be holy persons who are on the path to Buddhahood themselves (in other words, bodhisattvas) and they may assist the seeker toward a spiritual destiny his own poor karma would never make feasible. Indeed it is this doctrine of the bodhisattva that separated Mahayana Buddhism from its predecessor.

Where did this new understanding come from? Mahayana texts (especially the *Saddharma-Pundarika*, or "Lotus Sutra of the True Law") portray the Buddha as, in his latter days, letting his disciples in on a secret: behind the doctrine they have always believed, and that he first taught them, there lies another, advanced version that makes the first look like nursery school pablum by contrast. The new doctrine, which they could never have accepted earlier, is, of course, the Mahayana Bodhisattva doctrine. Now it is time to grow up and embrace it. Nor must they stumble at its apparent novelty, clinging to outworn playthings—like the Four Noble Truths! This is all a transparent attempt to grandfather subsequent doctrines onto the founder so as to co-opt the pedigree of Theravada Buddhism.

THIS BUDDHA'S FOR YOU

We can witness the bodhisattva doctrine evolving from various important features already present in Theravada Buddhism. First, according to the much-beloved *Jataka Tales*, the Buddha had lived many previous lives accumulating good karma preparing to become worthy of his task. Second, even Theravadins believed Gautama was but the latest in a long chain of revealers, a belief shared with and perhaps derived from the similar Jainist religion. There had been twenty-four Buddhas before him, so it stood to reason that more could become Buddhas after him. Third, once he had been enlightened, the Buddha resisted Mara's temptation to escape samsara and immediately pass into Nirvana, electing instead to remain here for the good of others, to show them the way. Fourth, in the third century BCE the expectation arose that another Buddha, Maitreya, would come in five thousand years, at which time it would be a golden age of salvation. Play your karmic cards right and you'll be born then. At that time it will be as easy to attain Nirvana as it seemed in retrospect to have been in the time of Gautama when thousands were enlightened.

In retrospect it almost seems as if these potent chemicals had to mix together to form the bodhisattva doctrine: the belief that we ought to follow the example of the Buddha, deferring our own salvation to help all other beings, which after all is what he did. And presumably, so must all the previous Buddhas. And if Buddhahood was not unique to Gautama, it must be possible for anyone else with the needful gumption ("right effort"), so why not me? Why not you? It may seem a tall order, but if it took the Buddha himself many lifetimes of pious effort, we can undertake the same long journey. And though most folks will not embrace the bodhisattva path for themselves, they may hang onto the coattails of those who do, by faith, just as Theravada already allowed them to bank on being reborn in Maitreya's day.

ALL THE WORLD'S A STAGE

The bodhisattva doctrine evolves, with these results: the Arhat ideal is replaced by the bodhisattva ideal. One should strive not to be saved, but to become a savior, a Buddha, in one's own right. No one will be saved till all sentient beings are saved. The Four Noble Truths and the Eightfold Path are effectively replaced by the Six Perfections (*paramitas*) and the Ten Stages (*bhumis*). In the first six stages the bodhisattva attains each of the six perfections. Of these, the first is *giving*, the renunciation of property, just as Siddhartha did. The second is *morality* (the same as "right behavior"). The third is *patience*, the fourth *rigor*, the fifth *concentration*, and the sixth *wisdom*—that is, attaining the grasp of a particular esoteric doctrine, that of the Void, or *sunyata*, Emptiness, Thusness, or *tathata*, all of which pretty much amounts to nondualist idealism (see below). At this point, why is the bodhisattva not considered to have arrived already at Buddhahood? He seems to have learned all there is to know! The reason he is yet a bodhisattva is simply that he must recapitulate the last episodes of the Buddha narrative, doing everything Gautama Buddha did.

The seventh stage is the attainment of the seventh perfection, "*nonreturning*." Buddhahood is now inevitable; the bodhisattva has long since ceased accumulating any karma that would impact upon himself and necessitate his rebirth. The perfection of nonreturning answers an old question raised by Theravadin adepts: if you have attained Nirvana, can you kill yourself to prevent backsliding? The answer: once you have really been enlightened, that is nothing to worry about anymore.

Eighth comes a period of longer or shorter celestial existence in the *Sambogkya* (the glorious heaven of Buddhas and bodhisattvas).

During this time the bodhisattva, essentially already a divine savior, may answer prayers, send astral projections of himself to the earth to teach mortals (such projections are called *tulku*s or *tulpa*s), or even descend into hell to suffer for sinners! Such beings are not merely characters in the museum of theology; one may meet an itinerate holy man who has himself taken the bodhisattva vow or has attained to such an advanced degree of holiness that he can recall his previous lives (a feat claimed by many Hindu and Buddhist mystics), when he first undertook his mission. Also, the abbots of certain monasteries may inherit as part of their office the claim to be the *tulku* of a particular bodhisattva, as with the Dalai Lama (see below).

The ninth stage is a return to earth for the last time, to recapitulate the episodes of Gautama's life (though Buddhists would not put it that way, thinking that Gautama, too, just followed an already ancient pattern). This epiphany is not a true incarnation, for the bodhisattva only takes the outward semblance of human flesh. His humanity is a veil of illusion, or *maya*, and in fact his pseudo-incarnate state is called the *Nirmankya*, or "Transformation Body." Those with spiritual insight will see past this seemingly human form to the gigantic, glowing form of the superman beneath the illusion. It is the true spirit-body worn by the bodhisattva in the heavenly realm. Thus the bodhisattva is striving to go the very way the Buddha trod. But he is the exception that proves the rule! The doctrine has really been crafted for the benefit of the vast majority, the lazy laity who welcome the news that a few saviors are competing for their business.

At any rate, this stage takes the bodhisattva up to his taking a seat beneath the Bodhi Tree, as Gautama did. By now, obviously, the whole thing is a charade, a ritual, since there is no greater degree of enlightenment he can get than he got in stage six. He was essentially a Buddha then; the rest is mere formality. Finally, stage ten is (the semblance of) enlightenment at the Bodhi Tree. After this, he preaches until an apparent death, then ascends back to heaven, where he remains, a new Buddha, in the Sambogkaya in the company of other Buddhas and bodhisattvas, until that glorious day when all sentient beings shall have become Buddhas, too. Thus the bodhisattva is undertaking a course of millions of lifetimes of good works to accumulate more good karma than he could possibly need for his own salvation, used instead to share with poor mortals.

That the distinction between Buddha and bodhisattva has become entirely superfluous is evident from the simple fact that in Mahayana mythology the greatest of bodhisattvas is *Avalokitesvara*, "the Lord Who Looks Down" in compassionate providence. He is believed by his *bhaktas* (devotees) to encompass all other Buddhas and bodhisattvas in himself. Like the Virgin Mary and the personified Sabbath in Judaism, he even secures occasional relief for the damned in hell. In China he has become Kwan Yin, goddess of compassion. Avalokitesvara embodies the chief virtue of all the bodhisattvas, *karuna*, or disinterested, impartial compassion toward all beings.

Pure Land Buddhism provides the greatest example and the most extreme form of the bodhisattva doctrine. According to the *Sukhavati Sutras*, ages ago Amitabha Buddha (the Buddha of Infinite Light) vowed to create a Buddha field into which anyone might be reborn simply by virtue of calling on him in faith. Once born into this Pure Land, a world free of the distractions of sin, one would at once attain the stage of nonreturning and would subsequently become a Buddha. It was to this goal that he had dedicated his innumerable lifetimes of effort as a bodhisattva, and he succeeded. Here was a gospel of salvation, even of divinization, by grace through faith in the bodhisattva. This version of Buddhism originated in India, then passed into China, and then into Japan (where the Savior's name is rendered *Amida*). It is obviously quite close to the older Theravada belief in a future Buddha, Maitreya, on whom one might set one's hopes, to guarantee rebirth in his era, when salvation would be easy. Just as obviously, it grossly contradicts the still-earlier Theravada belief that no grace is either necessary or available!

A series of Pure Land patriarchs sought to purify the doctrine of any lingering vestige of reliance on "self power" and to secure complete and total reliance on "other power." Like all Mahayana Buddhists, they viewed the *goal* of Theravada (Hinayana) Buddhism as selfish. But they regarded the *method* of Mahayana Buddhism as self-assertive, relying as it did, at least in the case of the bodhisattva, on self-effort. The focus of the Pure Land school is the karmically bankrupt layman, not the self-sanctifying bodhisattva. Yes, one still aims to "become a savior" all right, but by the grace *of* a savior, which would seem to defeat the original point. According to the patriarch Shinran (1173–1262), founder of the Jodo Shinshu sect (or Shin Buddhism), the mere act of reciting Amida's name is to be taken as irrefutable evidence that Amida's grace has predestined one to salvation. The very moment one chants, one has attained the stage of nonreturning. At the moment of death, one finds oneself in the Pure Land, already fully a Buddha!

IS NOTHING SACRED?

The bodhisattva doctrine fits hand in glove with the doctrine of the Void; indeed, the latter undergirds the former. The greatest exponent of the doctrine of the Void was Nagarjuna (ca. 100–200 CE), who taught a form of nondualism. The doctrine of *maya*, shared with Hinduism, implies that all differences, all diversity and plurality, in the world of perception are illusory. Ultimately there is only the Void (*sunyata*), a pure and undifferentiated field of unitary experience, finally devoid of all the artificial distinctions we introduce so as to "slice the pie" of reality in order, as we think, to "make sense of it." All "truths" are half truths, causing the world to seem divided when it is not.

The Void is also called the *Buddha-nature*. All things "contain" it, since all things are illusory fragments of it. Again, the Void may be viewed as the highest level of experienced reality. (Buddhism does not pretend to describe "reality" per se. There is only experience.) As such it is called the *dharmakaya*, the Truth-Body or Truth-Mode of the Buddha. Buddhists speak of a three-tiered cosmology, centered about the manifestation of the Buddha on each plane. This doctrine is called the *trikaya*, the three bodies of the Buddha. First is the Dharmakaya or "dharma body," the Void of Buddha-nature. Second is the Sambogkya or "enjoyment body," the celestial realm in which the Buddhas and bodhisattvas exist. Third comes the Nirmankya or "transformation body": our world of *maya* in which the Buddhas appear by a phantom birth in a phantom body.

Nagarjuna formulated a dialectic that made possible a more positive evaluation of samsara, the realm of suffering and reincarnation. In this way he supplied the rationale for Buddhist art, but he also provided an undergirding for the bodhisattva doctrine. Remember, Theravada/Hinayana Buddhists sought to flee samsara to gain Nirvana. But Nagarjuna argued that as long as we do not overestimate samsara as real and desirable, as long as we recognize it as a tenuous film on the surface of a bubble, we need not despise its beauty. The world is not evil if one views it in the right per-spective. Samsara gives rise to frustration and suffering only insofar as one seeks from it a satisfaction it cannot offer. But this is not due to some deficiency in samsara. Rather, it is our fault for barking up the wrong tree. If one appreciates it for what it is, one need not despise it for failing to be what it is not. In fact, one must not flee samsara in search of Nirvana, but must instead seek Nir-vana in the very midst of samsara, beneath its outward forms. In light of this understanding, the Mahayana bodhisattva is no longer urgent to flee and shun samsara, as the Theravada Arhat was. He can be "in the world but not of the world." And not only does he seek to redeem the world; all the world is capable of being redeemed because it all contains the Buddha-nature.

The Yogacara School founded by the monks and brothers Vasubandhu (420–500 CE) and Asanga (410–500 CE) taught that the practice of yoga enables us to attain unto the realization of the One-ness which is then seen to be "Mind Only," a kind of collective unconscious. Whereas Theravada Buddhists took the *anatta* doctrine to mean that there is no self other than the *skandhas*, Yogacarins take it to mean there is no self apart from the One Universal Self. In either case, individual selfhood is the illusion. Picture someone with amnesia: part of himself, his past, what lies behind him, is shut off from him. Yogacara Buddhism suggests that each of us is like an amnesiac, only much worse, for we are cut off from the rest of our larger self which lies all around us *right now*, to either side, not just behind. When we imagine we are nothing more than the ego-self, we are wearing blinders and have forgotten what else there is to us now. Again, the importance of this insight for the bodhisattva program is obviously enormous. It is just absurd even to think of saving, much less of "liberating," my individual self! It is a contradiction in terms.

TOP SECRET

Zen Buddhism (the earliest known proponent of which was Bodhidharma, ca. 570 CE) seeks to return to a pure perception of Suchness, the Void minus our illusory distinctions. It aims at a direct apprehension of Thusness beyond *namarupa* ("name and form"), the barrier of words and concepts that supposedly convey reality to us but which actually substitute for it and hide it from us. "Talk doesn't cook the rice," as one famous Zen epigram has it. In other words, talking about enlightenment cannot get us enlightened for the simple reason that words and thoughts, while pretending to convey reality, in fact substitute for it, like currency which stands for but actually substitutes for traded goods and services. One needs to get beyond the veil of words to Suchness. And it is going to take something other than words, other than doctrines, to do the trick.

One implication of the Void doctrine is that there is finally no reality even to the sublime doctrines of Buddhism. Thus they are dispensable, having only utilitarian, instrumental value: if they help you toward *satori* (enlightenment), use them; if not, try something else. Zen monks have tried *koans* (riddles with no logical answer: "What is the sound of one hand clapping?") and sudden arbitrary gestures designed to propel one off the track and into the Void.

Vajrayana Buddhism (in Tibet; also the Shingon school in Japan) is a type of esoteric Buddhism, brought by sorcerer-saint Padma Sambhava from India to Tibet in 747 CE. It appears to represent a mixture of Buddhism with Tantra yoga and native Tibetan Bön shamanism. A notable aspect of Vajrayana Buddhism is its practice of Tantra or Tantric yoga, shared with Shaiva (Shiva-worshiping) Hindus. It is named for the Tantras ("treatises, tracts") in which it is expounded. It is based on another version of the Void doctrine. Tantric doctrine imagines the perceived world of difference and multiplicity, plurality, and so on, as arising from a primordial event analogous to sexual procreation in which the phallic *vajra*, or lightning bolt, fertilized the receptive *gharba* element, and the world was the result. (Sometimes the event is symbolized mythically as a great creator Buddha, Vairocana Buddha.) The Oneness of the Void is not lost but rather still invisibly underlies all things, as we have seen, and the object is to return, in mind and spirit, to that primordial oneness. Rituals designed to effect this passage into a trance state of Oneness aim at trans*cend*ing all worldly distinctions (half truths, remember) by trans*gress*ing them in an elevated, disinterested state of mind ("mere witness," "right mindfulness"). This is called the Left-Handed Path and requires the use of the "five forbidden substances": meat, beans, intoxicants, fish, and sex with a partner not one's spouse. These things would be mortally sinful if partaken of in a worldly attitude, but since they are approached as means of grace, they accrue no karma. One Tantric verse says: "By the same acts that cause some men to boil in Hell for one hundred thousand eons, the yogi gains his eternal salvation." The yogi engages in intercourse with his partner, all the while maintaining a fantastic degree of control over breath and even ejaculation, bringing the whole process to a crashing halt on the verge of climax. At this point he is catapulted, inwardly, back to the primordial state of cosmic Oneness. It is a trance state from which he will again emerge, as from all yogic trance states. But for the duration he has transcended the world.

DRAGON LADY

Pema Chödrön's type of Buddhism is a subsequent offshoot from Vajrayana Buddhism. And as with several dharma innovations summarized above, her tradition seems to have been born from someone's insight that one element of traditional Buddhist faith or practice was logically undermined by another. Mahayana Buddhists noticed that Theravada's Arhat ideal was made moot by a hidden aspect of selfishness. Pure Land Buddhists noticed how the selfless goal of Mahayana nonetheless retained the self-confidence that one possessed the ability to tread the bodhisattva path. Zen Buddhists noticed that the illusory nature of all things must extend equally to the dharma itself, which was thus negotiable. In precisely the same way, Pema's tradition is built on the insight of her preceptor, Chögyam Trungpa, that the quest for enlightenment is itself one more variety of craving, and that one must renounce this, too. Instead, the goal becomes the yogic state of "mere witness."

What is the source of our suffering? In a larger sense it is, of course, desire. But Pema's spin on it is this: we suffer because our posture toward life as it comes at us is to *resist* it and to *redact* it. That is, we tend not to take it as it comes, to go with the flow (à la Buddhism's cousin Taoism), but rather to resist it, to try to reroute or even dam up the river, because we think we would like it better that way. Life comes at us like a novel we are reading, but we cannot seem to just sit back and let the author lead us along. No, we keep wanting to edit it. It spoils a movie when some jerk next to you interrupts with observations such as "I'd have written that differently!" or "They should have done it this way instead!" How strange, then, that we keep interrupting the flowing text of our own experience, wanting to cut this, to rewrite that. Some writers fall prey to the temptation to keep on revising, which is why, for example, J. R. R. Tolkien's *Silmarillion* did not appear until four years after his death. His son had to harmonize a pile of drafts he had left. Some people have the inspiration to write, but they can never get more than a sentence or two down on paper because they cannot let it flow. They keep choking off the Muse, stopping and starting as in a traffic jam, to weigh and second-guess every word choice. It is agony for them to write. And that is how we experience our lives, because we do not like what we think and perceive, or we are told it is not good enough.

The basic misstep is that we early learn to seek comfort and to avoid pain, and this causes us to flee life or to try to edit it. If we are willing simply to experience both pain and pleasure, we will come to understand life and ourselves as we are. That is not just pop psychology; it is the Buddhist doctrine of Suchness (*tathata*). If we try to "improve" ourselves, we are doing an un-Buddhist thing: we are inflicting a subtle kind of aggression upon ourselves (Chödrön, pp. 1–2, 28). Pema says, "there's a kind of basic misunderstanding that we should try to be better than we already are, that we should try to improve ourselves, that we should try to get away from painful things" (p. 26). If we wish to exercise the Buddhist ideal of compassion, we will study ourselves, our thoughts, feelings, and inner speech, *nonjudgmentally*. We will sit back in the state of mere witness and be *mindful* of what is happening within us and without us. "Mindfulness is loving all the details of our lives, and awareness is the natural thing that happens" (p. 57).

But why should we feel it is an attack upon our authentic being to seek to be rid of what are essentially impediments and distortions? Our negativities are not diseases of which we may be healed with more or less negativity. That is the wrong analogy. We might better compare the situation to the Parable of the Wheat and the Tares (Matt. 13:24–30). A farmer's competitor sneaks into his field at night and sows seeds of darnel among the wheat. The two plants look much alike, and their root systems intertwine as they grow.

Once both types of plant begin to sprout, the farmer's workers realize what has happened. "Do you want us to uproot the tares?" they ask him. But he answers, "No, lest in pulling up the tares, you pull up the wheat too. Let both grow together till harvest." Just so, you are now what your experiences, positive as well as negative, have made you. It is too late to uproot the negative without tearing the whole thing asunder: "[O]ur hang-ups, unfortunately or fortunately, contain our wealth. Our neuroses and our wisdom are made out of the same material. If you throw out your neurosis, you also throw out your wisdom" (Chödrön, p. 28). Think of the scene in the movie *Star Trek V: The Final Frontier* when the Vulcan empath Sybok offers to relieve Captain Kirk of his deep-seated pain. Kirk refuses: "Damn it! I *need* my pain!" Yes, he does.

Desire is indeed the root of suffering; Pema's Buddhism does not deny that. But why is desire dysfunctional? In what sense? It makes one reject the reality that is *now*, because, like a stubborn brat making a scene on Christmas morning, what you got is not what you wanted. And perhaps it never will be. This is how desire creates suffering. You forever blame any apple for not being an orange, and the trouble is that you find yourself in an apple orchard! The thing to do is to open your eyes to the wonder of where you are now. "Acknowledging the preciousness of each day is a good way to live" (p. 54). There is the doctrine of impermanence as Nagarjuna redefined it: the fleeting world, so fleeting that it is not quite real, is all the more beautiful and dear because it vanishes so quickly. Every moment, like gold, is the more precious because it is so rare. The point of impermanence is not the pessimism of Ecclesiastes: "Vanity of vanities! All is vanity and a chasing after wind." Rather it is the lesson Faust learned from Mephistopheles: amid the dizzying carousel of life, never say,

"Stay a moment! You are so beautiful!" For then the merry-go-round will grind to a halt. But that is just what we tend to do: we seek to reinforce the illusion of unchanging stability by slowing or arresting change.

This habit of resistance, this doubling up of the rug to trip whoever passes, is another way of talking about the ego. The idea is much like that of Michel Foucault, who called the ego a "rhetorical fold." It is a trick of perspective resulting from the tendency of the experiencer to block off the free passage of experience. Pema says, "resisting the fact that we change and flow like the weather . . . resisting that is what's called ego" (p. 84). And to rid oneself of this charley horse, this squint, is to deny the self, to expunge the ego, as traditional Buddhism taught. But the goal is not to "improve yourself" because you don't like the hand you were dealt. No, it is precisely the opposite: to remove the obstacle of selection in perception, and to let the river flow free again. "If we don't protect ourselves from the trueness and the vividness and the immediacy and the lack of confirmation of simply being a part of life, then we are not this separate being who has to have things turn out our way" (p. 86).

The Mahayana realization that Buddhist doctrines, too, being purely instrumental, lack any stable reality, have no dharmas, is reflected in Pema's suspicion of orthodoxies and belief systems. A creedal belief shuts out everything not allowed. It is no longer perceived. "Holding on to beliefs limits our experience of life" (p. 70) because one's world is effectively produced by one's belief system (p. 73).

What sort of meditation might one expect to accompany such Buddhism? For one thing, it must not be a striving to extinguish mundane consciousness, except in the sense, mentioned just above, of removing curbs and defensive blocks on experience. In traditional meditation one is typically told to concentrate on a mantra or a candle flame or the end of one's nose, anything to focus attention. If one's mind starts to drift into thinking about this or that, one ought to gently bring oneself back to the subject at hand. But Pema's practice is rather different. One seeks simply to let consciousness and perception flow over one without obstruction. It is consistent with the Mahayana insight that Nirvana may be found right here in the midst of samsara. It is of a piece with the Zen *koan*, "What is Zen [which means 'meditation']? It is your everyday speech." "Meditation is a process of lightening up, or trusting the basic goodness of what we have and who we are, and of realizing that any wisdom that exists, exists in what we already have" (p. 9). Thus the meditator does not renounce ordinary thought but seeks enlightenment through the back door: by renouncing the "craving" for enlightenment! It is only when one catches oneself beginning to judge and to evaluate, to approve or disapprove, or when one's thoughts begin to blink at the bright light of the present moment, seeking retreat into the past or the future, that one needs to call oneself back to the path of mere witness (pp. 47, 77). "One of the main discoveries of meditation is seeing how we continually run away from the present moment, how we avoid being here just as we are. That's not considered a problem; the point is to see it" (p. 5). "The basic point of it all is just to learn to be extremely honest and also wholehearted about what exists in your mind—thoughts, emotions, bodily sensations, the whole thing that adds up to what we call 'me' or 'I'" (p. 46). But is this not a Buddhism remarkably tolerant of "I" and "me"? Is this not rather far off the beaten Eightfold Path? No, I think it is not. Pema is still speaking in terms of the "I" being a composite synthesis, not a unitary entity as Hinduism would suppose. Note the wording: "thoughts, emotions, bodily sensations, the whole thing that adds up to 'me' or 'I.'" These are the *skandhas*, the aggregate parts of what we have *instead* of an *Atman*.

What is the goal of Pema's version of Vajrayana? It sounds as if tailored to secular Western sensibilities, as may in fact be the case. But the result does seem to be in true continuity with Buddhist understanding. For instance, these words imply more of a this-worldly preoccupation than one might expect from Buddhism:

> The ground of loving-kindness is this sense of satisfaction with who we are and what we have. The path is a sense of wonder . . . wanting to know the unknowable things, beginning to question everything. We know we're never really going to find the answers, because these kinds of questions come from having a hunger and a passion for life—they have nothing to do with resolving anything or tying it all up into a neat little package. This kind of questioning is the journey itself. (p. 11)

Would a classical Buddhist recognize any of this? Well, Mahayana Buddhists have always realized there is no urgency to escape from this world, this life, as if Nirvana lay somewhere else, since it lurks beneath our feet, just waiting to be noticed. As for the incessant questioning, that is the essence of Zen, for there is but a thin line between "wonderment" at what one can never account for and "wondering" how to account for it. The Buddha spoke of "questions that tend not unto edification," referring to sophistical distractions from the proper business of enlightenment. But suppose enlightenment consists of a constant sense of wonder along with the satisfaction of remaining perpetually agape with astonishment? Desire is defeated when one realizes that the empty cup is full of the plenitude of the Void. The Void, after all, is a lack of what one does not need. "By 'cessation' we mean . . . the cessation of this resistance, this resentment . . . , trying to maintain this huge ME at any cost" (p. 86). And yet Pema's dharma does not promote the pathology of self-hate, something that frightens many of us away from Buddhism. No, "the idea isn't to get rid of ego but actually to begin to take an interest in ourselves, to investigate and be inquisitive about ourselves" (p. 4).

BUDDHISM WITHOUT *MAYA*

In J. D. Salinger's fascinating book *Franny and Zooey* (1961) we witness a dialogue between a college woman, Franny Glass, and one of her older brothers, Zooey. The pair find themselves at very different places in their spiritual pilgrimages. Franny has just had something of a breakdown brought on by her incessant chanting of the Eastern Orthodox Jesus Prayer, a kind of devotional mantra, or, as her brother suspects, by various life stresses from which she has sought to take refuge in meditation. For himself, Zooey feels he has graduated from spiritual sophomorics. He holds a view of spiritual matters that is about equal portions cynicism and deep respect. And he tries to impart some of his hard-won wisdom to Franny:

> As a matter of simple logic, there's no difference at all, that *I* can see, between the man who's greedy for material treasure—or even intellectual treasure—and the man who's greedy for spiritual treasure. As you say, treasure's treasure, God damn it, and it seems to me that ninety per cent of all the world-hating saints in history were just as *acqui*sitive and unattractive, basically, as the rest of us are. (p. 148)

It looks as if Pema Chödrön's mentor Chögyam Trungpa arrived at pretty much the same destination:

> We may feel these spiritual collections to be very precious. We have studied so much. We may have studied Western philosophy or Oriental philosophy, practiced yoga or perhaps have studied under dozens of great masters. We have achieved and we have learned. We believe that we have accumulated a hoard of knowledge. . . . Our vast collections of knowledge and experience are just part of ego's display, part of the grandiose quality of ego. We display them to the world and, in so doing, reassure ourselves that we exist, safe and secure, as "spiritual" people. But we have simply created a shop, an antique shop. We could be specializing in oriental antiques or medieval Christian antiques or antiques from some other civilization or time, but we are, nonetheless, running a shop. (p. 15)

Just as Jesus called people to renounce material wealth to follow him, Trungpa summons his disciples to renounce their spiritual wealth. It is not as simple as a criticism of "spiritual pride," the self-flattery of the puffed-up know-it-all who mistakes a big data bank for piety. No, Trungpa is saying something that goes deeper and is much more subtle: spirituality itself, even when genuine, may be an obstacle to true enlightenment. "Eventually we must give up trying to be something special. . . . What is really needed is for you to stop caring altogether, to completely drop the whole concern" (p. 59). In his 1970–71 set of lectures, already regarded as a classic, *Cutting through Spiritual Materialism*, the Westernized lama set forth a sort of "spirituality among the ruins" ideal. One might call it the dharma of disillusionment. In these talks

TOP SECRET

Trungpa performed another of those periodic exercises in ruthless self-scrutiny that has prompted the generation of new Buddhist sects and systems. One sees the settled result of this sort of thinking in his disciple Pema Chödrön, but in these lectures by her master, one sees the violent birth pangs of the perspective.

Contrary to Matthew 7:15–16, one cannot always distinguish false prophets by their fruits. That is, a teacher may prove personally unworthy of the mantle he bears. He or she may utterly fail to live up to his or her teaching, but that might be for any number of reasons. The teaching may still be good. And yet in this case, one must approach Trungpa's teaching with the question in mind: Did he set the bar too low? Does his anticlimactic spirituality make it easy to ask too little of oneself, as it seems he did? Indeed, reading some of his preachments in light of his later-revealed sexual exploits can be chilling.

> At the beginning a kind of courtship with the guru is taking place, a love affair. . . . A kind of love-hate relationship, a kind of surrendering and running away process develops. In other words, we begin to play a game, a game of wanting to open, wanting to be involved in a love affair with our guru, and then wanting to run away from him. . . . You tend to get too close to the teacher, but once you do, you get burned. (p. 43)

But enough of that. Time to look at his ideas. Trungpa's central insight can be summed up in one striking and devastating passage:

> Many people make the mistake of thinking that, since ego is the root of suffering, the goal of spirituality must be to conquer and destroy ego. They struggle to eliminate ego's heavy hand but . . .

that struggle is merely another expression of ego. We go around and around, trying to improve ourselves through struggle, until we realize that the ambition to improve ourselves is itself the problem. Insights come only when there are gaps in our struggle, only when we stop trying to rid ourselves of thought, when we cease siding with pious, good thoughts against bad, impure thoughts, only when we allow ourselves simply to see the nature of thought. . . . We need only drop the effort to secure and solidify ourselves and the awakened state is present. . . . We must walk a spiritual path. [But] ego must wear itself out like an old shoe, journeying from suffering to liberation. (p. 153)

It seems to me that Trungpa is making things difficult for his disciples nonetheless, for he seems to be promising them this letting go of illusions is a climax to which they cannot come until they have come to the point of exhausted frustration in conventional pursuit of enlightenment. Only then can they recognize the centrality of ego in the spiritual work at which they were so busy, and without apparent result. They reach a point of Socratic humility, becoming at last spiritual enough to see that they have only been exalting ego all along. But knowing that such a crossroads lies somewhere ahead doesn't get you there automatically (p. 202). Worse yet, knowing it lies up ahead makes it difficult to take the struggle to get there seriously enough to become frustrated with it. You already know it is a dead end! Hasn't it become a charade? Well, yes, I think so. But I am reminded of exactly the same charade that is a canonized spiritual discipline in the bodhisattva doctrine: the Ten Stages. Passing through this course one supposedly repeats the progress of Gautama Buddha, stage by stage, as he zeroed in on enlightenment and finally attained it. And yet no one embarks on the bodhisattva path unless he already knows good and well the doctrine that Gautama discovered at the end of the game. So how can one really repeat his struggle? It is a charade, a ritual recapitulation. Maybe Trungpa has created the same paradox, and maybe that paradox is maddening enough to bring the aspirant to the goal of frustration by a different route! "There is tremendous energy in realizing that we have given up trying to become the Buddha, that now we have the time to really live life, that we have gone beyond neurotic speed" (p. 176).

Trungpa advocates meditation as a means to attain unto the experience of *sunyata*, the Void. That much is basic to all Mahayana Buddhists, including the Tibetan Vajrayana. But what exactly does he mean by it? We have already glimpsed it in our discussion of Pema Chödrön's approach to meditation. But there is more to say about it. Trungpa lays the groundwork for their shared approach. Progress toward the Void, or Thusness, is progress beyond the realm of *namarupa*, name and form. Why? And what is it like when one arrives? First we must understand that we make the world we live in by naming it, ascribing meanings and value judgments to things and events. "We tend to conceptualize the object, which means that at this point we are no longer able to perceive things as they actually are. We have created a kind of padding, a filter, a veil between ourselves and the object" (p. 197). Often we do not decide on these values and definitions ourselves but have inherited them and taken them for granted. But we continue to project our constellation map onto the heavens, and we still think we see the bears, the centaur, the dragon, Princess Andromeda, belted Orion, and so on. The claim is not that we conjure the physical "reality" into being as a solipsistic dream. Nor it is just that the "meaning" of what surrounds us is not inherent in it but is projected onto it by ourselves. "Belief in anything is simply a way of labeling the mystery" (p. 194). And we ourselves receive an illusory appearance of reality by casting ourselves in the role of observers of the world and therefore objects within it (pp. 11, 122, 126). This dynamic corresponds to Jacques Lacan's "mirror stage" in personal development in which the child begins to form a self-image by associating himself among those he sees around him.

So what do we do about it? Would there be any advantage in ceasing to perceive the universe in the categories in which it makes sense to us? Remember the Zen saying: "Before I found enlightenment, a mountain was just a mountain. When I was enlightened, a mountain was no longer a mountain. Since I was enlightened, a mountain is just a mountain again." The enlightened meditator who penetrates the screen of projections to see what lies beyond sees the world again, but he has gained a new perspective on it, and beyond it. I am reminded of the Sophists, contemporaries of Socrates. They traveled around the Mediterranean, studying various societies. When they returned to Athens, they realized that the Athenian way was not the only way. But that did not mean it was not a perfectly good way, a good enough way. Their perspective had changed. It is the same with Buddhist meditation.

In the Mahavi pashana meditation practiced by Trungpa the method is, first of all, not to look to the future state of anticipated enlightenment. No, meditation is a matter of mindfully inhabiting the present moment. To look to the future with yearning or expectation assures your never getting there (p. 121). Let the future take care of itself. Put another way, you will never experience any future, only a series of ever new nows. So concentrate there. One tries to refrain from naming and judging and evaluating. One exists in the state of *mere witness*. One sees things in their unutterable *suchness* when one sees them in their *otherness*, not defining them in one's own terms or in any terms at all (pp. 169, 182, 188, 190). And since we created our world by naming and valuing it, this sort of meditation will help us dismantle that world. Doing so is attaining the Void. And what is that like? "Meditation practice is not an attempt to enter into a trance-like state of mind" (p. 153). "Having an experience of shunyata does not mean that the whole world completely dissolves into space" (p. 201). "Finally we come down to earth, we see things as they are. This does not mean having an inspired mystical vision with archangels, cherubs, and sweet music playing. . . . It is a question of seeing the world in a direct way without desiring 'higher' consciousness or significance or profundity. It is just directly perceiving things literally, as they are in their own right" (pp. 189–90). So what? "One begins to realize that whatever we do in everyday life is beautiful and meaningful. . . . You become aware that each precise moment has dignity. . . . Every act of our lives can contain simplicity and precision and can thus have tremendous beauty and dignity" (p. 156).

And this includes oneself. We have already seen that Trungpa warns the meditator not to try to flog his mind till it contains only true and noble thoughts. Pema Chödrön says the same. Just observe, unblinkingly and nonjudgmentally, what passes before your mind, your inner speech. But is not this to set the bar too low? Shouldn't we seek sanctification? No. Sanctification may be well and good, but, like happiness, it does not come by being sought.

> If we are speaking of a way out all the time, then we are dealing in fantasy, the dream of escape, salvation, enlightenment. We need to be practical. We must examine what is here, now, our neurotic mind. Once we are completely familiar with the negative

aspects of the state of our being, then we know the "way out" automatically. (Trungpa, p. 118)

Isn't that just what the Buddha did? He had to discern what the problem was, and then the solution appeared as a matter of course. He had to come to grips with suffering and craving before their remedy became plain, and then it did!

Speaking of looking back from the heightened perspective of Buddhist enlightenment to the mundane world, it is arresting to recognize how little the dharma of Chögyam Trungpa and Pema Chödrön depends upon any metaphysical much less supernatural assumptions. It is rather a way of regarding one's experience. Admittedly, Buddhists have traditionally offered opinions on questions like reincarnation, unseen worlds and natures, and so on, but the sort of radical Buddhism we are considering here regards all that as a set of questions that do not edify—unless, that is, we use them to stretch our minds and reignite our sense of wonder. Such ostensible entities are examples of "spiritual materialism" that must be cut through. If taken literally, they become creedal blinders that stifle our awareness rather than expand it. Secularists and skeptics cannot easily dismiss it. It would be misleading to call this dharma "religious." That, too, would be a cheap attempt to evade the mystery by labeling it.

Chapter 4

Practicing the Present

Eckhart Tolle, *The Power of Now: A Guide to Spiritual Enlightenment*

ANYWHERE BUT HERE, ANYTIME BUT NOW

Jacques Derrida, the great philosopher of deconstruction, carried on a tireless crusade against what he called "Presence Metaphysics." He was referring, in particular, to the claim of René Descartes that whatever *appeared* clearly and distinctly true in the mirror of the mind *was* necessarily true. For Descartes, all certainty depended upon this precept, this intuition. But Derrida turned Descartes's certainty upside down. Derrida, hardly claiming to be the first to do so, pointed out that what seems to the perceiver as the present moment, a glimpse of raw and unmediated experience, is in fact a construct, a product, and that, if one looks close enough, one can learn to spot the seams. As Wilhelm Dilthey had said in the nineteenth century, what seems the simple present moment is in fact a composite of the future and the past. From the past one inherits at least the categories of meaning into which one will, by interpretation, place new "present" events. From the future one receives a horizon of hopes, plans, and intentionality. Everything in every "now" moment is seen as a recurrence or a fulfillment or a defiance of the past, not something in its own right. Every present moment is considered a stepping-stone toward or a partial arrival of the future. Without the shadows of the past and the dawning rays of the future, we could not read that pattern of light and shadow cast on the present that enables us to read "meaning" across its barren expanse. As soon as we open the envelope, the sheet inside meets our eyes as "pre-inscribed" by the conditioning of the past and the anticipation of the future. And thus, says Derrida, we have no access to some self-evident, tacit, raw truth of the present moment. Whatever we think to experience then and there in all its freshness is formulated, edited, composed. It is never a field of virgin snow; the sun of perception already dawns on a field bearing countless crisscrossed tracks.

From this Derrida did not (nor do we have to) conclude that the present is an illusion, except, of course, in the sense that it is always slipping through our clutching fingers. What one might conclude instead, though, is that the present should be defined as a timeless state of mind or awareness, and one with no defined content. The error of Presence Metaphysics, said Derrida, was the erroneous belief that whatever *notion* or *idea* seems clear in the now-moment is veridical. As I understand Buddhism, it cherishes the same insight. If one could strip away the categories through which we color and interpret raw experience, what we would then experience would be sheer Thusness or Suchness (*tathata*). It would be a plenitude of emptiness, a Void, empty of all divisions, dichotomies, differences, distinctions, and definitions. Just perceiving *as is*. I think Derrida's deconstruction fits this approach perfectly. Just as the Buddha argued that there is no soul and really meant that what we think of as the soul is an illusion, so Derrida really intended, I think, to say that what we think of as Presence is not. We look at the writing on the page and think it has always been there on the page, like the watermark of the stationery. But what if there is a way to get hold of virgin paper on which no one, least of all ourselves, has ever written? That is the goal of Zen, and it is also the goal of spiritual writer Eckhart Tolle.

HE'LL TELL YOU IF YOUR SIN'S ORIGINAL

Tolle diagnoses the inauthenticity, the fatal distractedness of the run of humankind, as a kind of universal neurosis, stemming from some primordial flinching from the pure light of Being, or of Presence. This trauma was not something that happened to our first ancestors and which they passed on down to us, like a crippling mutation. No, rather Tolle is thinking of a fall from Presence that every individual undergoes, sooner rather than later.

> Ego is the unobserved mind that runs your life when you are not present as the witnessing consciousness, the watcher. The ego perceives itself as a separate fragment in a hostile universe, with no real inner connection to any other being, surrounded by other egos which it either sees as a potential threat or which it will attempt to use for its own ends. The basic ego patterns are designed to combat its own deep-seated fear and sense of lack. They are resistance, control, power, greed, defense, attack. Some of the ego's strategies are extremely clever, yet they never truly solve any of its problems, simply because the ego itself is the problem. (p. 150)

TOP SECRET

It would be hard not to see the resemblance to Buddhism and Hinduism in this, and indeed, as we go along, we will observe how fully Tolle appears to have made his own way to Buddhism. In my judgment, Tolle looks to have done what Deepak Chopra pretends to have done: made his own journey of discovery, without following the directions of an established path, only to find himself paralleling its trajectory and finally ending up at the same destination. Thus it does greater justice to his work if we follow something like Tolle's own path to his conclusion, which seems to have proceeded along the lines of an inquisitive phenomenology of consciousness. So, rather than rush to comparisons with Buddhist dharma, I would rather point out a helpful parallel to the thinking of Reinhold Niebuhr, who, like Tolle, was a German, but became an American neoorthodox theologian (he belonged to the Evangelical and Reformed Church before it merged with Congregationalism to form the United Church of Christ). Whereas liberal Protestant theologians were willing to chop off aspects of the Christian tradition they found outmoded or superstitious, the mark of neoorthodoxy was to try to retain as much of the old creeds as possible by reinterpreting them at those points where they seemed to contain wisdom, but in a premodern dress. As Niebuhr himself famously said, one may not be able to take them literally, but one still ought to take them seriously. Original sin was one such doctrine. Niebuhr sought to make sense of St. Augustine's doctrine that sin is constituted by "concupiscence," the overweening desire for something not properly one's own.

The way Niebuhr sees it, all of us become self-aware as one cell in a larger organism, a state in which we ought to find contentment in an interdependent fellowship of others like us. Every cell makes its contribution and meanwhile benefits from the care and contribution of the others. The normal and healthy attitude, then, should be one of peaceful trust. The community, the larger body, will see to one's welfare, as one does his share to care for everyone else. But the more one becomes aware of one's individuality, the more one begins to fear deprivation: how can we be sure our needs will be met? Perhaps I had best make my own future as sure as I can by seizing not only my share but that of another, even of as many others as I can. In this way, beginning from this root of paranoid insecurity, we isolate ourselves from others. And the tendency spreads like an infection. The more individual cells of the body become selfish and self-seeking, the more foolish it seems to the rest not to adopt the same tragic policy.

MYSTERIES OF THE ATAVACHRON

To pursue the Freudian metaphor of alienation from the present as a neurosis, we might observe that the trauma, buried however deeply, will make itself known in far-reaching symptoms. Freud would agree with Tolle (or perhaps vice versa) that the repressed neurosis of fleeing Presence shows itself perhaps most strikingly in our unwitting insistence on living life as a continually replaying loop of the past, specifically, the dysfunctional past, whether or not we understand what made it dysfunctional. We so fear risking a new trauma in the now that we retreat into the past. Our past is traumatic, but at least it is the devil we know. A new risk that went badly might have the disadvantage of being even worse! Like Oedipus, our very plans for avoiding the trauma lead us directly to fulfill it! "What you perceive as future is an intrinsic part of your state of consciousness now. If your mind carries a heavy burden of past, you will experience more of the same. The past perpetuates itself through lack of presence. The quality of your consciousness at this moment is what shapes your future" (Tolle, pp. 49–51).

This is what New Thoughters mean by "the law of attraction." Like attracts like. Specifically, negative attitudes inside one's head bring about negative external conditions to match them. But none of this involves anything spooky or paranormal. It is a matter of simple psychology and of selective perception, and of sending out subtle signals that invite negative reactions. "When you deny emotional pain, everything you do or think as well as your relationships become contaminated with it. You broadcast it, so to speak, as the energy you emanate, and others will pick it up subliminally. [Even if] they are unconscious [of your signals] they may even feel compelled to attack or hurt you in some way, or you may hurt them in an unconscious projection of your pain. You attract and manifest whatever corresponds to your inner state" (p. 185). Isn't that pretty much the same as Freud's notion of "the return of the repressed"?

I cannot help but think of a *Star Trek* episode in which all the inhabitants of a distant planet had to flee their world because of an impending nova. They were technologically advanced, but their genius lay in time travel, not space travel. So the entire populace chose different past eras of planetary history and went back in time via a time portal called the Atavachron. Thus when the end came, there was no one left to greet it. They had all died years or centuries before, after a long life—in the past! That is what we try to do: escape the dangers of the present by retreating into the past. Oh, we know our history! We are well aware of the inconveniences, even the terrible dangers of the past, but at least those pains are known, and we would rather stick with them. "A victim identity is the belief that the past is more powerful than the present, which is the opposite of the truth. It is belief that other people and what they did to you are responsible for who you are now, for your emotional pain or your inability to be your true self" (p. 140).

We often speak of "carrying baggage" from old traumas and disappointments. We do not merely mean that we retain memories. We mean that the old wounds are still bleeding, still painful, still open, because we keep opening them. Jainists speak of a "karma body" that builds up in an almost material way around the core of one's soul. The more of it comes to encase us, the faster we sink. In like manner, Eckhart speaks of "the pain-body" of the past that we carry like a corpse chained to us. "As long as you make an identity for yourself out of the pain, you cannot become free of it. As long as part of your sense of self is invested in your emotional pain, you will unconsciously resist or sabotage every attempt that you make to heal that pain. . . . The pain-body is an energy-field, almost like an entity, that has become temporarily lodged in your inner space. It is life energy that has become trapped, energy that is no longer flowing . . . It *is* the living past in you, and if you identify with it, you identify with the past" (p. 140).

BACK TO THE FUTURE

Those people in the *Star Trek* episode could only choose portals to the past, not the future, because their planet had none. It would soon be a cinder. But we do have the future as an imagined route of escape. And we take it just as often, Tolle reminds us. The ego "constantly projects itself into the future to ensure its continued survival and to seek some kind of release or fulfillment there. It says, 'One day, when this, that, or the other happens, I am going to be okay, happy, at peace" (p. 18). We discount the present moment as a mere rehearsal for opening night. "If you then become excessively focused on the goal, . . . the Now is no longer honored. It becomes reduced to a mere stepping stone to the future, with no intrinsic value" (p. 47). We think of our lives now as a run-through for the real thing, calisthenics before the big game. "Are you waiting to start living? If you develop such a mind pattern, no matter what you achieve or get, the present will never be good enough; the future will always seem better" (p. 71).

We may even justify moral compromises in this way, "under the implicit assumption that the highest good lies in the future and that therefore the end justifies the means" (p. 48). Our acts seem to us as (merely present) means to an end, which will be realer and better. In that far-off day we will scarcely remember what we "had" to do now, and so already we treat our dubious deeds as only half real, already fading phantoms. "'One day I'll make it.' Is your goal taking up so much of your attention that you reduce the present moment to a means to an end?" (p. 71).

"The future is an imagined Now, a projection of the mind. When the future comes, it comes as the Now" (p. 41). We spurn the living present for the imagined future. And it is not only imagined but actually imaginary because it will never come! Oh, tomorrow will come all right, but when it does, it will seem to us merely another "today" to endure on the way to an ever-receding future. As long as we are in the mode of anticipation, we simply cannot recognize it when the promise is fulfilled. It slips right by us because we are focused too far ahead, off in the mist. In the Gospel of Thomas, the disciples ask Jesus when the kingdom of God was due to arrive. His reply catches them up short: "What you expect has arrived, only you do not recognize it!" Indeed, Eckhart tells us, whether it has come or is still on its way is all a matter of perspective: Where are you looking? If you look about you now, in the present moment, you will find the kingdom of God. It was always right there under your nose. But if you insist on looking into the future you will never see anything that is not far off. "Waiting is a state of mind. Basically, it means that you want the future; you don't want the present. You don't want what you've got, and you want what you haven't got" (p. 71). You will have become farsighted in the eye-doctor sense: you *cannot* see the things that are *close* to you!

We suffer from "an endless preoccupation with past and future and an unwillingness to honor the present moment and *allow it to be*. The compulsion arises because the past gives you an identity and the future holds the promise of salvation, of fulfillment in whatever form. Both are illusions" (p. 40).

BLACK HOLE SUN

Well, Eckhart Tolle is asking and answering the question of why the human race always gives in to concupiscence, seeking for the one what was for the good of all (including the one). It is no accident. The first step down the slippery slope was the isolation of the ego itself, the withdrawing of one's hand from the grasp of one's neighbor's to form a clenching, selfish fist. The rest is a matter of course. The individual ego is the root of the problem. By cutting itself off from its wider identity and the source of its completion, it flees from the Presence which is empty of all such frivolous distinctions.

All cravings [remember concupiscence here, as well as Buddhist "desiring," *tanha*] are the mind seeking salvation or fulfillment in external things and in the future as a substitute for the joy of Being. As long as I am in my mind, I am these cravings, these needs, wants, attachments, and aversions, and apart from them there is no "I" except as a mere possibility, an unfulfilled potential, a seed that has not yet sprouted. In that state, even my desire to become free or enlightened is just another craving for fulfillment or completion in the future. (p. 25)

Tolle notes that "people will often enter a compulsive pursuit of ego-gratification and things to identify with in order to fill this hole they feel within. So they strive after possessions, money, success, power, recognition, or a special relationship, basically so that they can feel better about themselves, feel more complete. But even when they attain all these things, they soon find that the hole is still there, that it is bottomless" (p. 37). One might think of the "black holes" theorized by astronomers to explain the bending light where there appears to be no planetary body to attract it. The theory goes that the light thus pulled slightly off course has narrowly escaped the sucking pit of a star in its last stages of collapse. A superannuated star first expands into a red giant, having exhausted all its other elements. Then it goes nova in a terrific explosion. What is left, particularly dense elements, contracts to form a white dwarf star. In some cases, the great density of such an object entails such powerful gravity that hitherto irrelevant laws of physics begin to operate so that the star core commences to collapse upon itself *infinitely*. The denser it becomes in this manner, the greater the concomitant gravity becomes, until not even photons can escape the irresistible suction. This means the "star" is now absorbing light rather than emitting it. It has become a black hole, and anything passing nearby will be drawn ineluctably into its maw. Light passing just far enough away to avoid being swallowed altogether still may be yanked slightly off course.

The ego-self, then, fears and shuns the Void of the Now-moment, Presence, so it seeks desperately to fill that void and to silence the inevitable sense of yearning it feels for that with which it dares not satisfy itself. Not surprisingly, nothing works. The more possessions and achievements get sucked into the vortex, the stronger the suction and the greater the yearning. The nature of that which causes the suction guarantees that merely shoveling more and more into it will never satisfy it. And this is why, Buddhists say, craving is the origin of suffering, since it can never, in the nature of the case, be satisfied, only transcended. How does one do that? Oddly enough, as Tantric Buddhists say, the Void is somehow also like a womb. It is fertilized by the lightning strike of enlightenment (much as primordial lightning blasts ignited life in the rich stew of the chemical oceans of the newly made earth). And this imagery suggests that the Void is a portal that wants to face *outward*. It is a birth canal. (And thus it is a perfect example of what Derrida calls, metaphorically, "the hymen," a concept in which the direction of logic and signification is indeterminate and seems to go both ways.) One's task is somehow to brace the walls of the Void open, stop trying to clog the space, so that what is on the other side may emerge into consciousness. What seeks to emerge from it into our world? Why, a new Selfhood, and one harmonious with pure, inarticulate, uninscribed Being. It would be a Selfhood that does not cut itself off from the rest of Being by defining and judging it. The ongoing result would be a state the yogis call "mere witness," a perspective on life from which one is moved to admire all and have compassion upon all, instead of trying to secure one's ego by possessing and devouring everything in one's path.

Surrender is the simple but profound wisdom of *yielding to* rather than *opposing* the flow of life. The only place where you can experience the flow of life is the Now, so to surrender is to accept the present moment unconditionally and without reservation. It is to relinquish inner resistance to what *is*. Inner resistance is to say "no" to what *is*, through mental judgment and emotional negativity. It becomes particularly pronounced when things "go wrong," which means that there is a gap between the demands or rigid expectations of your mind and what *is*. That is the pain gap. If you have lived long enough, you will know that things "go wrong" quite often. It is precisely at those times that surrender needs to be practiced if you want to eliminate pain and sorrow from your life. Acceptance of what *is* immediately frees you from mind identification and thus reconnects you with Being. Resistance *is* the mind. (pp. 171–72)

As Michel Foucault said that the "I" is a "rhetorical fold," a trick of the light accidentally produced by the practice of speech, so Tolle is saying that the ego is nothing more, at its root, than a foolish Maginot Line built up to fortify oneself against resistless incursions from the outside world. Inevitably the guns you have posted along that fortress wall will be turned against its defenders. This is the suffering of the ego. It only suffers because it is swimming against the current. Heidegger says something similar: as we map ourselves and the worlds of our experience, we learn our limitations/capabilities by "bumping up" against the walls, like a prisoner exploring his lightless cell. Only Tolle is talking about pathology: beating our heads against the wall!

It is natural, though sophomoric, to object that Tolle appears to be counseling pathological passivity. What do you do when your tire goes flat on the highway. Just sit there and smile till the gents in the white coats show up? No, rather it is a matter of whether you see the problem as a mountain or a molehill, an obstacle or a challenge. "'Problem' means that you are dwelling on a situation mentally without there being a true intention or possibility of taking action now and that you are unconsciously making it a part of your sense of self" (p. 54). "Wouldn't you know it? I'm the kind of guy this always happens to, dammit! I guess the world's just out to get me!"

> Once you have identified with some form of negativity, you do not want to let go, and on a deeply unconscious level, you do not want positive change. It would threaten your identity as a depressed, angry, or hard-done-by person. You will then ignore, deny or sabotage the positive in your life. This is a common phenomenon. It is also insane. (p. 157)

Haven't you ever tried to cheer up a depressed friend and get them to see new solutions to their problems, new avenues forward for their lives—only to be rebuffed by a defensive array of excuses? This would never work because of that. That would never work because of this. If only it were as obvious to us when we are inside this bubble what a chain of bad excuses they are! How can we not see the nature of the Maginot Line mentality we have structured, and that we have built it to keep our own liberators at bay?

TODAY IS THE DAY OF SALVATION

We began with a comparison between Eckhart Tolle and Jacques Derrida. Here is another. Derrida speaks much of *différance*, a neologism by which he means to denote the element of language that inevitably defers and delays meaning. Each word we understand is a brick placed in the wall of a vast structure of overall meaning which we hope one day to sit back and admire, then to move into. This expectation passed from Greek Logos philosophy into Christian theology. In that context one speaks of that day when we will no longer know in part, but in full, when we shall know as we are known. In that day we will at last experience the "Parousia," the Presence of the Logos, the returned Christ, whose advent will answer all questions, right all wrongs, and wipe away every tear. One day we will know. One day, meaning will become clear. But Derrida says it can never happen. Any truth one expects to be made manifest in language is never going to come present, and this is, again, because of the nature of language itself. It is *differential*, not *referential*. Words are defined based on their contrasts and comparisons to the words next to them in the dictionary and in our minds. They are like adjacent jigsaw pieces. The shape of no individual piece makes any sense by itself; it assumes sense only in association with an adjacent piece. Words point to one another. Words stem from definitions and point toward still other words. Ultimately language cannot convey pure Truth because of the self-referentiality of it. It is finally like the experience every student has of looking up a word only to find that the ostensible definition of the word contains the word itself! Final meaning is never going to arrive. Nor can it, for the "final," that is, certain or definitive, meaning of a text, even of a single sentence, remains forever open to debate. We look to the future, even to the "future" of completely understanding a lone sentence, in vain.

Likewise, Eckhart Tolle is saying, as I read him, that the fulfillment we seek can be discovered only in the present moment, that now from which we flee because we imagine fulfillment lies in another direction, that of the future (or the past).

> True salvation is a state of freedom—from fear, from suffering, from a perceived state of lack and insufficiency and therefore from all wanting, needing, grasping, and clinging. It is freedom from compulsive thinking, from negativity, and above all from past and future as a psychological need. Your mind is telling you that you cannot get there from here. Something needs to happen, or you need to become this or that before you can be free and fulfilled. It is saying, in fact, that you need time—that you need to find, sort out, do, achieve, acquire, become, or understand something before you can be free and complete. You see time as the means to salvation, whereas in truth it is the greatest obstacle to salvation. You think that you can't get there from where and who you are at this moment because you are not yet complete or good enough, but the truth is that here and now is the only point from where you *can* get there. You "get" there by realizing that you *are* there already. (p. 122)

> You cannot be free in the future. Presence is the key to freedom, so you can only be free now. (p. 51)

> The moment you grasp it, there is a shift in consciousness from mind to Being, from time to presence. Suddenly everything feels alive, radiates energy, emanates Being. (p. 42)

AGAINST INTERPRETATION

I have described Eckhart Tolle's approach as being much like Buddhism, Zen in particular, if not actually another form of it. He leaves us in no doubt that he is talking mysticism, though, as I have said, he is entitled to it, having derived it from an honest phenomenology of consciousness.

> Beyond the beauty of the external forms, there is more here: something that cannot be named, something ineffable, some deep, inner, holy essence. Whenever and wherever there is beauty, this inner essence shines through somehow. It only reveals itself when you are present. (p. 80)

Why do we have but fleeting glimpses of this vista? There is a deep, deep gap, though it is very narrow to jump, between awareness and interpretation. It is the difference between knowledge and thought.

> The time gap was so small that it seemed to be a single process. The truth is, however, that the moment thought came in, all you had was a memory of it [i.e., of the perception]. The wider the time gap between perception and thought, the more depth there is to you as a human being, which is to say the more conscious you are. Many people are so imprisoned in their minds that the beauty of nature does not really exist for them. They might say, "What a pretty flower," but that's just a mechanical mental labeling. Because they are not still, not present, they don't truly see the flower, don't feel its essence, its holiness—just as they don't know themselves, don't feel their own essence, their own holiness. (pp. 80–81)

All right, then, how do you lengthen the gap between perception and thought? I think it has something to do with bracing open the closing walls of the Void. Tolle's suggestion is simple:

To listen to the silence, wherever you are, is an easy and direct way of becoming present. Even if there is noise, there is always some silence underneath and in between the sounds. Listening to the silence immediately creates stillness inside you. Only the stillness in you can perceive the silence outside. And what is stillness other than presence, consciousness freed from thought forms? Here is the living realization of what we have been talking about. (p. 85)

No matter how simple something may seem in principle, there will usually be room for at least a couple more requests for clarification. If children persist in asking, "Why?" adults ask again and again, "How?" Tolle gets a bit more specific: "Be where you are. Look around. Just look, don't interpret. See the light, shapes, colors, textures. Be aware of the silent presence of each thing. Be aware of the space that allows everything to be" (p. 52). Here is something resembling the "phenomenological epoche" (bracketing) we meet in Edmund Husserl's phenomenology: just examine the lay of the land as it appears to consciousness without imposing evaluative and analytical categories upon it, like surveyors' lines looking to partition the turf and divide it up. We may recognize here the same advice Chögyam Trungpa gave: Do not judge and name and value what you behold, because the moment you do, you have created a world of illusion and made yourself one more character in the delusive world of virtual reality.

Come to think of it, it is quite astonishing how the world around us, especially the media, demands of us an opinion on every issue. "What do you think about this?" "What is your position on that?" Do I have to have one? Maybe I do. Sometimes I don't. There are many, many stones that I am not obliged to pick up and cast into the pond of my peace of mind. There are many things (to say nothing of people) about which I need to form no judgment. There are so many races in which I have no horse. Why worry about them! Better to live, as far as possible, in a world of delighted wonderment, just beholding. So it would be worth asking oneself, as soon as anxiety arises, "Do I need to have a judgment about this? An opinion about that? Do I need to care one way or the other?" Maybe not.

Tolle also invites his readers to try another exercise, a kind of "spot meditation" designed for odd moments: "Close your eyes and say to yourself: 'I wonder what my next thought is going to be.' Then become very alert and wait for the next thought. Be like a cat watching a mouse hole. What thought is going to come out of the mouse hole?" (p. 77). It will probably take a while before your mind begins to wander. Even then, you can direct it back, but the point is that the technique prolongs a prerational period of pure perception in the Now. "As long as you are in a state of intense presence, you are free of thought. You are still, yet highly alert. The instant your conscious attention sinks below a certain level, thought rushes in. The mental noise returns; the stillness is lost. You are back in time" (p. 77).

I am reminded of David Hume's argument that we cannot, from sheer empirical observation, prove the existence of the observing self, since all we can really say we observe is a continual parade of sensations and ideas across the stage of awareness. Hume's point was not to argue for a Buddhistic notion of No-Mind such as Tolle propounds, but how strikingly similar is the result! There is awareness, and there is a gratuitous inference of selfhood from the occurrence of perceptions. Assuming the existence of such a self only obscures the perceptions on the basis of which one posited the self in the first place.

There are rare individuals who seek out a life of silent meditation. More power to them, though personally I am not interested in that. But I hardly think that is what Tolle is advising or seeking. My own academic field is biblical studies, and from it I venture to draw an analogy, one not of doctrine but of mere punctuation. Did you know that originally the text of the Bible (as with all ancient texts) featured no paragraphs? No punctuation? Nor even any spaces between words? Hebrew writing did not even have vowels! The reader or copyist faced a formidable wall of letters of which he had to learn to make sense. Eventually some scribe had the bright idea of breaking up the text into readily identifiable words and sentences. It was by driving wedges into the mass of the text that the text became more readily understandable. I think it is the same with everyday experience. We need not try to flee it in order to have a better understanding. But it would help if we could break it up with intervals of silence and blankness so as not to get crushed by a heap of endless letters. The gaps between words, sentences, and paragraphs facilitate our understanding of all the words, sentences, and paragraphs. The empty spaces are just as crucial as the ones occupied by ink. We face, each day, a mass of wall-to-wall events, demands, jobs, and challenges. We need to seek out small zones of presence and stillness if only to gain perspective on the rest. Perhaps that is mysticism enough.

TURNING THE OTHER CHEEK AS JUJITSU

Tolle, like Pema Chödrön, suggests that the ego arises as a bulwark of resistance to events we decide we do not want to reach us. (How can there be anyone to make such a decision before the defensive wall erects itself? The two are simultaneous, neither moment preceding the other, two sides of a coin. It is the result not of logical derivation from a premise but from phenomenological introspection.) But if we were to open the sluice gates of perception, no more fearing to drown in the flood, but learning to surf on its crest, we might not have to worry about our dam breaking. We might not busy ourselves with safeguarding a dike threatening to crack under the pressure, because then there would *be* no pressure. "Accept—then act. Whatever the present moment contains, accept it as if you had chosen it. Always work with it, not against it. Make it your friend and ally, not your enemy. This will miraculously transform your whole life" (p. 29). To some, this may sound like vacant New Age drivel, but not so fast. Tolle's advice need have nothing to do with any troublesome myth, as some teach, about all of us choosing our lot before birth, up in some heavenly real estate office. That is a pernicious doctrine insofar as it leads to a "blame the victim" mentality.

No, the lesson I learn from Eckhart Tolle is that the events of your life are as much "you" as the genetic composition you inherited "from without," from your parents. You were not consulted in the choice of your genes and chromosomes. Yet it is healthy to affirm who you are and what you've got as you face life. Equally, insofar as events have conditioned you outside the boundaries of your control, they have made you what you are. They have dealt you the cards you hold as you join the game. Is it not just as sensible to affirm that outcome, too? Even Invictus does not claim he controlled his origin, only his destiny. So I take Tolle to mean that we must affirm ourselves as prior hands have made us. We did not choose them or the job they did at the time. We couldn't have. But we can affirm it now, own it as ourselves, and move on. Because, really, what is the alternative? Bemoaning opportunities and endowments others have but you do not is going to do you no good at all. It will only stymie any progress you might make. You must not begrudge the past. You must affirm the future, and that is tantamount to deciding you *did* choose your self, its equipment, and how it has turned out.

Then again, there is always the possibility that you *have* created your circumstances in some subtle way. We probably have much more influence on what comes our way than we notice. Our actions set in motion all manner of factors invisible to us at the time but in accord with the motive and the spirit in which we acted. It is not magical. It is not metaphysical. It is a matter of the unnoticed fine print in all the little transactions we make with named and unnamed individuals every day. Sometimes they come back to bite us (or to bless us). But, at any rate, we cannot do better than cutting our losses and allying ourselves with the conditions life, or blind fate, has assigned us. Maybe you did not choose them to begin with; indeed, you couldn't have. But if you affirm them now, it will be as if you chose them, because you are choosing them *now*.

The pain-body is a mass of psychic scar tissue that accumulates as we are chafed and battered by the friction produced by our resistance to so much that comes our way. Suppose you want to stop the process, even reverse it so that you will be willing to accept what comes your way, at worst, to roll with the punches. How would you do it? Vagueness is as useless as metaphysics to many of us. But Tolle does have something to offer in the way of specific volitional moves, maneuvers that will eventually accumulate, as Aristotle said such things do, to work a genuine change upon our habits of mind. What we need to do is to treat events as if they were people, for deep down we have the same reaction to both. We need to forgive them. Consciously we realize it would be primitive animism to get angry at mindless events. But that does not stop us from growing bitter, on a prerational level, against turns of events. We must not ignore emotional reactions, roosting as they do where rational scrutiny does not bother looking for them. So why not treat them consciously as we treat them unconsciously: as if they were offending entities? "Forgiveness of the present is even more important than forgiveness of the past. If you forgive every moment—allow it to be as it is—then there will be no accumulation of resentment that needs to be forgiven at some later time" (p. 148).

Most people seem to realize that, though they have the right not to forgive someone (it would hardly be an act of grace if you were obliged to do it), it is nonetheless in their own best interests to forgive. Justified though you may be to hold your grudge, watch out lest it eat you up inside. Take care lest your bitterness sour your whole life. It may even be that your bitterness is harming, punishing, no one else but yourself. Forgiveness drains away the poison. There is no reason the same emotional movement should not do the same for resentments one holds against Life, implicitly personified. It is absurd to be angry at life, to personify it as Life. But if that is what we tend to do subconsciously, then we had better root it out and deal with it on that level. Tolle is suggesting just that. It seems to work better than reasoning with yourself, trying to convince the rational mind of what it already knows.

Many people do not think of forgiving because they enjoy anger and resentment, even though such delight undermines the righteous character of their indignation. They have not really been put upon and harmed if they are enjoying the results. They are having so much fun resenting the SOB who ill treated them that they ought to thank him for it. They enjoy the indignation they feel because it gives them, in a silly sense, a sort of cause to identify with. It lends them a paranoid sense of importance, for contained in every twinge of resentment is a secret thought of "How dare they treat *me* in this manner!?" Oh, how important! Again we can see Tolle's point: resistance *is* the self. It gives the wall a sense of importance to feel handballs bounce off it. But what if the wall fell?

> All this can be transformed into spiritual practice. Feel yourself becoming transparent as it were, without the solidity of a material body. Now allow the noise, or whatever causes a negative reaction, to pass right through you. It is no longer hitting a solid "wall" inside you. As I said, practice the little things first. The car alarm, the dog barking, the children screaming, the traffic jam. Instead of having a wall of resistance inside you that gets constantly and painfully hit by things that "should not be happening," let everything pass through you.
>
> Somebody says something to you that is rude or designed to hurt. Instead of going into unconscious reaction and negativity, such as attack, defense, or withdrawal, you let it pass right through you. Offer no resistance. It is as if there is nobody there to get hurt anymore. *That* is forgiveness. In this way, you become invulnerable. You can still tell that person that his or her behavior is unacceptable, if that is what you choose to do. But that person no longer has the power to control your inner state. (p. 160)

Have you heard something like this before? I'm sure you have. It would be a simple matter to show how much of it is paralleled in ancient Stoicism. But let me point to another parallel, near and dear to my arrested-adolescent heart. Tolle's advice sounds remarkably like the Bene Gesserit litany against fear that the Lady Jessica taught Paul Atreides in Frank Herbert's *Dune*:

I must not fear. Fear is the mind-killer. Fear is the little-death that brings total obliteration. I will face my fear. I will permit it to pass over me and through me. And when it has gone past I will turn the inner eye to see its path. Where the fear has gone there will be nothing. Only I will remain. (p. 15)

THE SILENT TOLLING OF BEING

Speaking of science fiction and fantasy, it must be admitted that Eckhart Tolle once or twice manages to reach escape velocity and to go where no man has gone before—at least not by means of rational inquiry or psychological introspection. "There are countless beings whose consciousness frequency is so different from yours that you are probably unaware of their existence, as they are of yours. Highly conscious beings who are aware of their connectedness with the Source and with each other would inhabit a world that to you [note: not "to *us*"!] would appear as a heavenly realm" (p. 165). One feels sure that, if one asked Tolle which he intends, angels or aliens, he would not see much of a difference.

Tolle also believes that our world is to a large degree an illusion maintained by the shared delusions of the unenlightened. If enough of us could wake up, the world would assume the likeness, one must suppose, of the higher heaven-worlds of the aliens and angels (pp. 165–66). His creed also makes room for reincarnation (p. 118) and for pan-psychism, the sentimental ecodoctrine that "the Earth . . . is a living, intelligent organism" (p. 187). Like Charles Fillmore, founder of the Unity School of Christianity, and Deepak Chopra (*Ageless Body, Timeless Mind*), Tolle believes one can, via right thinking, banish physical aging:

When you become identified more with the timeless inner body than with the outer body, when presence becomes your normal mode of consciousness and past and future no longer dominate your attention, you do not accumulate time anymore in your psyche and in the cells of your body. The accumulation of time as the psychological burden of the past and future greatly impairs the cells' capacity for self-renewal. So if you inhabit the inner body, the outer body will grow old at a slower rate, and even when it does, your timeless essence will show through the outer form, and you will not give the appearance of an older person. (p. 102)

Notice how Tolle's claims retreat and shrink a little with every clause of this passage. He sounds at first like Dale Gribble of *King of the Hill* fame: "I'm not *goin'* to die. Chromium picolinate: every orifice, every day." Then he comes to Faustlike eternal youth, and finally to a mere promise of a spring in your walker-assisted step and a gleam in your rheumy eye. But the wimpiest assurance Tolle has to offer once he ventures into this crackpot territory is this: "*Is there any scientific evidence for this?* Try it out and you will *be* the evidence" (p. 102). He doesn't say whether your little experiment will be evidence *for* or *against* his wild claim.

For New Age readers, such claims and faith assertions present no problem. But it is a shame that they threaten to discredit the book in the eyes of those who are not ready simply to believe anything they are told. As I have sought to demonstrate in this chapter, very much of Eckhart Tolle's *The Power of Now* derives its considerable power from an unflinching and keen-eyed phenomenological scrutiny of how we flinch from the Now moment and the healing clarity it promises. By far, most of Tolle's analysis stands on its own and rings true against most people's experience. If one

TOP SECRET

finds, as I do, much genuine wisdom in Tolle's pages, one must not commit the ad hominem fallacy and discount those insights just because the messenger turns out to be something of an eccentric.

Chapter 5

A Course in Malarkey

Helen Schucman, *A Course in Miracles*

THIS IS A COURSE IN MIRACLES.
PLEASE TAKE NO-DOZ

*O*ne thing's for sure: if Mark Twain could have read *A Course in Miracles*, he never would have called the Book of Mormon "chloroform in print." Utterly without redeeming value (take that any way you want), the only conceivable importance of *A Course in Miracles* is as a testimony to the pathetic state of spiritual hunger and confusion on the part of late twentieth-century American "seekers." Leaden and tedious in style, the work is easily a hundred times longer than it needs to have been to convey its point.

A Course in Miracles is regarded, a bit loosely, as a "channeled" work, conveyed mediumistically to Dr. Helen Schucman, a secular Jew and psychiatrist. She never claimed to have gone into a trance to make way for a supplanting persona like Judy Zebra Knight's fictive alter ego, Ramtha. Rather, Dr. Schucman said she sensed a subtle voice intruding thoughts and words into her waking consciousness. The voice soon identified itself as none other than Jesus

Christ. Depending on whom one listens to, Schucman either had no further interest in the manuscript thus produced and did not accommodate her personal beliefs to its teachings; or, she was at any rate little inclined to practice the forgiving, affirmative attitudes urged by her scripture. Some claim she was familiar with occult and New Age/New Thought beliefs; others deny it. Her fans mean to deny that she, in and of herself, could have or would have produced the *Course*. They are trying to fit Dr. Schucman into the age-old apologetic for this or that revelation. How is Jesus so learned when he had never formally studied (John 7:15)? Because he's a divine revealer! Flesh and blood did not reveal the secret of Jesus' messianic identity to Simon Peter; it must have been the Father in heaven (Matt. 16:17). The Sanhedrin remarked upon Peter's eloquence, seeing that he was but a Galilean bumpkin; then they remembered he had been with Jesus (Acts 4:13). Muhammad could not have been the author of the suras of the Koran, for he protested his illiteracy to the angel Gabriel, just as Moses had when Jehovah told him to rebuke Pharaoh (Exod. 4:10). Joseph Smith could not have written a book like Mormon out of his unschooled imagination, so it must really be an ancient scripture. And so on. I must, however, regard *A Course in Miracles* as the work of Helen Schucman, however far from her familiar convictions (or lack of them) its doctrines may stray. The emergence of her quasi-Christianity from her subconscious is no more miraculous than the conversion of many a secular Jew to "Jews for Jesus" Christianity. In fact, we might even expect such a thing, as the notion of Jesus speaking to her is a potent symbol of her dissatisfaction with an inherited Judaism that apparently had never meant anything to her. If you wanted a symbol for a new revelation, not derivable from her own religious background, you could hardly think of a better one.

One may observe that, if we are to take seriously Dr. Schucman's claim to be the mouthpiece of Jesus Christ, one must regret Jesus' dreadful loss of his once-marvelous gift of gab. For one thing, Jesus seems not to know the proper use of the word *literally*. For another, he must have thought he was getting paid by the word. To compare the patronizing pedantry of *A Course in Miracles* with any line or two from the New Testament gospels is like comparing a washing machine repair manual with Shakespeare. While one must repair to the likes of, let's say, Kahlil Gibran's *Jesus the Son of Man* for authentic-sounding Jesus apocrypha, *A Course in Miracles* sounds more like Klaatu, the alien savant from *The Day the Earth Stood Still*, even like the superhero The Sphinx (in the comedy *Mystery Men*), a fountainhead of moebius-strip maxims like "He who doubts his training only succeeds in training himself to doubt."

> You denied Him because you loved Him, knowing that if you recognized your love for Him you would not deny Him. Your denial of Him therefore means that you love Him . . . and that you know He loves you. (p. 190)

> [The Holy Spirit] is the answer to everything because He knows what the answer to everything is. (p. 157)

> The ego's purpose is fear, because only the fearful can be egotistical. (p. 83)

What is staggering as one reads the wearying paragraphs (pretentiously divided among chapters and verses) of *A Course in Miracles* is the realization that anyone has been able to stay awake for any stretch of pages, much less to find solace or inspiration in them. If one feels that trusting the New Testament to the likes of fundamentalists is to cast pearls before swine, in the present case one cannot help thinking of the destitute prodigal looking to sate his hunger with the husks the pigs are munching.

CHURCH OF JESUS CHRIST, PSYCHIATRIST

Scholars used to (falsely) point to a use of medical terminology in Luke and Acts to vindicate the old tradition that these books were the work of Luke the beloved physician mentioned in Colossians 4:14. Henry Cadbury put an end to all that talk, but Dr. Schucman's authorship (not mere mediumship) of *A Course in Miracles* is evident on every page from the pervasive psychological, therapeutic perspective. Schucman's Jesus is obligingly easy on the reader: there is no sin of which to repent, no guilt for which to atone. Schucman is a kind of metaphysical Stuart Smalley, a mock self-help character from *Saturday Night Live*. Her ventriloquist-dummy Jesus cannot say enough to build up the self-esteem of the emotionally needy reader.

> You are a child of God, a priceless part of His Kingdom, which He created as part of Him. (p. 101)

> God created nothing beside you, and nothing beside you exists, for you are part of Him. (p. 181)

> Because I am always with you, *you* are the way, the truth, and the life. (p. 116)

You are the Will of God because that is how you were created. (p. 141)

Grandeur is of God, and only of Him. Therefore it is in you. . . . Can your grandeur be arrogant when God himself witnesses to it? (pp. 177, 179)

You are altogether irreplaceable in the Mind of God. (p. 179)

I treasure you beyond the value that you set on yourself, even unto the worth that God has placed you. . . . I thank the Father for your loveliness. (pp. 265–66)

He will never cease His praise of you. (p. 266)

This is the last resort of the self-hating. No one who has (or realizes he has) any genuine basis for self-esteem takes refuge in deductive syllogisms to prove his worth. To all appearances, I am a worthless waste of tissue, but I can rejoice to know that *in a hypothetical universe in which things are exactly opposite to the way they appear* I am pretty cool. For Schucman, the psychiatrist, this world is unremitting insanity, a word she uses incessantly. Human thoughts and thought patterns that do not conform to her metaphysic are "totally insane." This is not mere name-calling, but rather an index of how radical a departure in thinking she calls for. And it seems the patient is running the asylum.

According to Schucman, the plight of the reader in a miserable world is all illusion, even hallucination. Jesus is like Morpheus in *The Matrix*, trying at interminable length to convince the stupefied reader to awaken from an all-encompassing illusion, a bad dream of the (illusory) individual's (imaginary) separation from God. It is not quite like the Advaita and yoga doctrine of *maya*, according to which one suffers from delusion, misconstruing the *meaning* of all one sees. In that scenario, one gains enlightenment and henceforth passes life in a state of "mere witness," acting no longer from karma-accruing, mundane motivations, with no vested interest in the passing carnival show. One used to see a mountain until one gained Mukti, but since then one sees but a mountain again, albeit with a better perspective (could that be the "mountain-moving faith" of the New Testament?). But this is nothing to Schucman's paranoid cosmos—the reader beholds a world of sheer fantasy:

> Sit quietly. And look upon the world you see, and tell yourself: "The real world is not like this. It has no buildings and there are no streets where people walk alone and separate. There are no stores where people buy an endless list of things they do not need. It is not lit with artificial light, and night comes not upon it. There is no day that brightens and grows dim. . . . The world you see must be denied." (p. 254)

Every religion diagnoses a problem, to which it then prescribes a single solution. One often feels the problem has been derived from the solution so as to provide a felt need for it, in the manner of Madison Avenue. In Schucman's case, the doctrines of hamartology (how things went wrong) and cosmogony (the origin of the world) are one. In the beginning was only God. Schucman appears to conceive of the Deity somewhat sloppily in terms now of nondualism (Only God exists), now of pantheism (All is God), now of panentheism (All is *in* God). The first is the Advaita Vedanta Hindu teaching of Gaudapada and Shankara, whereby all apparent beings are illusory masks of God, who alone is real. The second is the doctrine of the Stoics and Baruch Spinoza: God is the pervasive essence within all things, the reality of which all existing entities are faces and forms, all real, but none autonomous, all secretly divine. The third would be the teaching of Ramanuja, founder of Visistadvaita ("qualified nondualism" or "difference-in-identity") Vedanta Hinduism and of modern Process theologians like Charles Hartshorne, John Cobb, Schubert Ogden, David Ray Griffin, and Norman Pittenger. This is the belief that God includes all things and indwells them. As the Upanishads put it, Brahman emanated the cosmos from himself, then entered into it "up to the fingernails." God is the soul of the world; the world is the body of God. Human souls straddle the distinction, being part of God's body but sharing his sentience. God thus exists in three modes: a physical world, human souls, and a personal God who may be worshiped. It is analogous to the Trinity, but it cuts the pie differently, including everything and everyone.

Schucman's Jesus seems sometimes to assume pantheism, the virtual identity between God, Christ, and the reader: "you are part of Him. What except him can exist?" (p. 181). But closer examination reveals distinctions between the major players which are not going away, not even after enlightenment. She seems, then, to be a panentheist, more or less. (This is no criticism: a scripture need not present a consistent theology. Few ever have. That is not their function.) It is perhaps confusing that she says God the Father "created Christ," as this implies less than real divinity, as per the fourth-century Council of Nicea. A created being by definition does not share the eternal, impassible nature of the Godhead. But elsewhere she does seem to picture Jesus as assuming his eternal unity with the Father. Where does the reader come in? Schucman/Jesus tells us that the reader is an aspect of "the Sonship." All sentient beings are the Son of God. Not the Sons of God, much less Sons and Daughters of God, because every aspect of the whole contains the whole—one of many dubious metaphysical fiats by which Schucman simplifies her worldview. "You are the Kingdom of God" (p. 69) is another. Indeed, one grows irritated with the number of times one thing is declared to be the same as another with the italicized word *is*. I feel I must give you some idea of her stylistic excess at this point:

> To know your brother *is* to know God. (p. 69)

> You must learn to change your mind about your mind. Only by this can you learn that it *is* changeless. (p. 121)

> This allegiance [to fear] makes it treacherous to love because you *are* love. (p. 124)

> What you want to be *is* what you think you are. (p. 127)

> Your will is as powerful as His because it *is* his. (p. 134)

> The Father's Will *is* the Son. (p. 135)

> The miracle is therefore a lesson in what joy is. Being a lesson in sharing it is a lesson in love, which *is* joy. (p. 135)

> This is His Will for everyone because He speaks for the Kingdom of God, which *is* joy. (p. 136)

> There are no exceptions to this lesson, because the lack of exceptions *is* the lesson. (p. 136)

Knowledge *is* His Will. (p. 138)

Ask for light and learn that you *are* light. (p. 141)

The world *is* the belief that love is impossible. (p. 144)

God's Will *is* thought. It cannot be contradicted *by* thought. (p. 149)

The acceptance of peace is the denial of illusion, and sickness *is* illusion. (pp. 185–86)

The temple still is holy, for the Presence that dwells within it *is* holiness. (p. 291)

For the ego *is* chaos. (p. 294)

This is not only very bad writing and annoyingly smug conde-scension. It is also a cheating shortcut in argumentation. Where Schucman owes it to the reader to build a bridge between claim and proof, premise and conclusion, she takes a shortcut by popping out of the phenomenal dreamworld in which argument takes place, and into the "real" world in which everything is the same as everything else, since there is only Oneness anyway. Identifying Hitler with Gandhi is easy in that subspace dimension, and then she pops back into the land of rational arguments, having made a quick identification of two points in her argument without covering the distance between.

She speaks of the reader, of any human being, and of Jesus interchangeably as "the Son of God." "The Sonship" to which the humble reader no less than Jesus Christ belongs is a collective entity analogous, one supposes, to the Mystical Body of Christ, or the Light-Man of Gnosticism (the latter is historically the probable origin of the former). But this applies only so far, for the multiplicity of the Sonship appears mostly to reflect nondualism. In other words, it seems that the single created Son has been divided only from the standpoint of illusion, just as Shankara said that the indivisible Oneness of the Brahman appears to be refracted like sunlight into colors through the prism of the "limiting conditions" (*upadis*) of lower knowledge, relative ignorance (*avidya*). It is on this lower level of *maya* that the (illusory) individual, according to Shankara, experiences his existence among other individuals as well as his pious relation with a personal Creator. This lower level is dreamlike, not the ultimate reality on the other side of enlightenment, a higher realm where all is One. And yet it is not completely unreal either. It is true as far as it goes.

Schucman seems to picture the reader and his "brothers" (no equal-opportunity "sisters" are in evidence) as separated on the plane of illusion which the reader is told he occupies, implying that there is no actual division between them or Jesus Christ on the level where Jesus is, and where we, too, *really* are, if only we knew it. The goal of the "course," of course, is to get to know it. Now how did the reader come to be in this sorry state? The Son (here denoting the reader) once hatched the crazy scheme of asking God the Father to allow him to experience pain. This request a loving Father could not grant, since pain is not his to give. Like a spoiled child, the Son of God decided to fake it himself and plunged into a coma of delusion in which he believes/d that he was in fact alienated from God. Henceforth he wallowed in a world of pain, fearing God for good reason: the reader/Son of God had meantime fallen under the nefarious spell of the ego, a false self, equally illusory, and the ego knows that he can maintain his pseudoexistence only by leaning on the reader, and to do this, he must keep the reader believing it is a good thing to stay away from the Father. If the Son/reader were to snap out of it, like the Prodigal Son in his self-imposed exile from his father, the ego's fiefdom of existence would pop like a bubble. "The bleak little world will vanish into nothingness, and your heart will be so filled with joy that it will leap into Heaven, and into the Presence of God" (p. 198).

THE FALLEN SOPHIA

Right at this point, Schucmanism breaks away from nondualism and veers toward Gnosticism. What led to the individual's perceived existence as an individual? Shankara chalked it up to the *maya*-character of the lower knowledge level. Part and parcel of the mystery of things as we see them now. But Gnosticism explained it. For Valentinus, the greatest of the Gnostics, it all began with a fall within the Godhead. The Unknown Father had emanated from himself one hundred eighty-two pairs of Aions, or divine beings, each pair begetting or emanating the next in a vast chain. Collectively, they constituted the pleroma, the cosmic Fullness of Light. Finally there appeared the three-hundred-sixty-fifth Aion, lonely Sophia ("wisdom"). Farthest from the fountain of divinity, Sophia yearned to "conceive" in both senses: to bear offspring, albeit without a mate, and to understand the secret of the Godhead. Existing on the rim of the pleroma, just beyond the barrier, she was in ignorance. She managed to beget a defective being, Ialdabaoth, who confusedly imagined himself to be the Supreme Being (he was, understandably, more ignorant than his well-meaning mother).

He sought to create his own version of the pleroma by making the Archons, the angelic rulers of the world (essentially the planetary gods of Babylon, the elemental spirits of Stoicism, or the weather-angels of Judaism). These cheap counterfeits of the immortal Aions were to assist their Lord in ruling the mud-pie earth, created by the Demiurge ("Craftsman, Creator"), Ialdabaoth. But the earth, including Adam, was inert. So the Archons contrived to steal some of the heavenly light and entrap it within matter, where it would function like self-replicating DNA to give life and order to the world. (Where they obtained the light differs in different versions of the myth. Some Gnostics said it was the light reflected off Sophia in the placid lake-surface of the newly made earth. Others said the Archons dismembered the Primal Man, a heavenly Adam Aion who ventured too close.) The Archons raped Eve, and the human race eventuated as the bastard spawn of that union. Centuries later, the Demiurge, whom Gnostics identified as the Hebrew God, assigned laws to Moses, laws from which Gnostics considered themselves exempt.

Not all humans have one of the divine sparks inside them, but the ones who did were redeemable. So the Christ Aion (himself somehow identified with the Primal Man) entered the world to reveal to these elite the unsuspected truth of their origin and destiny. They might depart this life and return to the bliss of the pleroma if they heeded the teaching of the Christ. Actually, Eve had evaded the lustful Archons, leaving behind a phantom double for them to think they defiled. In like manner, the Archons now imagined themselves to have gotten hold of the Christ and crucified him, but this, too, was a phantom semblance. Christ returned to the pleroma, to await the return of his enlightened brethren. The Gnostics, of course, understood themselves to be the illuminati, kindred of Christ, destined for divinity.

Schucman's myth of the Fall is strikingly akin to that of Valentinus and the Gnostics. The Fall occurs within the Godhead. And it is a fall into ignorance. The main difference is almost trivial: Schucman combines the fallen Sophia with her son, the Demiurge. The reader takes the combined role. It is this Son's ill-advised curiosity that causes the "Separation." The Christ is sent to Helen Schucman to enlighten all who will listen to the fact that they are parts of him. They are to understand that they are members of Adam/Jesus, the dispersed Son of God, lost in the false world of darkness and pain.

The reader is sometimes identified with the evil ego, other times distinguished from him. The more seriously we take the distinction between the ego-phantom and the reader/Son, the closer is the Gnostic parallel, for then we might identify the reader/Son with the fallen Sophia and the ego with the Demiurge, her son. Schucman even provides the Demiurgic ego with the requisite band of Archontic henchmen, barring the souls of the Gnostics from the pleromatic world of light: "The sentinels of darkness watch over it carefully, and you who made these guardians of illusion out of nothing are now afraid of them" (p. 285). Further, "your sentinels . . . serve to guard the dark doors behind which nothing at all is carefully concealed. We must open all doors and let the light come streaming through" (p. 286). The dastardly ego is, like his Demiurgic counterpart, a stern law-giver: "The ego's laws are strict, and breaches are severely punished" (p. 260).

How has the Christ effected the salvation of his brethren/ aspects? He has done it through the atonement. Not that he died on the cross. He didn't: that was part of the ego-orchestrated shadow play of illusion. The Christ has never really departed heaven. Neither has the reader! For the atonement is the retroactive undoing of the separation. It never happened! "The message the crucifixion was intended to teach was that it is not necessary to perceive any form of assault or persecution, because you cannot *be* persecuted" (p. 92). In other words, your apparent sufferings are just as "docetic" (an optical illusion) as Jesus' were. How can that be, you ask? "The body is *not* part of you" (p. 101). And that, as you might be surmising by now, leads directly into the arms of Mary Baker Eddy: "A sick body does not make any sense. It could not make any sense because sickness is not what the body is for" (p. 156). I guess Dr. Jesus and Dr. Schucman remain unfazed by the many, many deaths that have resulted from this doctrine over the decades. Good luck with that.

I'VE NEVER MADE A MISTAKE.
I THOUGHT I DID ONCE, BUT I WAS WRONG.

The whole atonement notion appears to be superfluous, however, for we already have an entirely different reason for our freedom from the separation, the Fall, into illusion. And that is the fact that nothing outside of God is real. The world we perceive and the pain thereof are objects of experience, as objects in a dream. They are phenomenal events, but they have no substance. They might be called *ontic* but not *ontological*. Thus ego, evil, guilt, and sin have no existence, though they are experienced on the level of lower knowledge.

Schucman reveals a fatal confusion at this point. On the one hand, she wants the *maya* level not to exist at all. That way, we need not take it seriously and we can slough off the whole damn thing. On the other hand, she needs the *maya* level to exist, since there is manifestly the problem that the reader perceives himself to occupy a world of diversity, separation, and pain. For there to be a problem for the *Course* to solve, the lower level must exist ontically, phenomenologically, as a force to be reckoned with. Schucman induces the reader to plant a foot in each world: if the illusion world is not powerfully real (to us), there is no problem; unless the illusion world is totally unreal, there is no solution. As in all nondualism, one can always say that the illusory world is real on a lower level, "less real" than the divine world, and that the two coexist, like first class and tourist class cabins, separated by a curtain. And the poor reader is simultaneously on both levels. On one he suffers; on the other he does not and never has. But what good does that do for the tourist class version of the reader? To solve the problem, the reader would have to be shown that the world of pain is false *on its own level*, not on the one above it. And Schucman does in fact wind up saying just this.

> The ego is nothing more than a part of your belief about yourself. Your other life has continued without interruption, and has been and always will be totally unaffected by your attempts to dissociate it. (p. 67)

> Since the Holy Spirit is in your mind, your mind can believe only what is true. . . . He tells you to return your whole mind to God, because it has never left him. If it has never left Him, you need only perceive it as it is to be returned. The full awareness of the Atonement, then, is the recognition that *the separation never occurred*. The ego cannot prevail against this because it is an explicit statement that the ego never occurred. (p. 98)

> Through His power and glory all your wrong decisions are undone completely, releasing you and your brother from every

imprisoning thought any part of the Sonship holds. Wrong decisions have no power, because they are not true. The imprisonment they seem to produce is no more true than they are. (p. 143)

You have condemned yourself, but condemnation is not of God. Therefore it is not true. No more are any of its seeming results. (p. 154)

What has no effect does not exist, and to the Holy Spirit the effects are nonexistent. By steadily canceling out all its effects, everywhere and in all respects, He teaches that the ego does not exist and proves it. (p. 169)

God would not have His Son embattled, and so His Son's imagined "enemy" is unreal. You are but trying to escape a bitter war from which you *have* escaped. . . . Nothing destructive ever was or will be. The war, the guilt, the past are gone as one into the unreality from which they came. (p. 266)

His peace still flows to you from Him Whose Will is peace. You have it now. (p. 268)

When He willed that His Son be free, His Son *was* free. (p. 349)

So you don't even *have* a problem, not even on the illusory level! But Schucman's glowing reassurances have overshot the mark. If what she says is true, then there is after all no problem to solve.

I find it helpful to contrast what Schucman says with traditional Christian Universalism. (By that I do not mean to imply that most Christians have espoused the view I am about to describe, only that it is an old belief within some quarters of orthodox Protestantism.)

Universalism teaches that Jesus Christ died for the sins of the human race—and it worked. The efficacy of his atoning sacrifice is in no way dependent upon whether or not anyone or everyone accepts or even acknowledges it. If they do, all the better, for then they have the benefit of spiritual communion with their Savior already in this life. But when they die, all human beings will find themselves in heaven, with their sinfulness fading away like static from a better phone connection. What has happened here is that God has effected reconciliation on the level of objective reality as he sees it. An unrepentant/unbelieving sinner here below is out of step with reality for the present, here below. Eventually the slack will be taken up when everyone arrives, perhaps surprised, in heaven. Schucman also says that God has taken care of reconciliation and is waiting for us to catch up, but in her version, God is said to have made things right not only on *his* level but on *ours* as well, even though we don't see it. But "our level" means no more than "the way we see things." He has dispelled our illusion on the only level where it exists: the illusory level. And yet we still experience illusion. We still find ourselves like Timothy Leary: on the outside, looking in.

Schucman appears to think she is like the ancient Eleatic philosopher Zeno, disciple of Parmenides. Parmenides, a major influence upon Plato, held that the world of the senses cannot be real in any aspect since it contradicts reason. Reason demands (for reasons too abstruse to pursue here) that reality be recognized as a massive, perfect sphere with no parts or distinctions between them. Zeno sought to demonstrate this by tying his hearers in knots. How can a runner even reach the finish line of a race? We see runners do so all the time. But they cannot be doing it, since to reach the finish line implies passing the midpoint of the distance, then passing the midpoint of the *remaining* distance, then the midpoint of the distance left after *that*, and so on. Since the remaining space will always be infinitely divisible into microns and theoretical, dimensionless mathematical points, the runner is faced with the impossible challenge of passing an infinite number of points in a finite amount of time. Thus things cannot be as they seem. Schucman triumphantly points out the absurdities she sees in life as we think we live it. But I should say rather that she has only reduced her own system to absurdity. If it is true, then you don't have any problem for her to solve. She does not seem to realize who the joke is on.

HE AIN'T HEAVY

The same self-stultifying glitch becomes even more severe when Schucman gets to the matter of how to deal with one's "brothers." One is told they are the Son, and equally perfect, in their real essence, where Christ and the Father see them on the heavenly level. If, down here below, we "refuse" to see them that way, we are reinforcing and perpetuating the illusion of the separation. Why? Because we are acting on the assumption that our brother is not the same person as we are. We are like the psychotic protagonist of Chuck Palahniuk's *Fight Club* before he comes to the realization that he and the mysterious Tyler Durden are the same person. For instance, the *Course* warns us never to presume to condemn, even to correct our brother, for correction is condemnation, which implies that our brother partakes of guilt, which, *as the Son of God*, he does not and cannot. And as long as we see our brother as someone else, and separated from God by guilt, we are perpetuating the error that he is not us, we are not God, and I am not the walrus.

When you react at all to errors, you are not listening to the Holy
Spirit. He has merely disregarded them, and if you attend to them,
you are not hearing Him. . . . When a brother behaves insanely,
you can heal him only by perceiving the sanity in him. If you perceive his errors and accept them, you are accepting yours. If you
want to give yours over to the Holy Spirit, you must do the same
with his . . . To perceive errors in anyone, and to react to them as
if they were real, is to make them real to you. (p. 167)

Lay not his guilt upon him, for his guilt lies in his secret thought
that he has done this unto you. Would you, then, teach him he is
right in his delusion? The idea that the guiltless Son of God can
attack himself and make himself guilty is insane. . . . For sin and
condemnation are the same. (p. 261)

Likewise, if we pray and seek some answer from God, we can
only expect to get it from our brother, even the most annoying of
the brethren. He only offends us because of what we are projecting
onto him. It is we who are attacking him by perceiving offense
where none can really have been, since he is really just as much a
Jesus as you are and as Christ is. So if you learn to hear him right,
you will hear the answer to your prayer.

The message your brother gives you is up to you. What does he
say to you? What would you have him say? Your decision about
him determines the message you receive. Remember that the
Holy Spirit is in him, and His Voice speaks to you through him.
What can so holy a brother tell you except truth? But are you listening to it? . . . His words are the Holy Spirit's answer to you. Is
your faith in him strong enough to let you hear? (p. 164)

But, pray tell, Jesus, just what is the element of projection here? If some lout is abusing me, and I decide he is really imparting Christlike wisdom, am I not simply disregarding what is coming out of his mind and his mouth and ascribing to him what I might wish he would say if he were a Christlike fellow? It all sounds sweet, but I am unpersuaded that anything at all significant is being proposed here. I am not to condemn my brother, an incarnation of Jesus named Jeffrey Dahmer. How dare I attribute guilt to old Jeff? He is Jesus! The problem is that he is Jesus on the wrong level. On the level we are both stuck on, I had better watch my ass, or Jeff will be having it for supper. Is Schucman's Jesus simply telling us that all people are potentially Christlike? I can accept that. But then what happens when they have let themselves become a child molester, a drug fiend, a terrorist? Is such a person not susceptible to correction or condemnation? Or is Schucman merely telling me to love the sinner and to hate the sin? I can even accept that. As C. S. Lewis once quipped, we all seem to take precisely that generous approach when it comes to ourselves, so why not others? But that is no revelation. That is no big deal. We still cannot ignore the evil that men do. And if Schucman is saying that we ought to, then it is she who is inviting us into a madhouse universe.

I have mentioned the similarity at some points between Schucmanism and Stoicism, another pantheism. Here is another, though I think Schucman is confused where the Stoics had clarity. The helpful element of truth in what she is saying is that ultimately my weal or woe lies with me, not with another. That is, no one can "make" me angry or sorrowful, as if I were a robot and the other person had the control box. We fail to grasp this wisdom every time we say that someone "pushed my buttons." The buttons are no one else's to press. It is theirs to bait us, ours whether or not we are going to fall for it. So, yes, it is ultimately our fault if they get our goat, and we never have to let them do it. We are in control. But we don't need to project a faultless perfection onto a knave in order to do it. It is Schucman who urges delusion upon us.

COMMUNICATIO IDIOMATUM

Remember how panentheism in effect makes everybody and everything into persons of the Trinity? Let me pursue the Trinitarian implications a step further. The Trinity doctrine is an extension of the doctrine of the dual natures of Christ. Early Christians wanted to strike a balance between understanding Jesus as human and understanding him as divine. Too divine a Jesus would be too remote for humans to relate to, while too human a Jesus would share our predicament and be unable to save us. So they wanted to find a way of seeing him as fully divine and fully human, yet without mixing the two natures. The final formula, promulgated at the Council of Chalcedon in 451 CE, was that Jesus Christ was fully God and fully Man, the two natures being inseparable but unmingled. The implication of this trade-off was a doctrine, really a manner of speaking, called the "Communication of Properties." This meant that Christians might (almost metaphorically) speak of one nature in terms of the other since a single individual possessed both natures. Suppose one said, "Jesus of Nazareth walked on water." That implies Jesus the man, the Galilean carpenter, defied gravity, something he certainly did not do in his capacity as a human being of flesh and blood. It would be more literally accurate to say, "The Son of God walked on water," since the action stemmed from the divine nature. Likewise, one might say, during an impassioned Good Friday sermon, "God died on the cross for your sins!" Technically the divine nature is impassible and cannot suffer. Only mortals suffer and die. Nonetheless, since the man who died on the cross was also God, one can *say* that God died on the cross. This is how Catholics can say Mary is the Mother of God. They don't mean to make her a goddess in her own right. They mean that her son, though a mortal human, was also possessed of divine nature. It is a kind of theological "legal fiction." And if you go further than that, if you mean it literally, you're confusing the two natures.

Schucman sounds to me as if she is applying the Communication of Properties doctrine to all individuals as interchangeable members of the Sonship. For her, what is true of Jesus Christ can be predicated of all his brethren who are united with him, in some manner, in the Sonship. So if Jesus is unfallen and perfect, then so are you, and so is Charlie Manson. But Schucman is confused: she fails to grasp that what is true of the one may be predicated of the other only in a manner of speaking, so as to highlight a unity that is real on a different and unseen level. If there is a comatose Son of God in a stupor of illusion and separation, then I should say *that particular* Son of God, or aspect of the Sonship, is *not* simultaneously sharing the perfection of God. One might say that Otis Campbell sleeping it off in the drunk tank is "really" a better man, a sober man, a family man. But it does no good to then release him, dead drunk, back onto the streets of Mayberry.

The confusion of levels, and of what is relevant to each, confronts us again in the question of the reader's guilt or lack of it. As Anton van Harskamp has pointed out, the *Course in Miracles* is a source of psychologically perilous mixed signals. On the one hand, as we have seen, it goes out of its way to absolve the reader of any and all guilt. The separation is just a mistake, that's all, and one, furthermore, that has been erased from history (though we still suffer from its nonexistent effects). On the other, the blame for a nightmare history of massacres and holocausts is placed squarely on the reader's sagging shoulders. For it is "he" who has dreamed it all up! He is "guiltless," then, in only a Pickwickian sense, on some other plane of existence where pigs can fly. On the level where it matters, the reader is guilty as hell.

And if he has created the mess, it is he who can end it. So why doesn't he? Here is where Schucman drops the Acme anvil onto her hapless readers' heads. They can read and reread this tiresome tome as many times as Tolkien fanatics have read *The Lord of the Rings*, and the universe is not going to wink out. (Or, if it does, they will soon find themselves ensconced between padded walls.) And here comes infinite regress. Let's see: "I" created this crazy world, but on the level of God's truth it has been corrected. Then I don't have a problem anymore, do I? But I guess I do, since I find myself still here! So I guess I was "really" freed from the illusion, and it is just an illusion that I'm still captive to it! I guess Christ-Schucman has really freed you from *that* illusion, too. But why can't you perceive that? Must be another level, a subbasement, of illusion. And there will prove to be another below that, and so on, and so on. Again, I say she has performed a reduction ad absurdum on her own doctrine. It is the same predicament that Christian Science and Pentecostal faith healers assign their adherents: the victim takes the blame. Why didn't it work? It can't have been God's fault, so who is left to blame? I guess I didn't have enough faith, and I don't know how I can get any more, so I'm worse off than when I started!

Oh, and one more thing: the book *never once defines miracles*, nor is it at all clear even by implication. One thing Schucman seem

Chapter 6

U-Turn to Love

Marianne Williamson, *A Return to Love*

REMEDIAL COURSE IN MIRACLES

*M*arianne Williamson is a self-proclaimed apostle for the gospel contained in Helen Schucman's compendium of gibberish, *A Course in Miracles*. Good for her! Paul, too, was self-appointed, at least in human terms. He always fiercely declared his independence of the Jerusalem apostles, maintaining his call came straight from Christ. The prophet Joseph Smith and the Reverend Sun Myung Moon, too, claimed no earthly sanction. And yet Williamson is quick to disclaim any original insight. What she is is a popularizer, which is never a bad thing, so long as one does not dilute the product in the process. She attempts, in her lectures and books, to convey Schucman's (or Jesus') insights to audiences, I guess, like me. I found the experience of reading *A Course in Miracles* pretty much like what I imagine it would be like to play "Great Balls of Fire" on the piano with my forehead. By contrast, Marianne Williamson's treatment of the same themes is winsome and reader friendly. And I suggest that her faithfulness to the material may be gauged by the extent to which many of the leading ideas in *A Return to Love* remain offensive and counterintuitive. Even if one does not agree with her, one may admire her integrity for refusing to compromise her message.

It is worth noting that Marianne Williamson is by no means the only spiritual teacher to be influenced by *A Course in Miracles*. Wayne Dyer, Eckhart Tolle, Neale Donald Walsch, and David R. Hawkins also express their debt to Schucman's revelations. But these others merely use it as one more pinch of spice in their stew, though Walsch may be said to have derived the whole idea of his own channeled scripture, *Conversations with God*, from Schucman's venture, or from her financial success with it. Williamson seems largely content to remain in Schucman's shadow, as an exegete and preacher of her mentor's scripture. But would to God Schucman had called in Williamson to edit her material! But I guess such an appeal would have fallen on ears as deaf as Ayn Rand's when editor Bennett Cerf told her that her magnum opus *Atlas Shrugged* needed some trimming, and Rand replied, "Would you edit the Bible?"

ALL YOU SEE IS LOVE

What you see isn't what you get. Not by a long shot. "The world of the human storyline, of all our concentration on behavior and all the things that occur outside us, is a world of illusion. It's a veil in front of a more real world, [it is] a collective dream" (Williamson, p. 58). When someone says that everything reduces to one fundamental reality, it sounds like they are making a metaphysical statement, but I should say they are making more of a value judgment. They have decided to take only one aspect of things seriously. And for

Williamson, as may already be surmised, that is *love*: "Only love is real. Nothing else actually exists" (p. 84). Now what is that supposed to mean? Philosophers draw a distinction between the ontic and the ontological. The former is judged to be metaphysically real in the fullest possible sense; the latter may be dream or delusion, but admittedly we encounter the ontic in our experience. We may discount it as "unreal," but it does exist as something we encounter, maybe even something from which we suffer, and when we say it is unreal we mean to say we are going to refuse to take it seriously. And then it becomes a mirror game: which side of the glass shows us reality? The more one refuses to take seriously what surrounds one, the more effectively one operates "in denial." Paul says, "I am crucified to the world, and the world is crucified to me" (Gal. 6:14). Where is reality? The mystic who retreats from what he considers a world of *maya* dwells happily on the plane of reality, as far as he is concerned, but the rest of us may look at him and deem him fit for a padded cell, completely out of touch with reality. Who is right? It is all in the point of view. Thus to say that "only love is real" amounts to saying, "I am rejecting other emotions. I will seek to feel only love and to act only from love. I will pay attention to nothing else, even the repercussions of my loving behavior if they do not seem conducive to love. I shall dismiss them all as 'illusion,' and that way nothing can possibly challenge the validity of this stance I am taking." One rationalizes this sanctified stubbornness with one or another philosophy or theology, and in Marianne Williamson's case, she derives from the claustrophobic pages of *A Course in Miracles* something resembling Yogacara, "Mind-Only" Buddhist idealism. In other words, "*A Course in Miracles* says that one day we will realize that nothing occurs outside our minds" (p. 109). She equates Jung's Collective Unconscious model with the divine mind and chalks up our seeming individual consciousnesses as mere *skandhas*, or "aggregates," making up the ever-shifting personalities we like to think of as ourselves.

> The concept of a divine, or "Christ" mind, is the idea that, at our core, we are not just identical, but actually the same being. . . . There's only one of us in here. . . . We're like spokes on a wheel, all radiating out from the same center. If you define us according to our position on the rim, we seem separate and distinct from one another. But if you define us according to our starting point, our source—the center of the wheel—we're a shared identity. . . . [A]t the bottom of it all, what we are is love. . . . There's actually no place where God stops and you start, and no place where you stop and I start. . . . We are all part of a vast sea of love, one indivisible divine mind. This truth of who we really are doesn't change; we just forget it." (p. 29)

> We awaken from the dream that we are finite, isolated creatures, and recognize that we are glorious, infinitely creative spirits. We awaken from the dream that we are weak, and accept that the power of the universe is within us. (p. 30)

I will admit up front, as I did during the consideration of *A Course in Miracles*, that I think someone is looking through the wrong end of the scope. In terms of the world we live in, the one we may not like but don't have to deny whole regions of in order to save face for our preferred worldview, which is the reality and which the dream? It would be nice to wield the power of the universe, as Captain America's foe the Red Skull does (in *Tales of Suspense* no. 80, 1966) when he gains the all-powerful weapon called the Cosmic Cube, enabling him to reshape reality at a whim, but that does not happen outside of comic books—and *A Course in Miracles*. It is hyped-up rhetoric. Which seems more relevant? Our differences, which dictate so much of what happens between us, good and bad? Or our common origin, the fact that we are all "starstuff," or more mundanely put: hydrogen atoms? What we have in common is in most ways the least important thing about us, our lowest common denominator, not our highest. And which of the following seems more like a dream: that we are finite, though resourceful, creatures, or that we are infinite spirits despite all the wall-to-wall evidence that we are not? Or, to put it another way, how would Williamson or Schucman say we could falsify their assertions? I mean, what would even *count* as evidence against the notion that I am the infinite God, and so are you? Our inability to command reality by whim does not count against it, because we can always say we have forgotten our all-powerful deity. The fact that the almighty, omniscient deity was able to forget in the first place does not count against the belief, for we need only draw a distinction between the way God "really is" on the plane of the Dharmakaya, and the refracted distortion of the truth as it appears to us, the fragments of God here on a lower plane. But then, once we introduce such a two-level system, we are back to observing that we do live in an experience-world that includes diversity. And our assertion that "we" live in a singular microdot of almighty love seems to be reduced to merely stubborn assertion after all. In other words, it seems impossible to name anything that would be logically entailed in the claim if it were true. It is hard, the way Williamson and her friends hedge their bets, even to describe how the world should look if all *were* God versus if all were *not* God. Thus the claim is not so much *false* as *useless*. Even if it were true, it wouldn't make any difference. It is a course in gibberish.

METAPHYSICAL MEDICINE SHOW

A great deal of the power religion holds lies in its tendency to over-simplify the baffling complexities of our problems. Their causes are multiform and usually largely untraceable. Years of therapy often leave them undiscovered and firmly in place. So when someone comes along with a simple "cure fer what ails ye," many people are eager to buy a bottle. There can be a simple solution only if there is a simple problem that everything else boils down to. So religions, cults, and pop therapies are quick to announce their patented distillation of all human ills down to one faulty connection, one bad apple. And then it is simple to fix, though perhaps not inexpensive. Such oversimple solutions invariably wind up creating more neurotic suffering than before, since they cannot work, the world and its ills being far too complex, and then the seeker/sufferer feels worse than before, since he now has religious failure to add to his rap sheet. He has managed even to bungle the supernatural, surefire cure. And in the meantime, he is clueless, given no guidance to help him reach maturity. "Gospels" have to minimize the differences between individuals because their whole appeal is their claim that "one size fits all." Any problems you have that don't fit, don't count. A fresh new convert only seems to glow with excitement, relief, and a sense of purpose for a while because, in the thrill of his initial zeal, he has simply stopped paying attention to those aspects of his life that had been problematical before. But it will not be long till they are knocking on the door, demanding attention again. The product representative (the evangelist, guru, spiritual director, etc.) will prescribe a more powerful dose of zeal for the cause, and that, too, may work for a while. But eventually the limit is reached. This is why there is such a turnover rate in cults and new religions, why so tiny a percentage of Billy Graham converts stick with it. It is all aptly summed up in the bogus claim of Transcendental Meditation and its front men like Deepak Chopra that if you learn their technique, you can fly. But the sad fact is your feet never stay off the ground, no matter how high you may bounce. And even then your bottom is going to hurt too much to continue.

Marianne Williamson fits the pattern: "Denying love is the only problem" (p. 73). Of course, it's never quite as simple as it appears! Why should the want of love be the root of all evil? If it requires an explanation, we have already taken a big step away from the simplicity we were promised. And we have. It turns out that "denying love" is code for a larger framework much like that we have found in Eckhart Tolle (and in Reinhold Niebuhr): We were individual, albeit redundant, cells belonging to a single reality. God in some unimaginable fashion did the last thing one might expect from an omniscient entity and forgot who he was! (Are things still "simple"?) Suddenly (and erroneously) finding ourselves alone, we began to fear for our sustenance and security, no longer trusting the whole to care for us. Mistrust (which came from . . . where?) corrupted love. We need now "simply" return to faith, or to love (as per the book's title), which must be the same thing as faith. "Faith is believing the universe is on our side, and that the universe knows what it's doing" (p. 46). Apparently, faith is also taking for granted that Marianne Williamson knows what she's talking about, because reason will not tell us so. For it is quite a different thing to believe that the universe is on your side as opposed to believing that there is no side to be on, for all is One. Whole religions can and do fall comfortably between these two stools.

Is *any* old thing to be deemed "true" which hath charm to soothe the savage breast? One must infer that Williamson and her colleagues have no trouble leaping from one conceptual province to another because they believe, somehow, that, like apparently different individual souls, diverse doctrines, too, are identical beneath the surface. And in that case, all she wants you to do is to start at any point along the rim and slide down any spoke to the common center.

MANIFEST DESTINY

Marianne Williamson qualifies as among those I denominated "New Age New Thoughters" in a previous chapter. That is, as I read her, she adds various secondary elements into the New Thought formula, elements that may or may not fit. Now I would like to take a look at her major innovation, which is a new spin on the venerable New Thought axiom of affirmation-visualization-manifestation. To anticipate, I will suggest that she is making a legitimate extrapolation from the traditional doctrine, one logically in accord with it yet one that is probably an error nonetheless. (Of course, you may think differently.)

As to her solid New Thought character, I need only indicate her emphasis, familiar by now from Chögyam Trungpa, Venice Bloodworth, Shakti Gawain, Wayne Dyer, and especially Eckhart Tolle, upon engaging the present instead of fleeing to the future. "Waiting for a powerful future is a way of making sure it never gets here. An adolescent dreams of what will be. An adult takes joy in today" (p. 241). "We sometimes fail to work on ourselves in the relationships that are right in front of us, thinking that 'real life' begins when *they* [Mr. Right or Ms. Right] get here. This is just a ploy of the ego once again, making sure that we'll seek but not find" (p. 109). "We don't get to the light through endless exploration of the darkness. . . . The only way to the light is through entering the light" now, not waiting in case it decides to dawn someday (pp. 110–11).

On a related theme, also common to New Thought, indeed perhaps, its most popular emphasis, there is the idea of financial miracles. Here is where, even more than in the case of spontaneous healing, New Thought approaches magical thinking and merits inclusion among sociologist Bryan Wilson's "cults of manipulation." In its crassest version, the doctrine teaches that one can rub the Aladdin's lamp of "affirmation" and get rich quick. But I believe Williamson's approach to the money question avoids crass materialism. Her attitude is more along the lines of the optimism of the gospels: "Do not concern yourselves over what you shall eat, what you shall drink, or where you shall stay. For all these things the pagans seek, and your heavenly Father knows that you need them. Seek first his kingdom and his righteousness, and all these things will be provided you" (Matt. 6:31–33). Williamson affirms that one's heavenly mindedness need not be discredited by one's being no earthly good. Spiritual pursuits will not embarrass you. "A responsible attitude toward money is one in which we're open to whatever comes, and trusting that it always will" (p. 170). Nor does this amount simply to living on a wing and a prayer. Williamson tries to spiritualize the matter of making a living, since something that occupies such a lion's share of one's time ought to be approached as a dharma, a spiritual calling as well as a means to pay the bills. "I have heard it said that living out of our vision is more powerful than living out of our circumstances. Holding on to a vision invokes the circumstances by which the vision is achieved" (p. 186). This would hold true for specific projects as well as a career path. Shakti Gawain's book *Living in the Light* is entirely devoted to living by intuition as a fundamental component of the

New Thought lifestyle. And it is important to remember that such confidence need not imply the metaphysical window dressing set forth by some of its advocates. It is just a matter of the wisdom of humankind, as when Ray Bradbury, no mystic, advised those uncertain whether to make a career of their dreams as he did. Sometimes you just have to jump out the window and grow your wings on the way down!

Marianne Williamson's handling of the delicate balance between seeking prosperity and being charitable is also quite helpful. One receives the uncomfortable impression from some New Thought writers that giving is a way of priming the pump, and that if it were not, mere compassion for the needs of others would not be sufficient motivation. Instead, Williamson nicely shows how the two motives, self-directed and other-directed, mesh naturally:

> When our desire is to give instead of get, our core belief is that we have so much abundance, we can afford to give it away. The subconscious mind takes its clue from our core beliefs, and brilliantly manufactures situations that reflect them. Our willingness to give directs the universe to give to us. (p. 181)

She envisions a kind of "trickle-up" economics whereby good sought for others reflects back upon the giver.

ONE STEP BEYOND

All this is wisdom well put. Marianne Williamson makes her own the New Thought counsel to visualize the future, the desired goal, as if present as a means of causing our everyday reality to realign itself accordingly. But Williamson takes it a major step farther. Traditional New Thoughters usually embrace a nondualist metaphysic to explain how it is they can manipulate reality in the way they describe (though their most recent advocates translate the whole thing into terms of quantum physics). They are interested in their divine identity and the entailed access to divine, world-shaping power. But Williamson, under the influence of *A Course in Miracles*, turns to the allied question of one's unity with those around one, and the implications of their common identity with God. What sort of visualization and affirmation would be appropriate there? What sort of yet-unseen reality would one seek to manifest in that dimension? Here Williamson's love monism comes to the fore. We find ourselves at odds with others, competing against them, bitter against them, afraid of harm they may do us, disgusted by their evil behavior. But this sort of experience belies the fundamental fact of our identical oneness with them. So if we want to manifest that oneness in the form of actual harmony between (seeming) individuals, the thing to do is to affirm the basic (unseen) truth about them: they have done nothing wrong; they pose no threat; they are lovable, not hateful. And then that is how it will appear to us.

I fear this is a self-sealing premise, an invulnerable delusion subject to the same criterion of falsification I invoked above. First, I admit that answering hatred with love can sometimes work like magic in showing a new, unguessed opportunity to someone raised on and warped by hate. Second, I do not believe that will always work, and it will be dangerous to insist that it is working when it is not. The more one stubbornly insists that things are not the way they seem, that people are really being good when they are being bad, the more of a fool and a sucker one will become. One not only looks on the bright side but refuses to admit there might be a dark side. Any lingering awareness of the other person's evil will be dismissed as one's own fault. "They wouldn't be coming across to me as vicious if I weren't somehow projecting it onto them!" This is classic blaming the victim stuff. Abused wives are experts at it.

And I do not believe I am criticizing Williamson's approach on the basis of some unforeseen implication I am weaving out in a perverse manner, making the exception into the rule. She herself says, "Pain doesn't stem from the love we're denied by others, but rather from the love that we deny them" (p. 89). This mad doctrine is in turn based on the solipsism of *A Course in Miracles*, as we should expect: "Only what you have not given can be lacking in any situation" (quoted in Williamson, p. 111). You see, this is what *has* to be true if we are to take the solipsism of the system seriously. It is not some maxim of shrewd observation about human experience. It is a way of keeping everything that happens to you safely within the monad of your existence, you being the only one who does. It is the interpersonal relations equivalent of the Christian Science approach to healing (which New Thought also typically espouses). Yes, yes, that we may make ourselves sick, even unto death, by unhealthy attitudes is part of the received wisdom of humankind. But to insist, on the basis of the arbitrary axiom that "We are God, and God cannot be ill, so neither are we"—well, that is nobody's wisdom. It is perverse dogmatism that refuses to learn wisdom from the faith-generated deaths of sick believers who threw out their insulin, and so on, thinking that they would be healed by "Dr. Jesus" or "Jesus Christ, Scientist."

We do not need to charge Williamson with repression: she boasts of it and elevates it to a technique of sanctification. We must "seek a greater capacity for love and forgiveness within ourselves. We do this through a 'selective remembering,' a conscious decision to remember only loving thoughts [about people] and let go of any fearful ones" (p. 61). But would this reprogramming really expand one's capacity to forgive? I think not, since the strategy appears to be one of denial rather than open-eyed reconciliation.

> In the Course . . . we're taught . . . that there *is* no guilt in anyone, because only love is real . . . , to see through the illusion of guilt, to the innocence that lies beyond. . . . Actually, then, there is nothing to forgive. The traditional notion of forgiveness—what *A Course in Miracles* calls "forgiveness to destroy"—is then an act of judgment. It is the arrogance of someone who sees themselves [*sic*] as better than someone else, or perhaps equally as sinful, which is still a misconception and the arrogance of the ego. (p. 61)

> An attack on a brother is a reminder of his guilty past. In choosing to affirm a brother's guilt, we are choosing to experience more of it. The future is programmed in the present. To let the past go is to remember that in the present, my brother is innocent. It is an act of gracious generosity to accept a person based on what we know to be the truth about them, regardless of whether or not they are in touch with that truth themselves. (p. 84)

The tragic foolishness of all this is obvious. What we have here is therapeutic liberalism: an anti-ethic, a rejection of good and evil because if we accepted that anyone was culpable for their actions, then we, too, might be culpable, and we are much too fragile to withstand guilt feelings. So, in terror of feeling them, we declare all things good. As if that were not pathetic enough, consider the political implications, which are all too evident around us today: this is precisely the rationale implicit in releasing convicted child rapists back into the public and being concerned with their privacy rights, with less concern for their future victims. It is Pollyanna liberalism. No matter what outrages and enormities come, such a person always has the option of retreating from the pain caused by outward events into an inner world where crimes and wrongs are, as Williamson calls them, "hallucinations" (p. 84). The only thing worth protecting is the belief in solipsism: I alone exist, so I must be in control, so everything must, despite appearances, be copacetic.

And, once again, one must ask: even if true, what does this doctrine even *mean*, this affirmation against appearances, that everyone is good? Williamson assures us, "when we see the total truth about someone," we see that "[t]hey *are* perfect. That's not just our imagination" (p. 106). Criminals of every type are legion. They are not rare exceptions, though, thankfully, neither are they the majority. But one must reckon with a considerable portion of the human race being malevolent and dangerous. To see Charles Manson, Jeffrey Dahmer, countless child-raping priests, innumerable demagogues, and dictators as truly innocent is hardly "seeing the total truth about them." No, plainly it is Marianne Williamson and Helen Schucman who are missing a significant element of the truth about them. It reminds me of an experiment James Randi conducted with a famous Russian psychic who claimed to be able to read a person's character and deeds from a single portrait photo. Randi showed her a snapshot of mass murderer Richard Speck. Her clairvoyant powers told her about Speck's long-standing interest in music, which was true enough, but somehow she didn't get a clue about those grisly murders he committed. Who is seeing the "total truth," and who is captive to their "imagination"? I just cannot see how the fact that the molester priest and his victim are made of the same "starstuff" or "Godstuff" is nearly as important as what the perpetrator has done.

Is the traditional (i.e., the dictionary's) definition of forgiveness really so bad? Does it entail a moral judgment? You bet it does! And that is the greatness of forgiveness: it is what Paul Tillich calls "creative justice." It recognizes that a breach has occurred. A wrong has been done. And it moves on from there. It is difficult work to seek restoration of a broken relationship sundered by one partner's violation. But the one who forgives shoulders that task. How much easier, by contrast, to let it slide and say, "Oh, it was only an illusion? Whew! No harm *done*, eh?" That is the way of the emotional coward who grants forgiveness for fear he is not up to the task of standing up for himself. That is the way of pathetic inauthenticity and moralistic hypocrisy that sooner or later undermines all moral standards by making everyone innocent by fiat. That is not a return to love, but a retreat into denial. And don't worry—you can be sure that the repressed will return.

WEIRD ROMANCE

The reader of any self-help book must be on guard in case it seems a writer is hastily generalizing from his or her own experience. Western Christendom has been suffering for centuries from St. Augustine doing that. I wonder if what we are hearing from *A Course in Miracles* and from Schucman's disciples Marianne Williamson and Eckhart Tolle is not the "theologizing" of their unhappy love lives. Williamson sums it up: "Our desire to find one 'special person,' . . . is hurtful because it is delusional. It means we're seeking salvation in separation rather than in oneness. The only love that completes us is the love of God" (p. 95). "The ego . . . argues that the love we need must come from someone else, and that there's one special person out there who can fill up that whole. Since the desire for that person actually stems from our belief that we're separate from God, then the desire itself symbolizes the separation and the guilt we feel because of it" (p. 96). "The ego isn't looking for someone to love; it's looking for someone to attack. Its dictate in love is 'Seek, and do not find.' It looks for a reflection of itself, another mask that hides the face of Christ. In a special relationship, I'm afraid to show you the real truth about myself—my fears, my weaknesses—because I'm afraid that if you see them, you'll leave. I'm assuming you're as judgmental as I am" (p. 98).

Eckhart Tolle, another grateful reader of *A Course in Miracles*, belongs to the same Lonely Heart's Club Band:

> Unless and until you access the consciousness frequency of presence, all relationships, and particularly intimate relationships, are deeply flawed and ultimately dysfunctional. They may seem perfect for a while, such as when you are "in love," but invariably that apparent perfection gets disrupted as arguments, conflicts, dissatisfaction, and emotional or even physical violence occurs with increasing frequency. It sees that most "love relationships" become love/hate relationships before long. Love can then turn into savage attack, feelings of hostility, or complete withdrawal of affection at the flick of a switch. This is considered normal. . . . It may appear that if you could only eliminate the negative or destructive cycles, then all would be well, and the relationship would flower beautifully—but alas, this is not possible. (p. 123)

You expect Tolle next to say what a difference it makes in a relationship when both partners are living in the Now. But he doesn't. He seems to be describing romantic relationships per se, which he sees as a subtype of addiction. He damns relationships with the faintest praise:

> Avoidance of relationships in an attempt to avoid pain is not the answer either. The pain is there anyway. Three failed relationships in as many years are more likely to force you into awakening than three years on a desert island or shut away in your room. But if you could bring intense presence into your aloneness, that would work for you, too. (p. 127)

Finally, almost grudgingly, he finds himself forced to admit, on a technicality, that a sound relationship *might* be *possible*:

> Love is not selective, just as the light of the sun is not selective. It does not make one person special. It is not exclusive. Exclusivity is not the love of God but the "love" of ego. However, the intensity with which true love is felt can vary. There may be one person who reflects your love back to you more clearly and more intensely than others, and if that person feels the same towards you, it can be said that you are in a love relationship with him or her. (p. 129)

Note the clinical tone of the anthropologist, as if such arcane behaviors are alien to the writer. What we've got here are the New Age equivalents to comedian Chris Farley's motivational speaker character, Matt Foley. He is a bitter failure, being thrice divorced and living in a van down by the river. He is exactly the wrong kind of person from whom to listen to a lecture called "Go for it!"

Why do *A Course in Miracles* and *A Return to Love*, and *The Power of Now* offer such bizarre and romance-dooming nuggets of advice? Again, I suspect that their authors' love lives have been unsatisfactory, and they are committing the great sin of designing the future in the shape of the past. But on another level, they are again safeguarding the padded cell view of reality they elsewhere espouse: they are alone in a delusional world of their own making in which they are God, hence all that they say is infallible, and so are you, so what looks good to them must be good for you, too. But finally, the two levels are one: they have chosen solipsism as a neurotic protection strategy, and that is nowhere clearer than in these whispered words of anti-romance. For to be open to receive love makes one dangerously vulnerable, and Williamson's fear of rejection is palpable on the page. Again, her metaphysics is no antidote to fear, as she promises, but rather a desperate defense against it. She is not offering armor against the blows of what she fears. She is offering a numbing anesthetic to take away the pain. And that numbness she mistakes for peace. Just like frostbite. The forgiveness she offers is cheap and predicated on systematic denial; the love she receives is Platonic for fear of the real thing; the esteem she accords to others is the flip side of her own inability to face the sting of guilt. Is she returning *to* or *from* love?

Chapter 7
Idol Conversations

Neale Donald Walsch,
Conversations with God

Your contemplation is worth whatever your being is worth; your God is the god you deserve.
—Henry Corbin, *The Man of Light in Iranian Sufism* (p. 92)

WHAT IF GOD WAS ONE OF US?
JUST A SLOB LIKE ONE OF US?

*C*hanneling supernatural entities appears to be getting easier all the time. Usually we picture a dramatic shtick in which the ostensible oracle shudders to shrug off his/her mundane ego so that it may be temporarily supplanted by the ghost of, let's say, an Atlantean warlord (in the case of Judy Zebra Knight) or an Atlantean adulteress (Shirley MacLaine). But Helen Schucman channeled the whole of the interminable *A Course in Miracles* in a state of normal consciousness, just speaking what came into her head, the words seeming to be formed by an inaudible but distinct inner voice—a voice, I guess, like the one that once whispered to me, "Slow down," just before I rounded a bend in the highway and got nabbed by a state trooper. But easier still, one supposes, was the scribal task of Neale Donald Walsch, who found himself one day venting his frustrations by penning a complaint letter to God (he had often used this clever technique to let off steam in letters to friends or employers, wisely refraining from sending them); as soon as he thought he was done, he felt impelled to keep writing, this time transcribing the *answer* to the legal pad epistle he had just scribbled. The result was *Conversations with God: An Uncommon Dialogue.*

The parallel with Schucman's New Age Bible *A Course in Miracles* is not purely fortuitous. One may suspect Walsch's effort to have been in some measure inspired by it. Indeed, I am tempted to view *Conversations with God* as his own version of *A Course in Miracles.* He liked it and, somewhere deep down, wanted to write his own version, like pulp author Robert E. Howard, who, reading a story by H. P. Lovecraft featuring the latter's imaginary *Necronomicon*, liked it very much and decided to fabricate his own nightmare volume for use in horror tales, *Nameless Cults.* Walsch and his pet deity even give a shout-out to Schucman. God says, "All attack is a call for help." Walsch replies, "I read that in *A Course in Miracles.*" God promptly takes advantage of the straight-man line thus offered: "I put it there" (p. 90). This is typical of the rim-shot revelations which abound in this book.

Not surprisingly, Walsch/God goes on to offer specific insights derived straight from Schucman's older testament: "All human actions are motivated at their deepest level by one of two emotions—fear or love" (p. 15). "Every human thought, word, or deed is based in one emotion or the other. You have no choice about this, because there is nothing else from which to choose. But you have free choice about which of these to select" (p. 19). Here Walsch even imitates the *Outer Limits* control voice style of Schucman's book. We think again of Schucman when we read in Walsch that "even the term 'wrong thinking' is a misnomer, because there is no such thing as that which is wrong" (p. 40), a bumbling misapplication of the Platonic-Augustinian Privation Theory of evil. Even the mode of presentation comes from Schucman's *Course*: "Now that we're moving this rapidly through the material . . ." (p. 203).

The attraction Walsch's book has for many readers appears to be its no-nonsense, straight talk, commonsense approach to major religious questions. Readers find it refreshing to hear God echoing their own unvoiced skepticisms. They rejoice to learn that God is more like their wiseacre old uncle than the pious clergy whose sermons he used to mock at Sunday dinner. "In most cases, you don't want to make your parents, your schools, your religions, your traditions your holy scriptures wrong—so you *deny your own* experience in favor of what you have been *told to think*" (p. 63). Yeah! Give 'em hell, God! And yet one begins to feel that perhaps Walsch has taken God down one peg too many. Sometimes he comes across as "Your Assholiness." And this approach to theology and revelation by means of puncturing religious pomposity turns out to be quite ironic, since eventually we are going to find that Walsch takes his yellow-pad oracles as seriously as fundamentalists take the Bible and expects the reader to do so as well. Walsch, it seems, is flippant and irreverent to traditional deities, not so much to his own.

MY WORLD AND WELCOME TO IT

Conversations with God is a prime example of what Jacques Derrida called "the myth of the voice," that is, the illusion that portentous pronouncements appear to issue not only into the reverberating silence but also from it, an essentially sourceless epiphany of self-creating truth offered to the hearer to accept or reject. The myth of the voice is nowhere more mythic than in religion, when the voice is that of a *bath kol*, a divine calling from heaven. For example, in the Jordan baptism scene in Mark's Gospel, there is an apparently simple and spontaneous declaration in the voice of God from the sky, which says, "You are my Son, the beloved, in whom I am well pleased" (Mark 1:11). In fact, it seems to represent the careful scribal cobbling together of at least three scriptural texts": "Take now your son, your only son, whom you love, and go to the land of Moriah, and offer him there as a burnt offering" (Gen. 22:2); "I will surely tell of the decree of Yahve: he said to me, 'You are my son; today I have begotten you'" (Ps. 2:7); and "Behold my servant, whom I uphold; my chosen one, in whom my soul delights" (Isa. 42:1). What first appears as a bolt from the blue is really an artificial, editorial compilation.

Even so, Walsch's declamations are offered as telegrams from God, truth speaking for itself, cutting through the fog of human opinion. As revelations, they offer objective truth, the facts about the universe. But what we are really getting is one mortal's opinions, the distillation of one man's reading and thinking, and only the punch line. It is obvious that Walsch had already made quite a study of Eastern faiths and New Age/New Thought metaphysics, and, posing as God, he passes on his synthesis of his various favorite notions. But he doesn't argue for his conclusions. He doesn't tell us how he got there, because he wants to create the illusion that he *didn't* get there. He wants us to believe the truth came to him one day, straight from the blue, with no human fingerprints on it. Well, wherever he got it, what does he teach about the world and our place in it?

Mainly he seems to be a panentheist. His God announces, if possible, in accents more grandiose than Jesus' Father or even the great and powerful Oz: "Now I will explain to you the ultimate mystery: your exact and true relationship to me. YOU ARE MY BODY. As *your* body is to *your* mind and soul, so, too, are *you* to *My* mind and soul" (p. 197). I guess that settles *that*. Might as well forget about those philosophy courses you were planning to take.

Kabbalistic Jews are panentheists, too, believing that all things share the divine nature, having been formed out of the Godstuff, but that there remains left over a personal center of divine consciousness that we may worship as a person analogous to ourselves. Kabbalists developed a fascinating theory to explain the origin of evil and adversity, which would at first seem incompatible with the divine origin and character of the world. It seems that God, filling all space, being infinite, had to contract into himself somewhat to provide ontological space where a created world might be placed. He did so, and this cosmic contraction is called the *Tsimtsum*. And yet God, being infinite by nature, cannot become less so. Thus even the apparent gap he left empty was a part of him, albeit his shadow side (something like the charged vacuity left behind upon the decay of a positron). It was from this Dark Side of God, which was without form and void, that the creation emanated, including evil. Walsch borrows the Tsimtsum: "God has contrived to create 'something else' other than itself (though in strictest terms this is impossible, since God is—I AM—All That Is)" (p. 57).

Panentheism is a close cousin to both pantheism (all things are manifestations of divine substance, without a personal God) and nondualism (all things are illusions since there is nothing but the divine substance), and, like many New Age gurus, Walsch tends to hover between all three options, something no one ought to blame him for, given the admittedly mind-boggling character of the divine. If even physical phenomena only more or less fit the theoretical paradigms we formulate, who would expect the phenomena of the divine to do so? Anyway, Walsch borrows a page from Stoicism, the most popular ancient form of pantheism, drawing its inference of a providential order to things, along with the moral implications: "You see, suffering has nothing to do with events, but with one's reaction to them. *What's happening is merely what's happening. How you feel about it is another matter.* I have given you the tools with which to respond and react to events in a way which reduces—in fact, *eliminates*—pain, but you have not used them" (p. 105). In the Stoic playbook the reference would be to the wisdom of valuing only virtue and evaluating every seeming catastrophe as a welcome opportunity to grow more virtuous. But, given the nondualism Walsch elsewhere espouses, and his claim that his conceptual "tools" can wholly eliminate suffering, he is probably talking about Christian Science denial of the reality of pain, for all the good that's liable to do anyone.

Walsch's divine alter-ego tells him, "There *is* no coincidence, and *nothing* happens 'by accident.' Each event and adventure is called *to* your Self *by* your Self in order that you might create and experience Who You Really Are" (pp. 51–52). This would be Stoicism, with its trust in the all-permeating Logos of God (Zeus) which orders all circumstances for our ultimate good, except that Walsch (again, like all New Agers) crosses it with nondualism, according to which one's nature is the same as the divine Brahman. In that case, you yourself have orchestrated your existence. Not that you remember doing it. No one claims that. The idea is analogous to the distinction drawn by literary critics in a first-person narrative between the "narrating I" and the "narrated I." The latter is the character as embroiled in the events of the moment. He may not know their cause or their outcome at the moment, but the narrating I has since learned these things and may share them with the reader as he is telling the tale of his own past adventures, like Odysseus or John Carter of Mars. Even so, the apparent individual with your name on his tag cannot see very far outside the circle of light cast by the present moment, but the true, divine being within, which is secretly the same as the Brahman and all other persons, does understand what is happening and why. The short-term goal is to accept that what you are undergoing is all according to (your own) plan and to try to learn the intended lesson, which in Walsch's case is that you gradually remember your divine origin and identity. All events are meant to wake you up again. And it is you who meant them to do so when once you wrote this particular life like a stage play. Nor is this the only play in which you are likely to perform, as it may take several (or zillions) of incarnations to learn your lesson (p. 204), all the more if you are in the habit of spending your life watching TV.

To Walsch's credit, he seems to have given a bit of thought to the implications of holding to nondualism on the one hand and talking with a personal God on the other. À la Shankara, he understands that the formless Brahman who is far beyond personality is reflected on the lower levels of perception as Isvara or Brahma, a traditional theistic-style deity, and Walsch seems to realize that this latter is the one with whom he is in dialogue. God drops a hint: "For even as you are the body of Me, I am the body of another." Walsch: "You mean, You are *not God?*" God replies: "Yes, I am God, as you understand Him. . . . I am the Conceiver and the Creator of Everything you now know and experience, and you are My children . . . even as I am the child of another." A surprised-sounding Walsch: "Are You trying to tell me that even God has a God?" A coy demi-

179

deity replies: "I am telling you that your perception of ultimate reality is more limited than you thought, and that Truth is more *un*limited than you can imagine" (p. 197).

THE NODDING GOD

So, as in some Hindu systems, the universe is a great game devised by God, a game of hide-and-seek in which God's lower-order facet reflections, imagining themselves autonomous individuals, have the object of rediscovering their original identity with Brahman. "This is My plan for you. This is My Ideal: that I should become realized through you. That thus, concept is turned into experience, that I might know my Self *experientially*" (p. 43). Everyone can win, and eventually everyone will, but it takes a long, long time, since some don't understand either the rules or the object of the game, or even that there *is* a game, and that they're playing. Uh, if they're all God, why *don't* they? That's because, somewhere along the line, this one or that one, acting in amnesiac ignorance, committed some deeds to which a high karmic price tag attaches, and this only deepens their funk.

But isn't this approach rather haphazard? Not at all. In a shrewd version of the Free Will Defense, Walsch/God explains:

Upon entering the physical universe, you *relinquished your remembrance of yourself.* This allows you to *choose* to be Who You Are, rather than simply wake up in the castle, so to speak. It is the act of choosing to be, rather than simply being told that you are, a part of God that you *experience* yourself as being a total choice, which is what, by definition, God is. Yet how can you have a choice about something over which there *is* no choice? You cannot *not* be My offspring no matter how hard you try—but you *can forget*. (p. 28)

The goal, then, is the experience of self-discovery, not simply the knowledge one is thereby discovering. God already knew that good and well. But not even God can know what finite experience, including self-discovery, is like unless he becomes an ignorant human who needs to discover himself. So that is what he has done. The point is much the same as the great Sufi mystics who taught that God created Man, the heavenly Man of Light, in order to behold his own glory. How does he do this? The Primal Man, a finite image of Allah, sharing all his attributes, is in turn the prototype of the creation, including human beings, in whom the world first becomes self-aware. As individuals become aware of their ultimate identity with Allah (though seventy thousand veils separate them from him) and seek to experience it again, they grow closer to the divine prototype of humanity (its perfect historical manifestations being the Prophet Muhammad and, by his own confession, Mohyiddin Ibn al-Arabi); they come to contemplate, then, with the inner eye, to behold the glory from which they stem and in which they partake. And in that moment, God knows himself through their eyes. This I judge to be the most profound depth of *Conversations with God*.

Usually the goal of a nondualist system is liberation by means of knowledge. But Walsch applies his worldview of illusion and cosmic sleight-of-hand also to matters of this world. If the world of seeming is our own creation, and if we can in some measure regain our ability to wield such demiurgic authority, then we ought to be able to manipulate the dreamstuff of which the samsaric world is made. This belief, though not wholly absent from Eastern faiths, probably reflects instead Walsch's debt to New Thought meta-physics, where the vision is more thisworldly. New Thought culti-vates belief in visualizing the way one wants things to be, believing that what one visualizes will "manifest" in external events. "You will not have that for which you ask, nor can you have anything you want. This is because your very request is a statement of lack, and you're saying you want a thing only works to produce that precise experience—wanting—in your reality" (p. 11). "Instead of think-ing, 'I want success,' think 'I have success" (p. 179).

Even the venerable notion of the individual's inherent Godhood seems to serve worldly, selfish ends, as if the Prophet Walsch were losing his focus. In a slippage seemingly endemic to New Age reli-gion, "Self" gradually slides back over into "ego." It is supposed to denote the unconditioned, divine Atman but winds up denoting instead the conditioned, psychological jiva. Thus we are treated to the spectacle of Shirley MacLaine standing in the surf, arms spread wide, yelling into the night air, "I am God!" No, like Felix Unger, we must remind Oscar Madison, "Now, this is the *real* you . . . that's underneath the *other* real you!" I see Walsch sliding over into this marshy territory in such utterances as "The first step in changing *anything* is to know and accept that you have chosen it to be what it is. If you can't accept this on a personal level, agree to it through your understanding that We are all One. Seek then to create change not because a thing is wrong, but because it no longer makes an accurate statement of Who You Are" (p. 36). Can you pic-ture the poor delusional slob who twists his mind till he actually thinks this way? *"There is only one reason to do anything: as a statement to the universe of Who You Are.* Used in this way, life becomes self-creative. You use life to create your Self as Who You Are, and Who You've Always Wanted to *Be"* (p. 36).

Walsch/God hardly stops here. The narcissistic infantilism gets even worse: "If there is some aspect of creation you find you do not enjoy, bless it and simply change it. Choose again. Call forth a new reality. Think a new thought. Say a new word. Do a new thing. Do this magnificently and the rest of the world will follow you. Ask it to. Call for it to. Say, 'I am the Life and the Way, follow me'" (p. 92). That's nice. Now it's time for your meds.

You might find yourself thinking, "If *this* guy can be a spiritual master, what's stopping me? And then you start thinking, "Where did I leave that ordination application to the Universal Life Church?" Go ahead! Walsch encourages what we might call guru inflation: "*Each soul is a Master*—though some do not remember their origins or their heritages" (p. 33). "All of you are special" (p. 143). Remember that *Seinfeld* episode where Jerry and George cringe when the hostess at a party yells from her window to the legion of runners in the New York City Marathon, "You're *all* winners!"

But if there is a winner to the narcissism game, it is you know who. "Many Masters have been sent to the Earth to demonstrate Eternal Truth. Others, such as John the Baptist, have been sent as messengers, telling of the Truth in glowing terms, speaking of God with unmistakable clarity. These special messengers have been gifted with extraordinary insight and the very special power to see and receive Eternal Truth, plus the ability to communicate complex concepts in ways that can and will be understood by the masses. You are such a messenger" (p. 143).

And the importance of *Conversations with God*? It turns out to be instrumental to the task of correcting the false un-Walsch teaching which has for so long plunged the world into woe. "You can undo the teaching by reading and re-reading this book. Over and over again, read it. Until you understand every passages. Until you're familiar with every word. When you can quote its passage to others, when you can bring its phrases to mind in the midst of the darkest hour, then you will have 'undone the teaching'" (p. 120).

The only thing more nauseating than imaging some poor sucker cherishing in his secret heart the tone-deaf texts of this pancake-flat book is the self-congratulation Walsch offers himself with his hand up God's back: "It takes great courage to announce oneself as a man of God" (p. 145). *Sniff.* Bra-*vo*, man!

WOODEN NICKELS

Early on, Walsch asks God how a poor mortal is supposed to be able to tell genuine revelations from false ones, something about which he seems to be little troubled by the end of the book.

> The challenge is one of discernment. The difficulty is knowing the difference between messages from God and data from other sources. Discrimination is a simple matter with the application of a basic rule: *Mine is always your Highest Thought, your Clearest Word, your Grandest Feeling. Anything less is from another source.* Now the task of differentiation becomes easy, for it should not be difficult for even the beginning student [Catch the lingering Schucmanism here?] to identify the Highest, the Clearest, and the Grandest. Yet I will give you these guidelines: The Highest Thought is always that thought which contains joy. The Clearest Words are those words which contain truth. The Grandest Feeling is that feeling which you call love. (pp. 4–5)

Belief in revelation is a great temptation for those who prefer a shortcut, who want to leapfrog the tedious labor (as they deem it)

184

of thinking. Hence the disdain of some religious people for philosophy. In the present case, one thinks of Derrida's warning against Walsch's approach. Walsch's criterion for genuine revelation is a perfect case of the error denounced by Derrida as "Presence Metaphysics," the glib assurance that whatever appears "clear and distinct" (Descartes) to the contemplating mind must ipso facto be regarded as true. But there *is* no self-evident truth, as ought to be evident from the fact that not everyone accepts any proposed candidate for the crown of metaphysical truth. Every notion, despite its seeming single-malt simplicity, turns out to have seams, to represent combination, conflation, derivation from prior premises. Even the purity of the Now moment, of which our mystics make so much, dissolves upon closer inspection into an amalgam of recollection of the past and anticipation of the future in various recipes; otherwise the present moment must appear contentless, not a perception of anything. The ancient skeptics had already cast grave doubt on Walsch's thumbnail epistemology. Have you ever been absolutely convinced of the obvious truth of a thing, only to discover later that you were wrong? Of course you have. Then how can you be so sure of anything henceforth? You can't. Walsch can't either, but he doesn't seem to know it.

But it's worse. Why does Walsch, who is so skeptical of traditional religion with its pat answers, not think to question whether his divine pen pal is telling him the truth when he asks him for criteria? He is willing to accept whatever criteria his deity may supply. But how can he know *these* revelations are genuine? I, for one, have my doubts that they are.

The criteria given are uselessly subjective and vague, hinging the matter of truth on the way it seems at gut level to the poor humans who are so confused as to require revelation in the first place. Walsch/God seems to realize this as soon as he has given the criteria: just how are we to define "Highest, Grandest, Purest"? Hitler, the great cliché whipping boy, was pretty sure he had the highest truth of the grandest race of Aryan purity, and to hell with Jews. So Walsch's God decides to tighten up the criteria a bit by defining the signature mark of Highest, Grandest, Purest. "Highest" thoughts are accompanied by joy (even though Adolf rejoiced to receive the crematorium statistics). Grandest thoughts are accompanied by love (like that which Hitler had for the German nation?). And the Clearest are the thoughts that are *true*. Uh, that's great. But isn't it fatally circular? What we are supposed to be getting here are rules to follow to tell *whether* thoughts are true in the first place. Let's see: true notions are Clear ones, which are true ones. Of course, the point is that all of Walsch's thoughts are true, and the seeker need trouble himself no further. Look, if Walsch is not simply pulling rank on you, why does he ascribe everything he says to Almighty God?

And if something God/Walsch says strikes you as doubtful, don't worry, he's got that one covered, too: "We should listen to God even when what's being said seems wrong? Especially when it seems wrong. If you think you are right about everything, who needs to talk to God?" (p. 7). Say, *good point*, Neale! If we can figure out the truth well enough with our best judgment, what *do* we need with divine revelation? Never mind whether the George Costanza approach to "doing the opposite" comports with what we read two pages earlier about going with the truth of our clearest thoughts.

ER, *GOOD* ONE, MEIN FÜHRER!

As if to demonstrate the utter uselessness of his epistemological criteria for would-be revelations, Walsch implicates the divine voice in all manner of silly declamations. "Think you [like that phony King James idiom?] that God cannot laugh? Do you imagine that God does not enjoy a good joke? Is it your knowing [= assumption?] that God is without humor? I tell you, God *invented* humor" (p. 60). Yeah, yeah. It is so sophomoric, so sitcom sentimental. *Please* don't let this be a real revelation from God. It reminds me of a time my dad and I sat watching some campaign news during the 1988 election, and George H. W. Bush, trying to look like a real Texan, claimed to enjoy pork rinds. My father asked me, "You think he's lying?" I replied, "I *hope* he's lying!"

For the inventor of humor, Walsch's God hasn't got much of a sense of it. Jesus and the Buddha taught in parables; the divine Walsch uses bad puns, the kind of stuff you see on church message boards: "It is *your* sole purpose. That is to say, your *soul purpose*" (p. 28). "If you do not go within, you go without" (p. 44). "You will never find Me in your mind. In order to truly know God, you have to be out of your mind" (p. 94). "Yet even 'fate' can be an acronym for 'from all thoughts everywhere.' In other words, the consciousness of the planet" (p. 106). "You don't need to have a reason for anything. Just *be cause*. Be the cause of your experience" (p. 206). If we didn't realize these were Walsch's own pathetic witticisms, we would have to pity him for having to feign amusement whenever God cracked these groaners—like some nervous crony of Saddam Hussein or Hitler, the tyrant having offered some lame jest. Better make that laughter sound convincing!

Walsch's God is a pseudoscientific crank. "Like energy attracts like energy—forming (to use simple words) 'clumps' of energy of like kind. When enough similar 'clumps' crisscross each other—run into each other—they '*stick to*' each other (to use another simple term). It takes an incomprehensibly huge amount of similar energy 'sticking together,' thusly to form matter" (pp. 54–55). I don't need to know what else this book says; anyone who uses terms like "clumps of energy" simply cannot be the real God. "Jesus did this regularly. He understood how to manipulate energy and matter, how to arrange it, how to redistribute it, how to utterly control it. Many Masters have known this. Many know it now. *You* can know it. Right now" (p. 55). Whether Walsch learned this secret, which would presumably put him on the same level with *Star Trek* characters like Q or Trelaine, the Squire of Gothos, we are not told. My guess is that he leaves it hanging to tantalize his credulous followers with what he may or may not be able to do. But I don't think he did learn the trick. He can't even turn printer's ink into sensible words.

God is also a conspiracy nut, a sucker for urban legends: "What if I told you your own medical profession *holds back* cures, refuses to approve alternative medicines and procedures because they threaten the very structure of the 'healing' profession?" (p. 89). God/Walsch chides "the governments of the world" because they "do not *want* to end world hunger" (pp. 49, 89). But what's wrong with that? Presumably Walsch doesn't want to either, since he figures all those poor human skeletons *chose* their rib-protruding lot in order to learn some damn karmic lesson (p. 46).

God is a Leftist, too: "Your industrial-military complex ... opposes mightily any attempt to install a war-no-more government-anywhere" (p. 48). This might be true, though I doubt it. But do you see the problem here? Walsch offers no data, no evidence for such assertions: they are presented as simple dicta from God. There is a name for that: demagoguery. In this case, demagoguery from a demigod. (How often do you get to use that phrase?)

BLAMING THE VICTIM, BLESSING THE VILLAIN

Perhaps the most chilling moment of Rob Zombie's movie *House of a Thousand Corpses* comes early on, when in a pseudodocumentary shot, the sociopathic vixen Baby casually remarks, "There's no 'wrong.'" This is the rusty faucet from which all the film's ensuing horrors flow. Likewise, one of the really frightening things about the New Age movement, even worse than its fondness for superstition and pseudoscience, is its moral nihilism. New Age gurus seem to want to comfort guilt-ridden wretches beaten down by fundamentalism or Roman Catholicism. That is a good thing, but then Walsch and his colleagues throw the baby out along with the baptismal water. They assure us there is no such thing as sin or guilt, even morality. "There are no 'shoulds' or 'shouldn'ts' in God's world. Do what you want to do. Do what reflects, what represents you as a grander version of your Self. If you want to feel bad, feel bad" (p. 38). "Those who taught you were wrong. I have never set down a 'right' or 'wrong,' a 'do' or a 'don't.' To do so would be to strip you completely of your greatest gift—the opportunity to do as you please, and experience the results of that. . . . To say that something—a thought, a word, an action—is 'wrong' would be as much as to tell you not to do it. . . . To restrict you would be to deny the reality of Who You Really Are" (p. 39). "Put away your pointless taboos and restrictions upon sexual energy— rather, help others to truly understand its wonder, and to channel it properly. Do *these* things and you will go a long way toward ending robbery and rape forever" (p. 51). So it's the laws against sexual excess that produce sexual excess? This sounds to me like the naiveté of anarchists who imagine that police are the cause of crime. If God says it, he's wrong.

New Age gurus are inconsistent in their dismissal of guilt, since they proceed to pile the weight of all the world's ills on each of us: "You are *all* at root cause for the conditions which exist which create in the robber the desire, or the perceived need, to steal. You have all created the consciousness which makes rape possible. It is when you see *in yourself* that which caused the crime that you begin, at last, to heal the condition from which it sprang" (p. 51). "There are no victims in the world, and no villains. And neither are you a victim of the choices of others. At some level you have *all* created that which you say you detest—and having created it, you have *chosen* it. . . . So long as you entertain the notion that there is something or someone else out there 'doing it' to you, you disempower yourself to do anything about it. Only when you say, 'I *did* this' can you find the power to change it. *It is much easier to change what you are doing than to change what another is doing*" (pp. 35–36). The sum of this Orwellian reasoning is that the actual murderers and molesters are *not* guilty, but everyone else *is*. This is the kind of ultraliberal doctrine Frank Miller satirized in his 1985 graphic novel, *Batman: The Dark Knight Returns*, where a future Gotham City administration hunts down Batman as a vigilante and paroles the Joker and Two-Face as hapless victims of society! Walsch would not blame poor Jack Napier (Joker) or Harvey Dent (Two-Face) either. "It is not appropriate to interfere with choice, nor to question it. It is particularly inappropriate to condemn it. . . . Be watchful, therefore, of the choices of others, but not judgmental.

Know that their choice is perfect for them in this moment now" (p. 47). Let me get this straight: God gives Walsch detailed instruction on how to avoid making the wrong choices, which assumes he might easily otherwise make them. But we must assume that everyone else is constantly and automatically making the right one? And notice how Walsch dances around using the word *wrong*, using *inappropriate* instead—he wouldn't want to sound like he condemns something just because he condemns it!

Here we see the actually dangerous, not merely philosophically lame, consequences of New Age thinking. On the one hand, there is this notion that the innocent must blame themselves for the crimes of the guilty and then strive to improve social conditions by cultivating good vibrations. This marks a retreat to the magical thinking of the infant.

On the other hand, there is the mind-over-matter approach inherited from Christian Science: "Illness and disease . . . are made manifest in your reality at your behest. You cannot be ill without at some level causing yourself to be, and you can be well again in a moment by simply deciding to be" (p. 32). This is surely as deadly a hoax as any perpetrated by the ecclesiastical tyrants whom Walsch's God repudiates. Nobody ever died from eating a communion wafer. Walsch rightly ridicules those who claim that God both allows free will and yet imposes hell—some choice! Christian apologists flinch at saying that God imposes the torments of hell, so, absurdly, they claim the sinners asked for it! But is it any less cruel or crazy to claim that the cancer patient or the one poisoned by asbestos asked for it? Someone will point out that there is in fact a good deal to be said for the notion that faith and positive thinking are powerful weapons in keeping up one's immunity and in recovering from illness or surgery. Is Walsch, like Mary Baker Eddy, to be condemned for pointing out what medical science now accepts? In answer, I should say there is a spectrum of possibilities here. On the one end there is the idea that affirmation and the will to live can prevent or mitigate disease. It is not impossible that the confident will is the differential between smokers who contract cancer and those who don't. It may be that their positivity strengthens the hardiness of their cells. My mother, who was as sweet as sugar but as tough as nails, smoked for over half a century and did not get cancer. But take this a little further and you will wind up with the delusions of the Boxer Rebellion. The Boxer warriors were persuaded that, if they were in the proper state of spiritual determination, the bullets of their enemies would not harm them. That is the same sort of thinking taken to an extreme, isn't it? Positive thinking steeling the flesh against assault, in this case, by hot lead? Though the same delusion has been surprisingly recurrent in third world messianic movements in the last couple of centuries, no New Agers go so far. And this is because the experiments of the Boxers and others have been definitive. The results are in. We know the principle doesn't apply that far. But by the same token, aren't the results of Christian Science healing in, too? How many more deaths from people using faith instead of medicine do we need to convince us?

What sense the bizarre preachments of Walsch, like those of Helen Schucman and others, seem to make is an illusion born merely of the author's willingness to spin out all the nonsensical implications of his premises and to accept them, no matter how absurd the results. A strange but consistent system is the result. One might compare it to those rare geometric "proofs" which combine axioms in perverse ways to demonstrate that, for example, two different lines may be drawn from a single point above a line to the line below, both of them meeting it at right angles. It is a clever sleight-of-hand trick, producing a consistent theorem, but one that, if one has any common sense at all, is patently false.

THE DIVINE VENTRILOQUIST DUMMY

The God of Neale Donald Walsch is the one he sees in the mirror every morning. The holy water is rising no higher than its source. God as channeled by Walsch is a self-congratulatory pseudo-intellectual who likes iconoclasm if he can then pick up the pieces to build an idol in his own image. That seems pretty clear to me, so I guess it must be the truth, right?

Chapter 8

The Cellophane Prophecy

James Redfield, *The Celestine Prophecy*

SEEING THROUGH IT

*J*ames Redfield offers a set of nine insights to readers of his didactic, barely fictive, novel *The Celestine Prophecy*. It is barely fictive not in the sense of being slightly varnished historical reporting (like, say, *The Serpent and the Rainbow*) but in the sense of utilizing narrative as a vehicle for exposition in only the most skimpy and rudimentary sense. The narrative is curiously humdrum and nondramatic, plainly existing merely as a medium for didacticism. Like a porn movie, the narrative is just itching to get from one juicy scene, in this case, of revelation and exposition, to another.

Before we get to the insights the book imparts, we ought to spend a moment, but only a moment, on the literary quality of the book. It deserves no more since there is so little to the "adventure" as the book subtitles itself. What is remarkable is that, with a book featuring so little in the way of story, it is nonetheless so bad. The wide and avid readership of the book was either very forgiving or completely oblivious.

The lead character is not really a "protagonist," since that word would imply he is other than purely passive. The narrator is simply and completely an intranarrative incarnation of the narrative. He *is* the story as it progresses from one equivalent scene to another. The goal of the book is to catechize the reader with one New Age lesson after another, so the narrator, standing for the reader, marches dutifully from chapter to chapter, which is to say from classroom to classroom, learning each lesson in turn. Every one of the characters the narrator encounters shares the same actantial role: all are "donor" figures placed in the story at regular intervals to give the hero the information he needs when he needs it, and to keep the illusion of narrative movement going. "I thought about it. He was right. I had met just the right people at just the right time: Charlene, Dobson, Wil, Dale, Phil, Reneau, Father Sanchez and Father Carl, now Pablo" (p. 175). "I recalled Wil's soothing attitude when I was on the verge of panic in Lima, and Sanchez's fatherly hospitality, and Father Carl's and Pablo's and Karla's concerned counsel. And now Julia's. They all had the same look in their eyes" (p. 199). That's because they're all pretty much the same character. They even have the same names: Carl, Karla, Charlene, Wil, Phil, Dale. A better novel, or one might say, a *real* novel, would vary the types of characters and actantial roles. More would be going on than aimless, circular travels, nominally fleeing from enemies who ultimately present no danger, and looking for friends who may either return or be replaced by narrative clones—it hardly makes any difference.

For what it's worth, the "story" is that the narrator learns of an enigmatic "Manuscript" recently discovered in Peru. His first interlocutor, Charlene, has been able to find no real leads on the mystery but says enough about it to intrigue the narrator, who finds himself just then at loose ends. So he jets to Peru, meeting another Manuscript seeker in the seat next to him on the plane. It shortly develops that there is almost no one in Peru who *doesn't* know of the Manuscript, and the country is embroiled in a near-inquisition by which church and state alike seek to suppress the Manuscript and its believers. Once our man gets there, gunmen shortly separate him from his seatmate, but there is always someone around the next corner who is well versed in the lore of the Manuscript and who has been clumsily stationed at his or her post by author Redfield to hand the narrator (really the reader/catechumen) down the receiving line to the next stop. Eventually the hero learns all nine insights from fragments of the Manuscript or from those who have read it.

The writing style is unobtrusive and inoffensive. One feels that if Redfield could discover some plot for a novel, he would be able to write one. But this is not that book. The pages of *The Celestine Prophecy* are merely like a bunch of Tibetan prayer flags flapping in the wind. All forward drive is illusory, but it is not much of an illusion. The "action" moves forward only by the most unimaginative shoves of one's shoulder against one's stubborn donkey's intransigent rump. Redfield saves himself work by the ubiquitous use of wild Dickensian coincidences justified as examples of the kind of synchronicity the reader can supposedly expect to experience the further into the nine insights he or she penetrates. How convenient. Similarly, narrative motivation is constantly cut short by clairvoyance. The author just tells the character what to do next, speaking through this or that psychic character.

THE BOOK WITHIN THE BOOK

Now what of the Manuscript? H. P. Lovecraft once said that the aspiring writer, to make a fictional creation convincing, must apply all the careful ingenuity he should muster if he were mounting a real hoax, hoping to deceive the reader. Lovecraft succeeded so well in his own efforts that he was never able to dissuade many readers that his fictive grimoire, the *Necronomicon* of the mad Arab Abdul Alhazred, was a real book. He had done his work too well, composing "translated" excerpts in a properly archaic style and inventing a plausible publishing history of the book. Even today many are convinced the *Necronomicon* exists.

Lovecraft's creation of the *Necronomicon* forms one boundary of a zone of ambiguity of which Joseph Smith's biblical pastiche the Book of Mormon forms another, and James Redfield's *Celestine Prophecy* still another. Lovecraft appeared to be citing a real but little-known tome, though he admitted it was all fiction. Smith composed a plausibly ancient-sounding text and extended the fiction so far as to claim publicly that the Book of Mormon actually was an ancient book he had discovered. He not only applied the requisite ingenuity, as Lovecraft would later advise; Smith went the whole way and turned a literary creation into a full-fledged hoax. Perhaps in the end he had come to believe it himself. But Redfield, making no attempt at claiming historical antiquity for his invented Manuscript, yet trades upon the mystical ambience of the gimmick in order to lend his nine insights a sense of venerable ancient wisdom they might not seem to deserve if evaluated as what they are: the speculative postulates and platitudes of New Age psychobabble. In short, because of the narrative frame of the nine insights being discovered in a suppressed and ancient manuscript, readers seem willing to grant its (Redfield's) teaching an unearned scriptural gravity.

Redfield's achievement is all the more ironic since he has not managed to the least degree to create the requisite plausibility Lovecraft thought necessary. The conception of the Manuscript teems with vitiating anachronisms and absurd conceptions. Redfield tells us that the Manuscript is an Aramaic document dating from the sixth century BCE, about the time of the Babylonian exile of the Jews. The novel's epigraph, a quotation of Daniel 12:3–4, implies Redfield may have modeled this aspect of the Manuscript on Daniel, the stories of which are set in the sixth century BCE, though the book was actually written in the second century BCE. Daniel is partly written in Aramaic. But then what is it doing over in South America? Here we must think of the Book of Mormon again. According to its account of itself, the Book of Mormon is a collection of writings beginning with the testimony of the patriarch Lehi and his sons Nephi and Laman, who departed from Jerusalem shortly before the Babylonian invasion of Judea in the sixth century BCE. Its ostensible language, however, is not Aramaic, but "Reformed Egyptian," which is a way of saying Smith wanted the glyphs he supposedly transcribed from the Golden Plates of Mormon to look like Egyptian hieroglyphics, though he had only a vague notion of how they should look. He could explain any great differences between his imaginary hieroglyphics and the real ones as if the differences between original hieroglyphics and the "reformed" variety. Anyway, Lehi and his family sailed from Jerusalem to the New World, where they established a branch Israel surviving for many centuries until they were destroyed by internecine warfare, leaving behind only the Book of Mormon as their memorial. All this bears a striking resemblance to the Manuscript in *The Celestine Prophecy*: a manuscript written in a Near Eastern language and stemming from the sixth century BCE somehow shows up in the Western Hemisphere with great revelations to share. One wonders if Redfield is not trying to hitch his wagon to Mormonism. Did he have in mind that the Manuscript was brought over by Lehi and Nephi, perhaps as shelf liner in their ark?

TOP SECRET

Redfield has given precious little thought to what is and is not appropriate to an ancient manuscript from a premodern culture. The gross anachronisms of which he is guilty would demonstrate the spurious character of his Manuscript if he had seriously offered it as an antique discovery. But the Manuscript is just too thickly inscribed, margin to margin, with anachronisms to be taken seriously even as a fictive prop. The most resounding blunder must be the Manuscript's *pre-Christian* division of history into BC (BCE) and AD (CE). It predicts a turning point for the history of the human race toward the end of the second millennium. The *what*? Can we imagine a writer in what we call the sixth century BCE conceiving historical chronology in such terms? Not only that, but as we shall see, it foretells the history of the Western world in such detail as to stymie and render superfluous all scientific and geographical discovery before it happened! If you know in advance that so-and-so is going to be discovered, then you have advanced the discovery of it to your own day, haven't you?

NINE PRINCIPLES IN AMBER

But these anachronisms, no matter how glaring, utterly pale next to the tenor and content of the nine insights themselves, which can never have proceeded from any ancient mind. Let us distill these insights from their narrative encrustation.

The First Insight occurs when we become conscious of the *coincidences* in our lives [p. 6]. The First Insight is a reconsideration of the inherent mystery that surrounds our individual lives on this planet [p. 7]. The Manuscript says the number of people who are

200

conscious of such coincidences would begin to grow dramati-
cally in the sixth decade of the twentieth century.... [T]his
growth would continue until sometime near the beginning of the
following century, when we would reach a specific level of such
individuals.... The Manuscript predicts ... that once we reach
this critical mass, the entire culture will begin to take these coin-
cidental experiences seriously. We will wonder, in mass, what
mysterious process underlies human life on this planet. And it
will be this question, asked at the same time by enough people,
that will allow the other insights to also come into consciousness—because according to the Manuscript, when a sufficient
number of individuals seriously question what's going on in life,
we will begin to find out. The other insights will be revealed ...
one after the other. [p. 8]

In fact, people in the sixth century BCE already had no trouble
seeing vast significance in everyday coincidences, major or minor.
They called them omens and lived their lives by them. The Manuscript appears to be written (as of course in fact it is) by a person of
the late twentieth century who is taking a break from critical
thinking and retreating into superstition. It speaks of a second
naiveté, when, at the time of the Manuscript's ostensible composition, humanity had not nearly begun to emerge from the *first*
naiveté. Nor did anyone then alive stop to wonder what life was
about. This is a distinctly modern preoccupation and presupposes
the bankruptcy of all traditional religious worldviews, crumbling
under the assault of science.

The Second Insight ... puts our current awareness into a longer
historical perspective.... It says that at the close of the second
millennium—that's now—we will be able to see that entire period

of history as a whole, and we will identify a particular preoccupation that developed during the latter half of this millennium, in what has been called the Modern Age. Our awareness of the coincidences today represents a kind of awakening from this preoccupation [p. 21]. The manuscript says that the important thing to understand here is that every aspect of the Medieval world is defined in other-worldly terms. All the phenomena of life . . . is [*sic*] defined either as the will of God or as the malice of the devil. There is no concept of weather or geological forces or horticulture or disease. . . . The Medieval world view . . . begins to fall apart in the fourteenth and fifteenth centuries [p. 23]. You knew you had lost your certainty about a God-ruled universe and, because of that, your certainty about the nature of God himself. But you felt you had a method, a consensus-building process through which you could discover the nature of everything around you, including God, and including the true purpose of mankind's existence on the planet [p. 25]. . . . The Second Insight . . . describes how explorers would be sent out into the world utilizing the scientific method to discover the meaning of human life on this planet [p. 35] . . . but because of the complexity of the universe they weren't able to return right away. [p. 25]

So the ancients already knew about the scientific method as well as modern global exploration? They already knew the differences between the self-understandings of medieval man and modern man? This is not just knowing certain events in advance, like Nostradamus supposedly foretelling the rise of Hitler ("Hister"); rather, here are historical reflections necessarily made by those who have lived through great events already past. Or, to put it another way, if the people of the sixth century BCE already knew about global exploration, why *was* there any subsequent global exploration? I often sense the same paradox in any Superman comic in which NASA is mentioned: if there were really a Superman, he would have rendered all space exploration superfluous. He could just tell us what we want to know!

> The Third Insight . . . describes a new understanding of the physical world. It says we humans will learn to perceive what was formerly an invisible type of energy [p. 40]. In other words, the basic stuff of the universe, at its core, is looking like a kind of pure energy that is malleable to human intention and expectation [p. 42]. The Manuscript said the human perception of this energy first begins with a heightened sensitivity to beauty [p. 43]. The Third Insight elaborated on the nature of beauty, describing this perception as the one through which humans would eventually learn to observe energy fields. Once this occurred, it said, then our understanding of the physical universe would quickly transform. For instance, we would begin to eat more foods which were still alive with this energy, and we would become conscious that certain locations radiate more energy than others, the highest radiation coming from old natural environments, especially forests. [pp. 63–64]

Well, here's your health food, environmentalist New Ageism. You knew it was coming sooner or later. The third insight gratuitously promises that people can learn to see haloes and auras, which they will in fact not see unless they just squint and kid themselves. But at least in the case of the third insight, we do have (minus the vague, pseudoscientific "energy field" jargon) something that we can picture the ancients conceptualizing, unless it is perhaps *too* ancient for the sixth century BCE. And that is a belief in natural "luck-force" or *mana*. This is the force that "explains" why one Samoan has more pigs than his neighbors. Equally primitive is the notion that certain places are filled with *mana*, so that one only need to sleep there for some of the luck to wear off onto one. Here we are, in the name of advancement, back at the belief in sacred tree groves in which Baal made his presence known. But this is what we have come to expect from New Ageism: neoprimitivism labeled as scientific progress.

> The Fourth Insight . . . said that eventually humans would see the universe as comprised of one dynamic energy, an energy that can sustain us and respond to our expectations. Yet we would also see that we have been disconnected from the larger source of this energy, that we have cut ourselves off and so have felt weak and insecure and lacking. In the face of this deficit we humans have always sought to increase our personal energy in the only manner we have known: by seeking to psychologically steal it from others—an unconscious competition that underlies all human conflict in the world. [pp. 65–66]

As elsewhere in the book, the fourth insight is afloat in hippie metaphysics of which no one in the ancient Near East or pre-Columbian America could have made any sense at all. But the repeated use of "we humans" in this and other insights may provide a clue as to the supposed origin of the mysterious Manuscript: are we to infer that the text is the product of an extraterrestrial civilization? Presumably these superintellects would know of the predictable cycles of evolution of intelligent species like our own and might attempt to guide it, like the masters of the Monolith in Arthur C. Clarke's *2001: A Space Odyssey*. They would occupy a historical and scientific perspective like that of self-assured New Age gurus such as Redfield. Even this consideration, however, does not absolve Redfield as a writer, since there is just no way the New Age concepts he places in the Manuscript could ever even be communicated in the ancient Aramaic language. Think of the manner in which Hal Lindsey and other "Bible prophecy" buffs read the ancient apocalypses including Daniel and the Revelation of John. The only way they can pretend to discover in them references to modern weaponry and political arrangements (Soviet helicopter gunships, the Common Market, the Warsaw Pact) is to read them into the fantasy imagery on which the apocalyptic genre thrives: hydra-headed dragons, twelve-winged eagles, and so on. This is because Lindsey and his pals realize good and well that the ancient languages of the Bible had no words to describe modern science or warfare directly. If we try to imagine what it would be like if they did, we get something like Woody Allen's parody on the discovery of the Dead Sea Scrolls where he says some scholars doubted their authenticity because of the occurrence in the texts of the word *Oldsmobile*. Or something like *The Celestine Prophecy*.

> This shortage of energy can be remedied . . . when we connect with the higher source. The universe can provide all we need if we can only open up to it. That is the revelation of the Fifth Insight [pp. 119–20]. As I'm sure you learned in the Fifth Insight, each time we fill up with energy and a coincidence occurs to lead us forward in our lives, we institute this level of energy in ourselves, and so we can exist at a higher vibration. Our children take our level of vibration and raise it even higher. This is how we, as humans, continue evolution. [p. 149]

The Celestine Prophecy, like most New Age writings, uses the term "evolution" in a misleading way. Obviously the word may refer metaphorically to any process of transformation, but the context here implies Redfield wants his characters to be carrying on the legacy of Darwin. Only they do not quite seem to understand it. Evolution properly refers to the slow emergence of new species through the process of natural selection. The gradual accumulation of favorable genetic mutations within a species eventually marks off a new species from its forebears, with which they can no longer reproduce. It is true that natural selection is not the end of the line for humanity. Where natural selection leaves off, cultural selection begins. Human decisions in the long run, if they are wide enough in their effects, can to some degree influence the direction of our collective existence and thus, in a sense, further evolution. An example would be the invention of medicine. If natural selection were left to operate spontaneously, the human race would soon evolve beyond susceptibility to various illnesses. Those who suffered from them would die. The hardier specimens, those who (or whose ancestors) happened to have evolved genetic features which rendered them immune, would be the ones to survive, and they would pass down their immunity to the next generation. Thanks to the deaths of most nonimmune specimens, the immune members of the species would contribute a disproportionate percentage of the next generation. Thus, in a matter of time, the human race would have purified itself of vulnerability to one disease after another. But at what a cost! Many loved ones would die. And we don't want that. So we as a culture have decided to choose short-term survival for individual members of our species over long-term immunity. Similarly, nearsightedness would be bred out of the human race because the nearsighted would perish from dangers they could not see to avoid. It would be good to have a race who would have perfect eyesight, but we have decided to protect the safety and enhance the life quality of individuals in the short run. All of this is cultural selection. What Redfield's characters are talking about seems to be better described as personal growth. But that doesn't have the same scientific ambience he desires.

[The Sixth Insight:] Let me explain the classifications spoken of in the Manuscript . . . everyone manipulates for energy either aggressively, directly forcing people to pay attention to them, or passively, playing on people's sympathy or curiosity to gain attention. For instance, if someone threatens you, either verbally or physically, then you are forced, for fear of something bad happening to you, to pay attention to him and so to give him energy. The person threatening you would be pulling you into the most aggressive kind of drama, what the Sixth Insight calls the intimidator. If, on the other hand, someone tells you all the horrible things that are already happening to them, implying perhaps that you are responsible, and that, if you refuse to help, these horrible things are going to continue, then this person is seeking to control at the most passive level, with what the Manuscript calls a poor me drama. . . . If a person is subtle in their aggression, finding fault and slowly undermining your world in order to get your energy, then . . . this person would be an interrogator. Less passive than the poor me would be your aloofness drama. So the order of dramas goes this way: intimidator, interrogator, aloof, and poor me. [pp. 128–29]

When you fully integrate this view of your life, you will have achieved what the Manuscript calls a clear awareness of your spiritual path. According to the Manuscript we must all spend as much time as necessary going though this process of clearing your [*sic*] path. Most of us have a control drama we have to transcend but once we do, we can comprehend the higher meaning for why we were born to our particular parents, and what all the twists and turns of our lives were preparing us to do. We all have a spiritual purpose, a mission, that we have been pursuing without being fully aware of it, and once we bring it completely into consciousness, our lives can take off. [p. 146]

The sixth insight reads like the lost chapters of *I'm OK—You're OK* by Thomas Harris or maybe *Games People Play* by Eric Berne. It is a set of possibly helpful, though hardly revelatory, observations about the dysfunctional ways we are liable to interact with one another. But again, to imagine anyone, prophet, sage, or seer, in the sixth century BCE thinking in such terms is comical. This template of interpersonal strategies is what we call *pop* psychology. By its very nature it is derivative of genuine analysis and a grossly simplified, shorthand version of it. Thus the sixth insight already presupposes the whole history of psychoanalysis, instead of anticipating it, as if the wise old ancients already knew everything we do. And can we really imagine an ancient Aramaic document referring to something like a "poor me control drama"? We will have no better luck imagining extraterrestrials occupying themselves with such psychobabble either.

Seven deals with the process of consciously evolving yourself, of staying alert to the meaning of every coincidence, every answer the universe provides for you [p. 156]. The Seventh Insight talks of dreams. . . . It says to compare the story of the dream to the story of your life [p. 164]. We must assume every event has significance and contains a message that somehow pertains to our questions. This especially applies to what we used to call bad things. The Seventh Insight says that the challenge is to find the silver lining in every event, no matter how negative. [p. 178]

The book is what Tzvetan Todorov calls a "ritual narrative," a "narrative of substitutions," a series of icons or stained-glass windows depicting the same lesson again and again. There is no real progression of events. And this structure is quite appropriate to *The Celestine Prophecy*, since, instead of life lived and enjoyed for its own sake, this book promotes a view of life as a puppet theater, a blank screen for symbolic communications from an unseen realm. Living is just staring at the bottom of the teacup for the next revelation it may yield. Some readers may find the prospect of a universe wallpapered with fortune cookies a comfort. But if one has lived for any length of time in Christian fundamentalism, one can see only too clearly where all this is headed. Redfield is prescribing a condition of anxious paranoia where random events are to be treated as divine portents, somehow to be deciphered. Such a world is a Skinner box with oneself as the lab rat. One comes to live in fear of missing some message God must have sent through some chance encounter or circumstance. Here as everywhere, the New Age movement seeks to push human thinking back to the days of superstition.

> "The Eighth Insight . . . is about using energy in a new way when relating to people in general, but it begins at the beginning, with children. . . . We should view them as they really are, as end points in evolution that lead us forward. But in order to learn to evolve they need our energy on a constant basis, unconditionally. The worst thing that can be done to children is to drain their energy while correcting them. This is what creates control dramas in them. . . . But these learned manipulations on the child's part can be avoided if the adults give them all the energy they need no matter what the situation. That is why they should always be

included in conversations, especially conversations about them. And you should never take responsibility for more children than you can give attention to." "The Manuscript says all this?" I asked. "Yes," she said, "And the point about the number of children is highly stressed. . . . Because any one adult can only focus on and give attention to one child at a time. If there are too many children for the number of adults, then the adults become overwhelmed and unable to give enough energy. The children begin to compete with each other for the adult's time. . . . The Manuscript says that this problem is more important than people think. . . . The Manuscript says that humans will slowly understand that they should not bring children into the world unless there is at least one adult committed to focus full attention, all of the time, on each child. . . . The Manuscript says humans will learn to extend their families beyond blood ties. So that someone else is able to provide one on one attention." [pp. 184–85]

Again, no ancient would or could have said such things. On the one hand, ancient people considered children a joyous gift of God and were glad to have ever more of such wealth. On the other, given the horrible child mortality rate as well as the need for labor on one's homestead, it must have seemed insanity had anyone suggested limiting the number of children. And how would they have done it? There were rudimentary means of birth control and abortion, but infanticide by exposure was probably the preferred method, and pardon me if I think I detect here a New Age apologia for abortion.

The complacent and complete modernity of this supposedly ancient message is nowhere better displayed than in the "It Takes a Manuscript" approach of the eighth insight: Redfield seems to have forgotten entirely the modern origin of the nuclear family arrangement. Until very recently families contained several generations of blood kin under the same roof, and this arrangement allowed for the division of child-rearing duties. But to hear Redfield tell it, family life has always been pretty much like the "Yorkshire" sequence in *Monty Python's Meaning of Life*.

> What the Eighth Insight says about addiction to people [is:] When one first learns to be clear and to engage one's evolution, any of us can be stopped, suddenly, by an addiction to another person. . . . [T]he idea of an addiction, as used in the Manuscript, explains why power struggles arise in romantic relationships. We've always wondered what causes the bliss and euphoria of love to end, to suddenly turn into conflict, and now we know. It is a result of the flow of energy between the individuals involved. [p. 191]

We must be forgiven for finding this portion of the eighth insight, and the reaction of Redfield's characters to it, so laughable. Here they are, as if in their lab coats, whispering in awe over the scientific "discovery" of why love fades. And it's because of some kind of wiring goof! By all means, call the electrician! How can Redfield be so oblivious of the fact that such nonsense depersonalizes human experience in precisely the same way he and his ilk blame the "mechanistic" theories of modern science for doing?

> Oh, we can still have romance. . . . But first we have to complete the circle on our own. We have to stabilize our channel with the universe. That takes time, but afterward, we are never susceptible to this problem again and we can have what the Manuscript calls a higher-relationship. When we connect romantically with another whole person after that, we create a super-person . . . but it never pulls us from the path of our individual evolution. [pp. 194–95]

TOP SECRET

There is reason to wonder if people living at the time of the Manuscript's writing even knew what romantic relationships *were*, what with the arranged and polygamous unions. And, again, one wonders what the original Aramaic said that is being "translated" here as "higher-relationship."

> The Manuscript . . . says that whenever people cross our paths, there is always a message for us. Chance encounters do not exist. But how we respond to these encounters determines whether we're able to receive the message. If we have a conversation with someone who crosses our path and we do not see a message pertaining to our current questions, it does not mean there was no message. It only means we did not receive it for some reason. . . . The Manuscript says that what we should do . . . is to stop what we are doing, no matter what, and find out the message we have for that person, and that the person has for us. The Manuscript predicts that once humans grasp this reality, our interaction will slow down and become more purposeful and deliberate. . . . The Manuscript outlines the procedures . . . the exact way we're supposed to treat each other [p. 200]. The Manuscript says we will learn that sudden, spontaneous eye contact is a sign that two people should talk. . . . [When] some people look familiar [it] just says that we are members of the same thought group with certain other people. Thought groups are usually evolving along the same lines of interest. They think the same and that creates the same expression and outward experience. We intuitively recognize members of our thought group and very often they provide messages for us. [p. 208]

Again, if any readers have ever escaped from the binding coils of fundamentalist Christianity with its hag-ridden paranoia, one will recognize here the directions for a return to it. Anyone who looks at life as Redfield's revelation tells him to is asking for a daily round of anxiety as one flogs oneself for failing to discern divine guidance that was never there in the beginning. One cannot merely say "hello" to a passerby or someone seated next to oneself on a plane. Just as the fundamentalist must recognize every "chance" meeting as a God-assigned appointment for personal evangelism, so must the Redfielder bear the burden of seeing every encounter as a strategic meeting, one's whole day an unbroken series of appointments which one dare not miss for fear of skipping some portentous message from the universe.

The Ninth Insight explains how human culture will change in the next millennium as a result of conscious evolution. It describes a significantly different way of life. For instance, the Manuscript predicts that we humans will voluntarily decrease our population so that we all may live in the most powerful and beautiful places on the Earth. But remarkably, many more of these places will exist in the future, because we will intentionally let the forests go uncut so that they can mature and build energy.

According to the Ninth Insight, by the middle of the next millennium . . . humans will typically live among five hundred year old trees and carefully tended gardens, yet within easy travel distance of an urban area of incredible technological wizardry. By then, the means of survival—foodstuffs and clothing and transport—will all be totally automated and at everyone's disposal. Our needs will be completely met without the exchange of any currency, yet also without any overindulgence or laziness.

Guided by their intuitions, everyone will know precisely what to do and when to do it, and this will fit harmoniously with the actions of others. No one will consume excessively because we will have to let go of the need to possess and to control for security. In the next millennium life will have become about something else.

According to the Manuscript . . . our sense of purpose will be satisfied by the thrill of our own evolution—by the elation of receiving intuitions and then watching closely as our destinies unfold. The Ninth predicts a world in which everyone has slowed down and become more alert, ever vigilant for the next meaningful encounter that comes along. [pp. 222–23]

Redfield's Manuscript confuses the form with the material, the means with the end: What is one evolving *for*? What is the goal? Just to *evolve*? This is a mark of a shallow and superficial "spirituality," the very hallmark of New Ageism, if one may be forgiven for saying so. How long before the novelty of synchronic coincidences loses its shine? According to Jung, synchronicity is a clue to the meaning of the universe. It is not itself the meaning of the universe. It is as if some pathetic loser sat beside the mailbox every day rejoicing in the simple fact of getting mail at all, and never feeling the need to open it. Indeed, if it were all a flood of junk mail, that would be just as good, because the point is: he is getting messages!

The Ninth Insight . . . says that as we humans continue to in - crease our vibration, an amazing thing will begin to happen. Whole groups of people, once they reach a certain level, will suddenly become invisible to those who are vibrating at a lower level. It will appear to people on this lower level that the others just disappeared, but the group themselves will feel as though they are still right here—only they will feel lighter. [p. 241]

Well, why not? *The Celestine Prophecy* is, after all, science fiction, isn't it? But just this is the question. It seems like we are supposed to be taking the ideas of this novel quite seriously. It is only the vehicle that is nonfactual, right? That is the general impression. But then one grows uneasy: Is Redfield, and are his fans, actually convinced they are going to start vibrating on a higher frequency and become invisible? One may hope not. At any rate, in this conceit we have the book's explanation for the mysterious disappearance of the Mayas: "According to the Ninth Insight, the Mayans crossed over together" (p. 242). Like so much else in this book and in the philosophy it espouses, this is patently absurd. Unlike their modern descendants, the ancient Mayas must have been a bunch of faceless aborigines with no more individual personality than a litter of cats. How could it be otherwise when there was pretty much nothing to do but dodge jaguars and hoe maize? One requires hobbies, possessions, things to have opinions about, in order to become any sort of individual, and this comes only with affluence and technological advancement. To imagine these ancient people as a race of philosopher-supermen is the acme of the politically correct romanticization of the American Indian. And what really happened to them? Archaeology shows that they used to reapply several inches of stucco to the walls of their pyramids on a frequent basis and that eventually they must have decimated the surrounding forests to get the wood pulp for enough stucco. This must have ruined their soil and in turn destroyed their crops and their food supply. After this came incessant warfare over scarce resources (ruins show the late building of defensive walls), and they just died out. Too bad they weren't as reverent toward their forests as Redfield seems to imagine.

Chapter 9
Know-It-Alls

Modern Gnostics:
Carl Jung, Stephan A. Hoeller,
Timothy Freke, and Peter Gandy

JUNG AT HEART

"Gnosticism" is an ancient family of religions and philosophy that drew upon various sources of inspiration, including esoteric Judaism, Zoroastrianism, Hermeticism, and Platonism. The name comes from the Greek word for "knowledge," or *gnosis*. It denotes people who are privy to an elite revelation that would prove offensive to the religious rank and file since it departs so drastically from the superficial understanding of the laity. Though Gnosticism contributed much to the normative Christianity of the fourth century, imperial and ecclesiastical authorities did their best to stamp it out. Gnostic beliefs continued to surface throughout the Middle Ages, whether via the underground transmission of ideas and texts, below the radar of heresy hunters, or simply because inventive human minds, faced with the same theological questions in every age, kept reinventing the Gnostic wheel. It is hard to tell. But Gnosticism has always exerted a powerful attraction on those religiously inclined yet alienated from the simplistic creeds of the

217

churches. James Ingall Wedgwood founded a new Gnostic movement in 1916, which he called the Liberal Catholic Church. C. W.
Leadbeater, one of the great leaders of the Theosophical Society,
became its chief theologian. Other Gnostic revivals included the
Pre-Nicene Catholic Church (late 1950s) and the Gnostic Society
of Los Angeles founded in 1959 by Dr. Stephan Hoeller, a Jungian
psychologist as well as a theologian. With genuine erudition and a
lively sense of humor, Dr. Hoeller has been the longest lasting and
most creative (as well as intellectually respectable) of the modern
Gnostic leaders. In 1959 he managed to get a look at Carl Jung's
then privately circulated text *The Seven Sermons to the Dead* in
which Jung, in a visionary state, wrote under the persona of the
second-century Gnostic Basilides. At once Hoeller was captured,
instantly recognizing that Jung himself was the heir to the ancient
Gnostic heresiarchs and that he had created a new, demythologized
version of Gnosticism, "stripped of certain archaic and outdated
historical features," for modern man (Hoeller, *The Gnostic Jung*, p.
33). (In fact, Rudolf Bultmann's famous demythologizing program
had its origins in Bultmann's reading of his student Hans Jonas's
interpretation of Gnostic cosmology as a mythicizing projection of
the inner alienation and transformation of the psyche.)

Jung saw himself as something of a Gnostic mystagogue. He
christened the old Gnostics "the first psychoanalysts," but his
interest in them went much further than simply seeking an ancient
parallel or precedent for what he was doing. He entered into the
spirit of Gnosticism to a degree that makes many of his latter-day
interpreters uneasy, and a debate still rages among Jungians as to
how "spooky" Jung intended to be. In the present chapter I want to
expound, first, the demythologized Gnosticism of Jung and Hoeller
(for the latter disavows any role as an innovator, seeking only to

convey Jung's insights on the matter, which he does surpassingly well).

ANCIENT GNOSTICS AND WHAT THEY KNEW

An ideal type, or "split the difference," sketch of Gnostic doctrine might read as follows.

Gnostics worried about the prevalent evil in a world ostensibly created by a good deity, so they sought to disassociate the creation from God, making it the work of a subordinate several rungs down the ladder. They posited the existence of a supreme deity, the Unknown Father, who did not create anything but rather emanated from himself, like light from the sun, a large series of divine entities, or hypostases (like the Old Testament "Spirit," "Shekinah," "Word," "Wisdom," "Name," "Glory," and so on). They emerged from his essence in pairs, yolk-fellows (*syzygies*), each pair begetting and bearing (emanating) the next. In this way a whole pleroma (fullness) of divine light came to be, in which no less than 365 such entities (Aeons) existed. The very last one, Sophia (wisdom), wanted to overreach her appointed limits. On the one hand, she, too, wanted to conceive Aeons. On the other, she longed to peer inside the inner core of the pleroma, where the Father dwelt. But she could do neither, lacking a partner and being posted just outside the Barrier. She managed to give birth to an abomination ("the Abortion"), henceforth to be called the Demiurge ("Craftsman"), who would go on to create a physical world of matter. The Demiurge, variously called Sabaoth or Ialdabaoth, was identified as the "God" of conventional Judaism and Christianity: Jehovah. He vainly imagined himself to be the ultimate being, but his declaration of the same only prompted laughter from his mother Sophia/wisdom.

TOP SECRET

In an attempt to ape the pleroma of the Father, the Demiurge created a set of Archons ("rulers"), who were the same as the gods ruling the planets in traditional Mithraic and other astronomies.

The material creation was not much to brag about because the Demiurge lacked any ability to impart life to what he had made. The newly made earth stood like a stagnant pond until the Archons contrived to steal a bit of the light of the pleroma. This they did by either inducing Sophia to stoop down and look into the dark expanse of the world, stealing the photons (as we should say) of her reflection, or by ambushing and dismembering the Primal Man, another of the Aeons. In either case, the Archons used the light to give order and life to the cosmos, injecting it to function like self-replicating DNA. The result is that many sparks of the divine light are now imprisoned within matter, from whence Gnosticism proposes to release them. Specifically, Gnostic myth says that Adam lay inert upon the ground in Eden until the heavenly Aeon Eve, or the Serpent (or both, though sometimes they are identical), arrived to give knowledge and life to him. But the Archons lusted after her and pursued her. She evaded their clutches by turning into a tree (as Daphne did when chased by lustful Apollo) and leaving a phantom semblance in her place. The Archons raped this holo-Eve, and the result was the depraved race of Cain.

The human race falls into three categories: First are the *pneumatics*, or "spiritual" ones. They contain the divine spark. They suffer as strangers in a strange land, but they know not why, being ignorant of their heavenly origin. They reincarnate upon death because their spirits, attempting to rise up to the pleroma where they belong, are turned back by the Archons who are always vigilant like East German soldiers along the Berlin wall. But, being immortal spirits, they cannot die, so they reincarnate. Second there are the *psychics*, the "soulish" or "natural" ones. Not children of Cain, they nonetheless lack the divine spark. These are the pious of the conventional religions. They are not automatically saved by nature, but they can be redeemed by special measures. Third are the *hylics*, the "material" or "wooden" ones, also called the *sarkics*, or "fleshly" ones. They are basically two-legged animals, living for pleasure, lacking any real conscience. They are irredeemable.

The Father takes pity upon humankind, especially the pneumatics, who share his own nature. So he sends the Christ, another Aeon somehow identified with the Primal Man, into the world to awaken the pneumatics to their true origin and destiny. He temporarily joins with the human Jesus, who serves as his channeler, beginning with the descent of the Christ-Spirit upon him at the baptism and ending at the crucifixion ("My God, my God, why have you forsaken me?"). Some Gnostics did not draw this line between Jesus and Christ but posited a Jesus who was, like Eve, a phantom who only seemed to be made of flesh. But the model that saw Jesus and Christ as distinct though allied beings allowed for a two-track salvation system. The Christ communicated to the more discerning pneumatics among his hearers through the esoteric sense of his parables, which only they could grasp. As for the natural ones, Jesus had maxims of worldly wisdom for them, and he even died a redemptive death on their behalf, something not necessary for the pneumatics, already saved by nature. As for the carnal? Too bad, but they're only animated matter anyway.

Gnostics portrayed Christ, especially after the resurrection of Jesus or before the ascension (or even on a return visit of some years duration *after* the ascension!), supplying the elite with secret information, such as passwords and formulas to ward off the Archons as they attempted to turn one back. Once all the sparks of light should be regathered from the world, the unity of the Primal Man would be restored, all his sundered fragments replaced in the cosmos-spanning Mystical Body of Christ (as Catholicism calls it). In that day the creation should collapse back into its natural, inert state, and all suffering would be over. The Gnostics sought to hasten that day by spreading their message, though they had to be very careful about it. They attended church with non-Gnostics, where they would tactfully ferret out the like-minded, being careful not to "come out of the closet" to the wrong people. They knew good and well how offensive their doctrine sounded in the ears of the natural ones; hence the warnings not to cast one's pearls before swine, lest they trample them underfoot, turn on you, and tear you to pieces. And, of course, that is exactly what eventually happened.

BASILIDES REDIVIVUS

As is well known, Sigmund Freud dismissed religion as "the universal obsessive neurosis of mankind." His disciple Carl Jung did not agree. While he did not challenge Freud's verdict on the neurotic forms religion might take, he saw them as an abuse of religion rather than as the inevitable implications of religious belief. For Freud, religion was always an impediment to psychological maturity since it meant a stubborn refusal to transcend childish dependence on (imaginary) parental authority: that of "God." It led to wishful thinking and a refusal to stand on one's own two feet. But for Jung, it was just the opposite: religion is an invaluable factor facilitating psychological maturation, or "individuation" (Hoeller, *The Gnostic Jung*, p. 113). Jung believed that all people share a common brain structure called the Collective Unconscious. Among

the built-in contents of this unconscious mind are certain fundamental archetypes, images, symbols, numbers, characters, and so
on. They are like computer icons to activate new programs. The
various programs are latent in the computer, but in order to become
a skilled computer user, one must learn to activate those programs.
One is alerted to their presence by the symbolic icons on the
desktop screen. To access them, one clicks on the icons. The archetypes appear on our "screen," that is, to our conscious minds, as we
encounter them in myths, dreams, religious symbolism, fairy tales,
and so on. How do we "click on" them? Ritual is one important
method. Jung (like Joseph Campbell) thought that "Christ" represented the universal Hero Archetype and that the eucharist and baptism were ways of entering into that powerful symbol (see Slusser,
From Jung to Jesus, passim).

It is important to note that Jung deduced from all this, both the
origin of religious symbols and the way they appear to function, that
there is no necessary connection to belief. "To believe is vastly inferior to perceiving the symbols whereby truth is revealed" (Hoeller,
The Gnostic Jung, p. 129). No, he regarded *imagination* as the
needful faculty for religion. Again, for Jung, religion is a matter of
experience, not of belief. He once famously remarked that he did not
"believe" in God; he did not have to: he *knew*. But what kind of
God, and what sort of knowledge? It is the Archetype of God,
located inside us, and it is quite as powerful as any God outside us.
"To Jung, God is never a theological or philosophical postulate, but
a psychological reality; not an essence, but an experience" (Hoeller,
The Gnostic Jung, p. 200). And as for knowledge, it is neither speculation nor faith, but intuitive experience. Like his friend and colleague Paul Tillich, Jung regarded belief in symbols and doctrine as
literal truths a form of idolatry. And just as Kant rejected any mir-

acle story in scripture as worthless insofar as it did not somehow inculcate moral growth, so did Jung disregard any element of Gnosticism that one could not render into psychological terms.

And, just as religious symbols provide useful means for psychological integration, so does psychology help to explain the differences among religions. Jung saw the God images of various cultures in given periods as defining the possibilities of individuation available at each time and place. The liberal Protestant doctrine of Progressive Revelation says much the same thing: "What has actually happened is the production of a Book which from lowly beginnings to great conclusions records the development of truth about God and his will. . . . I do not believe that man ever found God when God was not seeking to be found. The under side of the process is man's discovery; the upper side is God's revelation" (Fosdick, p. 30). "The revelation given by God to half savage men must needs be morally imperfect. They are given as much as they can receive, and as their natures are gradually purified and enlarged they are given more. Thus the revelation must needs be morally progressive" (Gladden, p. 75). "The Bible is a record of man's laboratory work in the spiritual realm" (Abbott, p. 56). In fact, it is the constancy of the archetypes as part of the human psychic mechanism that explained for Jung how Gnosticism kept resurfacing, being recreated, throughout history. This is also the verdict of Gnosticism specialist Ioan P. Couliano in *The Tree of Gnosis: Gnostic Mythology from Early Christianity to Modern Nihilism* (see esp. pp. xiv, 57–59).

Jung was much influenced by Friedrich Nietzsche, but he declined to affirm the death of God, because Jung considered "God" to be a form of our inner, psychic reality, and we can therefore not dispense with God without injuring ourselves. Of course, had Nietzsche viewed God in a similar light, he very likely would not have affirmed the death of God. For Nietzsche, "God" referred to an external entity that threatened human autonomy. "Our degree of morality is really never fully known to us until we retreat from externally imposed laws and regulations and allow our internal ethics to set the guidelines for its own sake and for no other reason" (Hoeller, *The Gnostic Jung*, p. 114).

TIME WARP AND WOOF

These days Jung is popularly associated with his theory of synchronicity perhaps more than with anything else. He tried to establish "an acausal principle" behind striking, meaningful coincidences. Everyone sooner or later experiences such things, and no one is likely to forget them. We treasure these mystifying moments as a signal that there may after all be something "magic" going on in the world, even impinging upon *us*. Jung described a patient recounting to him a dream of the previous night; it involved an Egyptian scarab. Just as she was telling Jung the dream, the two of them noticed a distinct tapping on the windowpane next to the patient's face. It was a scarabaeid beetle trying to get in!

Similarly, one afternoon, many years ago, while I was attending graduate school, I was napping in my dorm room and dreamed I was on my knees searching through a pile of papers, leaves, and other things, intent on finding something I had lost. As the spectator of the dream I did not know what it was that I, as a character in the dream, was looking for. Then I realized I was beginning to wake up, just as I found the missing possession. I strained to see it before it was too late. It looked like a small plaque emblazoned with a single word: *hope*. Now this was at a time when I was having to reevaluate my long-held religious beliefs. It was a frightening process, yet an invigorating one, since I felt that, as my adolescent faith faded, my native personality was beginning to reemerge. Thus finding lost hope made sense to me. I didn't realize it at the time, until a professor pointed it out to me, but the dream shared the central image with the Pandora myth: by questioning my faith, I had "opened Pandora's box," and all manner of confusion had ensued. But left at the bottom of the box was one thing: hope. Well, the very next day I was in a stationary store and looked at a revolving rack of posters. I stopped in awe as I saw one depicting a candle flame and featuring the words "Hope is a waking dream"!

What did Jung say is happening in moments like these (and in cases of successful horoscopes, answered prayer, or *I Ching* castings)? He ruled out the possibility of one of the events causing the other. The beetle tapping on the window, in other words, did not and could not have sent some sort of signal back in time to create the dream. Nor did the dream send forth a psychic signal summoning the beetle to the therapist's window. As Ira Progoff spins out the theory, synchronicity seems to presuppose a correspondence (such as that posited by much ancient philosophy) between *macrocosm* and *microcosm*, the reality without and that within. "The mystery of the two eternities of microcosm and macrocosm which meet in the human psyche is closely related to what Jung . . . came to call synchronicity" (Hoeller, *The Gnostic Jung*, p. 179). Jung suggested that there is a meaning structure in the universe and that the archetypes reproduce or reflect it in the human mind. Striking synchronous experiences, then, are momentary flashes in which that correspondence is disclosed, hence their felt meaningfulness. One would expect synchronistic moments at significant junctures along the road to individuation. They would function as counterparts to the symbolic tribal masks used in rites of passage in many societies. Such masks, depicting elements of human and animal, life and death, and so on, express and embody the "liminality" of the situation of the ritual initiate as he is passing from one life stage to another. Such trappings of the carefully orchestrated rites even facilitate the passage and the attendant psychological disintegration/reintegration of the boy becoming a man, and so on. In the same way, synchronous experiences would reflect a leaping up of the fire of meaning at a crucial point in the journey of self-discovery. "The archetype then, when manifesting in a sychronistic phenomenon, is truly awesome if not outright miraculous—an uncanny dweller on the threshold" (Hoeller, *The Gnostic Jung*, p. 184). There, exactly, is the common element of *liminality*, passage between one realm and another.

New Age and New Thought teachers frequently refer to synchronicity as a sign, even as tangible evidence, of "the law of attraction" whereby visualization brings about manifestation (see Deepak Chopra's book *Synchronicity*). Such an interpretation of synchronicity at first sounds like the very sort of superstitious pseudocausative element that Jung rejected at the outset. But perhaps it is not. A closer scrutiny of the New Age/New Thought teaching reveals that it often goes hand in hand with the discovery of one's true path, one's dharma or life purpose, as in Shakti Gawain's pair of books, *Creative Visualization* and *Living in the Light*, the former about manipulating reality by envisioning it the way you want it, the latter dealing with the need for obeying the inner voice of intuition. But, insofar as there is a genuine element of temporal succession and cause and effect in the New Thought doctrine, it might be better to classify it as an example of Paul Kammerer's "Seriality" principle, whereby he would explain the conspicuous clustering together of related events which do not actually lead to one another in terms of immanent causation (Koestler, pp. 82–88).

As Progoff demonstrates, however, the philosophical implications of Jungian synchronicity are scarcely less overarching even if one does not see fit to pursue the New Thought direction. For it implies a universal, predetermined "monadology" whereby all entities mirror one another to the point of being contained within one another, and all events are thus predestined. Otherwise such coordination as synchronous moments appear to reveal would be impossible. Though, as far as I know, Jung did not connect synchronicity with Gnostic cosmology, it would certainly fit, since ancient Gnosticism presupposed the validity of astrology, the planetary gods and astral spirits governing the sublunar world. It was from such constraints, imposed by the Demiurge and his lieutenants, that the revelation of *gnosis* freed the pneumatic. Then he knew he was higher than the beings that imprisoned him, and he could defeat them. "The unenlightened or unconscious person is ruled by the planets, or by the psychological forces and complexes which are signified by the planets," that is, unsuspected determinants of behavior (Hoeller, *Gnostic Jung* p. 88).

IN THE CABINET OF DR. CALIGARI

"Jung's psychology," Hoeller writes, "is in some ways but a practical restatement of Gnosticism, and as such it shows innumerable analogies and equivalencies to the ancient Gnostic systems. The place of the Divine existence is taken by the archetypes, and the sum of these archetypes is none other than the psychological analogy of the Pleroma" (*The Gnostic Jung*, p. 69). What Jung does with Gnosticism is a strict case of demythologizing as Bultmann framed it, for it does not merely subtract the ancient myth but rather interprets it on the assumption that "every assertion about God is simultaneously an assertion about man and vice versa" (Bultmann, "New Testament and Mythology," p. 191). All myths, at least myths of the human place in the world and of the cosmic predicament from which we suffer, arise from the existential situation of the people who tell the myth to understand themselves. Thus they are prescientific, but nonetheless quite valid expositions of the/a human condition. This is why Bultmann felt the New Testament message of Jesus could easily survive the eclipse and collapse of the prescientific worldview of the ancients. Jung and Hoeller do precisely the same thing with the adjacent and overlapping Gnostic mythology of the ancients. "Jung thus employed himself . . . in stripping various esoteric doctrines of their metaphysical wrappings and making them objects of psychology. By this he did not intend a project of reductionism but rather a strict principle of psychological application of metaphysical statements" (Hoeller, *The Gnostic Jung*, p. 71). If the bizarre myths of the Gnostics had not been built on the subtext of human alienation and integration, it is hard to see what would have given them the power they obviously exerted over so many people. Ancient salvation myths, too, really depict the salvation "of the suffering mind by the paradigm of the individuated ego" (Hoeller, *The Gnostic Jung*, p. 177).

And for Jung, that subtext is a map of the shape and function of the collective unconscious. For instance, the pleroma of divine light "contains all dualities but they cancel each other out" (Hoeller, *The Gnostic Jung*, p. 49), being ultimately reconciled on the highest level as by some sort of Hegelian synthesis. As Merlin says to Morgana in the film *Excalibur*, as he shows her the Crystal Cave: "Here all things meet their opposites." As Tillich says, all the polarities of existence participate in the Being from which they arise, differentiating from one another as they both separate from their common source. "In created things," however, the polarities actually exist and therefore must reach reconciliation by means of conflict and compromise" (Hoeller, *The Gnostic Jung*, p. 49). The pleroma would represent the "macrocosm" of the collective unconsciousness, the common pattern and psychic potentiality of humans as such, while the "microcosm" would correspond to the conscious personality of the individual in the process of individuation. In just a moment we will consider the moral aspect of maturity as a prime example of this reconciliation of opposites.

On the one level there is the pleroma; on the other is the Gnostic pneumatic. Between them ought to stand as both barrier and door, the Demiurge. And it does. Drawing on a minor strand of the Gnostic tradition, Jung denominates the Demiurge as Abraxas. "Between linear, historical ego-consciousness and a circular, ahistorical unconsciousness, Abraxas stands as the third possibility of the eternally available timeless moment, the eternal now . . . which brings freedom from time both in its linear and its cyclic aspects" (Hoeller, *The Gnostic Jung*, p. 87). Abraxas is something of a personification of the pleroma, just as the Demiurge is a low-level mock-up of the Unknown Father. This means, among other things, that whereas the pleroma (the collective unconscious) could be an already reconciled transcendence of polarities, Abraxas, being finite, approximates this paradoxicality as closely as it can by embodying all sets of contradictions at once, hence its Januslike depiction as a god with opposite faces. Whereas the pleroma is beyond polarity, Abraxas actually features both poles. If the pleroma is, for instance, beyond good and evil, Abraxas is both good and evil. It is from the struggle of polarities within us that creativity is born, and so Abraxas, embodying liminality, is the threshold, the interstice, both the gate and the guardian of the gate.

> The living of meaning is then a mysterious process revealed by the poetic lucidity of myth, dream and imagination rather than by the concerns of the conscious ego. . . . This answer . . . is to be found in a curious process, an interaction or interplay of the opposites of being revealed in the experience of the psyche. (Hoeller, *The Gnostic Jung*, p. 152)

Morality is perhaps the most important example of how individuation requires the process of reconciliation of inner opposites. Jung says we have been wrong to picture good and evil as external realities, and that we must cleave to the good and shun the evil. Rather, we must see that good and evil are inside us, so that our struggle is to deal with both, not to enlist on behalf of one against the other. Dr. Jekyll found that out the hard way. Contrast with either the pleroma or Abraxas the conventional God of Western religion: "the Jewish-Christian-Islamic God-concept . . . is personal, and therefore moral in nature" (Hoeller, *The Gnostic Jung*, p. 96). Here it is helpful to remind ourselves of Jung's dichotomy of the Persona and the Shadow. The Persona is much like Freud's concept of the ego-ideal: one chooses or fashions the character goal toward which one strives. Much the same is true of Jung's version. The Persona (the drama "mask" of the ancient Greeks) is the goal of conscious behavior. But the Shadow is our hidden aspect, our dark side. We have two choices in dealing with it. We can either suppress it, pretending it does not exist, or, more realistically, face and fight it. But neither strategy is much good in the long run. Eventually the Shadow, whether browbeaten or ignored, will return with a vengeance. We are likely either to explode in a baffling display of the anger or lust we worked so hard to banish, or we will start projecting our own lustful or hateful motives and desires onto others, scapegoating them. (The latter process is pretty much the same as what Freud called "reaction formation," seeing the splinter in your neighbor's eye while there is an unsuspected two-by-four sticking out of your own.) These are the dangers of what Jungian Erich Neumann calls the old ethic of virtue. Instead, he says Jung calls for a new ethic of wholeness.

This new ethic would entail "giving the devil his due," acknowledging the Shadow and even indulging it—though never freely, because there is no use in closing off the conscience of the Persona either. Such an airtight sealing off of the Persona and the Shadow from each other would achieve nothing but schizophrenia. One may "cover the ground" by fantasizing one column of the moral menu and acting out the other. Though a Freudian in orientation, Bruno Bettelheim spoke from the same perspective vis-à-vis the Shadow when he denounced the misguided counsel of some so-called child development experts for parents to keep their children away from the traditional fairy tales with their mayhem and murder. Bettelheim could see that Hansel and Gretel teaches a child something that the Care Bears do not: the old tales feed both sides of the psyche, while finally putting the accent where it belongs, in the choice of which characters live happily ever after. Frederic Wertham made the same mistake in his inquisition against comic books in the 1950s. He imagined that the gruel and gore of *Tales from the Crypt* were making adolescents into giggling sadists. But the "longitudinal study" of seeing how those kids grew up readily demonstrates that Jung, Neumann, and Bettelheim were right: One needs to feed the Shadow in order to prevent it from becoming fierce and desperate from starvation. The psyche thrives on the balance. "We owe worship to the light, but the darkness needs and deserves our homage also" (Hoeller, *The Gnostic Jung*, p. 81).

But it is not simply a matter of persuading the angel on one shoulder to shake hands with the devil on the other. Jung puts the matter into the context of the individuation process. Moral growth requires the transcendence of an earlier set of laws if one is to graduate to a more mature set, and that transcendence must occur by an act of transgression. And this is where the whole idea is genuinely Gnostic:

> The religions of the masses demand obedience to God's will, while the Gnosis demands both obedience and disobedience. Not all commandments come from the true God, said the ancient Gnostics, for many come from a Demiurge, whose law may be useful to the unenlightened (the psychics, or men of soul) but is counterproductive to the true Gnostics (the pneumatics, or men of spirit). The will of nature is not that of supernature. The law of the morning which is appropriate for spiritual infants must be broken by those who have progressed to the law of the evening, where the light of differentiated consciousness must be dimmed in order to admit the luminosity of the midnight sun of individuation. (Hoeller, *The Gnostic Jung*, p. 81)

Where is individuation going? Does Jung envision an anonymous merging of the individual ego with a cosmic self? No, he thinks in terms of a self-centered ego maturing into an inclusive self, open to and approachable by all others, but retaining a sense of its own identity. The direction of individuation after all is a separation of the ego from the direction of the collectivity around him. Jung's Gnosticism therefore differs from the nondualism of some Hindu and Buddhist paths. Jung warned against the danger of losing the individual self in the pleroma. "We would be missing the mark indeed if we were to attribute some Advaitin non-dualism to the deeper strata of the psyche" (Hoeller, *The Gnostic Jung*, p. 98). No, the old dualities are present even there, in the depths, although they no more exist in conflict and competition. Rather, they have assumed the mutually complementary roles of yin and yang. "Here, then, we might say, is the veritable heart and center of Jung's Gnosis. The experience of the psyche . . . is the maker of meaning, the creator of truth" (Hoeller, *The Gnostic Jung*, pp. 152–53).

GNOSTICISM LITE

Timothy Freke and Peter Gandy believe that there was very likely no historical Jesus, but that the character was based on a sectarian Jewish adaptation of pagan god-men such as Dionysus, Osiris, and Attis, a view I happen to share. They argue in their book *The Jesus Mysteries* (1999) that Jesus functioned as an allegorical cipher for a specific kind of ancient spirituality, the Gnostic/Mystery cult variety. In the sequel, *Jesus and the Lost Goddess*, Freke and Gandy employ the term "Gnostic" in a much wider sense, referring to any ancient or modern religious people who transcend scriptural literalism in favor of an esoteric reading tending toward nondualist mysticism. I must register a bit of dissatisfaction with the repeated assertion that Freke and Gandy have herewith excavated "the secret teachings of the original Christians." That seems to me something of an extravagant and immodest claim. Freke and Gandy are telling us that the first Christians were a Jewish version of Vedanta, of nondualism. For them, it is hardly too much to say, earliest Christianity was Mahayana Buddhism plus Neoplatonism. This is a dangerous game.

The authors are in danger of engaging in what Derrida called "the dangerous supplement," supplanting a thing by pretending/trying merely to elaborate it. One takes aim at a product of culture, making it suffer by comparison with its newly discovered "natural, original" counterpart—while forgetting that this hypothetical "original" has not been found via time travel but only fashioned by research, thus no less a product of culture, albeit perhaps counterculture. Thus does every "historical Jesus" (re?)construction seek to supplant traditional Christology with what is only a newer Christology (at least as far as we will ever be able to verify). Every mysticism performs this operation, claiming only to restore the original profundity of the parent tradition by interpreting it nonliterally. The Sufis, Philo, and others made such claims, but how plausible are they? Usually such hermeneutical attempts are really efforts at modernizing an outmoded faith that has become an embarrassment to its latter-day adherents. Was the belief of the Stoics really older than that of Homer and Hesiod? I doubt it. Freke and Gandy may well be offering us a better version of Christianity, but that is a very different matter than offering us the original version.

Let me not be misunderstood, though: I do think that Gnostic sects predated Christianity and that Catholic-Orthodox Christianity is a secondary form of the faith, combining elements from Gnosticism, Mystery Religions, and hero cultism. But I cannot help suspecting that what the authors are doing is closer to Carl Jung and Hans Jonas than what the ancient Gnostics were doing. I think

Freke and Gandy are skipping a step: they are demythologizing and psychologizing Gnostic mythology and then attributing the result to the ancients themselves. It is a slippery business, and they may be right. But there is reason to doubt it. Put it this way: as Paul Veyne once asked whether the ancient Greeks believed their myths, I ask whether the Gnostics believed in their myths of the Demiurge, Sophia, the Primal Man, the Aions, the Archons, and so on. I suspect that they did. What was the supposed esoteric truth of which the Gnostics boasted? Was it a psychologization such as this book expounds? If it was, my guess is that they would simply have interpreted our familiar gospels and epistles in an allegorical way (and of course that was going on, too). Whence all the superextravagant mythology of multiple redeemers and cosmogonies? I picture the ancient Gnostics as no less superstitious than their Catholic cousins, just addicted to more elaborate theosophical fantasies analogous to those of Madame Blavatsky. Their *gnosis*, I imagine, was privileged possession of sophistical speculations of which outsiders were impatient and deemed unworthy. I imagine that their knowledge was like that of New Age believers today: just more elaborate and syncretic versions of what most people believed. Yes, Plotinus counted some Gnostics among his students, but I suspect that even this implies these few were looking for a more sophisticated, more genuinely philosophical, mysticism than Gnosticism offered them.

In the end, I think Freke and Gandy are offering readers the same sort of gospel as that preached by Stephan A. Hoeller in his "Gnostic Society: A Demythologization of Gnosticism" for moderns, conducted along Jungian lines—which is fine by me. Like Jung, they are demonstrating the unsuspected contemporary relevance of ancient writings too easily dismissed as the delusional rantings of crazed hermits. But, unlike Jung, they do not bother to show how specific elements of ancient Gnosticism in particular correspond to the psychological challenges and potentialities of people today. They rush to advocate a modernizing, world-affirming religious philosophy that they much too hastily christen as "Gnosticism." It is just hard to believe any ancient Gnostic would agree that the gist of the Gnosis is "Life is essentially good" (Freke and Gandy, *Lost Goddess*, p. 183). Nor would you really need lists of the names of hermaphrodite angels for that. The great danger of allegorizing myth is to rationalize it by reducing it to acceptable platitudes. This is the ubiquitous process of "natural-izing" the text (as Jonathan Culler calls it) whereby we try to smooth away the rough edges of a puzzling text by making it mean something we *can* understand. We reduce its daunting strangeness at the cost of learning less from it, since we make it synonymous with something we already knew. Philo and Origen often did just this when they allegorized the Bible, reducing it to tepid moralisms or pointlessly coded typologies of the human psyche. Is this what the erudite moderns Freke and Gandy have done, appealing to ancient forebears in the manner of ecologists idealizing the American Indians?

Or think of the anxiety of the Gnostics preparing for their antic-ipated heavenward journey, rehearsing all their magic formulas to stammer at the interrogating archons trying to bar their way to the pleroma. Can we imagine that these people were just tooling along in the laid-back manner prescribed by Freke and Gandy? People who looked at this world as if they were Steve McQueen in *The Great Escape*? It is as hard to believe that Freke and Gandy are really describing the ancient Gnostics as it is to imagine the enthu-siasts of ancient Corinth having anything in common with Bult-mann or Burton Mack.

TOP SECRET

What is supposed to be so darn great about Gnosticism? That is a question some treatments of the subject can skirt. Elaine Pagels, in her classic *The Gnostic Gospels*, seems to invoke Gnosticism mainly as an ancient precedent for freethinking Christian modernism, as if to say, "Look! *We* have early Christians on *our* side, too!" But Freke and Gandy have obligated themselves to go a good second mile farther than Pagels did. They are heavily invested in rehabilitating *gnosis* as "good news for modern man." Set aside the essentially adolescent self-satisfaction of the gloater over secret mysteries. What is the enlightened life of the person who accepts the Gnostic evangel as preached by Freke and Gandy (literally, at traveling seminars)?

For one thing, as one might expect from the large-scale parallels to Oriental nondualism, a Gnostic lifestyle would include the yogic element of *detachment*, "mere witness," the distancing of oneself from emotional investment in the passing sideshow of life. Of course, Stoicism counsels the same. I think of an anecdote concerning, I think, Sri Ramakrishna, who once had to undergo sensitive throat surgery without benefit of anesthesia: he asked the doctor to give him a minute, then meditated into an inner zone in which he distanced the witnessing Atman from the experiencing ego and successfully prescinded from the pain. Whether Freke and Gandy would offer us that power, I don't know.

But, as in Buddhism, such detachment does not serve selfishness. Rather it frees the enlightened person from any vested ego interests so he can look upon all beings with impartial compassion and act gladly on their behalf. (If he were more compassionate than me, he might even take the trouble to use gender-neutral pronouns, if there are any.)

Freke and Gandy prescribe a life of working on one's virtue and character development, punctuated by periods of blissful absorption into nondual consciousness. The first is life on the *psychical* plane, the penultimate existence as an individual reflecting the One but still distinct from it, still on the plane of samsaric existence. The second is a series of adventures into the *pneumatic* plane where one experiences identity with/as the One. À la the dialectic of Nagarjuna, one rejoices in the ephemeral beauty of the samsaric world because one can see through it to its Nirvanic Ground of Being. No longer falsely expecting samsara to provide ultimate satisfaction, one can appreciate it for what it is, neither making it into an idol of *maya* nor ascetically despising it for not being what it is not.

And even everyday life, the longer periods of *psychical* existence, the neo-Gnostic learns to experience as living myth, noticing the pleasant coincidences of Jungian synchronicity and taking them as signs of hidden meaning. To me, this is getting uncomfortably close to the delusions of reference in which fundamentalists indulge when they take minor coincidences as "confirmations" of divine guidance, like God getting them parking spaces. But ultimately, Freke and Gandy seem to take Gnosticism as more or less equivalent to liberal tolerance and a spirituality of seeking, and of openness to all traditions. I wonder if they are not so far from Pagels after all.

The authors are quite effective in conveying a coherent and clear account of nondualism as a realistic, almost commonsensical, outlook on the world. They are in this respect reminiscent of Alan Watts, the C. S. Lewis of Buddhism. But their presentation smacks more of Neoplatonism (partly via Dionysius the Areopagite) than of Buddhism. First there is the One, which is not even self-aware, since that would imply a subject-object distinction of which it is blissfully free. But for love to exist, as well as knowledge, on a lower level of reality/experience, the One bifurcates into con-sciousness and psyche, the knowledge and the knower. Further down the scale, the One is manifest in many fragmentary forms or images. Insofar as consciousness occupies the standpoint of these images, it begins to identify with them, and the illusion of indi-vidual ego-identities is born. But through Gnostic initiation these images may, like Freke and Gandy themselves, begin to slide back down the spokes to the central hub of consciousness, and to remember their uniative mutual identity.

I find myself thinking of the recent New Age exploitation flick about quantum physics, *What the Bleep Do We Know?* In it we are told that the tantalizing bafflements of quantum physics, such as the alleged fact that subatomic particles can be in two places at once, ought to revolutionize our living of everyday life. Characters plagiarize lines that sounded impressive in *Dune* and *The Matrix*, fantasy movies in which characters "fold space" and cause flying bullets to drop from their trajectories. People in *What the Bleep* suddenly morph into younger versions of themselves or find them-selves dribbling multiple basketballs all over the court at the same time, somehow because of the Heisenberg uncertainty principle. I guess the producers hope the viewer does not notice that such things in fact never happen in real life and are not going to start happening to him after seeing this film either. The film jumps from the way things happen on a subatomic level to the way they sup-posedly might happen on the macro level where we live. But the film is wrong. Quantum physics is just trying to throw new light on the unsuspected inner workings of the same old mundane world we have always lived in. It is not telling us that things happen differ-ently or that they might. B. F. Skinner said it well in *Beyond Freedom and Dignity*: "A theory about a thing does not change the thing the theory is about." A couple of times I saw Skinner strolling through Harvard Yard. He didn't move like a robot because he espoused determinism.

Ramanuja, the great exponent of the leading alternative to Shankara's nondualist Vedanta, namely, Visistadvaita ("difference-in-identity" or qualified nondualism), had the same reservation about nondualism: Even if it's true, why is it any more than an explanation of the way things are and how they work? Why isn't metaphysics like physics? Why would understanding how things get from there to here be a warrant for going someplace *else* than here? Ramanuja admitted that nondualists could work their way into nondual awareness, but when they had done so, he figured, they had merely experienced the undifferentiated ground out of which everything emerged. But the articulated reality was where the action and the meaning are. Ramanuja anticipated Freud's judgment on mysticism as merely a retrogressive attainment of the oceanic feeling of the womb, no advance but a retreat. He was even closer to modern brain physiologists who say nondual experiences are simply a function of an induced malfunction in the temporal parietal lobe of the brain, whereby the little gizmo that comes on line in infancy to differentiate self from others goes temporarily back offline. For Ramanuja, that's all you're doing. Once you snap out of it, a mountain's just a mountain again.

In the end, Freke and Gandy reduce (and expand) Gnosticism into a Socratic refusal to think one has everything all figured out. Their enlightenment is to gaze and gape at the Mystery of Being. And in that, I think they are very wise. But if anybody ever thought they had the whole thing figured out, it was the ancient Gnostics, whether they were the "original Christians" or not.

Chapter 10
Going Kabbalistic

Michael Berg, *The Way: Using the Kabbalah for Spiritual Transformation and Fulfillment*

COSMIC SCHTETL

*M*y house is filled with clutter (as some, perhaps including my wife, would view it): a vast collection of knickknacks, toys, photos, statuettes, even CDs, videos, DVDs, and zillions of books. They make me feel that I am living in my own private microcosm. That is, I have taken the world of meaning in which I live and move and have my being, and I have externalized it into a physical environment filled with tokens of these meanings. I move daily in a concrete realm of signification. Imagine my delight to see a beautiful depiction of the same thing in one of my favorite Ingmar Bergman films, *Fanny and Alexander*. The title siblings go to stay for a while with a friend of the family ("Uncle Isak") who is a dealer in antiques and curiosities, as well as being a pious Kabbalistic Jew. His nephew Aaron, a puppeteer, gives them the tour of the place. It is a universe behind closed doors, filled with treasures, winding corridors, eerie puppets that seem to move by themselves, and—central to the place—a locked chamber in which Aaron's brother Ishmael lives, locked away. All fear his dangerous prophetic and magical powers. During the walk through Uncle Isak's store/house, Aaron comments that

> Uncle Isak says we are surrounded by realities, one outside the other. He says that there are swarms of ghosts, spirits, phantoms, souls, poltergeists, demons, angels, and devils. He says that the smallest pebble has a life of its own. . . . Everything is alive. Everything is God or God's thought, not only what is good but also the cruelest things. . . . I for my part am an atheist. (Bergman, pp. 194–95)

I like Uncle Isak's worldview very much, but I also agree with Aaron. The swarms of dybbuks and ghosts and souls in which I make my residence are the swirling vortex of memory, imagination, and meaning. I think it is only in my head. But it is no less powerful for that.

In general, Jews have perforce created a sacred cosmos in the midst of a profane and often hostile world. If they want to safeguard their cultural distinctives, which are precious, they have little choice but to fashion and shore up a "finite province of meaning" (Berger and Luckmann, p. 25) in the midst of a non-Jewish cultural universe. The need is all the greater if a Jew's surroundings are comfortable, nonthreatening, even attractive. A spiritual mini-world is all the more necessary as a bulwark against assimilation. And Uncle Isak's shop is a cameo of such a refuge. And, I submit, so is the sacred cosmos of Jewish belief in general and of Kabbalah specifically. In this chapter, I want to deal with a modern appropriation of the brand of Kabbalah springing from the great sixteenth-century mystic Isaac Luria, who dreamed and taught his disciples in Safed, Galilee. This tradition has never died out, so we must not speak of its revival, only of its new popularity among unlikely audiences, including pop icon Madonna.

In *On the Kabbalah and Its Symbolism*, Gershom Scholem's remarks apply to our subject matter, regardless of which religion we are talking about.

> Paul had a mystical experience which he interpreted in such a way that it shattered the traditional authority. He could not keep it intact; but since he did not wish to forego the authority of the Holy Scriptures as such, he was forced to declare that it was limited in time and hence abrogated. A purely mystical exegesis of the old words replaced the original frame and provided the foundation of the new authority which he felt called upon to establish. This mystic's clash with religious authority was clear and sharp. In a manner of speaking, Paul read the Old Testament "against the grain." The incredible violence with which he did so shows not only how incompatible his experience was with the meaning of the old books, but also how determined he was to preserve, if only by purely mystical exegeses, his bond with the sacred text. The result was the paradox that never ceases to amaze us when we read the Pauline Epistles: on the one hand the Old Testament is preserved, on the other, its meaning is completely set aside. The new authority that is set up, for which the Pauline Epistles themselves serve as a holy text, is revolutionary in nature. Having found a new source, it breaks away from the authority constituted in Judaism, but continues in part to clothe itself in the images of the old authority, which has been reinterpreted in purely spiritual terms. (pp. 14–15)

It is generally known that allegorical interpretations arise spontaneously whenever a conflict between new ideas and those expressed in a sacred book necessitates some form of compromise. What is true of allegorical interpretation is still more applicable to the specifically mystical interpretation of such texts. (p. 33)

Actually the thought processes of mystics are largely unconscious, and they may be quite unaware of the clash between old and new which is of such passionate interest to the historian. They are thoroughly steeped in the religious tradition in which they have grown up, and many notions which strike a modern reader as fantastic distortions of a text spring from a conception of Scripture which to the mystic seems perfectly natural. (p. 33)

Similarity of purpose and hence in the fundamental structure of the mystical ideas about the Holy Scriptures accounts for the parallels between certain Kabbalistic statements about the Torah and those of Islamic mystics about the Koran or of Christian mystics about their Biblical canon. (p. 35)

Kabbalah simply means "tradition" but denotes a particular strand of Jewish mystical tradition, called "the Lore of Creation." It dates back to about the second to third century CE, as far as we can tell. Its chief documents include the *Sepher Yetsirah* (Book of Creation, second to third century), the *Bahir* (late twelfth century), and the encyclopedic compendium of mystical Torah commentary, the *Zohar* (Book of Splendor). This last is the work of a Spanish rabbi, Moses de Leon, at the start of the thirteenth century CE, though it is pseudepigraphical, written under the pseudonym of the second-century master Simeon ben Yochai.

The teaching of the Kabbalah, especially of Isaac Luria, is panentheistic: the cosmos is made out of the being of God, and yet (unlike pantheism) the cosmos is not all there is of God. Rather, a personal deity still stands over the world he has emanated from himself. Luria's doctrine explained how we came to have a world filled with the dark shadows of pain and evil, and yet gleaming with divine glory even in the darkest of shadows. This doctrine was embraced by most Jews of his time.

God at first filled all things, as he must by definition, being Infinite, All-in-all. (As such he was the En-Sof.) Where would there be "room" for anything else? So to allow for a created world, God withdrew or contracted into himself (the *Tsimtsum*), leaving ontological space for a world to be, and he created it "out of nothing," only, being Infinite, God could never really stop encompassing all things, so the hole left was still part of him! (Think of an antiproton, which is a charged hole in the ether of space.) This apparent nullity, negativity, cavity is really the shadow side of God. It is because the world was emanated from this Dark Side of the Deity that it contains evil and sorrow.

From his own being, God emanated a giant duplicate of himself, represented as both a Tree of Life and a heavenly Adam (the *Adam Kadmon*), each representing the collection of the Ten *Sephiroth* (spheres as well as letters of Torah, which means the world is created by word: "And God said, 'Let there be . . .'"). God had already prepared a set of "shells" (*Kelipoth*), the crystalline outline or outer form of what was intended as a resplendent creation of spirit and light. These were to hold, like fine wine, streams of divine light (the *Shekinah* or glory of God) which now streamed forth from the Adam Kadmon, from his eyes, nostrils, ears, and mouth. But this light proved too powerful, and the cosmic shells shattered on impact. They formed a jagged ruin of shards, having condensed into the world of matter. What about the divine light? It was lost, scattered amid the ruin of matter. To the heavenly Adam was assigned the task of regathering all the sparks of light for a new attempt at creation. He had nearly fulfilled his task when he somehow erred, spilling the whole collection of divine photons. For this failure, he was greatly reduced in size, though still a giant compared to us. God enclosed him in a prison of leathery hide: our accustomed bodies of flesh and blood. This is what Genesis 3:21 means when it says, "[H]e gave them coats of skin to wear."

Note that the Fall includes not only humans but God, God's Shekinah glory. God needs salvation as much as we do. (The Gnostic character of all this is obvious.) What is now to be done to right the situation? That is the job of pious Jews. By their acts of righteous devotion and good works (*tikkun*, or "purification"), they will gradually free the divine sparks from their imprisonment in matter. (Each soul has its appointed tasks. If it fails to accomplish them, it will be reincarnated to finish the job, perhaps with the aid of a more powerful soul.) This historic-cosmic vista is easily the match in symbolic power of the Christian doctrine of divine incarnation: in both we have profound symbols of the divine sharing of the plight of humanity. In the Jewish version, God himself shares the exile of his people, and he can only save them once they save him.

When this process is complete, the Messiah will arrive to usher in the new creation as God first intended it. The notion that repentance among God's people could hasten or bring about the coming of the Messiah is an old one in Judaism and is evident in Acts 3:19–20, "Repent, therefore and return [to God], so that your sins may be wiped away, in order that times of refreshing may come from the presence of the Lord; and that he may send the Christ appointed for you."

TIKKUN AND TEXTUALITY

All this has been derived, by hook or by crook, from scripture: "[J]ust as the microcosm, man, reveals the pattern of the Supreme Creator and Macrocosm, the Law of this microcosm makes known the Eternal Law of the Macrocosm. And since this cannot be discovered in the literal sense, you must acknowledge it to be drawn from the cabalistic or allegorical sense" (Blau, pp. 68–69).

Isaac the Blind, active 1190–1210, with his disciples Ezra and Azarael, lived in southern France and Spain. They developed the doctrine of the world emanating from God. They also suggested the doctrine of metempsychosis/reincarnation. Soon thereafter, Eliezar of Worms (active ca. 1220) and his disciples introduced numerical and alphabetical techniques (though they had existed in the second century CE at least). On their heels, Abraham ben Samuel Abulafia (1240–ca. 1292), a self-proclaimed messiah, combined and further refined the elements of his predecessors, both theoretically and practically (that is, by devotionalism and by scriptural study). His disciple Joseph ben Abraham Gikatilia (ca. 1247–1305) was the greatest systematizer yet and greatly developed the three famous techniques of esoteric interpretation widely used by their followers, including later Hasidic Jews, for the purpose of finding their beloved Kabbalistic doctrines in scripture. They are:

- *Gematria*, or "the calculation of the numerical value of Hebrew words and the search for connections with other words or phrases of equal values" (Scholem, *Jewish Mysticism*, p. 100). "It involved the use of the fact that in ancient languages, including Hebrew, the letters of the alphabet also represented numbers. This suggested that, when the sum of the numerical equivalents of the letters of two or more words was the same, the words might be considered identical and used interchangeably" (Blau, p. 8).

- *Notarikon*, or "interpretation of the letters of a word as abbreviations of whole sentences" (Scholem, *Jewish Mysticism*, p. 100). "The initial or final letters of the words of a phrase might be joined to form a word which was then given occult significance. The significance of another word might be explained by expanding it into a phrase, using each letter of the original as [the] initial letter of one word of the phrase. Finally, two words might be joined as one and thus given new meaning" (Blau, p. 8).

- *Temurah* is the "interchange of letters according to certain systematic rules" (Scholem, *Jewish Mysticism*, p. 100). "*Themurah*, which means 'transposition," is actually a combination of the letter substitutions of the code and the anagrammatic interchange of the resultant letters. Since an alphabet of twenty-two consonants provides twenty-one codes, and since vowel sounds are not printed in Hebrew, an almost infinite number of letter combinations can be produced from any one Hebrew word, and some few of these combinations are likely to form words. This method, then, is likely to be fruitful" (Blau, pp. 8–9).

Moses de Leon, the thirteenth-century author of the *Zohar* and the *Pardes* (Paradise), counted four separate levels of meaning in the Torah and listed them in a pun on *Pardes*.

P is for *peshat*, "designating the literal or simple meaning, which is preserved even in the mystical transfiguration, though it has been made transparent by the mystical light shining through it" (Scholem, *Jewish Mysticism*, p. 56).

R stands for *remez*, the allegorical meaning.

D stands for *derasha* (cf. *Midrash*), the haggadic or Talmudic meaning (legal, casuistic interpretation).

S stands for *sod*, the mystical meaning (the sort of exegesis that grounded Isaac Luria's system).

Later he added *Gematria* as a fifth, though it was more a means of unlocking the others, not a separate level of meaning in its own right.

Today's deconstructive critics, several of them Jews, take quite seriously the basic Kabbalistic insight about textuality as a material, not just a formal, aspect of writing. The medium itself is inseparable from the message. As Marshall McLuhan observed, the medium *is* the message, but it is much more. The text is a massive continent just beneath the ocean surface, and the plain-sense reading of the text is like an archipelago of islands, really mountain peaks revealed to our gaze, but signaling a greater, vaster reality below. Just as Kabbalah is panentheistic, all things being included in God, Kabbalah sees the sacred text as something like a divine totality from which specific messages, words and sentences, temporarily detach themselves, only to fall back into the ocean of a greater whole. Maurice Saussere distinguished between the bottomless abyss of language (*langue*) and individual usages of it (*parole*); Kabbalah sees the biblical text as a bubbling volcano, by virtue of the unstable, living character of the divine word which constitutes it. Any revelation may emerge from it at any moment as the learned read the text, using the various techniques developed by the masters of Kabbalah.

MADONNA'S GURU

Rabbi Michael Berg, director of the Kabbalah Centre, stands in the Lurianic tradition, as tweaked by Rabbi Yehuda Aschlag, who wrote during the Second World War, obviously a dire time for Jews and an unavoidable occasion for them to reexamine their relationship to God and their place in the scheme of things. We have already seen the extensive parallels between Lurianic Kabbalah and ancient Gnosticism. Aschlag drew the two systems even closer. He posited an explanation for the failure of the *Kelipoth*, the light shells, to catch and contain the divine light streaming forth from the Adam Kadmon. Why would they have proven inadequate to their assigned task? Who could be blamed but their Creator? That seems an odd loose end, and Rabbi Aschlag ventured to tie it up by personifying the *Kelipoth*. In his vision of things, the *Kelipoth* are like the frustrated Sophia of Valentinian Gnosticism. She was the last emanation from the Godhead, and she desired to know the Father, from whom however she found herself separated by the intervening 364 aions. Symbolizing the desire of the mind to "conceive" the truth, the Gnostic myth had it that Sophia managed to "conceive" offspring, just as the previous aions had. They had emerged in pairs from the Godhead, and so their conception of new Aions was natural. (Their ability to "conceive" stands for their knowledge of the Father, which

Sophia lacked.) Sophia contrives a virginal conception, and her off-spring is the confused and maligned Demiurge, the Creator. So Sophia's frustrated urge to know/conceive led to the Fall. According to Rabbi Aschlag, the trouble began because the *Kelipoth* yearned to reciprocate the loving advance of the onrushing divine light, not merely to receive it passively. But for this the light was not ready and it flinched, momentarily withdrawing and leaving a vacuum in the space between itself and the welcoming *Kelipoth*. The light then rushed back in reflexively to fill the vacuum thus created, and it was this impact that caused the *Kelipoth* to shatter.

As Rudolf Bultmann said, every statement of theology is at the same time a statement of anthropology. We may think we are speaking about God, but we are also speaking about human exis-tence. Everything we say about God is relevant to some aspect of our existence. If there is any extrahuman truth about God, we wouldn't have the equipment to pick up on it. Well, Rabbi Aschlag's innovation is a prime illustration of Bultmann's dictum. The overenthusiasm of the (anthropopathized) *Kelipoth* is not merely a theological integer to clear up a theoretical difficulty in the system. It also provides a jack which the individual Kabbalist can use to plug into the system spiritually. For it turns out that the individual must seek to become like the *Kelipoth*, fervently seeking to greet and contain the divine light. The spiritual practices of *tikkun* are the means by which we strengthen our own spiritual con-stitutions, so that we will not shatter upon impact like the original *Kelipoth* during the creation. "When we recognize our need for God's assistance, we create an egofree space within ourselves. [One might call this our own private *Tsimtsum*, or contraction.] Kabbalah describes this as 'creating a Vessel into which the Light can flow'" (Berg, p. 89).

TOP SECRET

Kabbalah has always been panentheistic, seeing everything as a part of God, but the way Rabbi Berg explains things, it appears to have become outright monistic, skipping pantheism in one great leap. According to pantheism, remember, all reality is a face of God, while for monism, all "reality" is a mask of God, hiding the underlying Oneness, not revealing it. For monism, diversity is an illusion. "In our everyday lives, we are like stones that have been carried away from the mountain. We assume individual identities for a time, but when we return to our point of origin we are no longer separate objects. We are again part of the mountain. . . . Separation from the Creator is recognized as an illusion, and Oneness is revealed as the supreme truth" (Berg, p. 57).

If absolute Oneness, an absence of diversity, prevails on the macrocosmic level, this unity is reflected (as well as refracted) by a condition of harmony among diversity here on our microcosmic level. The latter presupposes distinctions absent from the former, and yet their harmony points to the still unity of the higher plane. This is much like Jung's definition of Abraxas: a finite image of the infinite, symbolizing the ultimate lack of polarity under the form of a harmonizing of poles. And, just as Ira Progoff saw Jungian synchronicity as a series of flashes illuminating a harmonic universe of Leibnizian monads, so does Rabbi Berg envision synchronicity as the natural outworking on our plane of the nondual reality of the macrocosm.

When synchronicity strikes, we are momentarily taken aback at the revelation of what at least seems to be a usually hidden pattern of correspondences. But what about when no such order is evident? That is when we walk by faith, confident that, because of ultimate Oneness, even on our level of existence there are no coincidences. Everything is happening according to plan, and in our own best interests (Berg, pp. 114, 190–91).

From his Kabbalistic nondualism, Berg infers a doctrine of salvation right out of Mahayana Buddhism: Since there is no ultimate individuality, final salvation must be a package deal. It cannot exclude anybody. That is to say, it cannot exclude any individual because ultimately there are no individuals. Everyone is to be saved if anyone is to be. Berg uses the metaphor of a jigsaw puzzle: salvation is restoring the visible order to all the pieces of the "big picture." That goal is going to languish unaccomplished as long as anyone remains unenlightened, stuck in the illusion of individual existence (pp. 73–74, 75).

Think again of the puppets crowding the house-cosmos of Uncle Isak. They even included a seven-foot-tall effigy of God. This is an important image for Kabbalah as Rabbi Berg explains it: "A passage in the Zohar explains that we are like wonderful marionettes whose strings reach up to connect us to countless supernal worlds. But instead of these strings controlling us, *we* control the strings. Our actions in the world influence the spiritual worlds above us. A simple act of kindness allows more kindness to flow down into our level of experience—and this, in turn, empowers others to act kindly as well" (p. 101). Kabbalah tends to communicate in myth rather than in philosophy, but the point seems to be much the same as the main premise of New Thought, especially as New Thought pioneer Thomas Troward puts it. There has to be a way for us to send feedback into the Platonic realm of Forms so that we may play the role of the Demiurge, causing material reality to conform to an ideal reality we envision in the upper realm. For Troward and for New Thought, one seeds the subconscious with affirmations and visualizations, and since the subconscious ostensibly exists, like God, outside of space-time strictures (cf. Berg: "everyday notions of time and space are not applicable in matters of spirituality," p. 102), the mind may become a cause as well as an effect of the realm of Ideas and Forms. I am not sure this metaphysical version is really much more theoretical, less mythological, than Berg's version.

If New Thought makes the individual into the Demiurge, the Platonic creator, translator of form into matter, Rabbi Berg takes the parallel ever further. Just as the Gnostic Demiurge created Archons, angels, to do his bidding in his newly created world, so Rabbi Berg tells us that

> the idea that we create our own angels is a basic kabbalistic teaching. These angels are not white-robed beings with wings and halos. They are the direct expression of what is in our hearts and minds. These angels fundamentally influence our experience of the world, and we ourselves bring them into being. From this it follows that we must accept responsibility for whatever we encounter in the world, even those things that most distress us. Difficult as it may seem, we must realize that we ourselves are to some extent responsible for any and all suffering, no matter how remote it may seem from our lives. We must face the realization that if we had been better people, perhaps this might not have happened. (pp. 101–102)

Throughout *The Way*, Rabbi Berg seems to me to be tightrope walking between psychology and superstition. In the passage just reproduced I find a striking metaphor for a significant fact, often overlooked: each of us has such strong, though usually unsuspected, influence over others, ruining or making someone's day with a single comment, changing the course of a life with a compliment or a suggestion, that it is literally and entirely true to say that we are co-creators of the worlds of those we daily contact. We underestimate the power of our actions, oblivious of the fact that our own words and acts will rebound upon us as they set in motion people's reactions to us. Berg's kabbalistic angels are our words that do not return unto us void, failing to accomplish their mission, even if we do not realize what mission our careless speaking sent them on.

But then, I think, the good rabbi steps over the line into delusions of reference. He gives us a charter for feeling guilty about events to which we have contributed nothing. He only thinks we have because of his underlying nondualism: there is fundamentally no difference between the murderer and his victim, the slanderer and the object of her hatred. Here is liberal self-hatred elevated to a metaphysical worldview: no matter what happens, I can and should feel guilty for it. I have myself to blame for the deaths of the Kennedys and Dr. King. We all do! (And to think, Madonna renounced guilt-tripping Catholicism for this?) My belief is that liberal self-hatred, which gives rise to liberal politics, stems ultimately from survivor guilt. One imagines the envy and injustice felt by innocent victims of persecution or disaster toward those of us who did not so suffer, and for no good reason. We were just lucky. We were no more "worthy" of survival than they, damn us! And so *resentment* forms, the *resentment* that would ordinarily be directed at the fortunate by the unfortunate. Only liberals internalize this hatred and aim it at themselves. In this way, they seek to salve their consciences by thus "empathizing" with the sufferers, implicitly regarding it as the price (and a license) for keeping hold of one's affluence. This, I think, explains many of their social policies that intend to spread the guilt around and make the rest of the fortunate, by God, pay for their good fortune. It is an undeserved guilt, and it results in neurosis and neurotic beliefs and policies. Rabbi Berg has provided a theological rationale for it.

SACRED SUPERSTITION

Enlightenment, with its product scientific criticism, has not yet managed to disenchant the world of Rabbi Berg's Kabbalah. For one thing, he is completely precritical when it comes to the Bible. One of the great advantages of allegorical interpretation of scripture has always been the breathing room it allowed: the reader could allow, as Origen of Alexandria did, for historical errors in a text, viewing them as red lights signaling the reader to delve deeper than any literal meaning. But Rabbi Berg still believes that "Adam and Eve were real people who did eat a fruit from the forbidden tree. . . . Abraham, Isaac, Jacob, Rachel, and Leah are not literary characters. They were real people whose lives are chronicled in the Bible" (p. 25). One is tempted to doubt either the honesty or the sanity of anyone who would make such statements—until, that is, one recalls the power of what Peter Berger and Thomas Luckmann call "plausibility structures." These are carefully reinforced social units, peer groups of the like-minded, among whom the most inherently unlikely notions are taken for granted as self-evidently true simply by token of the fact that everyone in the group believes them. Everyone in the plausibility structure reinforces everyone else's belief. And that plausibility structure in this case is the bubble reality of Kabbalistic mysticism, an imaginary universe cosmic in its scope, yet existing behind the locked doors of tiny, pious conventicles.

Rabbi Berg's fundamentalism extends not only to the Bible but to the Kabbalistic *Book of Zohar* as well. He regards the great sages of Kabbalah as being literally divinely inspired (p. 200), like the authors of the Bible. And which of these sages, then, penned *Zohar*? It must have been he whose name appears upon it, the second-century mystic Shimon bar Yochai (p. 28), though critical scholars (e.g., Scholem) recognize the pseudonym as simply a technique to highlight the supposed antiquity of the teaching contained in the book, which was actually the work of Rabbi Moses de Leon in the early thirteenth century.

Earlier I mentioned the Kabbalistic apprehension of the textuality of the text, a potent notion rediscovered by today's deconstructive critics. But Jacques Derrida and Harold Bloom have nothing on Rabbi Berg when it come to the mystery of textuality.

> Kabbalah tells us that the Hebrew letters and the words built from them are like access codes granting us entry into the spiritual realm. In certain combinations, the Hebrew letters have the power to open us up to channels of Light in the Upper Worlds. . . . This is why Kabbalah urges us to scan the Hebrew text, even if we can't actually read it. The surface meaning of a passage is expressed in translation, but the spiritual power derives from the combination of Hebrew letters on the page. (p. 204)

Here the medium is not simply equated with the message; it has gone on to eclipse the message completely. The meanings of the text become, at best, a secondary epiphenomenon. Remember, according to the Kabbalistic creation myth, the divine light of creation streams forth from the Adam Kadmon who is also depicted as the Sephirotic Tree, a diagram of living Hebrew letters, each standing for or even constituting an attribute of God. In this way God creates "by the word" in the most literal possible sense. Thus, recalling Pythagoras's dictum that the world is made of numbers, Kabbalah implies the world is made of the letters of the Hebrew alphabet, which is no human-made language, but the very tongue of God.

It might seem difficult to evaluate such a doctrine. What possible contact with testable reality can it have? But in fact there is such an interface. What practice does the theory imply? We already know: Merely looking at the letters of a text one cannot read. It is like visual glossolalia, and the dyslexic is at no disadvantage. Surely we must call this superstition if there is such a thing. The whole doctrine thus reveals itself as a rationalization of a superstition. We know what superstition is like, and this is it. In the same way, a piece of theology that naturally yielded bigotry and hatred would ipso facto be discredited, since all, including adherents of said religion, profess to eschew bigotry and hatred. I may not be able to prove how many angels can dance on the point of a needle, or whether any do at all. But I can indeed tell what kind of tree I am looking at by its fruits.

Rabbi Berg also promotes a veneration for the Sabbath that comes across as manifestly superstitious. The notion of sacred time is far from superstititious. Any and all may readily see the point of a day set aside for spiritual contemplation for which one dare not pause during the hectic week. Anyone may admit that certain repeated occasions foster such contemplation because they are laden with cherished memories of when one has observed the holy occasion before. There is "magic" about the day, but nothing literally supernatural. But that is not enough for Rabbi Berg.

Shabbat is filled with the pure unadulterated energy of the Light. It's a free glimpse into the future, when humanity will be transformed and every day will be filled with the fulfillment of oneness with the Creator. Shabbat is the only day on which we are not required to *earn* our transformation. In fact, the Light of Shabbat is so great that we could not possibly earn it. Again, only one thing is required of us: that we prepare ourselves as fitting Vessels in which the Light can come to rest. (p. 180)

Anything and everything of a spiritual nature is amplified on the Sabbath. Prayers have more influence. . . . Study of spiritual texts is deeper and more revealing. (p. 181)

All this sounds to me like theological overkill. Do we really need such fanciful metaphysical claims on behalf of the Sabbath? Indeed, do they not implicitly denigrate the genius of the practice in a way that simple rational, psychological analysis would not? In the same way it implicitly insults scripture to claim divine inspiration as the basis for its authority, since what inherent moral authority it may have renders such extravagant praise superfluous. The excellence of the Sabbath can be demonstrated easily without hocus-pocus. A time set aside when we can forget everything else and delve into edifying discussion, unravel the puzzles of scripture, sing uplifting songs—assuming one has a taste for such things, as I admit I do—that is a delight and a treat not to be missed. I don't have to try to make myself believe that some dimensional portal has opened between this and another reality, and that the inhabitants of it are projecting golden rays into our world.

A WAY OF WISDOM

I do not want to leave a closing impression that Rabbi Berg's version of the Kabbalah is simply superstition. No, as with many premodern systems, there is much wisdom derived inductively from human experience, and not just alleged revelation derived deductively from someone's hallucinations. I would like to shift the focus to the former in conclusion.

Judaism in all its forms has always kept a healthy sense of priorities: doing good for other human beings trumps everything else. Piety means nothing without deeds of mercy. Worship is altogether without merit if one's heart is hard toward others. Even toward God one's acts must be sincerely felt and must partake of joy as well as fear, or it is an empty charade. The same sound priorities are on display in Berg's *The Way*. Yes, he seeks (and wants you to seek) mystical blessings and ecstasies. And that might seem like selfish navel gazing until we read, "We merit these divine gifts by becoming truly sharing beings and by performing acts of sharing in our daily lives" (p. 189). "Our intentions and our actions in this present environment are really only means for connecting with that other level of being" (p. 156). Again, to some, that may smack of crude barter, selling enough magazine subscriptions to win the prize. But that is not Berg's point. He is thinking of a transformation of our selfish nature. Real sharing, he says, and as anyone knows from experience, goes against our natural inclinations, and thus as we learn to share, we are growing past our initial character limitations. We are progressing, growing, achieving greater maturity and sanctification. To do this is to purify oneself of the impurities that cut one off from experiencing God to begin with (pp. 152–53).

In sharp contrast, I think, to the earlier advice to read the Hebrew text uncomprehendingly, comes Rabbi Berg's suggestion that individual scripture passages be memorized for meditation as odd moments through the day permit. It is like chanting a mantra, but it has nothing to do with belief in magical invocations. It is rather a technique to launder the inner speech of the mind. All day long one is incessantly engaged in random chatter anyway, much of it negative and critical. Why not run some detergent through the machine instead? Why not think upon edifying texts, and thus alter one's patterns of thinking and one's attitudes? If you don't happen to favor scriptures, your favorite quote from Bertrand Russell or Thomas Paine will no doubt have the same effect.

If that sounds like the mental techniques of New Thought, the similarity does not stop there. Rabbi Berg believes that the habits of giving and sharing we must inculcate in order to stretch ourselves for spiritual growth will, almost as a side effect, bring with them worldly compensations, too. "In fact, the benefits of giving are perhaps even greater when we have little: sharing is an opportunity to experience a consciousness of wealth and magnanimity, rather than poverty and scarcity" (p. 161). Eventually, this mode of consciousness will subtly cause our actions to catch up with our attitude, and we will have become more prosperous.

As with many other spiritual approaches discussed in this book, Michael Berg's Kabbalah invites criticism from the scientific observer at some points and admiration from the psychological observer at others. We often speak of bitter medicine going down easier with a spoonful of sugar. But I am willing to bet that for most of my readers, it is the medicinal element, the wholesome ideas and advice, that is being conveyed by a bitter coating: the superstition and pseudoscience of which our gurus cannot seem to rid themselves. Similarly, spiritual movements are often ill served by their most visible converts and supporters. If one is tempted to blame Rabbi Berg for the attraction his system has for narcissistic showbiz sirens, it might be well to remember that Jesus, too, had his Mary Magdalene.

Chapter 11

Are You Running with Me, Joel?

Joel Osteen, *Your Best Life Now*

The handsome, smiling Rev. Joel Osteen, as he stands before his congregation of thirty thousand, packed into what used to be a basketball stadium (to say nothing of his untold legions in TV land), is poised, many say, on the verge of becoming the leading evangelical minister in America. If anyone, he shares that distinction with the Reverend Rick Warren, author of *The Purpose-Driven Life*. Like Warren, Osteen has a best-selling book, *Your Best Life Now*. It is quite a different book, with quite a different message. I have dealt with Warren's book in my own *The Reason-Driven Life*, and here I will merely repeat my opinion that it is a repackaging of stale fundamentalism, nothing particularly new to anyone who has ever had any exposure to born-again Christianity. Osteen's book has little new to offer, either. Its message has been told and heard many, many times, only not among his particular audience, his own generation. It is my contention that Joel Osteen is the latest bearer of the perennially popular New Thought doctrine.

Joel Osteen is an evangelical Christian in both piety and theology, though neither is dominant in *Your Best Life Now*. His evangelicalism is almost vestigial, taken as read, as he conveys his central message of mind power and positive affirmations. In this chapter I would like to demonstrate that thesis, showing first how his preaching is readily recognizable as New Thought, pure and simple. Second, I will show how it is only cosmetically theological, God amounting to a conceptual fifth wheel in the system. Third, I will suggest that his gospel is virtually all of it sheer assertion, with only ornamental scriptural citations. Fourth, I hope to demonstrate how it is justified mainly by dubious anecdotal evidence. Fifth, I want to show how Osteen's residual belief in God contributes to two of the worst features of his approach, its superstitious character and its fatal inconsistency.

DO YOU FIND PAUL APPEALING OR PEALE APPALLING?

Joel Osteen is scarcely the first prominent American Protestant to promote New Thought as if it were an implication (or even the essence) of the New Testament message. Norman Vincent Peale, though he hailed from the staid Dutch Reformed Church, imbibed heavily of the literature of the Unity School of Christianity and fashioned from it a uniquely American gospel of Positive Thinking. Copies of his book *The Power of Positive Thinking* are still ubiquitous on the shelves of secondhand bookstores and garage sales. The depth of Peale's theology is revealed in the answer he gave to a reporter at the Super Bowl who wondered if some of Peale's parishioners might deem his presence there a violation of Reform Church sabbatarianism: "If Jesus were alive today, he'd be here!" *Yee-ouch.* As his influence waned somewhat in the 1970s, the baton was taken up by another Reformed Churchman (this time from the Christian Reformed branch), namely, Robert Schuller, whose variation on the theme was known as "possibility thinking." The shallowness of Schuller's feel-good evangel may be judged by his infamous quote, "The Cross is a plus sign!" But now a generation has arisen that does not know Peale or Schuller, and Joel Osteen is their oracle of New Thought.

It does not take much detective work to discover virtually the whole New Thought platform in Osteen's *Your Best Life Now*. First, God in this system begins to slip away from being a Father, a king, a person, toward being a vague cloud of positive energy upon which we draw by using certain techniques. Osteen has started down this path: "God is positive! There is nothing negative about him. If you are going to live God's way and be the person He wants you to be, you must line up your vision with His and learn to live in a positive frame of mind" (p. 105). "It's time . . . to tap into God's power" (p. 194). There is an implicit shift from having faith in God's almighty power toward imitating God, doing what he does when he does mighty works, namely, declaring something to be so, affirming it, and making it come into being. Despite the talk about God, it is really a matter of training the mind to expect and attract what we want in life: "We must realize that to a large extent, we can control our own destinies" (p. 103). "As a person thinks in his heart, so will he become" (p. 104). This paraphrases Proverbs 23:7, which also provided the title for one of the most famous New Thought classics, James Allen's *As a Man Thinketh*. "Fill your mind with good thoughts. Your mind is similar to a computer. What you program into it dictates how it will function" (p. 113). "You are reprogramming your mind" (p. 108).

One of the chief tenets of New Thought is the so-called Law of

Attraction, the mechanism of mind over matter: "Psychologists are convinced that our lives move in the direction of our most dominant thoughts. If thoughts of joy, peace, victory, abundance, and blessings dominate your thoughts throughout the day, you will move toward those things, drawing them to yourself at the same time" (p. 107). "Our thoughts contain tremendous power. Remember, we draw into our lives that which we constantly think about" (p. 109).

Osteen echoes the insight of New Thought that, as long as you think about your lacks and your problems, you merely reinforce them. The more you speak of them, you unwittingly affirm them and keep them coming: "Choose to dwell on what you have, not on what you don't have" (p. 115). "You must stop talking about the problem and start talking about the solution" (p. 128).

Not surprisingly, Osteen winds up recommending the use of daily affirmations, that self-coaching of which Al Franken (as "Stuart Smalley") makes so much fun. "If you are struggling with low self-esteem, you need to go overboard speaking positive, faith-filled words about your life. Get up each morning and look in the mirror and say, 'I am valuable. I am loved. God has a great plan for my life. . . . Everything I touch prospers and succeeds.' . . . There truly is power in your words" (p. 123). (In an earlier chapter, I defended the practice as a means of reprogramming one's habits of thought, not so ridiculous a practice after all. Nor do I mean to attack it here.)

WHO WILL ROLL AWAY THE FIFTH WHEEL FOR US?

Joel Osteen frequently mentions God, but one feels it is but the theological sugar that will make the New Thought medicine go down for his evangelical and charismatic audience. The New Thought pioneers, especially Charles A. Fillmore, founder of the Unity School of Christianity, were consistent in their pantheism. God for them was a force permeating all things, as the New Testament use of the Stoic Logos doctrine would imply. God is viewed as a set of eternal laws of thought, what Tillich called the "Logos Structure" of the universe. And the manipulation of it can bring us desired results. The New Thought deity did not so much as answer prayer by an act of will as yield the appropriate response to the proper stimulus, namely, the individual's affirmation. Osteen still believes in a personal deity, and this belief is what will get him in trouble, lending a crass magical character to his faith, as it will imply mortals can command God when what Osteen really wants to say is that human beings can manipulate the laws of thought and success. Actually, Osteen's system seems to work perfectly well without any role for the deity.

"Friend, that's what faith is all about. You have to start believing that good things are coming your way, and they will!" (p. 15). "She started expecting the supernatural favor of God. . . . She developed a 'can-do' mentality" (p. 27). In traditional Protestant, evangelical terms, a faith in God's supernatural favor and a "can-do" attitude would seem to be diametrically opposite each other. On the contrary, given the "He must increase, I must decrease," "My power is made perfect in wisdom" approach of evangelical pietism, wouldn't one require a "*can't*-do" attitude to reap the power of God through one's frail frame? Admittedly, Osteen says things like, "God says you can do all things through Christ" (p. 112). But it is hard to see why he wastes the ink adding "through Christ" to the sentence.

Here is the typical tune he sings: "[Y]ou must make room for increase in your own thinking, then God will bring those things to pass" (p. 6). Here, "God" seems to be code for "Life." When he says, "God has so much more in store for you" (p. 8), doesn't "God" simply mean "the future"? If you simply substituted "the future," would the sentence mean anything different? "Get beyond the barriers of your past and start expecting God to do great things in your life" (p. 9). Drop the words "God to do" and see if the sentence makes sense, the same sense as before. "God is opening a new door for them; all they have to do is step through it" (p. 21). Again, "God" is just a theological euphemism for "Life." "God has more in store for you" (p. 27). In other words, the future holds more in store for you. Osteen very nearly puts his cards on the table when he says, "If you want to point people to God, or simply to a better way of living, have some enthusiasm and be excited about life" (p. 299). That is because, as he implies, "God" for him means the same thing as "a better way of living."

THE GHOST OF GOD

But God's influence lingers in Osteen's pages like the moaning of a ghost. Insofar as Osteen retains the literalized mythology of "God" as a personal manipulator of circumstances, an answerer of prayers, and a providential will, he creates hobbling problems and paradoxes. New Thought is always delicately poised on the edge of superstition anyway, threatening to lend to its practitioners a sense of delusional grandeur. Osteen, far from avoiding the danger, only heightens it. The traditional New Thoughter may come to imagine he or she commands the forces of the universe. The Osteen believer must be careful or he will soon be regarding God as his genie. "Perhaps you're searching for a parking spot in a crowded lot. Say,

'Father, I thank you for leading me and guiding me. Your favor will cause me to get a good spot'" (p. 41). "God may intervene in your situation, replacing your supervisor so you can be promoted. One day, you may run that entire company!" (p. 22). Hear the word of Osteen the witch doctor: "I declare that any curse that has ever been spoken over you, any negative evil word that has ever come against you, is broken right now" (p. 140).

Once Osteen was stuck in sardine-can class aboard an airplane. At first the ticket counter personnel would not cooperate with him. And suddenly, as he did long ago at the Red Sea, God intervened in the causal nexus of mundane events. "She waved her hand and said, 'Oh, we needed the space in coach, so the computer just randomly picked somebody to bump up to first class.' I thought, *That's what you think!* I knew that it was my heavenly Father giving me preferential treatment" (p. 46). Personally, I cringe at Osteen's lapsing into the "Born-Again Super Race" arrogance of evangelical Christianity. "That was God giving me special advantages, giving me preferential treatment, not because I was a preacher's kid, or even a distinguished pastor's son, but because I am his child" (p. 47). He ought to have a bumper sticker on his car that says CHRISTIANS AREN'T PERFECT—JUST BETTER THAN YOU. That's sure the message he's sending with these anecdotes.

And yet, later on, he seems to feel guilty about this conceit. He gives an anecdote about a man from Saudi Arabia, a Muslim, who acted the way he says we should act and prospered as a result. Not exactly a born-again believer! Osteen explains that "the principles of giving are spiritual principles. They work regardless of nationality, skin color, or even religion" (p. 229). In other words, the principles work regardless of whether one is a born-again "child of God" or not. Does Osteen even realize the implications of what he is saying here?

TOP SECRET

"A woman . . . received a check in the mail from a relative who had died and left her $90,000. She had never met this man and didn't even know they were related. As she told us her story, I couldn't resist smiling and thinking. *God, give me some relatives like that!*" (p. 23). And kill 'em! This story betrays the narcissistic self-focus of the fundamentalist belief in providence: "Every event in the universe is happening as it does for *my personal benefit.* Oh, but I don't mean to be selfish! I want you to think that all events occur for *your* benefit." How can both be true? Who cares?

Consider the logical implications of this advice and this story: "Throughout the day, declare, 'The favor of God is causing this company to want to hire me'" (p. 40). A man who took Osteen's advice said, "When I went before that board of directors, they were literally scratching their heads. They said, 'We don't really know why we're hiring you. . . . We don't know what it is, but there's something about you that makes you shine above the rest'" (p. 41). Isn't this hoodoo, pure and simple? God, like an obliging genie, mind-controlled the board of directors to hire this fellow when they wouldn't have otherwise. That's magic. Even worse, what about the other poor jerks who, despite superior credentials, were passed over? What is this, the "God Old Boys" system? Did Osteen even bother thinking it out that far? Later on, he seems to, and he starts backpedaling: "[W]e must also understand that God will never change another person's will" (p. 178). But if that's the case, why didn't Osteen go back and delete the earlier stories that plainly depict God doing just that? As we will see, he believes one thing, then its opposite, as each comes in handy.

But suppose you were to drop the machinery of divine providence out of the picture? Suppose you simplified the whole scenario and dumped the deus ex machina of a God manipulating people? Then all you'd have to say is that the person who had primed himself for the interview with a lot of positive affirmation had come armed with a sense of self-confidence that the board found compelling. Others, despite better résumés, might not have been able to produce that, and so the Osteen man got the job. Presto! It would work better, as it implicitly does anyway, without the ghost of God haunting the system.

As might be expected, the magical nature of the whole approach implies it is egocentric. The financial theology is virtually the same that rationalized the sale of indulgences in the medieval church. "If you need a financial miracle, go buy somebody a cup of coffee tomorrow morning, or give a little extra in the offering at church" (p. 251, cf. p. 259). "If you are believing for a better car, instead of complaining about the one you have, sow a seed by giving somebody a ride" (p. 260). "When you give, you are storing up God's goodness and His favor so in your time of need, you'll have a great harvest out of which God can 'draw' to meet your need" (pp. 260–61). "God has witnessed when you have given sac-rificially, even giving money that perhaps you needed for yourself or your family" (p. 262). Here Osteen is willing to countenance what Jesus would not: "If a man tells his father or his mother, 'What you would have gained from me is Corban' (that is, given to God), then you no longer permit him to do anything for his father or mother'" (Mark 7:11–12).

This morning, my wife said she was setting a goal that within three years we would be able to afford some major home renova-tions: expanding the kitchen, adding a sunroom, and so on. She was affirming it in just the way New Thought teachers say you should. I said to her, "Fine by me!" I was seconding both her goal and her method. As I hope to have made clear by now, I think New Thought optimism is well founded simply as a matter of psychology. The focus of attention enables one to see opportunities otherwise missed, and so on. But suppose she had said to me, "I'm *praying that God will give us* enough money to do so-and-so home repairs." That's a different story. I think that's the way Joel Osteen would put it, and it is another instance of how the whole God business only mucks up a good thing. Making God a genie to answer selfish, Christmas-list prayers like that is somehow both infantile and odious. Here's my problem with it: it raises the question of why God is willing to grant my (or Joel's) wishes for home renovations or a good parking space, while his loving care for all the flood and famine and earthquake victims is conspicuous by its absence. Is there some reason I should expect to cut in line before these poor wretches trying to get God's attention? If I just decide not to think about the problem, I am becoming an accomplice to the neglect by an unfair God. There must be some reason God is doing me big favors while telling the poor Africans and Asians, "Eat cake!" But, hey! I'm not going to look a gift horse in the mouth! It's like accepting the gift of a watch you suspect is stolen goods, but you don't ask questions. You're just glad you got the Rolex.

Given the magical thinking Osteen propounds, it is not surprising he would eventually realize the need to provide a safety net for the Icarus-like believers who flew just too high on the wings of faith. Listen to him promise you the moon: "For all those years, runners believed what the experts were saying. They were convinced that it was impossible to run a mile in less than four minutes. . . . The barrier is in your mind. . . . Today, it's common for runners to break the four-minute-mile barrier. It's no big deal. Roger Bannister set a new standard. He cleared the path. Similarly, if you'll break through the barriers of your mind and start stepping out in faith, you will go beyond those old barriers" (p. 30). So, um, can you run the mile in *one* minute? One *second*? Is it foolish to believe those goals are impossible? Wise to believe they aren't?

DEVIL IN THE DETAILS

Of course, Osteen is setting people up for a fall. Don't forget to read the fine print: "But just because I didn't get what I wanted doesn't mean that I'm going to quit believing in the favor of God. No, I know that God has my best interests at heart, that He is working everything for my good. [What if you didn't get the prime parking space?] A delay may spare me from an accident. Or a delay may cause me to bump into somebody that needs to be encouraged, somebody that needs a smile. No matter what does or does not happen, keep believing for the favor of God in your life" (pp. 42–43). "Even if the bottom falls out of your life, your attitude should be: 'God, I know that you are going to turn this around and use it for my good. God, I believe that you are going to bring me out stronger than ever before'" (p. 75). Similarly, "If one dream dies, dream another dream" (p. 85). "Either your requests are not God's best and will probably not be answered the way you'd like, or it must not be the right time" (p. 198). Or it may be that God is having to take the hammer of adversity to you to chip away the rough edges (p. 210). Really, it could be anything; you never know. If things start to get discouraging, it is your job to take it like a man, to stick it out till God has shown you what he wants you to know, till you have emerged from the furnace purified, or whatever. This is essentially the stance of ancient Stoicism. Stoics taught that the only thing that matters, the only thing we ought to prize, is virtue. Thus there is no such thing as misfortune, because every trial may be welcomed as another opportunity to become more virtuous (precisely as in James 1:2–4). The pious Stoic would simply welcome whatever came, knowing it to be God's gracious gift for one's own good.

Stoicism is the fallback position of Osteen (as of the whole evangelical tradition). And it is not a bad philosophy. Certainly I don't mean to criticize it. But it is quite different from the one Osteen started out with, and you can't really embrace both at the same time. Joel Osteen takes away with one hand what he gives with the other. At first we are told that we may confidently affirm blessings we want (even something like a new car, more money), and we will get them. Osteen produces countless stories to reinforce that claim. But then he admits it may not work. So here comes the default mode: Stoicism. Adversity and disappointment could crop up at any time, for any of a number of reasons known only to God. *But then let's learn that lesson!* Since disappointment could happen at any time in the inscrutable providence of God, there is simply no reason to be so positive as Osteen told us to be at first, and still tells us. We should have learned that in any given case, God may want to bless us *or* try us. Either seems equally likely. We have no business expecting either one in any given case. How can that realization not undermine his policy of optimism? But instead, he goes right back to the straight New Thought ticket.

Osteen's system of blithe assurances grows unstable, so that he contradicts himself on a fundamental level. We read first that "Nobody—not even God—ever promised that life would be fair" (p. 144). But not to worry: "He'll make sure you get everything you deserve, and more!" (p. 167). "God is a God of justice. God is going to pay us back for doing the right thing" (p. 169). Why does Osteen put up with this odd seesawing, whereby one goes back and forth between invulnerable confidence to a humble acknowledgment that God may not answer prayer, and then back to the first? He dresses for the weather. If it's sunny, he preaches one thing. If it is rainy, he commiserates with the other. But that's the wrong analogy. He is really trying to wear two left shoes, each of which aims at fitting the same foot. Logically, forget it. But *psycho*logically it *is* consistent, since the real goal is to find some rationale for looking on the bright side in any circumstance.

YEA, HATH GOD SAID?

In the evangelical community, all discourse is garnished with scripture quotations. Whether they are on target or out of context, most pious reader do not know and cannot tell. For though they are great Bible readers, they have been coached to read every verse on any page as if it were a horoscope in a newspaper, applying directly to their moral or emotional life. Such an audience will not be put off by Joel Osteen's purely cosmetic use of Bible passages. Presently I will examine several of his Bible interpretations, but first it is surprising to notice the extent to which he bases his preaching on *sheer assertion*, as if he is an oracle of God in his own right. According to the prophet Joel, and I don't mean the one who has his name on a book of the Old Testament: "God wants us to be constantly increasing" (p. 5). "God wants to increase you financially" (p. 5). "God wants you to go further than your parents" (p. 8). "God is constantly trying to plant new seeds in your heart. He's constantly trying to get you to conceive, to give up antiquated ideas and spawn new bursts of creativity within" (p. 9). "Expect the favor of God. . . . Expect promotion" (p. 19). "God's dream for your life is so much bigger and greater than you can imagine" (p. 22). "God wants to give you your own house" (p. 35). "God wants you to lead your company in sales" (p. 36). "God wants us to have healthy, positive self-images, to see ourselves as priceless treasures" (p. 57). "Moreover, God sees you as a champion" (p. 58). "He regards you as a strong, courageous, successful, overcoming person" (p. 58). "God likes it all! God loves variety!" (p. 93). Where in the Bible does it say any of these things? It might come in handy for evangelical "relational theology," the "theology of the rap session" if the Bible said such things, but as far as I can tell, none of these subjects ever comes up. In fact, Osteen's blithe and gratuitous assertions make all the clearer the contrast between the Bible and our modern American therapeutic culture, to which it rather seems an entire stranger. It is comical, parodic even to imagine Jesus Christ patting self-obsessed neurotics on the back, telling them they are "not junk." Or imagine any apostle or prophet descending to the level of radio talk show psychobabble such as Osteen attributes to them.

Osteen's *Your Best Life Now* dwells in the worldview of Proverbs and of Job's comforters, a world designed so that nice guys finish first, and honesty is the best policy. "He'll make sure you get everything you deserve, and more!" (p. 167). "God is a God of justice. God is going to pay us back for doing the right thing" (p. 169). "The Bible says, 'If you walk with wise men, then you're going to become wise' [Prov. 13:32]. If you associate with successful people, before long you will become successful. Their enthusiasm will be contagious and you will catch that vision" (p. 19).

Osteen's message, like that of New Thought in general, is connected to the Bible by one stout umbilical cord: the small set of "blank check" promises, especially Mark 11:22–24, "And Jesus answered them, 'Have faith in God. Truly, I say to you, whoever says to this mountain, "Be taken up and cast into the sea," and does not doubt in his heart, but believes that what he says will come to pass, it will be done for him. Therefore I tell you, whatever you ask in prayer, believe that you have received it, and it will be yours.'"

Traditional evangelicals and Pentecostals have used this text almost as an incantation for confident prayer, and it has created as many embarrassments and generated as many face-saving rationalizations as Osteen uses, but that hardly matters here. The point is that, like his evangelical (and New Thought) forebears, at this particular point Osteen does at least seem to be citing scripture in context, without contrivance. He must be given credit for that, for we will not be able to congratulate him on the other instances of his using scripture. There, it must be said, he is quoting scripture like Satan does in the wilderness.

"The Scripture says that God wants to pour out 'His far and beyond favor'" (p. 5). This sentiment is supposed to be drawn from Ephesians 2:7, "that in the coming ages he might show the immeasurable riches of his grace in kindness toward us in Christ Jesus." The passage speaks of heavenly splendor following upon the end-time resurrection of the righteous, a glorified state enduring through eternity. It would seem to have nothing to do with an increasingly comfortable or lucrative life in this world.

"Interestingly, when Jesus wanted to encourage His followers to enlarge their visions, He reminded them, 'You can't put new wine into old wineskins.' Jesus was saying that you cannot have a larger life with restricted attitudes" (p. 6). Here we are referred to Matthew 9:17, part of a debate between Jesus and his critics over whether one ought to engage in ritual fasting. The point of his parable appears to most scholars to be that fasting has become pointless in view of the dawning of the kingdom of God. The reality of the kingdom is the new wine, the old ascetical practices the worn-out wineskins. Does it have a thing to do with enlarging one's life goals or professional ambitions, à la Osteen? Not that I can see. If he wants to use the phrase as a kind of metaphor for "thinking outside the box," fine with me. His point is a valuable one. But why does he think he needs the Bible to back him up?

"God says, 'Behold, I am doing a new thing. Do you not perceive it?' Notice, God is always ready to do new things in our lives" (p. 10). Is that really what Isaiah 43:19 is trying to tell its readers? As even a cursory glance at the context will show, the point is about the unheard-of event, thanks to Cyrus's decree, of a captive people being conducted home to rebuild their land and temple, the return of Jews from the Babylonian exile. Osteen seems to be trivializing scripture.

"God *wants* you to get your hopes up. We can't even have faith without hope. The Bible says, 'Faith is the substance of things hoped for.' [E.g., e]xpect to excel in your career" (p. 14). And that is what the writer of Hebrews 11:1 had in mind? Rather, he describes the dogged endurance of the heroes of the Jewish faith who would not give up their faith in God even in the teeth of persecution and torture. Does anyone really imagine he has the right to apply such a text to his hopes for a shiny new car?

Elijah told Elisha that, if he chanced to witness his miraculous departure, his request for twice Elijah's power would be granted (2 Kings 2:9–10). "Elijah was also saying, "If you can see it, then you can be it. If you can visualize it in your heart and mind . . . it can become a reality in your life" (p. 18). No, he wasn't. Anyone can see that. Osteen has stooped to merely picking sequences of words out of their context and placing them into a new one, then claiming the Bible supports what he says. His arbitrary approach isn't that much different from Michael Drosnin's *The Bible Code*.

"He said to them, 'You have dwelt long enough on this mountain.' I believe God is saying something similar to us. You've been wallowing where you are long enough. It's time to move on, to let go of past hurts, pains or failures. It's time to believe for bigger things" (p. 31). I'll agree with Joel Osteen; it is definitely time to put the past behind you and head for the future. But I sure can't see what on earth that has to do with his proof text, Deuteronomy 1:6, or why one would need a biblical text to buttress such an insight to begin with.

"The Bible promises that God will give us 'a twofold recompense for our former shame.' That means if you'll keep the right attitude, God will pay you back double for your trouble" (p. 31). Oh really, now? I'm not sure Isaiah would approve of Osteen snatching his words out of their historical context in this manner. Isaiah 61:7 is talking about God's plans to restore the fortunes of the people of ruined Judah after the Exile. To open the Bible to this verse and to "claim it as a promise" is like the old joke where the guy is seeking God's will by randomly letting the Bible fall open and reading whatever verse first strikes his eye. He sees "Judas went out and hanged himself." He hastily flips some pages, coming to "Go thou and do likewise." He tries again but only manages to come up with "What thou doest, do quickly."

"The Bible clearly states, 'God has crowned us with glory and honor.' In other words, God wants to make your life easier" (p. 38). Psalms 8:5 speaks in ringing tones of the paradox of humanity: a mote of cosmic dust in the scheme of things, and yet the possessor of divine glory thanks to his Creator. Osteen's ear could not be tinnier on this one. It's just a promise that you'll be able to take things easier? Can we really imagine the Bible saying such a thing in any case?

"When David told him that he was going to take care of him, the Bible says, 'Mephibosheth bowed his head low and he said, "Who am I that you should notice a dead dog like me?"'" Do you see his self-image? He saw himself as defeated, as a loser, as a dead dog. . . . How many times do we do the same thing? Our self-image is so contrary to the way God sees us that we miss out on God's best" (p. 89). Mephibosheth, the last surviving heir of David's deposed rival Saul, is simply using the courtly rhetoric of humility expected of a commoner before the king. His words have not a thing to do with the modern Western notion of "self-image." Mephibosheth wouldn't even have known what such a thing meant if you or Osteen tried to explain it to him.

"God said to Joshua, 'As I was with Moses, I will be with you.' Notice He didn't say, 'Joshua, you need to try to be just like Moses, then you'll be okay.' No, God said to Joshua, 'Be an original. Be who I made you to be, and then you'll be successful'" (p. 98). Never mind the fact that the story goes on to have Joshua recapitulate the greatest feats of Moses, leading Israel across the Jordan dry-shod as Moses did at the Red Sea, making a covenant of laws with them, leading miraculous battles, and so on. But there is no thought of what sort of "personality type" or "temperament" Joshua or Moses may have had. To suggest otherwise is comical, like a Monty Python skit.

"The Bible says, 'I have set before you life and death, blessings and curses, positive and negative; therefore God says choose life' [Deut. 30:19]. . . . We must choose to dwell on the positive, choose to dwell on the good" (p. 115). I agree with Osteen wholeheartedly on what we ought to do. But let him not quote a piece of Jewish scripture which threatens its readers with doom if they neglect to keep all the provisions of the Torah of Moses! I hope Osteen is not planning to have a ham sandwich anytime soon.

The most scripturally accurate exhortation in *Your Best Life Now* is probably this one: "You cannot go around all day long thinking about the people who have hurt you and all the mistakes you've made, and expect to live any kind of happy, positive life" (p. 115). However, the scripture it reflects so well is not the Bible at all, but rather the Buddhist *Dhammapada*:

> We are what we think.
> All that we are arises with our thoughts.
> With our thoughts we make the world.
> Speak or act with an impure mind
> And trouble will follow you
> As the wheel follows the ox that draws the cart.
> We are what we think.
> All that we are arises with our thoughts.
> With our thoughts we make the world.
> Speak or act with a pure mind
> And happiness will follow you
> As your shadow, unshakable.
> "Look how he abused me and hurt me,
> How he threw me down and robbed me."
> Live with such thoughts and you live in hate.
> "Look how he abused me and hurt me,
> How he threw me down and robbed me."
> Abandon such thoughts, and live in love.
> In this world
> Hate never yet dispelled hate.
> Only love dispels hate.
> This is the law,
> Ancient and inexhaustible.

A RUMOR WITH A VIEW

Joel Osteen's most natural, least contrived connection with the Bible, I suggested, is with the comforting viewpoint of the book of Proverbs. And Proverbs is a collection of wise observations, wise sayings, culled from sages of many nations, not unguessable revelations. The whole idea of a proverb is that it is something that rings true to common experience. It's not like a revelation, of which one may say, "Flesh and blood hath not revealed it unto thee, but my Father in heaven." No, proverbs embody wisdom human beings learned the hard way, at least some did, and now they are sharing it with you. An otherworldly revelation would not "click" as true, as if verified by your subconscious observations of life. You just have to take a revelation on faith. You shouldn't have to take a proverb on faith. Instead, your reaction should be, "Of course! Why didn't *I* think of that?"

That fits quite well with Osteen's general reliance upon anecdotal evidence. *Your Best Life Now* is filled from front to back with stories about his own and others' successes when they have dared to believe in God for good outcomes, personal advancement, and so on. All New Thought books do this. They have to, because, making the large claims they do, their writers know they need to show it is all more than mere theory. They need to bring forth satisfied customers, including themselves, to persuade readers. As I said in an earlier chapter, I believe they have done a good job in establishing the basic outlook of New Thought as a legacy of human wisdom. It is not a revelation. It is nothing new. It makes sense once you think about it. It does not require any sort of theology or metaphysic, whether Pentecostalism or pantheism. So I am quite sympathetic to Osteen's approach. By now it is obvious, however, that I believe he overloads his message with superfluous theology and bogus Bible quotes. But I must register a note of caution even where I think Osteen's case is the strongest. Any argument based on anecdotal evidence is prey to the hasty generalization fallacy. You can quote any number of cases and stories and testimonials, and it may still not be statistically significant. We may still be looking at a misleading, nonrepresentative sample of the evidence. If you ask for people to send you their success stories, you are automatically excluding all the possible cases where people have tried the same technique and failed. For instance, it is clear to me that the advertising of fundamentalist Christianity is grossly overblown and highly misleading for this very reason. You will hear nothing from them about the huge numbers of onetime converts who have dropped the whole thing in disillusionment.

But worse than this, Osteen relies on dubious anecdotal evidence derived illicitly from the Bible. What I mean is that he invokes biblical episodes that are by no means presented as typical. Osteen recalls how Paul and Silas were shackled in the Philippian prison, singing hymns to God (and no doubt dodging shoes from other jailbirds who wanted to get some shut-eye), and God responded by shaking the place with an earthquake localized so neatly that it merely shook the rivets holding their manacles to the walls and burst the cell doors off their hinges. So, says Osteen, we may extricate ourselves from tight spots by praising God (p. 191). But does the Bible mean to offer this story as a repeatable paradigm? Or isn't the whole point that it was exceptional? And there is much more like this in *Your Best Life Now*.

But it doesn't have to be *in* the Bible for Osteen to claim something as edifying biblical truth. "The apostle Paul wrote more than half of the New Testament while incarcerated, often in tiny prison cells not much bigger than a small bathroom. Some historians and Bible commentators believe that the sewage system of that day ran right through one of the dungeons in which he was imprisoned. Some commentaries state that it's possible that he could have written some of the great passages of what we now know as the New Testament standing in raw sewage that at times came all the way up to his waist. Yet Paul wrote such amazing faith-filled words as, 'I can do all things through Christ who strengthens me [Phil. 4:13, more or less]'" (p. 276). More likely, he'd have written, "I have suffered the loss of all things and count them as dung" (Phil. 3:8b). Actually, even if you think Paul wrote all thirteen epistles credited to him, they make up only a quarter of the New Testament. But the rest of it is just absurd. No commentators, no historians picture Paul in such a pickle. It just shows Osteen's utter ignorance of biblical scholarship. So should you imitate Paul in something he didn't even experience?

But it doesn't have to be biblical; it can still be bogus, and as long as Osteen likes the sound of it, it becomes evidence for his case. On pages 72 and following he tells the story of a man who was trapped overnight in a refrigerated boxcar. Sure that he was doomed, he settled down to await the end. And it came. He was dead when they found him the next morning. Only the freezing unit hadn't been on, and the heat had never gone below sixty degrees! He froze to death because he expected he would. Such, Osteen tells us, is the power of the mind over matter. Alas, poor Osteen has been taken in by a widespread urban legend that exists in various forms. In another version, the man thinks he is using up the air in a confined space, so he suffocates, even though air never stopped coming in through a hidden vent. But it's all one with the Mexican goat sucker and the hitchhiking angel. Check it out at the urban legends reference pages at snopes.com. Encouraging people with stories of what has happened to others and can happen to you is one thing. Deluding them with things that never happened to anyone is another.

Perhaps the most offensive set of anecdotes in *Your Best Life Now* are the many episodes from Joel Osteen's own life. No one is going to imagine he is Mr. Typical, as he seems to want to paint himself. Nor does it come across that way. He uses heroic tales starring himself as if the reader might emulate these things, but they give off mixed signals. On the one hand, they are clearly tales of the exceptional, adventures of the Golden Boy, or they would not be worth telling. On the other, they are presented as what can happen to anybody. Again, if they were typical, they would not bear telling in this manner. It's like a hero receiving an award and modestly saying, "Aw shucks, anybody could have done it." So what is the point of regaling the reader with the adventures of Joel Osteen, God's favorite on earth? It only serves the agenda of magnifying Osteen himself. Count the number of times he mentions his own name. It's a total of fifty-three by my count. They all occur in anecdotes in which someone has come to him for advice. This gives the same impression it does in Malcolm Boyd's once-popular collection of "slice of life" prayers, *Are You Running with Me, Jesus?* In it, the repeated punctuating of the text with second-person addresses to Jesus invokes the hovering presence of Jesus over the praying narrator's adventures. Only in this case, it is Joel Osteen himself who is drifting like a glory cloud over the proceedings.

Appendixes

fit perfectly. We want to use the typology to measure those differences so we can begin to explain them. In doing so, we will begin to understand the individual entity we are measuring against the ideal type. The goal is to understand each concrete phenomenon, not to pretend the phenomena are all the same and to cram them into the boxes whether they seem to fit or not! Much mischief has resulted from scholars forgetting the point of an ideal type.

CHURCH, SECT, CULT

For Weber, a "church" was an established religious community well integrated with the surrounding culture, affirming its values and even providing the spiritual or theological basis for them. Churches are allies of culture even when there is technical separation of church and state. This "at-homeness in the world" typically results in churches being world-affirming. Church values include a work ethic and discipline, what Weber called "worldly asceticism" and "love patriarchalism." Churches tend to be organized hierarchically according to inherited prerogative ("traditional authority") or technical competence ("rational-legal authority"). Accordingly, churches prize education and training. And if the surrounding society is stratified economically or classwise, the church will likely repeat the pattern or even justify it. People inherit membership in churches. They are baptized into membership before they know what is going on. They are confirmed as a matter of course. Faith may be basically an exterior matter, going to church, paying one's taxes, decent behavior. No one has to be too active, because on the one hand, the authorities will take care of everything, and on the other, there are so many people in the church, the individual's participation or lack of it doesn't matter much.

A "sect" splits off from a church. It may soon reproduce itself into several congregations, but it retains at least for a generation the posture of opposition to both the parent denomination/church and the sponsoring society. The sect splits off because certain individuals grow concerned that the parent group is not stringent enough in matters of doctrine or morality. Perhaps the society has drifted into tolerance of widespread sinfulness and the church has grown lazy and no longer acts as a prophetic conscience calling the larger society back to the commandments of God. The church has become worldly, too cushy and comfortable with the worldly order. Or perhaps the church's doctrine appears to have accommodated itself to worldly patterns of thought (in the fundamentalist-modernist controversy, for example). Or there is a dearth of piety and spirituality. Prayer has become formal and cold. Something must be done!

The resultant sectarian movements, though their goals may differ markedly (see below), commonly share a certain profile (here comes the ideal type): the sect finds itself in opposition to the corrupt and lax society/culture and views it with suspicion and fear as a Satan-controlled source of temptation. Sects accordingly are more otherworldly, as when evangelist Dwight L. Moody professed himself indifferent toward matters of social reform as a question of rearranging the furniture aboard the sinking *Titanic*: "God has given me a lifeboat and told me, 'Moody, save all you can!'" They may have a hostile attitude toward the larger society, projecting shadows of cosmic evil onto it, a reflection of the alienation they feel simply by virtue of being a pronounced and militant minority, whether or not they are persecuted or ridiculed.

Faith is more intense, more interior. Sects are revivalistic, pietistic, demanding a datable conversion, a "heart-warming" personal relationship with God. Often the sect's complaint against the parent church is not doctrinal but that the parent group lacks spiritual zeal. Pentecostal David du Plessis used to say that the mainline denominations and the Pentecostals had the same steak; it was just that the denominations kept it in the freezer, while the Pentecostals had it on the grill.

The sect requires every-member involvement or it will not float. It cannot afford to give anyone a free ride or it will sink. On the other hand, there is no hierarchy, not at first. Advanced education gives no advantage, nor is it welcomed, and it probably does not exist among the members. They rely on direct wisdom from the Spirit and take an optimistic view of the "perspicuity of scripture"—that is, any Joe off the street ought to be able adequately to interpret it. Sectarians are literalists unless their jumping-off point requires some manipulation of the text in order to smuggle in their new doctrines.

The sect is more likely to be egalitarian as well as democratic. Tertullian used to complain in the second century that Marcionites and Gnostics had female bishops or rotated the various church offices and duties among all the members indiscriminately. Early Pentecostals gave an equal share in leadership to women and had mixed black and white memberships because they believed ardently that what mattered was the Holy Spirit speaking through a mere human channel, so how could gender or ethnicity make any difference?

Weber described a cyclical process of evolution by which sects would eventually evolve into churches (perhaps already in the second generation, when children will have been born to the original members and raised in their faith). This means they will have reacclimated themselves to the surrounding culture and its values. They will have matured and left behind the essentially adolescent posture of the radical (see Billy Joel's song "The Angry Young Man"). A perfect paradigm of the transition sects face is provided by the Massachusetts Puritans and their "halfway covenant" dilemma. The first Puritans were sectarians who split from the Church of England. They were all zealous pietists. But as their numbers grew in the New World and they raised Christian children, fewer of the latter could claim conversion experiences: why should they, having believed in Christ since before they could remember? They had no "sinful past" to repent of. And yet Puritan polity demanded that to be eligible for church membership and taking communion, one had to be able to point to a discrete conversion, a "born-again" experience, a "work of grace." What were they to do with the new generations? Finally, Solomon Stoddard decided on the halfway covenant: the devout but "once-born" could vote as members of the congregation, but they could not take communion. This was an unstable dike doomed to give way as the Puritan sect inevitably became a church. Similarly, John Wesley mused how no revival could sustain itself forever, because the repentance people experienced would make them industrious and thrifty, simply as a matter of Christian character, and then they must inevitably gain wealth from their work. This affluence would in turn cause them to become worldly and spiritually complacent again.

Education, especially theological education, becomes important again when people tire of enthusiastic nonsense from the pulpit and if they begin to feel embarrassed when visitors come to church. Suddenly, seminaries don't sound so bad anymore. Maybe it's not so simple preaching the word of God as just opening your mouth and letting the Spirit fill it. More likely, one's own foot will fill it adequately. You know you have gone from sect to church when you stop calling theological seminaries "cemeteries."

APPENDIXES

SECTARIAN MENU

Sociologist of religion Bryan Wilson (not Brian Wilson of the Beach Boys!) proposed a typology of kinds of sects as divided according to their chief goals (see his *Magic and the Millennium: A Sociological Study of Religious Movements of Protest among Tribal and Third-World Peoples*). Churches may have no particular goals other than maintaining a sound spiritual family or haven. But sects feel they must accomplish something. What?

1. *Conversionist* sects understand salvation as an emotional and moral transformation of the individual, a new birth. His experience is a foretaste or a down payment of some future or heavenly state of large-scale salvation. The story is told of a Communist soapbox preacher pointing to a ragged bum and declaring, "Communism can put a new suit on that man!" A Salvation Army member in the crowd yelled out, "Christ can put a new man in that suit!" Salvation is a present reality: "Are you saved?" Baptist and Pentecostal groups fit in right here.

2. *Revolutionist* sects gleefully anticipate a soon-coming destruction of the social order and its replacement with a shining Millennium of righteousness. The role of individuals may be to help inaugurate the process or to herald it so people may be ready when it comes. Salvation is not present, but it will come soon, and its near approach may even provide a present "taste of the powers of the age to come" (Heb. 6:5). Qumran Essenes, Jehovah's Witnesses, Millerites, Cargo Cults, the Ghost Dance, and others would qualify.

3. *Introversionist* sects see the world around them as hope-

WHAT IS A CULT?

lessly corrupt. Salvation is sought in a collective withdrawal of the righteous into a "camp of the saints," a "city set on a hill," which by the sheer fact of its existence and its distinctive way of life (e.g., living out the ethics of the Sermon on the Mount) implicitly preaches the gospel to the rest of the world. Those who separate themselves out like this are already living as a sort of beachhead or colony of the future Millennium. Hutterites, Amish, Catholic Charismatics, Base Communities, Sojourners Community, Womanchurch, and other "intentional communities" are of this type.

4. *Manipulationist* sects believe that human misery is the result of the near-universal ignorance of how life works, or what the good life is. Manipulationists seek to make possible the living of a good life in this world for those who are willing to obey and practice certain forgotten laws or techniques or principles which will lead to being healthy, wealthy, and wise. No earthshaking conversion of either the individual sinner or of the world is necessary. It is a simple question of learning the rules of the game of life and starting to win. New Thought, Unity, Christian Science, Soka Gakkai, Transcendental Meditation, Ehrhardt Seminars Training (aka The Forum), and others would fall here.

5. *Thaumaturgical* (= magical or wonder-working) sects, like Manipulationists, seek to remedy particular problems, but in an immediate scope and by direct, supernatural means. Faith healers and their ministries (i.e., mailing lists of supporters and TV viewers) would count, as would Deliverance (exorcism) ministries.

6. *Reformist* sects have much in common with secular movements of social reform, the chief difference being the reli-

gious inspiration of the reforms. Quakers work for peace rather than waiting for God to bring it in his own sweet time. They believe that Christian pacifism provides an effective tool for seeking worldly peace. Dr. Martin Luther King Jr. learned the same sort of doctrine from the Hindu Mahatma Gandhi. Such a sect believes that providing a striking alternative to the world is not enough (contra the Introversionists), that Revolutionists (in Wilson's sense) are wasting their time, and that Utopians (next category) are fanatics. The thought of Reinhold Niebuhr was a good example of Reformist sectarianism. (He himself belonged to the Evangelical and Reformed Church, which later merged with the Congregational Church to form the socially liberal United Church of Christ.) Niebuhr (in his *Moral Man and Immoral Society*) argued that the "Christian Realist" approach should recognize the ethic of the Sermon on the Mount as a relevant but impossible ideal, and that Christians ought to try to come as close to it as possible. It would be fanatical delusion to believe that a Utopian Millennium will ever actually arrive, but the idea functions as a defining and beckoning symbol for Christian ethics and politics. Paul Tillich, who eventually took to attending Quaker meetings, argued along somewhat similar lines in his *The Socialist Decision*. As an activist in the Religious Socialist Party he got into trouble with the Nazis and had to flee to America.

7. *Utopian* sects anticipate the complete replacement of this corrupt society with a righteous one based on scripture. Only they do not merely wait for it like the so-called Revolutionist sects. Nor are their efforts as moderate as the Reformist sects. They undertake to usher in this change by voting or by

force. Post-Millennialism falls into this category, though the works Post-Millennialists assign themselves may be simply good works and evangelism, which, with a nudge from the Holy Spirit, should be enough to cause the desired wholesale change. The social and revivalistic crusades of the Holiness Movement of the nineteenth century were something on this order, as was the Social Gospel Movement of Liberal Protestantism shortly afterward. Today, Christian Reconstructionism and Islamic Jihadism would be two drastic examples.

WHERE CULTS DIFFER

Cults may be classified according to the same agenda options. Wherein do they differ from sects? There are two defining traits of a cult. First, a cult is a small group of zealous believers all completely devoted to a single charismatic leader whose authority rests on his followers' belief that he is divine or in touch with the divine. Thus they implicitly obey his every command. Naturally a cult will have to be small enough that the leader can relate to all members, but when it grows, it remains a cult as long as it can maintain complete leader-control over major aspects of the lives of members, perhaps through lieutenants or communication media. But once the leader dies or retires *or* he finds he must yield or divide his authority (and its application) among an administrative apparatus (see Moses in Exodus chapter 18 for a perfect example), the cult has begun to evolve into a sect. A sect is based on its doctrines, practices, and administrative structure. It is no crisis for a sect when the master dies. There is always a Joshua, or at least a Great Synagogue or the Seventy Elders, to take over in his absence. The

Buddha has died, but he has bequeathed adequate knowledge, as he said to his disciples gathered around his deathbed: "Be ye lamps unto yourselves." Socrates, about to imbibe the hemlock, told his followers, "Think not of Socrates, but think of the truth."

A great part of the perceived danger of the cult is this absolute control by its leader. Think of Jonestown. Robert J. Ellwood's book *The Gospel Time Bomb* provides many other good and disturbing case studies.

The second defining trait of a cult, though it is not applicable in all cases, is the foreign origin of the cult. Many cults are transplants from other countries and cultures. They may have come to America as missionaries to save us from sin or from our traditional but ineffective religions. The factor of foreignness helps to account for the full-blown ethical and ceremonial systems that seem so alien to most Americans. The alienness may not really be so much a matter of inherent oddity but rather simply of unfamiliarity. The mass weddings of the Unification Church do not seem so odd if one is familiar with the custom of arranged marriages in the East. The dancing and chanting of the Hare Krishna devotees no longer strikes one as a tasteless display of obsessive-compulsive behavior when one understand it is an outgrowth of a Hindu devotional tradition stemming from the fourteenth century.

And yet some cults' strangeness is more honestly come by. That is, it is hard for the rest of us to make excuses for it, lest we feel like fools ourselves. UFO cults are a good example. How are we to understand groups of numerous individuals who seriously believe not only that extraterrestrials have visited the earth (itself practically a mainstream belief by now) but that they are in touch with aliens or their representatives who supply teaching analogous to traditional religious revelations? Actually, it is not hard to explain. Keep in mind what Samuel Taylor Coleridge explained concerning "the willing temporary suspension of disbelief," that subtle transaction of mental compartmentalization whereby we are enabled to enter into a novel, a play, a movie, deeply enough to be affected by it as if it were real. Peter L. Berger and Thomas V. Luckmann (in their classic *The Social Construction of Reality*) argue that traditional religious services are no less "finite provinces of meaning" created artistically and entered into imaginatively by means of the temporary willing suspension of disbelief. Outside the church service it will not occur to us to believe in demons, though we hear about them in church. We may be slower or disinclined to believe in answered prayer outside the eleven o'clock hour Sunday morning. In the workaday world the Sermon on the Mount may seem to us neither relevant nor possible. We may believe that we should take intrachurch beliefs and commands seriously the rest of the week, and we will feel at least vaguely guilty for failing to do so.

But there are other social entities in which the members are fully cognizant of the fictive nature of their finite province of meaning. These include science fiction fandom: *Star Wars* and *Star Trek* geeks. Such heavy-duty fans show up at movie premieres, conventions, and parties wearing sophisticated costumes and makeup, sporting alter-ego names, autobiographies, and speaking made-up languages. The rest of the week they are meek accountants, but on occasional weekends they are Commander Klang of the Klingon Spacefleet. Such people realize their fantasy worlds are not real and that they are but imaginative zones of fictive escapism. These people, I suggest, are only analogous to average religious believers. But what if there were to be a bridge between the two tribes? There is one: the collection of Flying Saucer Religions including Heaven's Gate, the Aetherius Society, Scientology, the Raelians, Astara, the

Unarius Society, and so on. They have simply laced one more hole up the boot: like churchgoers, they have made it their business to believe the whole kit and caboodle all week long.

But the key to sustaining such a belief, which the believer knows is emphatically rejected by virtually everyone else, is *group solidarity, peer support.* Berger and Luckmann (*The Social Construction of Reality, The Sacred Canopy, The Invisible Religion*) have gone much further in explaining how belief is created and reinforced by a supportive matrix of other people committed to the same beliefs and that conversely belief is threatened and may erode if the believer finds him/herself among those not sharing his/her faith. Secure belief in a minority faith is a matter of remaining safe within a "plausibility structure." There may be several ways the leader(s) of a cult seek to legitimate their beliefs and to reassure the converts that it is all true. But more important is the simple fact of the plausibility structure. A *plausibility structure* is a social arrangement wherein one is surrounded by a consensus, an atmosphere conducive to reinforcing one's beliefs. There are many fellow believers who will say amen and live their lives by the rules of your faith. It may have taken a great act of courage to break with the inertia of convention to embrace new beliefs in the first place, but that is a tension one cannot sustain indefinitely. Thereafter, one must take refuge in the harbor with the rest of the ships.

Berger and Luckmann also discuss the *cognitive universe,* or the map of reality inside one's head. It is the set of values and assumptions that organize and color all your perceptions, that cause you to think something plausible or implausible, true or false, bad or good. It may be a set of explicit beliefs or of implicit assumptions. It is the lens through which you view the world. The people in your plausibility structure all live together in a shared cognitive universe, and indeed you assimilated it from them. Within the group, the creed seems self-evidently true, and one's only struggles are those of conscience as one seeks ever-greater repentance and sanctification. But outside the confines of the plausibility structure, doubts inevitable arise. The believer is like a submarine sailor surrounded by thousands of tons of water pressure. He had better have thick walls between him and that water! The plausibility structure provides them, and he must do his best to internalize the cognitive universe before he departs for the outer world of everyday society.

Sects and cults tend to be aggressively evangelistic. One reason is obvious: they have an urgent message to share with others for their good. But there is a hidden dimension of self-interest for the cultists, too. Remember, it is typical for cults to govern a new convert's relations with noncult friends and relatives so as to keep the boundaries of the plausibility structure secure. One's close associates have enough credibility with the new recruit that he might heed their doubts and urgings to quit the group, and we don't want that to happen. Well, for the same reason, cults send members on evangelistic missions, hoping to recruit more new members, certainly, but also to reinforce the self-image of the new convert. When he goes "witnessing," two things happen. First, by the simple fact of his evangelistic approach to an outsider, the convert casts him in a role that restricts the range of responses to a pair that will not threaten the new convert's faith. The outsider may sneer, "Scram!" Yes, that is a bit rude, but it is good, because the new convert has been told in advance that Satan controls the worldlings, and such a slammed door is an example of (albeit mild) persecution for the truth's sake. Like the apostles in Acts 5:41, the new convert will rejoice to lick his wounds, reinforced in his faith, now that he has put it on the line, risking public embarrassment. It is like a fraternity hazing. Having succeed him, as Jesus does in Matthew 18:15–20 and John 20:21–23. If he has ordained another charismatic individual to succeed him (e.g., Joseph Smith followed by Brigham Young, or the Bab by Baha'u'llah), the cult may well continue as such, a one-man show. But eventually the cult will survive as a sect. When the leader is replaced by an institution, we speak of the "routinization of charisma" (Weber). The founder possessed his own magnetic authority, but after him his successors reign by right of succession, "Shake the hand that shook the hand" (Harvey Cox). In Weber's terms, the leader exercised *charismatic authority*, but the institutional apparatchiks who come later exercise *traditional authority*.

And the sea change from cult to sect is not merely an organizational one. The further transition from sect to church has already implicitly been taken, too, because the status of the original leader has changed in such a way as to make the whole emphasis of the movement change as well. The founder will become idealized, perhaps even imagined as a god who came to earth to reveal himself, and he is identified with the divine creator. The creator of your new "cognitive universe" naturally becomes the creator of the natural universe as well, once the first becomes coextensive with the second. In other words, the new doctrines, which once seemed so radical and revolutionary, have come to be "felt as facts," as natural and "self-evident" as nature.

This process of deifying the founder goes hand in hand with the second-generation rapprochement between the culture and the new religion. As the latter happens, the inner zeal and commitment of the members begin to slack off for the simple reason that the pressure's off. So they can begin taking their faith for granted, just like people used to do in the old culture-wide religion. With less zeal, and feeling more at home in the world, the members can no longer

Membership Drive
Who Joins Cults and Why?

*D*uring the initial wave of anticult hysteria back in the early seventies, outsiders professed themselves baffled at why any sane person should wish to sign away his or her soul to an evil outfit. It was a case of begging the question. Starting with the assumption that cults were subversive and deleterious to those who joined them, it seemed natural to infer that people joined them for bad reasons. Cult recruits must have been pathetic losers and neurotics who would scrape the bottom of the barrel for a little respect, and given the caliber of such cannon fodder, the cults must have been satisfied with little more than a van full of warm bodies. If, on the other hand, some promising young people joined up, they must have been brainwashed and hypnotized. How else could their interest in cults be explained, since (outsiders assumed) cults had absolutely nothing to offer? The situation was much like that of heterosexuals today who ask what went wrong to turn someone into a homosexual. The gay person turns the question around on the one who asked it: What made you become a heterosexual? Even so, we might as well ask what makes someone a Methodist or an Orthodox

Jew or a Roman Catholic? It's not that there will be no interesting explanation forthcoming in either case. But we must step back and not take for granted that one allegiance is bad and the other is good. Again, one may turn out to be bad, but we have to conclude that, not assume it, if we want to make a sound judgment.

There are two research results we must keep in mind from the start. First, most people join cults/new religions not because of ingenious recruiting techniques or evangelistic rallies, but rather under the influence of friends or relatives, much as conservative Protestant churches grow.

This observation brings up an interesting parallel. In Rodney Stark's book *The Rise of Christianity*, the sociologist/historian examines the reasons and the rate for the growth of early Christianity in the Roman Empire. He shows how the rate need only have matched that of analogous sectarian new religions of modern times, like the Moonies and the Mormons, for the numbers to grow as they did from the mid-first century until Constantine's time. There was no miraculous or even surprising explosion such as Christian apologists sometimes like to claim as evidence of the supernatural origin of Christianity. Stark notes that there were many good reasons for the attractiveness of the new Christian faith, a fact implicitly neglected by claims that Christian growth was a miracle—it must be a pretty poor religion if that's the only way to explain people joining it.

But let us turn the scope around in the other direction: Stark's research obliquely but powerfully suggests to me that the mushroomlike growth of the Moonies (Unification Church) and the Mormons (Church of Jesus Christ of Latter-day Saints) was no more strange, in no more need of extraordinary explanations. We don't need to posit people being brainwashed, shanghaied into the new faith, any more than we require the direct compulsion of the Holy Ghost to account for early Christian numerical growth.

Second, it puts things in a considerably different light to know that the typical turnover rate for members of virtually all cults is over 90 percent. By far, most individuals who join cults remain in them long enough to accumulate interesting life experiences (for which they are often grateful, sometimes chagrinned, once they move on). No one dragged them in, kicking and screaming; nor did they have to climb the Berlin wall to escape. It is tragically ironic that if your children have joined some cult and you want to see them leave it, the absolute worst thing you can do is to forcibly remove them at the hands of deprogrammers, who will isolate them and berate them until they renounce their faith. Because if they are deprogrammed and relapse after the ordeal is over, you will have cemented their loyalty to the cult. Now you have made them a heroic martyr and confessor. They have suffered for the faith and will be much more firmly attached to it from then on. No, if you want them to come back to First Methodist and IBM, just give it a little time. That ought to do it.

A GOOD RINSE

Whence the common charges of brainwashing? Many cult critics, of course, charge that members have been induced to surrender their freedom of thought and choice on analogy to the efforts of North Korean interrogators who sought to "brainwash" American prisoners of war to make them into fifth-columnist Commie spies, as in *The Manchurian Candidate*. This is very unlikely.

For one thing, studies of these techniques and their use reveal that Communist brainwashing was virtually never effective as a tool of forced reeducation. One might induce a cowed and tortured wretch to feign an ideological conversion, just as any prisoner of war is advised to sign any confession in the knowledge that no one back home will take it seriously. And it is possible that a few POWs were converts to Communism via the Stockholm syndrome, whereby captives seek to ease their torment by actually coming to identify with their captors like dependent children. I have never heard of research suggesting that, but it may be true. And of course Communism is not without merit as a doctrine. Many believe in it freely, though I am not one of them. It is far from impossible that "reeducation" might actually result in convincement. But there is no real evidence that anyone has fallen victim to genuine mind-control through brainwashing, even in Chinese and North Korean POW camps, much less in American cults. In fact, the whole idea seems laughable. It belongs in James Bond movies and pulp maga-zines: hypnotized legions of cult zombies threatening the world.

For another, we must reckon with a historic prejudice against new and exotic religions, whether today's new religions like the Moonies and Krishnas, or the ancient Mystery Cults of Attis, Osiris, Mithras, and so on, transplanted from the Middle East into Europe in the centuries adjacent to the birth of Christianity. Many of the same terrible charges leveled at today's cults were aimed, almost verbatim, by the ancient Romans against Isis cultists, Cynic philosophers, and early Christians. See also the suspicions of the king of Thebes against the new Dionysian cult in Euripedes' *Bac-chae*. All were condemned as conspirators, cannibals, child mur-derers, orgiasts, incest-mongers, you name it. In his sixth satire, the first-century Roman satirist Juvenal paints a caricature portrait of cult leaders and gurus exploiting wealthy matrons for their money, alienating them from their husbands, and so on, that might, with the names changed, have been torn from the pages of today's anticult literature.

When Christians came to power, they turned the same guns on Jews, Gnostics, Marcionites, and other "heretics." For example, Gnostics were often defamed as immoral orgiasts, but when a huge cache of Gnostic documents was discovered in Egypt in 1945, the Nag Hammadi documents, it was striking that all of them advocated sexual continence, even celibacy. Our only evidence for libertine Gnostics remains the account of the fourth-century heresiologist ("heresy-buster") Epiphanius, Bishop of Salamis, that as a young man he had been unsuccessfully seduced into attending an orgiastic meeting of the Phibionite Gnostics. And who knows if he even knew what he was talking about? His impressions may have been the result of his own stereotyping.

So the tales one hears of brainwashing and other insidious and evil behaviors connected with cults may very likely be the products of deep-rooted instincts of prejudice against new and unfamiliar groups. Our fears take palpable form in bogeymen versions of cults. On the other hand, it must be said clearly that occasionally it seems cults have themselves conjured up the same dark fantasies and decided to live them out. No one will dismiss as baseless calumny the well-documented charges of drugs, orgies, and murder among the Manson family. The sadistic and paranoid megalomania of the Reverend Jim Jones (notwithstanding his equally genuine "Jeckyll" persona of a sincere social advocate and champion of the poor) resulted in astonishing abuses long before the famous Guyana suicides put an end to them. The seventeenth-century nihilistic Messiah Jakob Frank conjured into being an ultraviolet netherworld of secret orgies and blasphemies surpassing the imagination of any of today's anticult propagandists. If the ancient Attis cult required self-castration as its initiation rite, so did the modern sect of the Skoptsy in Russia, and neither cult could be suppressed. One must approach controversial religious movements with an initial presumption of innocence, given this historical perspective, but neither must one maintain an invulnerable Pollyanna optimism that new religions never deserve their opprobrium. Again, careful research must tell the tale in each case. One does not want to risk letting fear threaten freedom of religion.

But we are not dependent merely on the charges of complete outsiders for our suspicions of cults and their misdeeds, are we? There are books full of "atrocity stories" written by ex–cult members. They speak of having been brainwashed, mistreated, and so on. Are we not to believe them? Not necessarily. On the one hand, someone dissatisfied with a group is hardly an objective reporter about it. He will be tempted to justify his exit by blackening the group's reputation, even if unconsciously. Someone has said that deriving our view of cult life from alienated ex-members (apostates) is like getting a fair and balanced picture of marriage by interviewing only divorce lawyers. And yet who is a better source than someone who was an eyewitness of the life of the cult and is no longer bound by the desire to "spin" the information and to hide the dirty linen? We see we must critically sift our evidence, not reject whole bodies of evidence wholesale and a priori. How do we decide what to believe? Where to look for the facts? How to shave away bias and exaggeration?

We need to keep in mind what Peter L. Berger describes as "nihilation strategies." When someone embraces a new set of beliefs or a new allegiance, diametrically opposed to his former ones, he seeks to make sense of the old allegiance in terms of the new. He has a new perspective. "How wrong I was!" "I was sinking deep in sin, far from the peaceful shore." The temptation is often to exaggerate the dire degree of sin and lostness so as to highlight the new state of enlightenment or salvation. He may engage in self-vilification, to the greater glory of his savior. But he may also seek to mitigate his culpability for having been so terribly wrong. In the latter case, we are dealing with what Leon Festinger calls "cognitive dissonance reduction." One simply cannot deal with the chagrin of having been a "kooky cultist," and it comes in mighty handy to deny that one's choice for the previous state was voluntary. "I only joined up because they brainwashed me!" This is another way of saying, "You know, I must have been crazy to have joined that group!" Only it is no longer hyperbole. You are seeking to slough off the responsibility for a decision you now find embarrassing. I suspect the same thing happened in the early 1980s when porn star Linda Lovelace abandoned her film career and claimed, not that she had repented of her sins, but that she had escaped from slavery and brainwashing at the hands of her evil manager, who forced her to degrade herself in pornographic moviemaking. She was ashamed now of having done it, so ashamed that she could not imagine she had ever chosen to do it. Her story was a nihilation strategy to save face. And one suspects the atrocity tales of ex-cultists partake of the same.

If one has abandoned one's former membership through the intervention of a deprogrammer, one has in effect been through a "deconversion" experience fully as powerful as the original conversion whereby one entered the cult in the first place. One rejoices in a new identity, the person rescued ("saved") from the insidious cult. Note the déjà vu here. In light of one's rebirth experience, one must negate one's old life. In fact, when "nihilating" a former cult experience, even if one enjoyed it at the time, one must make it look pretty bad in retrospect precisely in order to justify one's new acquiescence in the deprogramming process. So that which one experienced as a new life in Christ (or the Divine Principle, or whatever) has retroactively, retrospectively, turned into a "life of sin." This is why we must at least be suspicious of the ex-cultist atrocity stories. At the very least there may be subtle recasting of the experience in view of the very different value judgments one now holds.

SPIN CYCLE

But are ex-cultists completely fabricating their stories when they claim they were brainwashed? No. One cannot deny that cults have often engaged in *manipulation* to gain new converts. This seems reprehensible to me, but I must admit it is not actual brainwashing or compulsion. Perhaps it is natural for me to see the difference because of my experience in various evangelistic ministries and an evangelistic Baptist congregation in which we used a battery of evangelistic strategies that I now view as manipulative, such as pretend surveys in which we would ask casual passersby which religious leader they knew the most about. We cared nothing about the results (at least until I insisted we submit the results to the town newspaper). We just wanted to con the hapless interviewees into talking with us about religion, and then we would start in with our version of the gospel message. So manipulation is no invention of the cults, whatever one thinks of it.

What is the nature of this manipulation? Probably the best paradigm case of recruitment manipulation known to me would be that practiced by the Oakland branch of the Unification Church in the

1970s and early 1980s. Moonies, whether students or not, would sit at an information table on a campus, where they would sign up interested students to attend some sort of experimental community retreat out in the wild. They would talk of idealistic values and education, but certainly no hint of anything religious, and no mention of Reverend Sun Myung Moon—until later. Once the buses unloaded far from campus, a tireless round of activities, games, hiking, and lectures would commence. Most present were clandestine Moonies, and the hosts would give loads of affection and attention ("love bombing") to the potential recruits. Joining in games, group singing, and encounter exercises helped forge a sense of community and group solidarity as well as shape behavior. One began by doing what the group did, and this primed one to accept the eventually revealed beliefs underlying the program. Early lecture sessions dealt in benign generalities about the needs of the world, for example, for harmony between religions and between science and religion, and eventually the Divine Principle would be presented as the answer. The potential recruit would have trodden a good deal of the desired path, and it would have been made more difficult to pull out and reverse course. Perhaps, as is common in such situations, cult-recruiting or not, there would be little opportunity for sleep, and maybe there would be a low-protein diet. And all this might make one suggestible, as in the *King of the Hill* episode where Luanne and Peggy join the Cult of Jane at the Arlen Community College. Hank and Dale prompt a mass exodus of cultists by grilling steaks right outside the iron fence of the cult sorority house.

Similarly, some cults have focused recruiting on freshmen and seniors more than other students. Obviously, this is because both groups face a present or impending period of anxiety-producing tension and ambiguity. The freshman faces the exciting but troublesome environment of overchoice, temptations, challenges, and opportunities. New ideas and people from new backgrounds promise to broaden his or her horizons, welcome or not. There is an exciting but daunting new degree of freedom from parental apron strings. Some will welcome the offer to regain a measure of the home-cooked guidance and shelter they left behind at home but may find again in a cult, a new "family." Seniors have adjusted to school, but now the free ride is over. No sooner have they learned the ropes and come to enjoy their new life on campus than it, too, is ripped away from them, and it is time to face the big bad world outside. At such a critical juncture, seniors, too, may welcome a port in the storm, especially if, like Dustin Hoffman in *The Graduate*, they are uncertain about the value of the career which they have prepared for.

Probably the least likely to join cults on campus are those with what Spong, Spiro, et al. call "the foreclosed personality." These are students who entered their major program knowing exactly what they wanted to do, or at least obedient to the plans of their parents. These students do not view college as a time of expanding horizons. It is essentially vocational school for them, and very little may change.

Again, when a new convert/recruit, whether gleaned from campus or not, joins a cult, there will very likely be an initial period of isolation from one's natural family and accustomed friends. This is to shelter the newcomer from old influences and so to facilitate new associations and new patterns of thought. One repudiates or at least temporarily puts natural family ties on hold so to strengthen ties to one's new spiritual family. Think of the gospel episodes where a new disciple is told to leave behind family, property, and occupation. Peter, Andrew, Philip, James, John, and Levi do precisely this. When Jesus' natural relations arrive to take charge of him, fearing for his sanity, he repudiates them in favor of his *true*, his spiritual or metaphorical, family (Mark 3:20–21, 31–35). It is tragically amusing to behold the irony of parents agonizing over the departure of their children for a cult instead of conventional Christianity—which itself seems to have begun with the very same social dynamics.

But no brainwashing has taken place in these scenarios. Only manipulation, reprehensible as it is. But there is a major difference. Any criticism, such as I would level, against such tactics must be aimed equally at all evangelistic groups with their peer-pressure and "brimstone-and-treacle" tactics. We are no longer talking only about cults.

UNUSUAL SUSPECTS

Interviews have shown very strongly that the mainstream of recruits to cults are not weirdos or losers. They tend to be more highly educated than most people and more idealistic. In fact, one very plausible reading of the dramatic growth of both the Jesus movement and the cults after the New Left radicalism of the 1960s is that refugees disappointed by the dead-end failure of these groups continued to look for a cause in which to reinvest their lives. Many found it in unconventional religion. Again, they did not stay long, but many left without bitterness, grateful for the experience, as for any experimental experience.

The late author and evangelist Francis A. Schaeffer (*The New Super-Spirituality*) tried to explain why many conventional evangelical-fundamentalist teenagers abandoned their suburban churches for radical cults like the Children of God/Family of Love. Perhaps ironically, many had complained of the legalism of their congregations only to embrace a far more severe version of the same thing in a cult. But Schaefer understood there was no inconsistency: the young people took more seriously all the radical discipleship talk they heard in sermons but never saw lived out except in the almost superstitious token form of not playing cards, dancing, or going to the movies. This was neither much of a social statement nor a spirituality. So they went where they could find something that answered to the discipleship rhetoric.

The same dynamic has long been evident in the phenomenon of fundamentalist church missionary conventions. A weeklong revival features missionaries temporarily returned from the field, driving home the need for workers to enter the ripe evangelistic fields—lest one be responsible for the damnation of far-flung tribesmen. The pew-potato church member, for the sake of one's preference for middle-class comforts, has long ago shirked his imagined missionary duty but now hopes to atone for it by sacrificing his own son or daughter to discharge the debt for him, in his place. What is happening here is that heady discipleship rhetoric, essentially of an adolescent caste, is aimed at those with ears keen to hear it: the congregation's youth. How proud they are when, at the close of the conference, Johnny and Mary have tearfully committed themselves to go to preach the gospel as a missionary to Zuphrenia or Slobbovia.

The same factor accounts for the predominance of Jewish youth attracted to cults and imported Eastern spiritualities (and to fundamentalist Christianity!). The children of secularized Jewish families are left with a sense of the importance of religion but without anything to fill the gap. So they will go where they can find it. It is a point worth considering. For those of us who do not relish indoctrinating our children with any creedal party line, are we kidding ourselves when we shelter them from faith instruction while assuring ourselves that one day our children will surely choose for themselves? The danger is that we will have successfully raised them to be areligious (not necessarily a bad thing, of course), or religiously frustrated, in which case we may have laid the groundwork for our own chagrin if they seek out a religion we find distasteful. One alternative is to educate them in one's inherited tradition but to emphasize that it is up to the child one day to decide whether or not to embrace it.

CAN GOD DELIVER A RELIGION ADDICT?

Sociologists of religion often speak of "conversion careers," the lifestyle of the constitutional "seeker" whose path seems to be one of frequent, temporary dalliance with this or that spiritual group until it is time to move, gypsy-like, on to another. The July–August 1977 (vol. 20, no. 6) issue of *American Behavioral Scientist* features many important discussions of such religious gypsies. Such individuals may correctly see the available range of movements (especially when many fall within the same wider theological spectrum, e.g., charismatic/Pentecostal, New Thought/Metaphysical, New Age) as so many items on a buffet and that there is nothing stopping them from picking and choosing as they wish, like frequenters of various fast-food outlets in a single town. The lack of brand loyalty may frustrate those who manage each cult, but perhaps they just need to come to grips with the fact that this is the only sort of ministry they can hope to offer a certain type of person at work on his or her own synthesis. Indeed, the same challenge increasingly faces all religious bodies in a radically pluralistic age of minimal religious brand-loyalty when the "heretical imperative" prevails (Berger, *The Heretical Imperative*).

The best chance of stopping the seeker-gypsy in his/her tracks, getting him/her to settle down with one's own group, seems to be to offer him/her a set of rewarding affective ties. We arrive again at "love bombing." This attempt to make newcomers welcome and to encourage identification with the group need in no way imply insincerity, as if the cult recruiter or members were on the level with used-car salesmen. They may well feel genuine friendly concern toward the new face, and once he joins, the old hands may feel genuine affection for him, like fraternity brothers presumably do with new members.

Yet those who suspect something phony is going on in such cases do, I suspect, have a handle on something. It is not precisely insincere motions they sense, but rather a subtle artificiality. The cult members (or church members) are stuck in what Paul Watzlawick (*How Real Is Real?*) calls "the 'Be Spontaneous' Paradox," when "genuine" friendship is *commanded*. We are all great rationalizers and doublethinkers, so perhaps we can perform emotionally on command. But we feel we shouldn't be able to turn it on and off. There is something fake here, and I think it is the *conditional* character of the affection offered. One is being welcomed *as a new brother/sister* in Christ (or whatever), and if the day comes when that bond is severed, if the convert decides he just can't buy it, he should not be surprised if the friendship that once felt like such warmth of spirit vanishes into thin air. Had it then been no more than a pretense all along? By no means, but it was predicated on a common religious allegiance, and very likely nothing more. One often hears compatriots in the faith say things like: "You can see the power of the Holy Spirit (or the strength of Christian love) in that it unites me and Charlie over there when ordinarily we would have nothing in common!" After all, were not the tax collector Matthew and the Communist agitator Simon both members of Jesus' circle? Or so we often hear. Yes, Christ (or whatever) *was* the only glue (and a powerful one) holding disparate individuals together, and when it was removed, the friendship evaporated. That is no surprise. There was no insincerity, only artificiality. That is the problem with love bombing.

It is all built into the religious notion of "agape," an early Christian term for unconditional love, the sort of nondiscriminating love God has for sinful mortals who can offer him nothing. The late Bishop Pike was probably the only Christian thinker ever to decry the condescension implied when we pretend to exercise agape toward one another, as if we occupied so high a pedestal.

But it is such agapaic love-bombing that may explain the cases we do find (though, again, they seem to be far from the majority) when a significant percentage of cult recruits do hail from the ranks of dweebs and losers. Some studies of Satanist groups imply that inveterate maladaptoids join the group to find a peer group of fellow lepers among whom they can feel significant. They may attain some degree of rank among the other ugly ducklings. The more degrees of initiation they amass, the higher their standing, just like the comic book geek who can tell you the vital statistics and secret identities of each and every comic book hero. And at the same time, the business of the cult is to teach them what they failed to pick up through normal channels, namely, skills to succeed in life. They may show the recruit some "tough love" and offer frank advice. Or they may deal in *ressentiment*, providing illusory and imaginary means to succeeding (e.g., magical spells of enrichment unsuspected by mere mortals) or getting even (how to hex or curse an enemy, maybe the school jock who ridicules you). In such cases we have a surprising but real parallel to the magical gestures of futility performed by primitive Cargo Cultists with their wooden-board rifles and orange crate radios, waiting for the cargo ship.

Again, what we are observing here is by no means confined to controversial or despised "cults." In his (in)famous book *The Case for Orthodox Theology* (i.e., as distinguished from liberal and neo-orthodox Protestantism), Edward J. Carnell lambasted fundamentalist Protestantism as "Orthodoxy gone cultic" and cited the example of the never-ceasing quest for intracultic brownie points the fundamentalist receives by witnessing to his faith, whether or not it produces any converts. He gets status in the cult.

HE REALLY IS SANTA CLAUS

My family and I watch *Miracle on 34th Street* every Christmas season and marvel anew at what a great movie it is, filled with fascinating and profound ideas. First, the film opens a window into the question of how religions begin and get off the ground. When Mrs. Walker, Mr. Shellhammer, and Kris Kringle's doctor discuss the matter of his mental health, the doctor assures them there's nothing to worry about. "His is a delusion for good." Between them, they all assume as a matter of course that Kris is crazy. But they admit he is functional, able to live a productive life, and not just despite but actually because of his delusion. And by the time the movie is over, they have all come to believe that he really is Santa Claus after all. Is the viewer supposed to share the belief that Kris is

Santa? I guess so, but technically the film ends on a question mark. The cane by the fireplace might have been left by the people who moved out. Yeah, maybe.

On the one hand, maybe we are to see that Kris's claim to be Santa has been vindicated. But another way to view it is that Gaily, Doris, Susie, and the others have come to share Kris's delusion. He has spread his net wide enough for them, too, to become entangled in it. And they have. A Santa cult has begun. And here I think we find an important clue as to the nature of religious belief systems. A religious belief system is a narrative universe, a story that at first exists inside the head of an individual who has somehow come to believe it and to live as if it is true. He might be able to live on the basis of those assumptions, but if he tries it in public, he will stick out like a sore thumb, as if he were the only one speaking a language, trying unsuccessfully to communicate with people around him.

That's the way religions begin, but as long as the individual prophet is the only one to believe as he does, we call him insane. We say he has a delusion, because he is the only one navigating by this compass on these particular seas. Like Kris Kringle, he is delusional. But then a few people begin to see that it is a delusion for good. Because Kris Kringle believes what he does, though factually he is mistaken, it is a fruitful mistake. He manages to get Macy and Gimble to shake hands and adopt a policy of putting the customer first. Good comes of the delusion, so others begin to adopt it. And after a while, when enough people believe it, we no longer call it a delusion. We call it a religion.

Religions are constituted by sets of attractive beliefs, such as the power of prayer and the richness of a cozy universe owned and operated by a God who has your personal welfare at heart. These beliefs, true or false, have good effects for people who believe in them. And we feel we have to respect a religion, unlike a delusion of the insane, which we feel entitled to laugh at.

The movie also gives us a keen insight into the process whereby individuals become converted to belief, to share the benevolent delusion. What is the bridge over which Doris, Susie, and Paul Gaily pass into belief in Santa, and that their friend Kris is Santa? They have first cultivated a series of relationships with him, and then a crisis tests their loyalty to him. His belief in his own Santaship is so central to his being that one cannot remain on his side without coming to share his belief.

We say "we believe in" someone when we have come to trust him, to count on him. It seldom comes to the point of having to affirm all that the person believes. But in Kris Kringle's case there was nothing left over. There was no way to ignore or to steer around his central belief. Mrs. Walker, Doris, discovers that as long as she says she loves the old man but agrees with his enemies that he is not Santa as he believes himself to be, she is their ally, not his. Kris's friends can only act on his behalf when they decide to commit themselves to his belief. To defend Kris, they must defend the belief that there *is* a Santa, and that *he* is Santa. And they discover that in order to defend the belief that he is Santa, they must embrace that belief themselves.

You will convert to a religion when you discover you cannot continue in your friendship or your relationship of love or trust unless you sign on for the other person's belief. It doesn't have to be the prophet, the founder. It need only be a believer, a follower. People are not just brains. They do not just think their way to their beliefs—even though they should!

People who need people join religions filled with the people they need. The beliefs are something they inherit. A person falls in love with a member of a different religion and, not surprisingly, switches to that religion. A person needs companionship, peer acceptance, and a group of religious people offer it to him. The belief follows in due course. If a religious recruiter can get you to do things with his group, to play games with them, sing their songs, you are in Rome doing as the Romans do. It will not be long before you become a Roman. And all this reflects the fact, and indeed is the same fact as in the history of religion, that ritual precedes myth. People do things before they know why. They may want to know why, and someone will explain it theologically, telling them a myth to rationalize it. But belief follows behavior.

But the most important lesson the film teaches is about faith. "Faith," we are told twice, "is believing when common sense tells you not to." I remember when I first watched this film, years ago, with a couple of skeptical pals. When we got to this line, we all exploded with laughter. Precisely what sort of belief is being mandated here? Belief in what sort of thing?

The first time we hear the maxim "faith is believing when common sense tells you not to," it is Gaily telling Doris to believe in him even though he has just quit his job at a high-paying law firm to defend Kris Kringle. She is so blinded by practical concerns that she cannot see that any sacrifice such as he has made can be worth it. She is too pragmatic to throw everything away for the sake of "intangibles" like love, hope, and compassion. And yet she believes in these things, too. She has just been disappointed in love and is afraid to trust, afraid to hope, again. And her daughter, hearing Doris urge her to believe even when common sense tells her not to, says, "In other words, 'If at first you don't succeed, try, try again.'"

The kind of faith we are being told to embrace, and told convincingly, is really *hope*, hope and the willingness to take the risk of commitment. Doris's problem, and Susie's, is that they have a low threshold for the pain of disappointment. They don't think they can afford to make the jump and fall short of the farther ledge again. So they have decided to shrink their worlds to small confines where they will not need to jump anywhere, because there will be no place else to go. Nothing to achieve that one cannot inch one's way to safely and predictably, without risk. No stretch to make, no wings to spread. But such a world will prove too confining, so confining in fact that you will begin to shrink to fit it. You will become a pessimist.

But the pessimist is not a realist. The pessimist is the one who cannot see a good thing when it comes along because he has lost the ability to recognize it. It will be invisible to him. This is why the pessimist thinks the optimist is a dreamer, hallucinating, seeing false hopes and pipe dreams that are not there. But they are.

It's not that the pessimist, the so-called pragmatist, doesn't want good things to happen. He just no longer thinks they can. He remembers hoping for good things, but he has been disappointed, and it hurt, maybe more than once or a few times, and he dares not take the risk again. This is easy to empathize with; we've all felt that way whether acutely or chronically. But on another level it's hard to understand. Because if you have become like Doris Walker, you are living in a constant slough of despond. You are already about as disappointed as you can get. But by this time if something really dramatic were to happen, it would at least add a thrill to life. It's like the joke where you are so far down you have to reach up to touch your toes.

Hope has become like Santa Claus—it has been a long time since you could believe in it, that the future would arrive with some gift you asked it for. But why not believe in the future again? Why not believe in possibility again? It is as simple as this: if Santa comes along with that gift, if the future appears and you have your eyes clenched shut in the assurance that the future will not come, you will not see it. If, on the other hand, your eyes are open, the future may not come, like Godot, but then again it may. And you will miss it. It will have come and gone without your knowing, and you will be without hope once again, only it will be your fault. You will be afraid to face the future, afraid to hope. But don't cringe! Fight! Elsewhere in the movie Santa says, "We may not win, but we can go down swinging!"

Doomsday Dawning

Why Do Some Cults Erupt in Violence?

*O*ne of the chief reasons the public is even aware of cults is the astonishing violence associated with them. The most notorious examples are the Manson family murders, the Peoples Temple mass suicide, the Waco conflagration, the three-wave suicide/murder of the Order of the Solar Temple (in Switzerland and Quebec), the Aum Shinrikyo sarin attack in the Tokyo subway, the Heaven's Gate suicides, and the cataclysmic end of the Movement for Restoring the Ten Commandments in Uganda where some 714 died. Indeed, some of the events led French and German authorities to recoil in horror and to declare war on nontraditional religious movements. Because of events like these, many people consider cults per se, any and all cults, to be potentially or actually dangerous. But a moment's reflection leads one to realize that there are literally thousands of cults, and only the tiniest fraction of them have been associated with violence, either suicidal or homicidal. This realization leads to the major question we must ask: *What makes a cult explode into violence, whether self-directed or outer-directed?* If we can figure out what the formula for disaster is, we will have come a long way toward discovering the formula for averting disaster.

TWIN ROOTS OF VIOLENCE

Again, there does not seem to be anything essential about cults that leads to violence. A cult simply as a cult is not especially liable to erupt into violence, but we can point to certain structural constants of cults that provide the potential for violence. There are two major characteristics.

1. Charismatic Leadership

The first is *charismatic leadership*. This does not help us narrow down the problem, since charismatic leadership is a trait of almost all cults. But understanding charismatic leadership does help us understand one of the major ways things can go wrong, and why.

One of the two defining traits of a "cult" as opposed to a "sect" is the focus on a single, central leader, whose word is law for his followers. This is one reason cults are by definition both *new* and *small*. As soon as they begin to grow beyond the level where the leader can keep track of everyone and have a personal connection to everyone, we are on the way to having a sect, because, as Max Weber said, charisma is becoming "routinized." This means it is becoming the theological authorization of a structure of secondary leaders. Charismatic authority is based on the dynamism of the individual, as opposed to the "traditional" and the "rational-legal" types of leadership. The former is leadership based on inherited prerogatives, like a hereditary monarchy. The latter is a constitutional office based on election or appointment on the basis of practical qualifications. The difference between charismatic leadership and the other types is well illustrated in Mark 1:27, when Jesus preaches in a synagogue and casts the demon out of a heckler, whereupon people exclaim: "What is this? A new teaching! And with authority!" Mark comments: "For he spoke with authority, and not like their scribes." The Jewish scribes, precursors to the rabbis, taught carefully and casuistically, judiciously reasoning from scriptural precedent. The charismatic leader sweeps all that away: "You have heard it was said to the men of old ABC, but I say to you . . ." (Matt. 5:27–28, etc.). If the business of the cult becomes too much for a single leader to manage, as it surely will once the numbers grow (see Moses having to share the authority for just this reason in Exodus 18), then the cult is ipso facto evolving into a sect.

"Charisma" is a Greek New Testament term (see 1 Corinthians 12–14) denoting an apparently supernatural gift of power or knowledge. When we speak of a politician, clergyman, rock star, and so on, as being charismatic or having charisma, we refer to a kind of dynamic magnetism that impresses and attracts others, motivates them to accept his challenges, even obey his commands. It takes such a person to launch a movement. It is this "rock star" quality, obviously, that leads to the danger of sexual abuse in ministerial relationships, whether mainstream or cultic. People tend to sense not only a parent figure but, in psychological terms, a living embodiment of the *ego ideal*. A charismatic leader summons his followers' best ideals and implicitly invites them to let him fulfill them for them, which can happen if they will yield their autonomy, their identity, to him.

Thus they identify with the cult leader or charismatic leader. It may be because of self-hatred, as in the mass movements Eric Hoffer studied in *The True Believer.* But it may simply be the promise of fulfillment that attracts the "seeker" type of personality—or anyone else in a weak moment. Such a total investment, whereby the members become something like emotional groupies, helps explain both why cult members are so tenaciously attached to the cult and why, if alienated, they turn against the cult with unabated scorn, sometimes going so far as to join countercult groups or become deprogrammers. And, as we will see, such scorned lovers, deconverts, often play a key role in inadvertently catalyzing cult violence.

Sociologists point to this give-and-take character of charisma, the fact that it must be received as well as given: it means that charisma is a relational quantity. It must be maintained and can be lost. Theologian Paul Tillich understands revelation in these terms. He says that if no one accepts the revelation, then there has been no revelation. Jesus is the Christ only insofar as he is recognized or received as such, as Peter does at Caesarea Philippi (Mark 8:29). This is an apt description of what happens with all cult leaders.

Okay, with these two factors in mind, that is, the "takes two to tango" character of charisma and the need to decentralize leadership once the membership grows, we can see one source of the unrest that can lead to violence—namely, that the leader may sense his absolute control slipping (John 6:66) and come, perhaps rightly, to suspect that his lieutenants, who are after all coming to share his mantel, are out to usurp or displace him. René Girard explains why they do this. It might seem odd for devoted followers to try to edge out their master and ideal, but it is not. Their devotion partakes of "mimetic discipleship" and therefore of "mimetic *rivalry.*" This means that the disciple so idolizes/idealizes the master that he seeks, basically, to *become* him (Gal. 4:14), and once committed to this trajectory, he eventually comes to realize there is not room enough for both the master and his new doppelgänger! This is why crazed fans kill their idols. This is why John Lennon died at the hand of his biggest fan. It is therefore not unreasonable for a cult leader to suspect his lieutenants are out to get him: "The disciple cannot become greater than the master; it is sufficient that he become like his master" (Matt. 10:24–25a). It may take no more than a concern like Jethro's in Exodus 18:13–23 to make the charismatic leader suspicious (is paranoia a special risk for the charismatic?). He may recoil as Jesus does at his relatives' seemingly innocent concern in Mark 3:32–35. He may set members of the inner circle against one another, or thin out the ranks of leadership by making new and arbitrary demands ("If anyone would follow me, let him hoist his own cross and follow me"; "From that time on, many of his disciples turned back from following him"). Or it may be that these demands ("If you really have faith, you'll make this sacrifice, believe this doctrine. Are you up to the challenge?") will thin out the ranks of the membership, reducing it to the old level where the leader could assert direct influence on everyone.

In any case, these leadership struggles, occasioned by the delicate dance of charismatic leadership, may eventuate in violence. One reason for this is that the leader will be narrowing the circle of those he trusts and will thus shield himself from negative feedback. Conversely, in their struggle to stay close to the leader, his remaining assistants may become yes-men and tell the leader what he wants to hear. You can see the difference in the depiction of Judas and Peter in the film *The Last Temptation of Christ*, where Judas dares to criticize and question Jesus, unlike Peter, who is an unimaginatively loyal yes-man. Judas proves the more valuable disciple because Jesus welcomes the challenges. Fearing betrayal from within, and increasingly out of touch with external reality, the cult leader may order some extraordinary action to assert and consolidate his authority. If it is suicide, it means he can keep in control to the end—by hastening the end.

To return to the scorned ex-devotees, they will become embittered against as well as disillusioned about their ex-leader. Some will work to bring him down. They may join cult-watch organizations and go to the media or the authorities with rumors and atrocity stories about the leader, true or not (things tend to look rather different in retrospect). This may focus unwelcome suspicion and hostile attention on the cult from the authorities, and out of his defensiveness (even paranoia) and the charged, isolated atmosphere inside the cult and/or its leadership circles, the cult leader, with possible delusions of grandeur, may react with desperate violence. In fact, alienated ex-members and relatives of members of the Peoples Temple, Aum Shinrikyo, Order of the Solar Temple, and the Branch Davidians instigated the eventual violence, both by telling their tales and by convincing authorities that cults were inherently violence-prone, thus stacking the deck in terms of how to deal with them.

2. Apocalyptic Faith

"Apocalyptic" comes from the Greek *apocalypse*, "the drawing back of the veil," thus the re-vel-ation. The book of Revelation is also called the Apocalypse. By extension, the word "apocalypse" is also used to refer to the explosive events of the End Times, for example, the Battle of Armageddon. Apocalyptic faith is the expectation that one lives in the End Times, and just as important, that one and one's group constitute the elect community, the camp of the saints, threatened and besieged by the Antichrist and awaiting deliverance at the Second Coming of Christ.

Many cults and even mainstream religions have avid apocalyptic faith and are completely peaceful. So apocalyptic faith is by no means some sort of doctrinal poison leading directly or inevitably to violence. In fact, usually apocalyptic groups are quietistic, hunkering down and patiently waiting for divine vindication from heaven. And yet apocalypticism is an important ingredient in a number of violent cultic flare-ups, and not by coincidence. Basically this is for two interlocking reasons.

First, an apocalyptic cult, by definition, feels itself estranged from a drastically evil and corrupt age. No one combines eager anticipation of the end of the world with a sunny optimism about how great it is to live here. You would only look forward to the end because, that way, as the old slave spiritual puts it, "Soon I will be done with the troubles of the world." As Peter L. Berger puts it in *The Sacred Canopy*, apocalyptic expectation is an *otherworldly, futuristic theodicy*. That is, things seem so bad to believers that they have ceased bothering to ponder why God allows such evil in the world (any proposed answer would be a "theodicy"); they are just willing to forgive and forget as long as it will be over *soon!* Apocalyptic expectation is necessarily expectation of the end coming very soon. So anyone holding such belief feels like a stranger in a strange land.

There is a built-in defensiveness toward the outside world, and not unlikely heightened suspicions and exaggerated judgments. Such faith easily breeds paranoia and alarmism. This is a great temptation because such an "us versus them," "the world's going to hell in a handbasket" belief allows one to oversimplify and saves one the trouble of complex political or moral analysis such as the rest of us are stuck with. And naturally, an apocalyptic cult is trip-wired to take any outside challenge or criticism as an assault of

Satan and his minions. Those who must for good reason challenge or offer criticism of them must be careful not to play the preassigned, scripted role ascribed to them in the apocalyptic scenario of the cult. That, alas, is exactly what the Bureau of Alcohol, Tobacco, and Firearms, then the FBI, did at Waco. More of that in a moment.

The second reason takes up the other half of Berger's phrase, a "futuristic *otherworldly* theodicy." It is not just that the future is liable to bring *some* reversal of the cult's perceived misfortunes. Apocalypticism entails that this deliverance is going to be otherworldly. Usually apocalyptic believers initially expect that their deliverance will be a catching up ("rapture") into the heavens into the waiting arms of Christ, or perhaps being beamed up to a waiting spaceship. Such believers, again, tend to be quietistic, waiting for their deliverance. But suppose things are getting a bit too hot. As in the disturbing 1991 film by Michael Tolkin, *The Rapture* (with Mimi Rogers and David Duchovny), the cult may conclude that they have things slightly out of order and that it is they who must take the initiative and cross over into the other world/heaven by means of suicide and/or homicide. If the mountain won't come to Muhammad . . . .

So apocalyptic faith looks toward a brightly lit EXIT sign. And that sign is pointing to death. This world is no longer good enough for apocalyptic believers. It is either too distressing or (in some cases, such as Heaven's Gate) too lackluster and mundane. As Michel de Rougement, in *Love in the Western World*, explains, the only way to attain that imagined world that is better than life—is to die. And so it is no surprise that apocalyptic believers are sooner or later more than willing to play that card. In an ultimate contest of wills, such as between the FBI and the Branch Davidians, the cult holds the trump card.

Apocalypticism begets polarization, the casting of one's group as "us" and everyone outside, most especially opponents of the group (ex-members, law enforcement, the Division of Youth and Family Services), as "them." We are the Children of Light; they/you are the Children of Darkness, exactly as in the Dead Sea Scrolls *War Scroll*, where the sectarians drew up battle plans for the day when open warfare must erupt between themselves, the Sons of Light, and the Sons of Darkness or Hordes of Beliar, a combined force of Roman occupiers and "lax" or apostate Jews (i.e., Jews not embracing the fanatically strict ascetical standards of the Scrolls sect).

MIXING THE CUP OF THE WRATH OF GOD

The cult already exists in a state of "nascent conflict" with the broader society simply insofar as it exists as a social-religious alternative to it, a "city on a hill." But at first the conflict is latent. Conflict emerges into the open and intensifies when outside critics and/or former members bring challenges to the group, perhaps in hope of shutting it down. For instance, the authorities, fed rumors (or truthful reports) about neglect or abuse of children, challenged cults including the Branch Davidians, the Church Universal and Triumphant (aka Summit Lighthouse), Children of God (aka Family of Love), and Krishna Consciousness. Children of the Children of God cult were simultaneously seized from many communes worldwide (though subsequent investigations revealed cult members had not in fact been guilty of child abuse, whereupon their children were returned). Jonestown settlers seem to have feared this would happen. Branch Davidians had reason to fear it. There was a wide range of reactions. The Krishna cult took the challenge to heart and completely revamped its approach to childcare. The Peoples Temple and the Branch Davidians ended real or anticipated sieges by the US government with "revolutionary suicide." The Church Universal and Triumphant, who had previously even stockpiled weapons in case violence should erupt, wound up cooperating and mainstreaming their children in local schools, from which they had hitherto segregated them.

This spectrum of responses implies that there are various options facing any challenged cult during a period of heightened tension and conflict. They may accede to the demands of their critics, as some have done. We can only admire the realism and broad-mindedness of groups that have done this, though here one begins to suspect such accommodation may be part of a search for legitimation of the cult in the eyes of the larger society, but that's good, too, since one only seeks legitimation in surrounding society if one seeks to live in peaceful coexistence with it or to gain persuasive influence over it, and then we are talking about a wholesale maturity beyond apocalyptic belief. The sect is on its way to becoming a church.

In his description of the early Christians of the Holy Land (*Sociology of Early Palestinian Christianity*), Gerd Theissen speculates that the Jesus movement reacted to wholesale public indifference to their message (something that, as we will see below, provoked murderous wrath on the part of Aum Shinrikyo and suicidal martyrdom among Heaven's Gate) by looking inward and consigning the unbelieving world to damnation—resorting to a species of what Nietzsche called *ressentiment*, a sour-grapes resentment in which one is too much of a coward to take overt revenge but conceals childish revenge fantasies beneath the cloak of pretended willingness to transcend offense and grudging. "Oh, *I'll* forgive you, but soon the Son of Man is going to come and kick your butt! *Then* you'll be sorry!" We can observe this turning point between two of the strata of sayings in the Q document, a collection of sayings attributed to Jesus and used by Matthew and Luke (see Mack, *The Lost Gospel: The Book of Q and Christian Origins*). In the original corpus of sayings we find a variety of wise and even sarcastic maxims similar to the street-corner wisdom of the ancient Stoic and Cynic soapbox preachers. Wisdom brings its own reward, foolishness its own comeuppance. But then suddenly we find a later set of sayings interlarded, threats of divine reprisal against the group's earlier hearers who refused to accept their wisdom: "Whoever rejects me and my words in this generation of sinners and adulterers, him will the Son of Man repudiate when he arrives with his angels" (Mark 8:38). We may wonder if such an interiorized, wishful-thinking response to indifference and opposition is more characteristic of a situation of only mild or intermittent conflict between the cult and its hostile public. Anyone who feels this way, who mutters grudging quotes of "Vengeance is mine; I will repay, saith the Lord," is still at least some major steps away from taking matters into his own hands.

Another means of resolving the conflict is to vote with your feet. The cultists may physically get up and go, adopting the theological model of Moses and the Exodus, looking for refuge in other countries where they can raise their children and worship their God in ways they see fit. The Children of God did this, abandoning the United States and heading for Europe, North Africa, and Asia.

Or violence may erupt, whether directed at the outsiders as part of the Last Battle, or self-directed as a way of passing peaceably through "heaven's gate."

What factors determine which strategy will prevail? We have

seen that much depends on what measures the charismatic guru feels are necessary to safeguard or vindicate his hold over the group. Group suicide, Masada-style, may be chosen as a way to secure the leader's grasp on his followers "for eternity." Or it may simply be a case of "If I can't have them, no one will." Also, theologically, it is surely better to descend from the messianic throne as a martyr-hero than as a bum hustled into the backseat of a police car. Dignity is charisma. (Thus, obviously, it is also self-defeating for negotiators and critics to treat the guru as a con man as the FBI finally did David Koresh. That is just asking him not to cooperate.) I think Vincent Bugliosi, though a hero, was mistaken in calling Charles Manson "Charles Con-man," refusing to take seriously Charlie's messianic status, but it didn't matter, because in that case the damage was already done. The murders were over; Bugliosi wasn't trying to avert them, only to vilify Manson and so assure the death penalty. Accordingly, I have always been glad Manson wasn't executed: it is more important to keep him available for study as an important piece of religious data.

If the cult guru is facing challenges from mimetic rivals within the group, again, choosing the death card is a final affirmation that trumps all others. No one can match that bet, and all opponents must fold. The guru goes out in style, charisma intact. In fact, his charisma may only increase once he becomes a martyr. This, obviously, is why governments prefer not to make rebels into martyrs, lest they become even more of a thorn in the side after their deaths. That certainly happened in the case of David Koresh, since, not only did someone continue to circulate epistles in his name, claiming he had survived, but Timothy McVeigh blew up the Oklahoma Federal Building to even the score for Koresh's martyrdom at Waco.

MEDIATING ARMAGEDDON

What can be done to dampen down the tension between the two factions in a polarized situation? One strategy is to introduce third parties into the discussion. In a sense one may consider the angry ex-members and relatives (e.g., Grace and Timothy Stoen) who initially sicced the authorities on the cult (Peoples Temple) to be a third party. But these really constitute one more head on the same hydra. In fact, with their knowledge or even guesses about the inner plans of the cult they used to belong to, the ex-members may actually make suicide scenarios into a self-fulfilling prophecy.

The desirable third party is a group of sympathetic outsiders, impartial anthropologists or sociologists of religion, those who understand where the cult and its guru are coming from without leveling judgments. They may also be able to appreciate marital and child-rearing arrangements that, while unfamiliar and shocking to American Protestants, may be ancient and traditional in other societies with which the cult may be connected. Plus, knowing how similar cult-versus-authorities confrontations have been resolved before (whether successfully or not), such specialists can make sure the full range of options are considered, as well as seek to prevent the imposition and embracing of dangerous stereotypes.

None of this means the cultists or the guru are not actually doing things most Americans find offensive. Polygamy, an adult guru having plural and young wives, corporeal punishment of wayward children, all these things may be happening. It need not be a case of mere misunderstanding. But the specialist or scholar may still be able to negotiate some understanding by making it clear that the actions are not intended or perceived as wrong by the cult. The goal will still be to work out some compromise, not just to declare relativism and go home.

APPENDIXES

And it may be that the guru is a paranoid madman, like Jim Jones, Charles Manson, or Shoko Asahara. But one does not want to draw such a conclusion hastily or ignorantly. To treat one who considers himself a messiah as no more than a crook is to provoke him into desperate acts he might not have previously thought necessary.

Needless to say, the third party specialists must not be used by the authorities as a front and a cynical stalling tactic as happened at Waco, where a theologian was having a good-faith dialogue with Koresh and thought he was getting somewhere but then got blindsided by the FBI assault when they decided they were tired of waiting.

It is important to realize that sometimes one cannot anticipate possible violence, that things may be working their way up a thermometer of polarized tension invisibly, in the paranoid imagination of a cult and its guru. For instance, Jim Jones perceived Congressman Leo Ryan's fact-finding visit, and especially his departure with disgruntled members, as a challenge to his control of the jungle-locked commune. He was right. He had not escaped the long arm of the hated US government. But he saw it through a haze of delusion, believing that the CIA was out to destroy his Socialist paradise and would torture his followers at the first opportunity. His paranoia (partly drug-induced, partly reinforced by isolation in a remote region with no radios, etc.) magnified the nature and extent of a genuine challenge. The results were catastrophic.

David Koresh, on the other hand, cherished delusional fantasies of his group surviving Armageddon when and if it occurred, but group members only became dangerous once the government obligingly played into their worst fears by besieging them.

Heaven's Gate, led by Marshal Herff Applewhite, experienced no real persecution except for massive rejection and occasional ridicule from the audience to whom the group preached. Nonetheless, this reaction, coupled with the death of Bonnie Lu Nettles, the coleader of the cult, plus the long delay of the expected arrival of a spaceship to take them to "the Next Level," finally ratcheted up the stakes to where the cult members decided to make their transition to the Next Level by means of suicide. In a sense, the clock, or the calendar, was their opponent, every tick, every passing date whispering the falsehood of their faith. Finally they sought the EXIT door.

Aum Shinrikyo carried on a similar one-sided confrontation with a larger society that for the most part did not suspect anything was going on. Like Heaven's Gate, cult members were antagonized by society's indifference to them. Their preaching fell largely on deaf ears. They did manage to gain a goodly number of converts, including some pretty big donors. But they had set themselves a goal of expansion throughout the world by an early deadline, and when it didn't happen, they decided it meant the world was doomed. When Shoko Asahara and some of his followers ran for office and were resoundingly defeated, they decided that what they had first anticipated as a spiritual war won through ascetical devotion and evangelism would now have to become a literal and bloody war, which they proceeded to declare against Japanese society. As is now notorious, they undertook the development of biological and chemical weapons, but they proved largely incompetent in delivering them, though a dozen died.

NEW TESTAMENT PARALLELS?

Anyone familiar with the history of New Testament scholarship will readily think of Albert Schweitzer's theory (*The Mystery of the Kingdom of God* and *The Quest of the Historical Jesus*) that Jesus harbored apocalyptic expectations such that by the preaching of repentance he hoped to usher in the kingdom of God, promising his followers that they should triumph after the crisis of the Great Tribulation, rising from the dead along with him. But, Schweitzer said, the general indifference of the public to Jesus' prophetic call led him to conclude that he must bear the tribulation alone, on behalf of his disciples. Hence he let himself be arrested, fully expecting to return from the dead days later as the supernatural Son of Man. Here is a striking analogy with the sheer impact of public indifference to the cult's preaching prompting a major reassessment of goals and methods.

Pivotal to Jesus' change of mind, so Schweitzer speculated, was the death of John the Baptist, whom Jesus had regarded as the returned prophet Elijah. He had expected some spectacular consummation to John's ministry, but when he died like a common criminal at the hands of Herod Antipas, Jesus realized that he, too, must undergo a worldly death (i.e., not an apocalyptic martyrdom at the hand of Satan) for God's plan of the ages to be advanced. Here we find a striking parallel to the change in Applewhite's thinking once Nettles died. Originally they supposed that both of them would die and rise from the dead (as the Two Witnesses of Revelation 11), an event ("the Demonstration") that would signal the advent of the spaceship to take followers aboard. As time went by, they decided they had been "crucified" by the media and that this was enough to fulfill the prophecy. They still expected, however, to be taken bodily into space aboard spaceships. But this changed when Nettles died of liver cancer. Applewhite began to realize that the members of the cult were not exempt from physical death after all. Rather, they should slough off their fleshly shells and be translated into a new existence aboard the spacecraft.

And in general we may see in these parallels the logic that leads apocalyptic groups to switch from a passive waiting for heavenly deliverance to an active resort to violence (either suicide or doomed collision with the authorities). Once bodies begin to fall, and the Last Trumpet has not sounded, one gets the signal that one has been misinterpreting the prophecy, and that, instead, God helps those who help themselves into the hereafter.

TERRORIST ORGANIZATIONS

Are groups like al Qaeda to be considered "cults"? I think so, though they might as easily be classified as "sects" if that makes any difference. The point is that they are sectlike in that they have split off from a more mainstream, world-affirming mother religion (a "church" in Weber's terminology) in an attempt to return to and to reinvigorate the (real or imagined) vital, more stringent ideals the religion had in its early days. The beliefs of the new entity may not be all that distinctive, though the Wahhabism underlying al Qaeda is "heretical" in that it posits that not only Trinitarian Christians but also Jews and non-Wahhabi Muslims are actually polytheists in that they revere human clergy and/or saints. These become lesser gods. As such, these polytheists deserve only death. (Why are Wahhabi leaders exempt from such condemnation? The old double standard!) But even this doctrinal innovation may be included under the rubric of sectarian tightening of the belt, retrenchment, and self-reformation. So in a sense they are more like sects than cults.

The thing that makes terrorist groups like cults is the feature of absolute obedience to a single charismatic leader, like the Taliban with Mullah Omar and al Qaeda with Osama bin Laden. And yet even here they are more sectlike in that the death of such a leader would not necessary spell the end of the movement. The rest, fiercely committed to the movement's ideology, could just as easily carry on by themselves.

Differentiating terrorist organizations from cults highlights a defining feature of cults that has not been very important in our discussion so far—namely, cults are often transplanted religions or religious sects from another country/culture. Back home, they may not have seemed cultic at all. Hare Krishna, for instance, is part of a Vaisnava movement in India dating from Lord Chaitanya in the fourteenth century. On the other hand, the Unification Church, while stemming from indigenous folk religion sources in Korea, was regarded as a cult even there. But terrorists groups arise from and seek to defend a traditional culture. This makes them *revitalization movements*.

A revitalization movement is the product of a large-scale invasion or unsettling influence upon one culture by another. The invading culture wins by virtue of superior technology (whether the weapons of colonial powers defeating Melanesian islanders or American Indians, or the superior communications technology of the West penetrating Iran, Saudi Arabia, etc.). The traditional culture is threatened with destruction as new ways take hold, either by forcible imposition or by tantalizing the natives with new technology, alcohol, and pornography, and by missionary efforts. The invading culture appears to the subjugated culture to have won by virtue of superior religion/magic. Revitalization movements attempt to save the traditional culture by a process of compromise: assimilating strategic elements of the invasive culture to use against it. This may include weapons and communications technology stolen or copied from the enemy. Or it may include elements of the

346

invaders' religion. In a number of cases in Melanesia and Africa, natives adopted the figure of Jesus or the Bible, claiming they were originally part of the native culture and were somehow stolen by the white invaders. And so Melanesian Cargo Cults have expected Jesus soon to come to them aboard a great plane or ship bearing, Santa-like, loads of TVs, washing machines, and other Western conveniences for them, as well as doom for the invaders. Similarly, African rebels have identified with biblical heroes. Thus Simon Peter Mpade, Jesus (Andre) Matswa, and so on, or Simon Kimbangu, dubbed the Christ of the Blacks, though he himself declined that honor. The emergent religious movement is both traditionalist and heretical, being a syncretistic combination of elements from the old religion and that of the invaders. It may find itself opposed by both traditional religious authorities and the invaders. Thus it is a new religion, again, like a cult.

This fact carries a number of implications. For one, believing in it is a very different matter from adherence to the traditional faith of the society, which could be largely taken for granted. The member of a revitalization movement (like the Indian Ghost Dance or the Cargo Cults) really has to go out on a limb, probably estranged from his friends and family who write him off as a nut. He may face persecution by both the authorities of his own people and those of the invaders. Even if the traditional faith was world-affirming, he will probably vilify the world as wicked since in fact he finds himself opposed to both cultures (albeit fighting, he thinks, on behalf of the traditional one). The traditional faith will have seen the structures of society as God-ordained, while the revitalization movement may instead see them as wicked, fallen powers and principalities, since its earthly representatives persecute the new religion.

Most revitalization movements come to a speedy end, but it

may be that Christianity and Rabbinic Judaism arose as revitalization movements, that is, as innovations arising out of already traditional faiths but with radical differences due to the crises which called them forth. John G. Gager argues for seeing early Christianity as a revitalization movement in reaction to Roman culture in his book *Kingdom and Community*, while one can see the xenophobic Hasmonean rebellion of Judah Maccabee and his brethren as a revitalization movement to stem the influence of Hellenism under Antiochus IV Epiphanes.

Religious terrorist movements like Hamas and al Qaeda see themselves as fighting a "cosmic war" (Juergenson, *Terror in the Mind of God*), which means not only that they believe traditional faith is endangered by Western/American secularism and hedonism but also that they regard their struggle as to some degree otherworldly and supernatural. They are like the Dead Sea Scrolls sect, who, in their scroll, *The War of the Sons of Light and the Sons of Darkness*, anticipated a final struggle in which they would drive out the Romans, but only with the aid of warrior angels swooping down from the heavens.

Religious terrorists realize that their struggle, though essentially political, could never be won by worldly means. Thus they posit God and his angels coming over the hill like the cavalry to win the day. In the meantime the faithful need only demonstrate their seriousness by mounting what efforts they can. If, like the destruction of the World Trade Center, these acts of "performance violence" (Juergenson) are more symbolic than strategic, that is all right. God will ultimately repay the sinners according to their works.

I think it is revealing to compare the acts of terrorists with the seemingly pathetic charades of the Cargo Cultists in the John Frum (or Prum) Cult in Melanesia. These simple people were so unfamiliar with technology that their attempts to ape the technology of the Western colonizers took the form, pretty much, of imitative magic (analogous to voodoo dolls); in other words, they had not the faintest notion of how a radio worked, so they just nailed some bottle caps onto a fruit crate and sat in front of it talking to it, in effect, praying for help. They had no idea of how rifles work but only knew like Indians in cowboy movies that they were "thunder sticks." So they would carve one-piece wooden "toy" rifles and drill with them, imitating colonial troops and hoping to gain power against them. They weren't so stupid as to believe they would defeat the Europeans with toys. No, they undertook symbolic gestures, the only level apparent to them, and hoped in this way to evoke supernatural forces to overthrow their enemies, the only hope they had against hopelessness. In the same way, groups like al Qaeda can never hope to defeat America on her own terms. They are merely lighting a fuse to God's keg of dynamite. Charlie Manson thought his murders would light the fuse of Armageddon in the same way.

And, as Juergenson points out, even if there is no likelihood of defeating one's enemy (something many terrorists do not even expect in their lifetime, though eventually God will do the deed), the symbolic, even ritual participation in a cosmic, sacred war lends the individual's life glorious meaning. Would you rather die of cancer in a hospital or become a martyr for the cause of God? Life is transfigured by imagining that one is fighting alongside Aragorn and Gandalf in the war against Sauron.

But as to the specific point of religious people resorting to the most morally loathsome tactics, the concept of an *eschatological interim ethic* comes in handy. Here I am adapting Albert Schweitzer's theory of the rationale for Jesus' commands for his followers to turn the other cheek, to give all their possessions and money to the poor, and so on. All such actions, as anybody can see, are unrealistic and irresponsible if history is assumed to march on as it always has. One will have bills to pay, property to secure, a future to plan on, kids to feed and send to college, and so on. Thus one must deal harshly with dangerous criminals, fight wars, save money for the future, and so on. But what if one knew there would *be* no mundane future? That very soon now the end of the world would be upon us? The final judgment, the resurrection of the dead? Then two things would become apparent: First, there would be no future to try to guarantee for oneself and one's loved ones. So one's money, possessions, and so on, would be available to feed those who are desperately poor and hungry now, in the eleventh hour. Helping them would in fact be one's only security since the good deed would come back to reward you soon at the Judgment. Second, since the final assize is at hand, one had best be extra right-eous to build up a stock of brownie points, and giving away every-thing, resisting the temptation to strike back, and so on, is now espe-cially incumbent: you better not pout, you better not cry—Santa Claus is coming to town! And so, Schweitzer reasoned, the radical demands of Jesus make eminent sense if one is assuming the soon coming of the end of the worldly order. What once was foolish is now required. It is an extraordinary ethic for an extraordinary time: an *interim ethic* for the brief window of opportunity before the end.

Various Jewish sects have taken the interim ethic even farther. Believing that the provisions of the Mosaic Torah were suited to the fallen age of sin, they reasoned that, at of the dawn of the messianic age, when sin would not exist, the meaning of the law would change to befit the new conditions of the Kingdom of God on earth. This meant that anything prohibited in the Torah now would be permitted or even commanded then. This is called a *deferred eschatological reversal*. Only if one believes, as these sectarians did (e.g., the sect of Messiah Jakob Frank in the seventeenth century), that the messianic age had dawned already, then there is no more deferral. Granted, the messianic age had not yet shown forth in all its glory, for every eye to see, but the faithful must demonstrate their faith by living out the (transvaluated) values of the kingdom which has come but which only they can see by the eye of faith. Thus, one undertook acts traditionally considered wicked. When the new age was fully come, the evil imagination of every heart would be eradicated. In the old age, sinful things were outlawed. But here in the mysterious zone between the secret inauguration of the new age and the complete passing away of the old age, one engages in an *interim ethic* of behavior ordinarily condemned.

That is perhaps why, as part of a cosmic war, Armageddon already here, al Qaeda feels justified in using terror and murder. Ordinarily these things would be wrong, but these are extraordinary times.

Again, terrorism is a species of what Calvinist Old Testament scholar Meredith Kline used to call "proleptic eschatology" when he sought to explain God's command for the ancient Israelites to eradicate every Canaanite, man, woman, child, and animal. It was not secular military strategy but rather *herem*, the killing of the defeated enemy as a sacrifice to the victory-giving God. It was holy war. Kline suggested that it was God's Final Judgment, the Day of Judgment, breaking into human history in advance. That is, genocide was an *interim ethic* appropriate to a strange time within time.

One of the central questions we have to face is how people ostensibly inspired by the high ideals of faith can wind up performing horrific acts of murder and terror against innocent civilians. Partly it is a matter of collective, corporate personality, the

Bibliography

Abbott, Lyman. *The Theology of an Evolutionist.* Boston and New York: Houghton Mifflin, 1900.

Addington, Jack Ensign. *Psychogenesis: Everything Begins in Mind.* Marina del Rey, CA: DeVorss, 1971.

Allen, James. *As a Man Thinketh.* Philadelphia: Running Press, 1989.

Bach, Marcus. *Strange Sects and Curious Cults.* New York: Dodd, Mead, 1961.

Berg, Michael. *The Way: Using the Kabbalah for Spiritual Transformation and Fulfillment.* New York: Wiley, 2001.

Berger, Peter L. *The Heretical Imperative: Contemporary Possibilities of Religious Affirmation.* Garden City, NY: Doubleday Anchor Books, 1980.

———. *The Sacred Canopy: Elements of a Sociological Theory of Religion.* Garden City, NY: Doubleday Anchor Books, 1969.

Berger, Peter L., and Thomas V. Luckmann. *The Social Construction of Reality: An Essay in the Sociology of Knowledge.* Garden City, NY: Doubleday Anchor Books, 1967.

Bergman, Ingmar. *Fanny and Alexander.* Translated by Alan Blair. New York: Pantheon Books, 1982.

Bettelheim, Bruno. *The Uses of Enchantment: The Meaning and Importance of Fairy Tales.* New York: Vintage Books, 1977.

BIBLIOGRAPHY

Blau, Joseph Leon. *The Christian Interpretation of the Cabala in the Renaissance*. New York: Columbia University Press, 1944.

Bloodworth, Venice J. *Key to Yourself*. Marina del Rey, CA: DeVorss, 1952.

Bromley, David G., and J. Gordon Melton, eds. *Cults, Religion, and Violence*. New York: Cambridge University Press, 2002.

Bugliosi, Vincent, with Curt Gentry. *Helter Skelter: The True Story of the Manson Murders*. New York: Bantam Books, 1975.

Bultmann, Rudolf. "New Testament and Mythology." In Bultmann, *New Testament and Mythology and Other Basic Writings*. Translated by Schubert M. Ogden. Minneapolis: Fortress Press, 1989.

———. *Theology of the New Testament*. Translated by Kenrick Grobel. New York: Scribner's, 1955.

Byrne, Rhonda. *The Secret*. New York: Atria Books/Beyond Words, 2006.

Carnell, Edward John. *The Case for Orthodox Theology*. Philadelphia: Westminster, 1959.

Chidester, David. *Salvation and Suicide: Jim Jones, the Peoples Temple, and Jonestown*. Rev. ed. Bloomington: Indiana University Press, 2003.

Chödrön, Pema. *Awakening Loving Kindness*. Shambhala Pocket Classics. Boulder, CO: Shambhala, 1996.

Chopra, Deepak. *How to Know God: The Soul's Journey into the Mystery of Mysteries*. New York: Harmony Books, 2000.

Chryssides, George D. *The Advent of Sun Myung Moon: The Origins, Beliefs and Practices of the Unification Church*. London: Macmillan, 1991.

Collier, Robert. *The Law of the Higher Potential*. Tarrytown, NY: Book of Gold, 1947.

Corbin, Henry. *The Man of Light in Iranian Sufism*. Translated by Nancy Pearson. New Lebanon, NY: Omega Publications, 1994.

Couliano, Ioan P. *The Tree of Gnosis: Gnostic Mythology from Early*

Christianity to Modern Nihilism. Translated by H. S. Wiesner and Ioan P. Couliano. San Francisco: HarperSanFrancisco, 1992.

Dawson, Lorne L. *Comprehending Cults: The Sociology of New Religious Movements.* Toronto: Oxford University Press, 1998.

Derleth, August W. *H.P. Lovecraft: Selected Letters.* Vol. 2. Sauk City, WI: Arkham House, 1968.

de Rougemont, Denis. *Love in the Western World.* Rev. ed. Translated by Montgomery Belgion. Garden City, NY: Doubleday Anchor Books, 1957.

Deussen, Paul. *The Philosophy of the Upanishads.* Translated by A. S. Geden. Edinburgh: T&T Clark, 1906.

Dyer, Wayne W. *The Power of Intention: Learning to Co-create Your World Your Way.* Carlsbad, CA: Hay House, 2004.

Ellwood, Roger S. *Religious and Spiritual Groups in Modern America.* Englewood Cliffs, NJ: Prentice-Hall, 1973.

Evans, Christopher. *Cults of Unreason.* New York: Dell Publishing/a Delta Book, 1973.

Festinger, Leon. *A Theory of Cognitive Dissonance.* Stanford, CA: Stanford University Press, 1962.

Festinger, Leon, Henry W. Riecken, and Stanley Schachter. *When Prophecy Fails: A Social and Psychological Study of a Modern Group That Predicted the Destruction of the World.* New York: Harper & Row Torchbooks, 1964.

Fosdick, Harry Emerson. *The Modern Use of the Bible.* 1924; reprint, New York: Macmillan, 1961.

Freke, Timothy, and Peter Gandy. *Jesus and the Lost Goddess: The Secret Teachings of the Original Christians.* New York: Harmony Books, 2001.

———. *The Jesus Mysteries: Was the "Original Jesus" a Pagan God?* New York: Harmony Books, 2000.

Gager, John G. *Kingdom and Community: The Social World of Early Christianity.* Prentice-Hall Studies in Religion Series. Englewood Cliffs, NJ: Prentice-Hall, 1975.

BIBLIOGRAPHY

Gawain, Shakti. *Creative Visualization.* New York: Bantam Books, 1982.

Gawain, Shakti, with Laurel King. *Living in the Light: A Guide to Personal and Planetary Transformation.* San Raphael, CA: New World Library, 1986.

Girard, Rene. *Violence and the Sacred.* Translated by Patrick Gregory. Baltimore, MD: Johns Hopkins University Press, 1977.

Gladden, Washington. *How Much Is Left of the Old Doctrines?* Boston and New York: Houghton Mifflin, 1899.

Hawkins, David R. *Power vs. Force: The Hidden Determinants of Human Behavior.* Carlsbad, CA: Hay House, 1995.

Hoeller, Stephan A. *The Gnostic Jung and the Seven Sermons to the Dead.* Wheaton, IL: Quest Books/Theosophical Publishing House, 1982.

———. *Jung and the Lost Gospels: Insights into the Dead Sea Scrolls and the Nag Hammadi Library.* Wheaton, IL: Quest Books/Theosophical Publishing House, 1989.

Jonas, Hans. *The Gnostic Religion: The Message of the Alien God and the Beginnings of Christianity.* 2nd ed. Boston: Beacon Press, 1963.

Juergensmeyer, Mark. *Terror in the Mind of God: The Global Rise of Religious Violence.* Rev. 3rd ed. Berkeley: University of California Press, 2003.

Jung, Carl. *Aion: Researches into the Phenomenology of the Self.* Bollingen Series XX. *Collected Works of C. G. Jung,* vol. 9, part II. Translated by R. F. C. Hull. Princeton, NJ: Bollingen Paperbacks/Princeton University Press, 1959.

———. *Synchronicity: An Acausal Connecting Principle.* Bollingen Series XX. *Collected Works of C. G. Jung,* vol. 8. Translated by R. F. C. Hull. Princeton, NJ: Bollingen Paperbacks/Princeton University Press, 1973.

Kaplan, E. David, and Andrew Marshall. *The Cult at the End of the World: The Terrifying Story of the Aum Doomsday Cult, from the Subways of Tokyo to the Nuclear Arsenals of Russia.* New York: Crown Publishers, 1996.

Kilduff, Marshall, and Ron Javers. *The Suicide Cult: The Inside Story of the Peoples Temple Sect and the Massacre in Guyana.* New York: Bantam Books, 1978.

Koestler, Arthur. *The Roots of Coincidence: An Excursion into Parapsychology.* New York: Random House Vintage Books, 1973.

Krause, Charles A. *Guyana Massacre: The Eyewitness Account.* New York: Berkley Books, 1978.

Lanternari, Vittorio. *The Religions of the Oppressed: A Study of Modern Messianic Cults.* Translated by Lisa Sergio. New York: New American Library/a Mentor Book, 1965.

Larsen, Egon. *Strange Sects and Cults: A Study of Their Origins and Influence.* New York: Haret Publishing, 1972.

Lessa, William A., and Evon Z. Vogt, eds. *Reader in Comparative Religion: An Anthropological Approach.* New York: Harper & Row, 1958.

Lewis, James R. *Legitimating New Religions.* New Brunswick, NJ: Rutgers University Press, 2003.

Lofland, John. *Doomsday Cult: A Study of Conversion, Proselytization, and Maintainance of Faith.* Englewood Cliffs, NJ: Prentice-Hall, 1966.

Mack, Burton L. *The Lost Gospel: The Book of Q and Christian Origins.* San Francisco: HarperSanFrancisco, 1993.

Martin, Marie-Louise. *Kimbangu: An African Prophet and His Church.* Grand Rapids, MI: Eermans, 1975.

Neumann, Erich. *Depth Psychology and a New Ethic.* Translated by Eugene Rolfe. New York: Harper & Row, 1973.

Noll, Richard. *The Aryan Christ: The Secret Life of Carl Jung.* New York: Random House, 1997.

———. *The Jung Cult: Origins of a Charismatic Movement.* New York: Free Press/Macmillan, 1997.

Oakes, Len. *Prophetic Charisma: The Psychology of Revolutionary Religious Personalities.* Syracuse, NY: Syracuse University Press, 1997.

BIBLIOGRAPHY

Osteen, Joel. *Your Best Life Now.* New York: FaithWords, 2004.

Progoff, Ira. *Jung, Synchronity, and Human Destiny: Noncausal Dimensions of Human Experience.* New York: Delta Books/Dell, 1973.

Ricci, Paul. *Introduction to the Lore of the Cabalists or Allegorizers.* Augsburg, 1515. In Joseph Leon Blau, *The Christian Interpretation of the Cabala in the Renaissance.* New York: Columbia University Press, 1944.

Richardson, James T., ed. "Conversion and Commitment in Contemporary Religion." *American Behavioral Scientist* 20, no. 6 (July/August 1977).

Salinger, J. D. *Franny and Zooey.* London: Heinemann, 1961.

Schaeffer, Francis A. *The New Super-Spirituality.* Downers Grove, IL: InterVarsity Press, 1972.

Scheler, Max. *Problems of a Sociology of Knowledge.* Translated by Manfred S. Frings. London: Routledge & Kegan Paul, 1980.

Scholem, Gershom. *Major Trends in Jewish Mysticism.* New York: Schocken Books, 1973.

———. *On the Kabbalah and Its Symbolism.* New York: Schocken Books, 1969.

Schucman, Helen. *A Course in Miracles.* Combined Edition. Glen Ellen, CA: Foundation for Inner Peace, 1992.

Shupe, Anson D., Jr., and David G. Bromley. *The New Vigilantes: Deprogrammers, Anti-Cultists, and the New Religions.* Sage Library of Social Research vol. 113. Beverly Hills, CA: Sage Publications, 1980.

Slusser, Gerald H. *From Jung to Jesus: Myth and Consciousness in the New Testament.* Atlanta: John Knox Press, 1986.

Stark, Rodney. *The Rise of Christianity: A Sociologist Reconsiders History.* Princeton, NJ: Princeton University Press, 1996.

Stevens, Anthony, and John Price. *Prophets, Cults and Madness.* London: Duckworth, 2000.

Streiker, Lowell D. *The Gospel Time Bomb: Ultrafundamentalism and the Future of America.* Amherst, NY: Prometheus Books, 1984.

Tabor, James D., and Eugene V. Gallagher. *Why Waco? Cults and the Battle for Religious Freedom in America.* Berkeley: University of California Press, 1995.

Theissen, Gerd. *Sociology of Early Palestinian Christianity.* Translated by John Bowden. Philadelphia: Fortress Press, 1978.

Tillich, Paul. *Existence and the Christ: Systematic Theology II.* Chicago: University of Chicago Press, 1957.

————. *Love, Power, and Justice: Ontological Analyses and Ethical Applications.* New York: Oxford University Press/a Galaxy Book, 1960.

Tolle, Eckhart. *The Power of Now: A Guide to Spiritual Enlightenment.* Novato, CA: New World Library, 1999.

Troward, Thomas. *Edinburgh Lectures on Mental Science.* New York: Dodd, Mead, 1909.

Trungpa, Chögyam. *Cutting through Spiritual Materialism.* Shambhala Dragon Editions. Boston: Shambhala Publications, 1987.

Turner, Victor. "Betwixt and Between: The Liminal Period in *Rites de Passage.*" *Proceedings of the American Ethnological Society*, Symposium on New Approaches to the Study of Religion, 1964, pp. 4–20.

Wallace, Anthony F. C. "Ritual as Revitalization." In Wallace, *Religion: An Anthropological View*, 157–66. New York: Random House, 1966.

Walsch, Neale Donald. *Conversations with God: An Uncommon Dialogue.* New York: Putnam's, 1995.

Watzlawick, Paul. *How Real Is Real? Confusion, Disinformation, Communication: An Anecdotal Introduction to Communications Theory.* New York: Random House Vintage Books, 1976.

Weber, Max. *The Theory of Social and Economic Organization.* Translated by A. M. Henderson and Talcott Parsons. New York: Macmillan Free Press, 1964.

Williamson, Marianne. *A Return to Love.* New York: HarperCollins, 1992.

Wilson, Bryan R. *Magic and the Millennium: A Sociological Study of Religious Movements of Protest among Tribal and Third-World Peoples.* New York: Harper & Row, 1973.

BIBLIOGRAPHY

Worsley, Peter. *The Trumpet Shall Sound: A Study of "Cargo" Cults in Melanesia.* New York: Schocken Books, 1968.

Zablocki, Benjamin, and Thomas Robbins, eds. *Misunderstanding Cults: Searching for Objectivity in a Controversial Field.* Toronto: University of Toronto Press, 2001.

Index

INDEX

INDEX

INDEX

INDEX

INDEX